$16.75

1. What kind of problems have particular distributions?
   Normal:

INTRODUCTORY
MATHEMATICAL
STATISTICS

INTRODUCTORY MATHEMATICAL STATISTICS

Principles and Methods

Erwin Kreyszig

JOHN WILEY & SONS, INC.

NEW YORK · LONDON · SYDNEY · TORONTO

Library of Congress Catalogue Card Number: 70-107583

SBN 471 50730 X

Printed in the United States of America

10 9 8 7 6 5 4 3

Preface

Purpose of the book. This book is intended to introduce the student to basic concepts, principles, and methods of mathematical statistics and its applications.

It is suitable for a one-semester course meeting three to five hours per week or for a two-semester course meeting two hours per week. Selected material for a short course is suggested at the end of the preface.

A course in elementary calculus is a sufficient prerequisite, and no prior acquaintance with probability theory or statistics is assumed.

The presentation has been influenced by practical work in statistics as well as by courses given in probability, statistical methods, general mathematical statistics, and applications to special fields. These lectures were presented to various audiences with diverse mathematical backgrounds and different practical interests on this continent and in Europe.

Content and arrangement. The book consists of three parts.

I. Descriptive statistics.
II. Probability theory.
III. Statistical inference.

Part I is short and mathematically very simple.

Part II provides the basis for mathematical models of distributions and for the statistical methods in Part III. It gives the conceptual framework within which the ideas of statistical inference may be discussed and emphasizes those concepts and methods which are essential to mathematical statistics. The presentation is relatively detailed, because experience shows that a good probabilistic background is helpful in gaining a deeper understanding of statistical methods.

Part III includes statistical methods of general interest, such as point and interval estimation, testing of hypotheses, quality control, acceptance sampling, an introduction to sequential analysis, goodness of fit, analysis of variance, regression and correlation analysis, an introduction to the theory of errors in physical measurements, some nonparametric methods, and the elements of decision theory.

Particular attention has been paid to the simplicity of the presentation and corresponding notation. To avoid confusion, we have denoted random variables by capital letters and the values which they assume by lowercase letters. The chapters have been kept as independent as possible. Certain proofs that are somewhat more advanced than the level of the book are separated from the text and included in Appendix 1.

Theory and applications. Since mathematical statistics has been growing at a spectacular rate for several decades, the selection of topics to be included in a book on this subject is more difficult than it would be in other fields. Preference is given here to methods of *general* practical importance, and I have sought to find a suitable balance between theory and application. It is hoped that this will aid the reader in developing an early appreciation for applications. In fact, much of statistical theory is not fully appreciated if it is removed from applications, since that theory developed from a need to solve real-life problems.

With a few obvious exceptions the statistical data in the text are taken from actual experiments and observations. Certain examples and problems are very elementary, to encourage the reader to start experiments and observations of his own.

Electronic and desk calculation. Electronic computers are of increasing importance in the numerical part of statistical work, and in several universities the use of computers in the teaching of introductory courses in statistics is being tried. This practice is sure to become more widespread. Of course, no matter whether the statistician intends to use an electronic computer or a desk calculator, he must know and understand some standard techniques of numerical analysis. This is the reason for the attention paid to numerical work in this book.

Problems and answers. Particularly in statistics, practical training is important in developing one's skill. The text includes about 1000 problems that are intended to help the reader in that respect and to provide him with opportunities to develop his intuition and increase his understanding and facility with the substance of mathematical statistics. The problems have been carefully selected from various fields. Answers to odd-numbered problems are given in Appendix 2. A teacher's manual of additional answers is available from the publisher for those adopting the book for classroom use.

References. A rather extensive list of selected books and papers for reference and further study is included in Appendix 3, and citations are made at various places in the text.

Tables. Appendix 4 contains tables of special distributions needed in Parts II and III as well as a table of random digits and tables of some auxiliary functions (for example, exponential function, binomial coefficients, and gamma function).

Selected material for a short course. Since the chapters (particularly in Part III) are relatively independent, material for short courses can be selected without difficulty. Here is one suggestion.

Frequency distributions of samples (Chap. 2)
Sample mean and sample variance (Secs. 3.1–3.3)
Fundamental concepts of probability theory (Secs. 4.1–4.9)
Probability distributions (Secs. 5.1–5.6)
Mean and variance of a distribution (Secs. 6.1–6.3)
Binomial, Poisson, and hypergeometric distributions (Secs. 7.1, 7.2, 7.4, 7.7)
Normal distribution (Secs. 8.1–8.4)
Distribution of several random variables (Secs. 9.1–9.3, 9.5)
Estimation of parameters (Secs. 11.1, 11.4–11.6)
Confidence intervals (Secs. 12.1, 12.3, 12.5)
Testing of hypotheses (Secs. 13.1–13.4)
Chi-square test (Secs. 15.1, 15.2)
Regression analysis (Secs. 17.1–17.5)
Correlation analysis (Chap. 18)
Nonparametric methods (Chap. 20)

Acknowledgement. Various parts of the manuscript were distributed to my classes in mimeographed form and returned to me, together with suggestions for improvement. I thank many of my colleagues and former students for advice and help in preparing this book, in particular Professors R. Bradley, H. O. Hartley, J. S. Hunter, H. Klinger, R. Roeloff, J. P. Spencer, and Dr. W. F. Taylor.

Finally, I am indebted to John Wiley and Sons for their effective cooperation and their great care in preparing this edition of the book.

Any further comment and suggestion for improvement of the book will be gratefully received.

Erwin Kreyszig

Contents

PART II   PROBABILITY THEORY

INTRODUCTORY
MATHEMATICAL
STATISTICS

CHAPTER 1

Introduction

This introductory chapter is intended to give the reader a first impression of the purpose and nature of mathematical statistics. It will also serve to give him an intuitive feeling for certain basic technical terms whose precise definition will be explained later in the text.

To help those readers to whom the field is entirely new, the material will be presented in a very simple fashion.

Mathematical statistics is of increasing importance in various fields, for example, in industrial mass production, medicine and biology, economics, politics, psychology, analysis of public opinion and other social sciences, agriculture, traffic studies, meteorology, physics, and engineering. Some reasons for its successful application will be explained in Sec. 1.2.

1.1 On the Nature of Mathematical Statistics

Mathematical statistics is concerned with the theory and application of methods for collecting statistical data, analyzing such data, and making inferences from them. Statistical data may consist of numbers arranged in tabular form or corresponding graphical representations. They may arise from traffic problems (number of cars on a certain road during given intervals of time, number of monthly traffic accidents in a community, etc.), medical experiments to determine the effect of a new drug, control of the quality of industrial products in a factory, gauging public opinion and voter preferences, and investigation of the cost of living, to mention a few examples.

Thus we see that statistical data may be collected in different fields. Nevertheless, such data have the common feature that they are derived from circumstances that are affected by "chance." That is, the situations are influenced by the presence of effects which we cannot predict because they result from factors that cannot be controlled or often even enumerated.

For instance, if we throw a die we know in advance that one of the numbers 1, 2, 3, 4, 5, 6 must turn up, but we cannot predict the "*outcome*" in any

1

performance of this *"random experiment"*; that is, we cannot predict which number will turn up in any throw. However, if the die is fair (geometrically regular and made from homogeneous material), then in the long run we observe that those six numbers turn up *about* the same number of times; for example, in 600 trials each number will turn up *about* 100 times.

Similarly, the birth of a single child may be regarded as a random experiment with two possible outcomes, "boy" and "girl." Again, we cannot make a prediction in any particular case, but experience shows that in a large population, for instance, in a large city, the two outcomes appear *about* equally often.

If we manufacture screws, we cannot predict whether the next screw to be produced will or will not be defective, but we may observe that every day the daily percentage of defective screws is almost the same, if the production process remains unchanged.

Similarly, we cannot predict at what age a certain person will die, but we can obtain life expectancy tables by considering a large population, and we may use these tables for calculating life insurance premiums. With respect to other types of insurance (fire, theft, collision, etc.), the situation is quite similar.

In our examples a single case shows a *"random irregularity"* that makes predictions impossible, but a large number of cases exhibit a *"statistical regularity."* It is important to discover details of such *"statistical laws,"* so that we may then set up a mathematical model. Such a model is helpful in understanding situations involving chance effects and may serve as a basis for predicting or influencing future behavior.

1.2   The Idea of Statistical Sampling

If, in a certain city, we wish to study the spreading of a disease (for example, ornithosis) by pigeons, it would clearly be impossible to catch *all* the pigeons in that city and examine them medically. Instead, we catch a small number n of them (for instance, $n = 50$ or 100 or 500 pigeons) and examine them to find out if they carry viruses which cause that disease (case 1) or if they do not (case 0). We could list the result by writing

$$1 \quad 1 \quad 0 \quad 1 \quad 0 \quad 0 \quad 0 \quad \cdots \quad 0 \quad 1 \quad 0,$$

which means that viruses were found on the first two animals, none was found on the third, etc. This string of numbers is called a *random sample* (briefly, a *sample*) from the *population*[1] (or *universe*) of all numbers that one would obtain by examining all the pigeons in the city. The numbers in the sample are called *sample values*, and their number n is called the *size* of the sample. If 15% of the sample values are 1's, we are inclined to conclude that *about* 15% of all the pigeons in that city carry those viruses. Of course, in

---

[1] The terms *population* and *sample* may also refer to the individuals measured.

this conclusion we must assume that our method of catching pigeons is such that all pigeons in the city have (about) the same chance of being caught, and thus the n pigeons actually caught represent a random selection of all pigeons in the city. This randomness requirement is basic and is further discussed below.

In other cases it often makes no sense to deal with the whole population instead of sampling. Typical of this situation is the destructive testing of bombs or light bulbs. Another example arises in connection with elections in a community. Even if we were able to ascertain the opinion of every adult in that community, the result would probably not be much more valuable than a sufficiently large sample because some of these persons might change their minds and others who first intended to vote might not do so, etc.

In many cases the population will be too large to be studied completely, so that time and cost may require sampling methods. For instance, inexpensive mass-produced articles (screws, bolts, radio resistors, rubber bands, pencils, paper clips, etc.) cannot be examined piece by piece because this would be too expensive and time consuming. With these examples in mind, we are not surprised to learn that in other applications of statistical methods, the situation is similar. In fact, this is the method which is basic to the whole of modern mathematical statistics—to take samples and from these samples to draw conclusions about the corresponding population.

In order to apply statistical methods for obtaining information about populations, it is important that the corresponding samples be random selections and that the trials by which a sample is obtained be independent of one another. We shall return to this point at the beginning of Part III of the book because, to define the notion of a sample properly, we shall need the concept of mathematical probability. For the time being, we emphasize that in random sampling the sampler must exercise no control over the specific choice of the units which are included in the sample. Any judgments such as a preference for "typical" units or an exclusion of "nontypical" ones destroy the randomness of the selection and the possibility of making useful inferences about the population by means of statistical methods.

It is interesting to note that the collecting of statistical data has existed at least since the days of the Roman Empire 2000 years ago. But the introduction of statistical methods into industry, physical and social sciences, and other fields began only a few decades ago, and all the implications have not yet been fully realized. Statistics has become important recently for two main reasons. First, mathematical methods have been invented that permit valuable conclusions from samples about corresponding populations ("*statistical inference*"). Of course, the very nature of these methods prevents the conclusions from being absolutely certain. However, we shall see that in each case we are able to choose a preassigned "probability" of obtaining a true conclusion (this probability can be chosen close to certainty if we want). Here *probability* is a precise mathematical term (to be defined in Part II), and in the present case it serves as a measure of the reliability of conclusions about populations from samples. Of course, all of these concepts and ideas will be discussed and explained in detail and illustrated by various examples; at present, we merely intend to give the reader a first general orientation.

The other reason for the increasing importance of mathematical statistics is the growing complexity of scientific, engineering, economic, and political problems, so that old-fashioned nonmathematical rules of thumb and empirical methods are becoming less and less reliable. Hence there is a great demand for better methods, and modern mathematical statistics is able to supply such methods for large classes of important practical problems.

Historically, we should note that a great impetus for the development of modern mathematical statistics came from Karl Pearson and his school [see E. S. Pearson (1938); cf. Appendix 3], W. S. Gosset [see Pearson and Wishart (1942)], and R. A. Fisher (1950, 1958, 1960). Outstanding work was also done by J. Neyman (1937), E. S. Pearson [see Neyman and Pearson (1933)], A. Wald (1947, 1950), and others.

1.3   Stages of a Statistical Investigation

Although the types of problems to which mathematical statistics can be applied are rather heterogeneous, in most cases the steps of a statistical investigation are the same.

1st step. Formulation of the problem. To investigate a problem successfully, we first have to create precise concepts, formulate clear questions, and impose suitable limitations on the problem, taking into account the available time and money and the skill of the investigators. Concepts such as *defective item*, *mental disease*, and *satisfactory customer service* may vary from case to case, and in each specific case we need to agree on appropriate definitions of the terms involved.

2nd step. Design of experiment. Our desire is to obtain a maximum of information using a minimum of cost and time. This implies, among other things, that we must determine the size of the sample or the amount and type of data that will solve the problem most efficiently. It turns out that this size will be affected by the mathematical method used in the last step (Step 5), and we have to select this method as well as a method for sampling. With respect to the latter we should note that it is not easy to obtain selections that are completely random. There is always a danger that a selection may be in some way biased. Various methods for overcoming this difficulty have been proposed and are used in practice. We shall consider this point at the beginning of Part III.

3rd step. Experimentation or collection of data. In general this will be the most time-consuming part of the whole investigation. It should adhere to strict rules. In fact, the less judgment the investigator uses, the better the results will be.

4th step. *Tabulation and description of results.* In this step the experimental data are put in readable form and are illustrated by graphical representations (diagrams, bar charts, etc.); furthermore, descriptive measures for the average size and the spread of the sample values are computed. The corresponding procedures are simple and will be discussed in Part I.

5th step. *Statistical inference and formulation of the answer.* By applying the statistical method selected in Step 2, we draw conclusions from the sample about the corresponding population (*statistical inference*) and formulate the answer to our problem.

There is no magic formula in mathematical statistics that takes care of all conceivable practical situations. Hence it is necessary to obtain general knowledge of the more important methods for making inferences. In each practical case the nature of the specific problem should be studied carefully, to make sure that the most appropriate method will be chosen.

PART I

DESCRIPTIVE STATISTICS

In this part of the book, we discuss methods for putting statistical data in a readable tabular form. Also we see how to illustrate these data graphically by bar charts, histograms, and the like. Furthermore, we introduce quantities that measure the average size of the values in a sample and their spread.

Starting with this part of statistics we can develop a better understanding of the whole field and its applications without the use of complicated mathematics.

CHAPTER **2**

Frequency Distribution of a Sample

In this chapter, methods for tabular and graphical representations of samples are discussed. Definitions are given for the concepts of absolute and relative frequencies, the frequency function $\tilde{f}(x)$, and the cumulative frequency function $\tilde{F}(x)$ of a sample; each of these two functions will give complete information about the size and distribution of the values of a sample.

2.1 Tabular Representation of Samples. Frequency

In the course of a statistical experiment, we usually obtain a sequence of observations (generally numbers) which we write down in the order in which they occur. A typical example is given in Table 2.1.1. The table shows the weights of 50 air mail envelopes of a certain type produced by a factory on a single day and randomly selected by the author. These data thus represent an example of a **sample** taken from the **population** of the weights of all those envelopes produced in that factory during that day. Our sample consists of 50 numbers, called **sample values,** so that the **size** of the sample is $n = 50$.

We already mentioned in Sec. 1.2 that in order to define the concept of a sample, we shall need the concept of mathematical probability. However, this will not affect our present discussion of tabular and graphical representations of samples. It will be sufficient to study corresponding methods in terms of our sample in Table 2.1.1. We begin with this topic because it requires very little mathematics.

Before going into detail, we should mention that if in a random experiment we observe two quantities simultaneously, for instance, the specific weight and iron content of iron ore, or the height and weight of adult persons, we obtain a sample in which each sample value is an ordered *pair* of measurements. Similarly, if we observe or measure three quantities, we obtain samples consisting of ordered *triples* of numbers, and so on.

Table 2.1.1. Sample of 50 Values of the Weight (in Ounces) of Air Mail Envelopes

0.098	0.103	0.104	0.100	0.108	0.099	0.105	0.101	0.110	0.095
0.106	0.105	0.096	0.107	0.101	0.115	0.100	0.103	0.097	0.103
0.103	0.098	0.107	0.099	0.105	0.092	0.104	0.106	0.102	0.111
0.108	0.097	0.109	0.110	0.096	0.102	0.101	0.094	0.104	0.100
0.101	0.104	0.094	0.102	0.112	0.103	0.099	0.107	0.098	0.108

To see what information is contained in Table 2.1.1, we must order the data. We write 0.092 (the smallest value), 0.093, 0.094, $\cdots$, 0.115 (the largest value) in a column. Then we examine Table 2.1.1 line by line and make a tally mark for each number that occurs. In this way we obtain a **tally chart** of our sample, which makes up the first two columns of Table 2.1.2. The number of tallies is then listed in the third column of the table. It indicates how often the corresponding value x occurs in the sample.

Table 2.1.2. Frequency Table of the Sample in Table 2.1.1

1 Weight x (in Ounces)	2 Frequency Tallies	3	4 Relative Frequency	5 Cumulative Frequency	6 Cumulative Relative Frequency
0.092			1	0.02	1	0.02
0.093		0	0	1	0.02
0.094	||	2	0.04	3	0.06
0.095			1	0.02	4	0.08
0.096	||	2	0.04	6	0.12
0.097	||	2	0.04	8	0.16
0.098	|||	3	0.06	11	0.22
0.099	|||	3	0.06	14	0.28
0.100	|||	3	0.06	17	0.34
0.101	||||	4	0.08	21	0.42
0.102	|||	3	0.06	24	0.48
0.103	⫫	5	0.10	29	0.58
0.104	||||	4	0.08	33	0.66
0.105	|||	3	0.06	36	0.72
0.106	||	2	0.04	38	0.76
0.107	|||	3	0.06	41	0.82
0.108	|||	3	0.06	44	0.88
0.109			1	0.02	45	0.90
0.110	||	2	0.04	47	0.94
0.111			1	0.02	48	0.96
0.112			1	0.02	49	0.98
0.113		0	0	49	0.98
0.114		0	0	49	0.98
0.115			1	0.02	50	1.00

The primitive method of tallying is well known, but it has serious disadvantages. In fact, it is subject to error and is rather difficult to check.

A better method is to put the data on individual cards, sort the cards into piles, and then count the number of cards in each pile. This approach can be carried out in a completely mechanistic fashion and will yield better results, particularly if the sample size is very large.

The number of times a value x occurs in a sample is called the *absolute frequency* or, more briefly, the **frequency** of that value x in the sample. Dividing it by the size n of the sample, we obtain the **relative frequency** shown in column 4 of Table 2.1.2; in this case, $n = 50$. Thus $x = 0.098$ has the frequency 3 and the relative frequency 0.06 or 6%.

If for a certain x we sum all the frequencies corresponding to the sample values which are smaller than or equal to that x, we obtain the **cumulative frequency** corresponding to that x. This yields column 5 in Table 2.1.2. For example, to $x = 0.105$ there corresponds the cumulative frequency 36, and this tells us that there are 36 sample values which are smaller than or equal to 0.105. Division by the size n of the sample yields the **cumulative relative frequency** in column 6. For example, from column 6 we see that 82% of the sample values are smaller than or equal to 0.107.

If a certain numerical value does not occur in a sample, its frequency is 0. If all the n values of the sample are numerically equal, then this number has the frequency n and, therefore, the relative frequency $n/n = 1$. Since these are the two extreme possible cases, we have:

Theorem 1. *The relative frequency is at least equal to* 0 *and at most equal to* 1.

Suppose that a given sample of size n consists of m *numerically different* values

$$x_1, \qquad x_2, \qquad \cdots, \qquad x_m \qquad\qquad (m \leqq n)$$

with corresponding relative frequencies

$$\tilde{f}_1, \qquad \tilde{f}_2, \qquad \cdots, \qquad \tilde{f}_m.$$

Then we may introduce the function $\tilde{f}(x)$, which for each $x = x_j$ equals the corresponding relative frequency $\tilde{f}_j$ and equals 0 for every x not appearing in the sample.[1] Expressed in terms of formulas,

(1)
$$\tilde{f}(x) = \begin{cases} \tilde{f}_j & \text{when } x = x_j \qquad (j = 1, 2, \cdots, m) \\ 0 & \text{otherwise.} \end{cases}$$

This function is called the **frequency function of the sample.** It shows how the values of the sample are distributed. Therefore we say that it determines the **frequency distribution** of the sample.

For example, in Table 2.1.2 the values of the frequency function are shown

---

[1] We write $\tilde{f}$ because we want to reserve the simple symbol f for the theoretical counterpart of the frequency function; f will appear more often in the book.

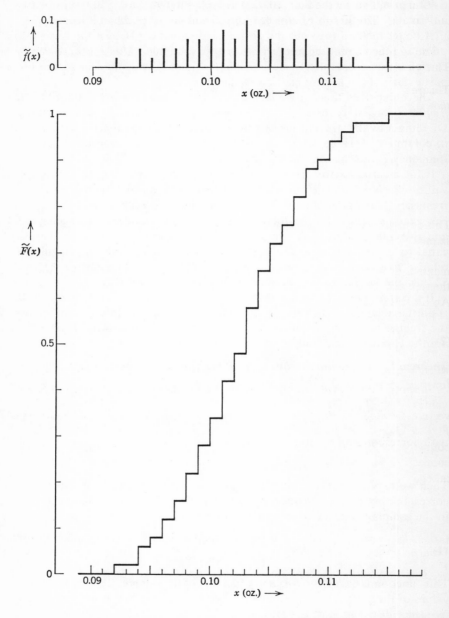

Fig. 2.1.1. Frequency function $\tilde{f}(x)$ and distribution function $\tilde{F}(x)$ of the sample in Table 2.1.2

in column 4, and we see that $\tilde{f}(0.092) = 0.02, \tilde{f}(0.093) = 0, \tilde{f}(0.094) = 0.04$, and so on. The graph of this function is shown in the upper part of Fig. 2.1.1.

The sum of all the frequencies in a sample of size n must equal n. (Why?) This yields:

Theorem 2. *The sum of all the relative frequencies in a sample equals* 1, *that is,*

$$\sum_{j=1}^{m} \tilde{f}(x_j) = \tilde{f}(x_1) + \tilde{f}(x_2) + \cdots + \tilde{f}(x_m) = 1.$$

We now introduce the function

$$\tilde{F}(x) = \textit{sum of the relative frequencies of all the sample}$$
$$\textit{values that are smaller than } x \textit{ or equal to } x.$$

This function is called the **cumulative frequency function of the sample** or the **sample distribution function.**

$\tilde{F}(x)$ is a *step function* (a piecewise constant function) having jumps of magnitude $\tilde{f}(x)$ precisely at those x at which $\tilde{f}(x) \neq 0$. The first jump is at the smallest sample value, and the last is at the largest. Afterwards $\tilde{F}(x) = 1$. An illustration of these properties is given in Fig. 2.1.1.

The relation between $\tilde{f}(x)$ and $\tilde{F}(x)$ is

(2) $$\tilde{F}(x) = \sum_{t \leq x} \tilde{f}(t),$$

where $t \leq x$ means that for a given x, we must form the sum of all those $\tilde{f}(t)$ for which t is less than or equal to x.

Clearly, from the values of $\tilde{f}(x)$ we may obtain those of $\tilde{F}(x)$ and conversely, so that either of the two functions describes the sample completely. $\tilde{F}(x)$ is less pictorial than $\tilde{f}(x)$ but is more important, since its theoretical counterpart $F(x)$ (to be introduced in Sec. 5.4) is more fundamental in connection with theoretical models of populations from which samples are taken.

Problems

1.–7. In each case make a frequency table of the given sample and graph the frequency function $\tilde{f}(x)$ and the cumulative frequency function $\tilde{F}(x)$.

1. Carbon content (percent) of coal

$$87 \quad 86 \quad 85 \quad 87 \quad 86 \quad 87 \quad 86 \quad 81 \quad 77 \quad 85$$
$$86 \quad 84 \quad 83 \quad 83 \quad 82 \quad 84 \quad 83 \quad 79 \quad 82 \quad 73$$

2. Tensile strength (kilograms/millimeter^2) of sheet steel

$$44 \quad 43 \quad 41 \quad 41 \quad 44 \quad 44 \quad 43 \quad 44 \quad 42 \quad 45 \quad 43 \quad 43 \quad 44 \quad 45 \quad 46$$
$$42 \quad 45 \quad 41 \quad 44 \quad 44 \quad 43 \quad 44 \quad 46 \quad 41 \quad 43 \quad 45 \quad 45 \quad 42 \quad 44 \quad 44$$

3. Numbers that turned up on a die

> 6   2   4   1   2   4   3   3   2   1   6   5   6   3   4

4. Release time (seconds) of a relay

> 1.3   1.4   1.1   1.5   1.4   1.3   1.2   1.4   1.5   1.3
> 1.2   1.3   1.5   1.4   1.4   1.6   1.3   1.5   1.1   1.4

5. Resistance (ohms) of resistors

> 99   100   102   101   98   103   100   102   99   101
> 100   100   99   101   100   102   99   101   98   100

6. Length (millimeters) of lamellas of a leaf of *Robinia pseudoacácia L.*

> 46   55   62   65   67   64   65   62   54   57
> 51   60   59   64   66   68   60   59   51

7. Number of seeds per pod of *Indigofera australis*

Number of seeds	3	4	5	6	7	8	9	10	11
Frequency	1	2	8	13	22	45	63	23	1

8. Throw a die 50 times, record the results, and represent them in a frequency table.

9. Throw 2 dice 100 times. For each trial, record the sum of the faces that turn up, make a frequency table, and graph $\tilde{f}(x)$ and $\tilde{F}(x)$.

10. Determine the relative frequency of the letters a, b, c, $\cdots$ on any page of a book. Repeat this experiment using another page of the same book and compare the results.

2.2   Graphical Representations of Samples

There are several simple ways of representing samples graphically. It is sufficient to discuss these methods in terms of the example used in Sec. 2.1.

Figure 2.2.1 shows the **dot frequency diagram** of that sample. This figure is related to the tally chart of column 2 in Table 2.1.2, but gives a better idea of the distribution of the sample values.

Figure 2.2.2 shows the **line graph** of the frequency function $\tilde{f}(x)$, whose values are given in column 4 of Table 2.1.2. We might also graph the absolute frequencies in a similar fashion. In the present case, where $n = 50$, both types of diagrams are equally convenient. However, if n were 37 or 84, for example, the graph of the absolute frequencies would be easier to plot.

Figure 2.2.2 may certainly be regarded as another graphical illustration of our sample. However, we must not draw from it the erroneous conclusion that the values of the quantity which we observed in this experiment (the weight of the envelopes) are restricted to finitely many discrete values. Of course, this would be true in experiments in which we *count*, for example, accidents, defective items, and recovered patients. However, in the present experiment in which we *measure*, this does not hold, and the appearance of Fig. 2.2.2 is a consequence of the process of rounding, not of the nature of

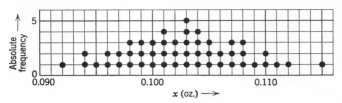

Fig. 2.2.1. Dot frequency diagram of the sample in Table 2.1.2

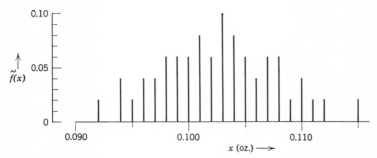

Fig. 2.2.2. Line graph of the frequency function $\tilde{f}(x)$ of the sample in Table 2.1.2

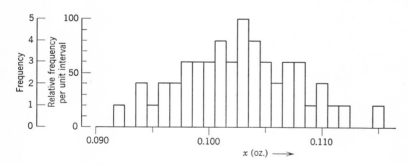

Fig. 2.2.3. Histogram of the sample in Table 2.1.2

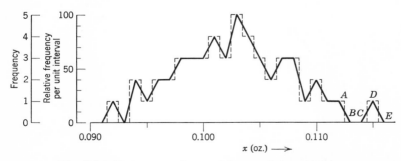

Fig. 2.2.4. Frequency polygon of the sample in Table 2.1.2

15

the experiment. It is obvious that any graph employed should so illustrate situations that misinterpretations are avoided as much as possible. With this in mind we see that here it is more suitable to use a **histogram** (Fig. 2.2.3). Instead of vertical line segments (rods) we now have rectangles, and the area of each of these rectangles is equal to the corresponding relative frequency, that is, this area equals the fraction of the corresponding x-value in the sample. From Theorem 2 in the last section it follows that the sum of the areas of all the rectangles must equal 1. The vertical scale (ordinate) must be adjusted accordingly. Since the areas of the rectangles equal relative frequencies, it follows that the ordinate must be labeled in terms of values of the relative frequency per unit interval of the x-axis. In this fashion we obtain the values shown in Fig. 2.2.3. In this figure the intervals on the x-axis (widths of the rectangles) are equal. Hence the values on the ordinate are proportional to the relative frequencies and to the frequencies. However, this would no longer be true if the intervals were of different lengths.

Finally, we mention the possibility of representing data by a **frequency polygon** (Fig. 2.2.4). This polygon can be obtained by connecting the midpoints of the tops of the rectangles in the histogram. It is customary to add the extensions AB, CD, DE (cf. Fig. 2.2.4) to the next lower and higher values (0.113, 0.114, 0.116) which have corresponding frequency 0 (and similarly at the left end of Fig. 2.2.4). Then the area under the frequency polygon equals the area of the rectangles of the histogram, which is 1.

Problems

1.–4. Graph a histogram of the following samples.

  1. Length of nails (in inches)

  0.80   0.81   0.81   0.82   0.81   0.82   0.80   0.82   0.81   0.81

  2. The sample in Problem 1, Sec. 2.1.
  3. The sample in Problem 2, Sec. 2.1.
  4. The sample in Problem 5, Sec. 2.1.

  5. Show that the area under the frequency polygon is the same as that of the rectangles of the corresponding histogram, which is 1.

2.3   Grouping

If a sample consists of too many numerically different sample values, its frequency function [cf. (1) in Sec. 2.1] and corresponding graphs are still rather complicated and perhaps even confusing. We may then want to eliminate unnecessary details. This can be done by the process of **grouping**, which we now describe.

A sample being given, we choose an interval I that contains all the sample values. For instance, if 42.3 and 63.9 are the smallest and the largest value in a sample, we may choose I to be $40 \leq x \leq 65$. We subdivide I into subintervals, which are called **class intervals** or *cells*. The midpoints of these intervals are called *class midpoints* or **class marks.** The sample values in each such interval are said to form a **class.** The number of values in a class is called the corresponding **class frequency.** Division by the sample size n gives the **relative class frequency.** This frequency, considered as a function of the class marks, is called the **frequency function of the grouped sample** and may be denoted by $\tilde{f}(x)$, as in the ungrouped case, without causing misunderstanding. The **cumulative frequency function of the grouped sample** will be denoted by $\tilde{F}(x)$ and is defined by

$$\tilde{F}(x) = \sum_{t \leq x} \tilde{f}(t)$$

where $\tilde{f}$ is the frequency function of the grouped sample.

For instance, the sample in Table 2.3.1, consisting of 125 values, may be grouped as shown in Table 2.3.2. We see that we have 12 class intervals. These intervals have the same length. The first interval contains the four sample values 408, 411, 411, and 412. These values no longer appear in the grouped sample, but are replaced by their class mark (410). The next class contains the sample values 414, 414, 416, 417, and 417, each of which is replaced by the class mark 415. The next class consists of the sample values 419, 419, 420, 420, 420, 420, 421, and 422, each of which is replaced by the class mark 420. For the other sample values the situation is similar. This illustrates that in the process of grouping, we *approximate* the sample values by the corresponding class marks. Comparing the histograms (*a*) and (*b*) in Fig. 2.3.1, we see the simplification obtained by grouping.

In many applications it will be possible to obey the following rules which are helpful in avoiding unnecessary complications in the later use of a grouped sample.

(1) All the class intervals should have the same length.

(2) The class intervals should be chosen so that the class marks correspond to simple numbers (numbers with few nonzero digits).

(3) If a sample value coincides with the common endpoint of two class intervals, we take it into account by adding $\frac{1}{2}$ to the class frequency of each of those two class intervals.[2] If possible we should choose the class intervals so that this coincidence does not happen.

The fewer classes we choose, the simpler the grouped sample will be, but the more information will be lost, since the original sample values will no longer appear explicitly. Grouping should be done in such a way that only unessential details are eliminated. In most practical applications we may choose between 10 and 20 class intervals.

Note that the grouped sample may change if we change the class marks, retaining the lengths and number of the class intervals. Thus we see that there are arbitrary factors in the process of grouping.

---

[2] Another method (not used here) is to place a value which falls on a boundary into the interval to the right of that value.

Table 2.3.1. Sample of 125 Values of the Splitting Tensile Strength (Pounds/Inch^2) of Concrete Cylinders (Diameter 6 in., Length 12 in.)

423	435	430	458	416	441	426	439	444	427
438	440	450	436	447	437	448	434	411	449
460	412	438	419	445	420	438	429	430	432
426	443	432	443	424	435	438	452	421	442
448	453	435	446	434	427	441	443	429	437
420	420	438	422	436	440	408	435	448	454
452	424	444	427	450	448	419	440	453	417
428	437	448	430	435	425	461	433	444	436
432	442	411	440	455	425	427	442	423	446
441	433	445	438	420	439	434	414	435	430
417	448	440	429	460	437	445	450	428	440
443	423	435	453	431	455	426	464	443	465
461	445	458	414	460					

D. L. Ivey, Splitting Tensile Tests on Structural Lightweight Aggregate Concrete. Texas Transportation Institute, College Station, Texas, 1965.

Of course, if we want to compare a sample with previously grouped material, it is important that the same grouping is chosen. For example, in vital statistics, age is ordinarily grouped into intervals of the first year of life, the next 4 years, and then in 5 (or 10) year intervals. If this convention were ignored, it would become difficult to compare results of different studies. Similar conventions are observed in handling data on personal incomes.

There is no doubt that grouping is useful for obtaining simpler graphical representations of samples that make clear their essential properties. However, grouping always means loss of information. Consequently, if statistical

Table 2.3.2. Frequency Table Obtained by Grouping the Sample in Table 2.3.1

Class Interval	Class Mark x	Class Frequency	$\tilde{f}(x)$	$\tilde{F}(x)$
407.5–412.5	410	4	0.032	0.032
412.5–417.5	415	5	0.040	0.072
417.5–422.5	420	8	0.064	0.136
422.5–427.5	425	14	0.112	0.248
427.5–432.5	430	13	0.104	0.352
432.5–437.5	435	19	0.152	0.504
437.5–442.5	440	20	0.160	0.664
442.5–447.5	445	15	0.120	0.784
447.5–452.5	450	12	0.096	0.880
452.5–457.5	455	6	0.048	0.928
457.5–462.5	460	7	0.056	0.984
462.5–467.5	465	2	0.016	1.000

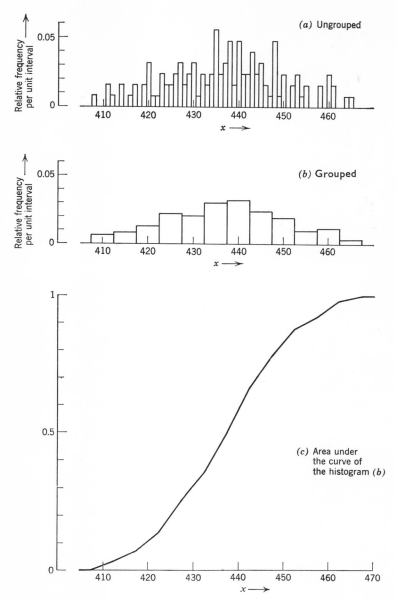

Fig. 2.3.1. Histograms of the ungrouped sample in Table 2.3.1 and the corresponding grouped sample in Table 2.3.2 and area under the curve of the histogram of the grouped sample

inference is to be based on the grouped data, this may create problems of varying degrees of severity, depending on the methods of inference to be employed. Hence, if we are unable to judge the effect of grouping, then under ordinary conditions (a sample that is not extremely large and computing facilities available) we should consider using the ungrouped original data.

We mention finally that some writers indicate class intervals by non-adjacent numbers, for example, 2.31–2.35, 2.36–2.40, 2.41–2.45, etc. Then the true boundaries are ordinarily halfway between the upper and lower recorded boundaries of adjacent intervals. Thus, in the example the true intervals are 2.305–2.355, 2.355–2.405, 2.405–2.455, etc. We shall not use this method of indicating class intervals.

Problems

1.–3. Graph the histogram of the following grouped samples.

1. Compressive strength (in kilograms/centimeter^2) of cubes of concrete

Class Mark	200	225	250	275	300	325	350	375	400	425	450	475	500
Class Frequency	1	4	6	9	10	19	17	11	7	2	3	0	1

2. Heights (in centimeters) of nine-year-old pines

Height	Class Frequency	Height	Class Frequency
55– 75	2	175–195	30.5
75– 95	0	195–215	19.5
95–115	4	215–235	10
115–135	8	235–255	5
135–155	17	255–275	2
155–175	27		

3. Lifetimes (in hours) of light bulbs

Lifetime	Class Frequency	Lifetime	Class Frequency
950–1050	4	1550–1650	53
1050–1150	9	1650–1750	37
1150–1250	19	1750–1850	20
1250–1350	36	1850–1950	9
1350–1450	51	1950–2050	3
1450–1550	58	2050–2150	1

4. Grouping involves arbitrariness. To illustrate this, group the sample in Table 2.3.1 in three different ways by choosing the class marks:
   (*a*) 408, 411, 414, · · · (length of intervals 3)
   (*b*) 410, 415, 420, · · · (length of intervals 5; cf. Table 2.3.2)
   (*c*) 410, 420, 430, · · · (length of intervals 10)
   Graph and compare the histograms.

5. Group the sample in Table 2.3.1 in different ways, choosing class intervals of the same length 5, but different sets of class marks:
   (*a*) 407, 412, 417, · · ·
   (*b*) 408, 413, 418, · · ·
   (*c*) 409, 414, 419, · · ·
   (*d*) 410, 415, 420, · · · (cf. Table 2.3.2)
   (*e*) 411, 416, 421, · · ·
   Graph and compare the histograms.

6. In Problem *5d*, obtain another grouping by uniting adjacent class intervals in pairs to get intervals of length 10 and class marks 412.5, 422.5, · · · . Graph the histogram and compare it with that in Problem *5d*.

7. In a sample of 400 values of strength of cotton yarn (pounds required to break a skein), the smallest value was 77 and the largest 129. Suggest class intervals and class marks for grouping.

8. The diameter of 150 iron bolts ranged from 0.342 to 0.467 in. Suggest class intervals and class marks for grouping.

9. Consider the following sample (strength of 50 lots of cotton, pounds required to break a skein).

74	100	90	99	97	89	108	94	87	79
101	90	105	83	91	96	81	98	81	98
105	110	91	99	101	94	106	98	93	82
90	86	96	88	97	103	85	106	92	115
97	101	102	96	100	76	96	81	101	93

   Make up a frequency table of the ungrouped sample. Group the sample, choosing class intervals of the same length, with class marks 75, 80, 85, 90, · · · . Graph and compare the histograms of the ungrouped and the grouped sample.

10. In Problem 9, unite adjacent class intervals in pairs to get intervals of length 10 with class marks 77.5, 87.5, · · · . Graph the histogram and compare it with that in Problem 9. Which grouping is more satisfactory?

CHAPTER **3**

Sample Mean
and Sample Variance

We have seen that the frequency function (or the distribution function) characterizes a given sample in detail. From this function we may compute measures for certain properties of the sample, such as the average size of the sample values, the spread, and the "asymmetry." In the present chapter we shall primarily consider the two most important of these quantities, which are called the *mean* and the *variance of the sample*. Roughly speaking, the mean is a measure of the central tendency (average size of the sample values), and the variance measures the spread (as does the square root of the variance, which is called the *standard deviation of the sample*). This chapter also includes some other measures of central tendency and spread.

We shall see later (in Chap. 6) that the sample mean and sample variance have theoretical counterparts, that is, certain parameters in the distribution of the population from which the sample is taken.

3.1   Mean and Variance of a Sample

Given a sample $x_1, x_2, \cdots, x_n$, we first want to introduce a measure for the average size of the sample values. The most common such measure is the *arithmetic mean*. It is denoted by $\bar{x}$ (read *x bar*); thus

(1)
$$\bar{x} = \frac{x_1 + x_2 + \cdots + x_n}{n},$$

and is briefly called the *mean value* or **mean** *of the sample*. Using the summation sign, we may write

$$\bar{x} = \frac{1}{n} \sum_{j=1}^{n} x_j.$$

Example 1.   Five randomly selected pieces of permalloy had the nickel content (in percent)

79.4   79.0   78.9   79.2   78.9.

The sum of these values is 395.4. Hence our sample has the mean

$$\bar{x} = \frac{395.4}{5} = 79.08.$$

This is the average of the percent nickel content.

Other somewhat less important measures for the average size of sample values will be considered in connection with the next set of problems (at the end of Sec. 3.2).

We shall now introduce a measure for the "spread" or "variation" of the sample values. To motivate our consideration, let us start with a simple example and compare the two samples

$$10 \quad 20 \quad 60 \quad \text{and} \quad 28 \quad 29 \quad 33.$$

Both have size 3 and mean 30. However, there is an essential difference because the values of the first lie much farther apart from each other (and therefore from the mean value) than do the values of the other sample. We want to introduce a measure of variability which will distinguish two samples such as these. The practical importance of such a measure is rather obvious; for example, in a production process small variability of the product may indicate high quality.

Let us consider the problem in general. For our purpose we may choose a quantity that measures the deviation of the sample values $x_1, \cdots, x_n$ from the mean $\bar{x}$. We require that *every* value of the sample is taken into account.

It is natural to consider using the sum of the deviations $x_1 - \bar{x}$, $x_2 - \bar{x}$, $\cdots, x_n - \bar{x}$. Unfortunately, this does not work, because this sum is zero:

$$(2) \qquad (x_1 - \bar{x}) + (x_2 - \bar{x}) + \cdots + (x_n - \bar{x}) = 0.$$

In fact, the expression on the left can be written

$$x_1 + x_2 + \cdots + x_n - n\bar{x},$$

and from (1) we see that the sum of the sample values is equal to $n\bar{x}$.

If all the sample values are equal, then $\bar{x}$ is equal to this common value. Except for this uninteresting case, the sum in (2) will contain positive as well as negative terms, and so our choice is unsuccessful. However, we may dispose of the sign by taking absolute values or by squaring each term. The latter procedure requires a bit more computation, but the theoretical justification for the statistical methods based on that procedure is simpler. Therefore, let us take squares and introduce the so-called **variance** of the sample, which is denoted by s^2 and is defined by the formula

$$(3) \qquad s^2 = \frac{1}{n-1} \sum_{j=1}^{n} (x_j - \bar{x})^2 \qquad (n > 1).$$

Except for the above uninteresting case, we always have

$$s^2 > 0.$$

The nonnegative square root of s^2 is called the **standard deviation** *of the sample* and is denoted by s. We see that the units of measurement of s are the same as those of the data; this will often be convenient.

Observe that the notation s^2 is suggestive; it reminds us that we have a sum of squares on the right; furthermore, we thus avoid introducing another letter for the standard deviation.

Formula (3) *defines* the variance, but is of no practical use in calculating it. Formulas for calculating variances will be introduced in the next section. Nevertheless, let us illustrate that we have accomplished what we had in mind.

Example 2.   The above samples have size $n = 3$, mean $\bar{x} = 30$, and variance

$$s^2 = \frac{1}{2}\,[(10 - 30)^2 + (20 - 30)^2 + (60 - 30)^2] = 700$$

and

$$s^2 = \frac{1}{2}\,[(28 - 30)^2 + (29 - 30)^2 + (33 - 30)^2] = 7,$$

respectively. The variance of the first sample is much larger than that of the second. The same holds for the standard deviations

$$s = \sqrt{700} = 26.46 \quad \text{and} \quad s = \sqrt{7} = 2.646.$$

Perhaps, the reader may wonder why the denominator of s^2 is $n - 1$, whereas that of $\bar{x}$ is n. The reason will be given in Sec. 11.2. The number $n - 1$ is called the number of *degrees of freedom* of that sum.

Problems will be included at the end of the next section. Other measures for the variation of the values in a sample (the *range* and the *interquartile range*) will be considered in connection with those problems.

3.2   Computation of Mean and Variance

Let us now derive some formulas which are quite important for computing sample means and variances.

The absolute values of the differences $x_j - \bar{x}$ in (3) may be small compared with the sample values, and this might cause a loss of significant figures (undetected in automatic calculation). To get rid of those differences, we substitute

$$(x_j - \bar{x})^2 = x_j{}^2 - 2x_j\bar{x} + \bar{x}^2$$

into (3), Sec. 3.1, and decompose the resulting formula into three sums. This yields

$$\sum (x_j - \bar{x})^2 = \sum x_j{}^2 - 2\bar{x}\sum x_j + \sum \bar{x}^2.$$

The last sum equals $n\bar{x}^2$. Using (1), Sec. 3.1, we see that

$$-2\bar{x}\sum x_j = -\frac{2}{n}(\sum x_j)^2 \quad \text{and} \quad n\bar{x}^2 = \frac{1}{n}(\sum x_j)^2.$$

Taking these two expressions together, we finally have

(1)
$$s^2 = \frac{1}{n-1}\left[\sum_{j=1}^{n} x_j^2 - \frac{1}{n}\left(\sum_{j=1}^{n} x_j\right)^2\right].$$

From (1), Sec. 3.1, it follows that we may replace $\sum x_j$ by $n\bar{x}$, obtaining

(2)
$$s^2 = \frac{1}{n-1}\left[\sum_{j=1}^{n} x_j^2 - n\bar{x}^2\right].$$

This looks simpler than (1), but is less direct, since to get $\bar{x}^2$, we divide $(\sum x_j)^2$ by n^2, and then in (2) we again multiply by n.

We are not yet finished because the numbers in (1) may be large. In this case we may set

(3) $x_j = c + x_j^*$ $(x_j^* = x_j - c)$

and choose the constant c so that the transformed sample values x_j^* are small in absolute value. Geometrically, (3) means that we shift the origin on the scale. We now compute the mean $\bar{x}^*$ of the transformed sample, that is,

$$\bar{x}^* = \frac{1}{n}(x_1^* + \cdots + x_n^*),$$

and then the desired mean

(4) $\bar{x} = c + \bar{x}^*.$

Furthermore, the original sample and the transformed sample have the same variance. The simple proof is left to the reader.

The method just described is sometimes called the method of **working origin** because, instead of the actual origin $x = 0$, for working we choose the convenient origin $x = c$ (for which $x^* = 0$). The advantage of the method is obvious in cases in which no calculator or computer is available or one does not want to use it for merely a quick check of a few data. Even in other cases it may have its merits because the expression in the brackets in (1) may be a small difference of two large numbers, so that there is a danger of losing digits. If the calculation is done by an electronic computer, we would perhaps not even notice the loss.

Example 1. In the case of the sample in Example 1, Sec. 3.1, we obtain from (3), Sec. 3.1, and Table 3.2.1 the variance

$$s^2 = \frac{0.1880}{4} = 0.047.$$

Formula (1) yields the same numerical value. In fact,

$$s^2 = \tfrac{1}{4}[31{,}268.42 - \tfrac{1}{5}(395.4)^2] = 0.047$$

(cf. Table 3.2.2). The computation becomes much simpler if we use (3) with $c = 79$. Then

$$x_j^* = x_j - 79.$$

Tables 3.2.1–3.2.3. **Computations in Example 1**

Table 3.2.1

x_j	$x_j - \bar{x}$	$(x_j - \bar{x})^2$
79.4	0.32	0.1024
79.0	−0.08	0.0064
78.9	−0.18	0.0324
79.2	0.12	0.0144
78.9	−0.18	0.0324
Sum	0.00	0.1880

Table 3.2.2

x_j	x_j^2
79.4	6304.36
79.0	6241.00
78.9	6225.21
79.2	6272.64
78.9	6225.21
395.4	31268.42

Table 3.2.3

x_j	$x_j{}^*$	$x_j{}^{*2}$
79.4	0.4	0.16
79.0	0.0	0.00
78.9	−0.1	0.01
79.2	0.2	0.04
78.9	−0.1	0.01
Sum	0.4	0.22

The mean $\bar{x}^*$ of the transformed values is (cf. Table 3.2.3)

$$\bar{x}^* = \frac{0.4}{5} = 0.08.$$

The variance s^{*2} of the transformed values is (cf. Table 3.2.3)

$$s^{*2} = \frac{1}{4}\left[0.22 - \frac{0.4^2}{5}\right] = \frac{0.188}{4} = 0.047.$$

This follows from (1) with x_j replaced by $x_j{}^*$. Applying (4), we see that the mean of the given values is

$$\bar{x} = 79 + 0.08 = 79.08.$$

The variance is

$$s^2 = s^{*2} = 0.047.$$

Observe that in (1) we had to calculate the difference

$$
\begin{array}{r}
31{,}268.420 \\
-31{,}268.232 \\
\hline
0.188
\end{array}
$$

and lost 5 digits, whereas in the method of working origin, we simply had to calculate

$$
\begin{array}{r}
0.220 \\
-0.032 \\
\hline
0.188.
\end{array}
$$

In many practical cases we may obtain further simplifications by setting

(5) $$x_j = c_1 x_j{}^* + c_2 \qquad \left[\text{thus } x_j{}^* = \frac{1}{c_1}(x_j - c_2)\right]$$

and choosing the constants c_1 and c_2 in this linear transformation so that the transformed values $x_1{}^*, \cdots, x_n{}^*$ become as simple as possible. We first compute the mean $\bar{x}^*$ and the variance s^{*2} of the transformed sample and then the mean $\bar{x}$ and the variance s^2 of the original sample, using

(6) $$\bar{x} = c_1\bar{x}^* + c_2$$

and

(7) $$s^2 = c_1{}^2 s^{*2}.$$

Table 3.2.4. Given and Coded Values in Example 2

x_j	$x_j{}^*$	$x_j{}^{*2}$
20	0	0
30	1	1
50	3	9
60	4	16
80	6	36
90	7	49
Sum	21	111

This method is called **coding**. When $c_1 = 1$, it reduces to the method of working origin. The proof of (6) and (7) is left to the reader (Problem 16).

Although we shall apply such shortcuts on several occasions in this book, their significance is small compared with the more fundamental ideas and concepts. However, the reader should appreciate their convenience and try to understand how they are to be used.

Example 2. Table 3.2.4 shows a sample of six student grades in a mathematics examination in the summer of 1962; the values are written in ascending order. The first three students failed the test, and none of the students earned the maximum grade (100). We want to compute the mean grade $\bar{x}$ and the variance s^2. Noting that the x_j are integral multiples of 10, we set

$$x_j = 10 x_j{}^* + 20.$$

Then we have

$$x_j{}^* = 0.1 x_j - 2.$$

From Table 3.2.4 we obtain the mean

$$\bar{x}^* = \frac{21}{6} = 3.5$$

and the variance

$$s^{*2} = \frac{1}{5}\left(111 - \frac{21^2}{6}\right) = \frac{37.5}{5} = 7.5.$$

Hence, by (6) and (7), the given sample has the mean

$$\bar{x} = 10 \cdot 3.5 + 20 = 55$$

and the variance

$$s^2 = 10^2 \cdot 7.5 = 750.$$

Problems

1. Compute the mean $\bar{x}$ of the sample (lengths of nails in inches)

0.80　0.81　0.81　0.82　0.81　0.82　0.80　0.82　0.81　0.81.

Compute s^2 (*a*) by the defining formula (3) in Sec. 3.1, (*b*) by formula (1), (*c*) by (5) and (7).

2. Boilers of a high-pressure steam-power plant had the efficiency (in percent)

$$90.3 \quad 91.6 \quad 90.9 \quad 90.4 \quad 90.3 \quad 91.0 \quad 87.9 \quad 89.4.$$

Graph a histogram of the sample, then guess the values of $\bar{x}$ and s by merely inspecting the histogram, and finally compute $\bar{x}$, s^2, and s.

3. Carry out the same procedure as in Problem 2 for the following sample of faces that turned up on a die:

$$2 \quad 1 \quad 4 \quad 5.$$

4. Graph and compare the frequency functions of the two samples in Example 2, Sec. 3.1.

5. Construct a sample of size 2 with mean 0 and variance 1.

6. Prove that if the values of a sample are not all equal, then $\bar{x}$ lies between the smallest and the largest sample value.

7. The difference between the largest and the smallest value in a sample is called the **range** of the sample. What is the range of the sample in Problem 2? Does grouping change the range?

8. What are the obvious advantages and disadvantages of the variance, compared with the range?

9. The *p*th **percentile** of a sample is a number Q_p such that at least $p\%$ of the sample values are smaller than or equal to Q_p and also at least $(100 - p)\%$ of those values are larger than or equal to Q_p. If there is more than one such number (in which case there will be an interval of them), the *p*th percentile is defined as the average of those numbers (midpoint of that interval). In particular, Q_{50} is called the **middle quartile** or **median** and is denoted by $\tilde{x}$. Find $\tilde{x}$ for the sample in Table 2.1.2.

10. The percentiles Q_{25} and Q_{75} of a sample are called the **lower** and **upper quartiles** of the sample, and $Q_{75} - Q_{25}$, which is a measure for the spread, is called the **interquartile range**. Find Q_{25}, Q_{75}, and $Q_{75} - Q_{25}$ for the sample in Table 2.1.2.

11. For given numbers $x_1, \cdots, x_n$ the expression

$$h(t) = \sum_{j=1}^{n} (x_j - t)^2$$

is a function of t. For what value of t is $h(t)$ a minimum?

12. Verify by direct calculation that the samples in Example 2 of Sec. 3.1 satisfy (2), Sec. 3.1.

13. Derive (2) from (1).

14. Prove (4).

15. Show that the variance s^2 remains unchanged under a translation (3).

16. Prove (6) and (7). *Hint.* Substitute (5) in the formulas that define $\bar{x}$ and s^2.

17. Show that the proportion of sample values that differ from $\bar{x}$ by as much as M is less than s^2/M^2.

18. A sample value that occurs most frequently is called a **mode** of the sample. What is the mode of the sample in Table 2.1.2? Give some intuitive arguments in favor of the mean, median, and mode as descriptive measures of a sample.

19. Show that for any sample,

$$\bar{x} \leqq \sqrt{\sum_{j=1}^{n} x_j^2/n}.$$

20. If the values of a sample are positive and are changed by (a) adding 50 to each value, (b) increasing each value by 50%, what effects will these changes have on the mean, the variance, and the standard deviation of the sample?

21. If the values of a sample are measured in feet and we express them in inches, how will this change affect the mean, the variance, and the standard deviation of the sample?

22. Show that if we unite two samples of sizes n_1 and n_2 with means $\bar{x}_1$ and $\bar{x}_2$, respectively, we obtain a sample of size $n = n_1 + n_2$ with mean

$$\bar{x} = \frac{1}{n_1 + n_2}(n_1\bar{x}_1 + n_2\bar{x}_2).$$

23. Find a formula for the variance s^2 of the united sample in Problem 22 in terms of the variances $s_1{}^2$ and $s_2{}^2$ of the original samples.

24. Find the mean, the mode, and the median of the sample

x	1	2	3	4	5	7	9
Frequency of x	3	4	3	2	1	1	1

Graph $\tilde{f}(x)$ and indicate the position of the mean, mode, and median.

25. (a) In what case will the mean, the mode, and the median of a sample coincide?
(b) In what case will the difference between the median and the mean be large? Give simple examples.

26. Find the mean, median, and mode of the following sample. Comment on the result.

Value of stocks owned	100	1000	100,000
Frequency	100	90	20

27. Show that if a sample $x_1, \cdots, x_n$ has mean $\bar{x}$ and standard deviation s, the sample of the transformed values $y_1, \cdots, y_n$, where

$$y_j = \frac{x_j - \bar{x}}{s},$$

has the mean 0 and the standard deviation 1. (These values y_j are sometimes called *standardized values*.)

3.3   Computation of Sample Mean and Variance from the Frequency Function

We shall now see how to compute the mean $\bar{x}$ and the variance s^2 of a given sample from the corresponding frequency function $\tilde{f}(x)$; this will be rather simple. Let us begin with a typical example.

Example 1.   Ten randomly selected nails had the following lengths (in inches):

  0.80   0.81   0.81   0.82   0.81   0.82   0.80   0.82   0.81   0.81.

From (1) in Sec. 3.1 we obtain the mean

$$\bar{x} = \tfrac{1}{10}(0.80 \cdot 2 + 0.81 \cdot 5 + 0.82 \cdot 3) = 0.811 \text{ (in.).}$$

Dividing by 10, we may write

$$\bar{x} = 0.80 \cdot 0.2 + 0.81 \cdot 0.5 + 0.82 \cdot 0.3.$$

This is the sum of the *numerically different* sample values, each multiplied by its relative frequency. That is, each of these three x_j is multiplied by the corresponding value $\tilde{f}(x_j)$ of the frequency function $\tilde{f}(x)$. Similarly, from (3) in Sec. 3.1 we obtain

$$s^2 = \tfrac{10}{9}[(0.800{-}0.811)^2 \cdot 0.2 + (0.810{-}0.811)^2 \cdot 0.5 + (0.820{-}0.811)^2 \cdot 0.3]$$
$$= 0.000\ 054 \text{ (sq in.)}.$$

Obviously, the formulas in this example are of the form

(1) $$\bar{x} = \frac{1}{n} \sum_{j=1}^{m} x_j n\tilde{f}(x_j) = \sum_{j=1}^{m} x_j \tilde{f}(x_j)$$

and

(2) $$s^2 = \frac{1}{n-1} \sum_{j=1}^{m} (x_j - \bar{x})^2 n\tilde{f}(x_j) = \frac{n}{n-1} \sum_{j=1}^{m} (x_j - \bar{x})^2 \tilde{f}(x_j)$$

where

$$x_1, \qquad x_2, \qquad \cdots, \qquad x_m \qquad\qquad (m \leqq n)$$

are the *numerically different* values in the sample $x_1, \cdots, x_n$. Clearly $n\tilde{f}(x_j)$ is the frequency. The derivation of (1) and (2) is simple and is left to the reader. Note that in (1), Sec. 3.1, and (3), Sec. 3.1, the number of terms equals the number of *all* the sample values but, in (1) and (2), that number equals the number of all *numerically different* sample values.

Of course, (1), Sec. 3.2, now takes the form

(2′) $$s^2 = \frac{1}{n-1}\left\{ \sum_{j=1}^{m} x_j^2 n\tilde{f}(x_j) - \frac{1}{n}\left[\sum_{j=1}^{m} x_j n\tilde{f}(x_j) \right]^2 \right\}.$$

From the computational point of view, the frequency $n\tilde{f}(x_j)$ is more convenient than the relative frequency $\tilde{f}(x_j)$.

Furthermore, in (6), Sec. 3.2, we now have

$$\bar{x}^* = \frac{1}{n} \sum_{j=1}^{m} x_j^* n\tilde{f}(x_j^*) = \sum_{j=1}^{m} x_j^* \tilde{f}(x_j^*),$$

and so on. Here $\tilde{f}(x_j^*) = \tilde{f}(x_j)$.

Example 2.   Table 3.3.1 shows the computation of the mean and variance of the sample in Table 2.1.2. Column 1 contains the numerically different sample values and column 2 the coded values

$$x_j^* = 1000(x_j - 0.100); \qquad \text{thus} \qquad x_j = 0.001 x_j^* + 0.100.$$

Note that this is (5) in Sec. 3.2 with $c_1 = 0.001$ and $c_2 = 0.100$. From column 4 we obtain

$$\bar{x}^* = \frac{132}{50} = 2.64.$$

Hence the sample has the mean [cf. (6) in Sec. 3.2]

$$\bar{x} = c_1 \bar{x}^* + c_2 = 0.001 \cdot 2.64 + 0.100 = 0.102\ 64 \text{ (oz)}.$$

From (7) in Sec. 3.2 and columns 4 and 6 we obtain the variance

$$s^2 = 0.001^2 s^{*2} = 0.000\ 001 \cdot \frac{1}{49}\left(1608 - \frac{1}{50} \cdot 132^2 \right) = 0.000\ 025\ 7$$

Table 3.3.1. Calculation of Mean and Variance in Example 2

1 x_j	2 $x_j{}^*$	3 $50\tilde{f}(x_j)$	4 $50x_j{}^*\tilde{f}(x_j)$	5 $x_j{}^{*2}$	6 $50x_j{}^{*2}\tilde{f}(x_j)$
0.092	−8	1	−8	64	64
0.093	−7	0	0	49	0
0.094	−6	2	−12	36	72
0.095	−5	1	−5	25	25
0.096	−4	2	−8	16	32
0.097	−3	2	−6	9	18
0.098	−2	3	−6	4	12
0.099	−1	3	−3	1	3
0.100	0	3	0	0	0
0.101	1	4	4	1	4
0.102	2	3	6	4	12
0.103	3	5	15	9	45
0.104	4	4	16	16	64
0.105	5	3	15	25	75
0.106	6	2	12	36	72
0.107	7	3	21	49	147
0.108	8	3	24	64	192
0.109	9	1	9	81	81
0.110	10	2	20	100	200
0.111	11	1	11	121	121
0.112	12	1	12	144	144
0.113	13	0	0	169	0
0.114	14	0	0	196	0
0.115	15	1	15	225	225
Sum		50	132		1608

and from this the standard deviation

$$s = \sqrt{s^2} = 0.005\ 07\ \text{(oz)}.$$

In the case of a **grouped sample** we define the mean by the formula

$$(3) \qquad \bar{x} = \sum_{j=1}^{K} x_j \tilde{f}(x_j) = \frac{1}{n} \sum_{j=1}^{K} x_j n \tilde{f}(x_j)$$

and the variance by the formula

$$(4) \qquad s^2 = \frac{n}{n-1} \sum_{j=1}^{K} (x_j - \bar{x})^2 \tilde{f}(x_j) = \frac{1}{n-1} \sum_{j=1}^{K} (x_j - \bar{x})^2 n \tilde{f}(x_j).$$

Here K is the number of class intervals, x_j is the jth class mark (midpoint of the jth class interval), and $\tilde{f}(x_j)$ is the corresponding relative class frequency (cf. Sec. 2.3); hence $n\tilde{f}(x_j)$ is the corresponding class frequency. From (4) we

Table 3.3.2. Sample from Table 2.1.2, Grouped

Class Interval	Class Mark x_j	Class Frequency $50\tilde{f}(x_j)$	x_j*	$50x_j*\tilde{f}(x_j)$	x_j*^2	$50x_j*^2\tilde{f}(x_j)$
0.0875–0.0925	0.090	1	-2	-2	4	4
0.0925–0.0975	0.095	7	-1	-7	1	7
0.0975–0.1025	0.100	16	0	0	0	0
0.1025–0.1075	0.105	17	1	17	1	17
0.1075–0.1125	0.110	8	2	16	4	32
0.1125–0.1175	0.115	1	3	3	9	9
	Sum	50		27		69

obtain the formula

$$(5) \qquad s^2 = \frac{1}{n-1}\left\{ \sum_{j=1}^{K} x_j{}^2 n\tilde{f}(x_j) - \frac{1}{n}\left[\sum_{j=1}^{K} x_j n\tilde{f}(x_j) \right]^2 \right\},$$

which is needed for computational purposes.

Example 3. We shall now illustrate the application of formulas (3) and (5) by a numerical example and see that grouping will, in general, change the values of the mean and the variance. For the sake of simplicity, let us take a small sample (which, in practice, we would perhaps use in its original ungrouped form).

The sample considered in the previous example may be grouped as shown in Table 3.3.2. We set

$$x_j = 0.005x_j* + 0.100; \qquad \text{thus} \qquad x_j* = 200(x_j - 0.100).$$

Then we obtain

$$\bar{x} = 0.005\bar{x}* + 0.100 = 0.005 \cdot \frac{27}{50} + 0.100 = 0.1027,$$

which differs from the result in the previous example. This difference is a result of grouping, and in other cases the effect may even be larger.

The variance of the coded values is

$$s*^2 = \frac{1}{49}\left(69 - \frac{1}{50} \cdot 27^2 \right) = 1.110\,6.$$

From (7) in Sec. 3.2 we thus obtain the variance

$$s^2 = 0.005^2 \cdot 1.110\,6 = 0.000\,027\,8$$

and the standard deviation

$$s = 0.005\,3.$$

These values differ from the corresponding values for the ungrouped sample (see above).

Table 3.3.3. Heights (in Centimeters) of 100 Austrian 18-Year-Old Girls

Height	Frequency	Height	Frequency	Height	Frequency
151	0	161	5	171	6
152	0	162	7	172	4
153	1	163	5	173	3
154	1	164	5	174	2
155	2	165	6	175	3
156	3	166	7	176	1
157	3	167	5	177	1
158	5	168	4	178	1
159	6	169	5	179	0
160	4	170	5	180	0

Problems

1.–6. Using frequency functions, compute the mean and the variance of the following samples.

1. The sample in Problem 1, Sec. 2.1.
2. The sample in Problem 2, Sec. 2.1.
3. The sample in Problem 3, Sec. 2.1.
4. The sample in Problem 5, Sec. 2.1.
5. The sample in Problem 3, Sec. 2.3.
6. The sample in Table 3.3.3.

7. In general, if a sample is being grouped, its mean will change. Show that in the case of class intervals of equal length l the change cannot exceed $l/2$.
8. Give a formal proof of (1) and (2).
9. Derive (2′) from (1) in Sec. 3.2.
10. Check the results in Example 3 by choosing another way of coding, for example, $x_j = x_j^* + 0.100$.

3.4 Analogy between Frequency Distributions and Mass Distributions

There is an interesting analogy between distributions of values in samples and distributions of mass points of total mass 1 on a straight line. The analogy is strictly quantitative.

Let $x_1, \cdots, x_m$ be the numerically different values in a given sample, and let $\tilde{f}_1, \cdots, \tilde{f}_m$ be the corresponding relative frequencies. The mechanical analogue of this sample is a distribution consisting of m masses, namely, the mass $\tilde{f}_1$ at the point x_1 on the x-axis, the mass $\tilde{f}_2$ at the point x_2, etc. The function that corresponds to the cumulative frequency function (2) in Sec. 2.1 is

$$\tilde{F}(x) = \sum_{x_j \leq x} \tilde{f}_j.$$

For each x this is the sum of the masses which are at the point x or to the left of that point.

That mass distribution has the center of gravity

$$\bar{x} = \sum_{j=1}^{m} x_j \tilde{f}_j.$$

The moment of inertia with respect to the center of gravity is

$$I = \sum_{j=1}^{m} (x_j - \bar{x})^2 \tilde{f}_j.$$

From this and (1) in Sec. 3.3 we see that *the sample mean corresponds to the center of gravity of that mass distribution.* Furthermore, from (2) in Sec. 3.3 it follows that *the variance corresponds to that moment of inertia*, except for a factor $n/(n-1)$.

The first moment with respect to the center of gravity equals zero. This is the mechanical analogue of formula (2) in Sec. 3.1.

PART II

PROBABILITY THEORY

Statistical experiments or observations yield samples from which we want to draw conclusions about the corresponding populations. Before we can do so, we must develop mathematical models of populations. This will require the theory of mathematical probability. Hence we see that this theory is of basic importance to mathematical statistics.

In this connection we should remember that mathematical models which aid in the solution of real-life problems are used in various fields. For example, in aerodynamics we may start from the basic laws of mechanics and obtain from them a mathematical model (a theory) of the motion of a certain type of airplane. Mathematical models should be as simple as possible, yet still describe with sufficient accuracy the main features and properties of the reality.

We shall now consider the fundamentals of probability theory[1] and, in particular, the concept of mathematical probability. Then we shall derive the most important probability distributions. These are theoretical distributions that serve as models of populations, in contrast to sample distributions, which are empirical.

[1] For a more extended treatment of probability theory, the reader is referred to the books by Feller (1961) and Parzen (1960) which are listed in Appendix 3. Also see Loève (1963).

CHAPTER 4

Fundamental Concepts

The theory of mathematical probability orginated from the theory of chance. Probabilistic studies of gambling problems were made by Pascal and Fermat as early as 1654. A systematic theory was developed by Jakob Bernoulli (*Ars coniectandi*, 1713), Abraham de Moivre (*The Doctrine of Chances*, 1718), and Pierre Simon de Laplace (*Théorie analytique des probabilités*, 1812). Probability theory also became important in astronomy and geodesy in connection with the theory of errors of measurements. Important contributions in this direction were made by Gauss and Laplace. For more historical information up to the middle of the nineteenth century, see Todhunter (1949) (cf. Appendix 3).

In the present chapter we discuss the concepts of probability theory that are important with respect to statistical methods.

4.1 Random Experiments, Outcomes, Events

In this section we shall explain several basic notions, some of which have already been mentioned before.

By a *random experiment* or *random observation*, or simply **experiment** or **observation,** we mean a process that has the following properties.

(1) It is performed according to a well-defined set of rules.
(2) It is repetitive in nature or can be so conceived.
(3) The result of each performance depends "on chance" (that is, on influences which we cannot control) and can therefore not be uniquely predicted.

The result of a single performance of the experiment is called the **outcome** of that trial.

Examples are games of chance such as throwing a die, flipping a coin, or drawing two cards from a shuffled deck of playing cards, technical experiments such as the random selection and inspection of 10 screws from a box containing 100 screws, the random selection of 5 pieces of sheet steel and the measurement of the Rockwell hardness, the measurement of the lifetimes of 50 light bulbs randomly selected from a lot of bulbs, the determination of the yield of a chemical process under various conditions, the relationship between working conditions (such as temperature and humidity) and output, the random selection of 20 persons from a group and the determination of their blood pressures or their opinions about a certain movie, etc.

An experiment in which several hogs are fed different rations may be performed only once with those same animals; nevertheless, the experiment has the above property (2). In fact, it can be regarded as being repetitive because it may be thought of as the first in an unlimited number of similar experiments.

The set of all possible outcomes of an experiment is called the **sample space** of the experiment and will be denoted by S. Each outcome is called an *element* or *point* of S. A sample space is said to be *finite* or *infinite*, depending on whether it consists of finitely many or infinitely many elements, respectively.

For example, with the random experiment of throwing a die we may associate the sample space

$$S = \{1, 2, 3, 4, 5, 6\}.$$

consisting of six elements corresponding to the six faces the die can turn up.

In tossing a coin there are 2 possible outcomes, namely, H (head) and T (tail). Hence, in this case the sample space S has 2 elements,

$$S = \{H, T\}.$$

These outcomes may also be expressed by numbers, for instance, H by 1 and T by 0. This is a convenient choice because the number indicates the number of heads obtained in a given toss.

In tossing a coin twice, there are 4 possible outcomes: HH, HT, TH, TT, where the first letter in each pair refers to the first toss and the other letter refers to the last toss. The corresponding ordered pairs of numbers are $(1, 1), (1, 0), (0, 1), (0, 0)$ and may be represented as points in a plane.

In connection with industrial production, we may draw an item to find out whether it is defective or nondefective. Then S consists of the two elements D (defective) and N (nondefective), which may also be characterized by numbers, for example, 0 (defective) and 1 (nondefective). If in this case we want to distinguish among several types of defects, we have a sample space consisting of more than two points.

The sample space of the experiment of measuring the strength of cotton is infinite because the outcome may be any positive number within a certain range. The same holds for experiments of measuring the lifetime of bulbs, the height of persons, the weight of animals, etc.

In most practical problems we are not so much interested in the individual outcomes as in whether an outcome belongs (or does not belong) to a certain

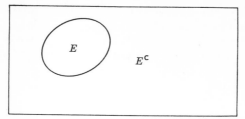

Fig. 4.1.1. Venn diagram representing a sample space S and events E and E^c

set of outcomes. Clearly, each such set A is a subset of the sample space S. It is called an **event.**

Note that each outcome is a subset of S and is thus an event, but a rather special one, sometimes called an *elementary event,* to distinguish it from other events consisting of more than one point of S. The notion of event also includes the entire sample space S as a special case.

Example 1. If we draw 2 gaskets from a set of 5 (numbered from 1 to 5), the sample space consists of the 10 possible outcomes

$$1,2 \quad 1,3 \quad 1,4 \quad 1,5 \quad 2,3 \quad 2,4 \quad 2,5 \quad 3,4 \quad 3,5 \quad 4,5,$$

but we may be interested in the number of defective gaskets we get in these drawings and thus distinguish among the 3 events

     A: No defective gaskets,   *B: 1 defective gasket,*   *C: 2 defective gaskets.*

Assuming that 3 gaskets, say 1, 2, 3, are defective, we see that

A occurs, if we draw	4, 5					
B occurs, if we draw	1, 4;	1, 5;	2, 4;	2, 5;	3, 4; or	3, 5
C occurs, if we draw	1, 2;	1, 3;	or	2, 3.		

A sample space S and the events of an experiment can be represented graphically by a **Venn diagram** as follows. Suppose that the set of points inside the rectangle in Fig. 4.1.1 represents S. Then the interior of a closed curve inside the rectangle represents an event which we denote by E. The set of all the elements (outcomes) not in E is called the **complement** *of E in S* and is denoted[1] by E^c.

For example, in throwing a die just once, the complement of the event

         E: The die turns up an even number

is the event

        E^c: The die turns up an odd number.

An event containing no elements is called the **impossible event** or *empty event* and is denoted by ϕ.

---

[1] Another notation for the complement of E is $\bar{E}$, but it is not used here, because the bar is used in set theory for another purpose.

Let us suppose that we perform an experiment n times and that in this series of n trials an event E occurs precisely k times. Then k is called the *absolute frequency* or, briefly, the **frequency,** and k/n the **relative frequency** of E in that series. This relative frequency will be denoted by $\tilde{f}(E)$. Thus

(1)
$$\tilde{f}(E) = \frac{k}{n}.$$

Since k cannot be negative and cannot exceed n, we always have the important relation

(2)
$$0 \leqq \tilde{f}(E) \leqq 1,$$

that is, *the relative frequency of an event is a nonnegative number that cannot exceed* 1.

If the event E is characterized by a number a, then our present consideration becomes identical with that in Sec. 2.1.

***Example* 2.**   Twenty-five randomly selected students obtained the following grades in calculus:

Grade	A	B	C	D	F
Number of students	2	4	8	3	8

We see that in this sample,

$$\tilde{f}(A) = \frac{2}{25}, \qquad \tilde{f}(B) = \frac{4}{25}, \qquad \tilde{f}(C) = \frac{8}{25}, \qquad \text{etc.}$$

Problems

1.–6. Graph the sample spaces corresponding to the following random experiments.

   1. Tossing a single coin.

   2. Tossing 2 coins.

   3. Throwing a die.

   4. Throwing 2 dice.

   5. Birth of a single child, the outcomes being B (boy) and G (girl).

   6. Drawing 3 gaskets from a set of 5 gaskets (cf. Example 1).

   7. In an experiment the lifetime of each of 3 electronic components is recorded. Define a corresponding sample space.

8.–10. In each case define a sample space S and find the complementary event of E.

   8. Throwing 2 dice; E: *The sum of the faces that turn up is an even number greater than* 5.

   9. Drilling a hole into a plate and measuring its diameter; E: *The diameter of the hole is at least* 2.3 *in. and at most* 2.4 *in.*

   10. Throwing 3 dice; E: *The three faces that turn up are different.*

4.2   Union and Intersection of Events, Mutually Exclusive Events

In applications of probability theory we are often concerned with several related events rather than with just one event. For this reason we shall now consider an arbitrary random experiment, with corresponding sample space S, and any two events A and B in the experiment. Then

$$A \cup B$$

denotes the event that occurs if and only if A occurs or B occurs, or both A and B occur. The event $A \cup B$ is called[2] the **union** of the events A and B.

Note that $A \cup B$ consists of all the elements of S contained in A or B, or both (cf. Fig. 4.2.1); hence the notation $A \cup B$ is in agreement with the usual notation in set theory, where $A \cup B$ denotes the union of two sets A and B.

Furthermore,

$$A \cap B$$

denotes the event that occurs if and only if both A and B occur simultaneously, that is, in the same performance of the experiment under consideration. The event $A \cap B$ is called[2] the **intersection** of the events A and B.

Note that $A \cap B$ consists of all the elements of the sample space S contained in both A and B (cf. Fig. 4.2.1); therefore the notation $A \cap B$ agrees with the usual notation in set theory, where $A \cap B$ denotes the intersection of two sets A and B.

If A and B cannot occur simultaneously, they are called **mutually exclusive events** or *disjoint events*. This is the case if and only if $A \cap B = \phi$, the empty event, so that A and B have no points in common. Note that this concept always refers to a definite random experiment.

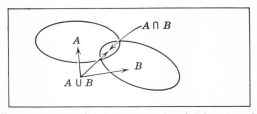

Fig. 4.2.1. Venn diagram representing two events A and B in a sample space S and their union $A \cup B$ and intersection $A \cap B$

[2] An older notation for $A \cup B$ is $A + B$, and an older corresponding term is *sum* of two events. Similarly, an older notation for $A \cap B$ is AB, and an older corresponding term is *product* of two events.

Example 1.   In rolling a die once, the events

> *A: The die turns up a number not smaller than* 4,
>
> *B: The die turns up a number divisible by* 3

have the union $A \cup B = \{3, 4, 5, 6\}$ and the intersection $A \cap B = \{6\}$ (cf. Fig. 4.2.2).

If all the elements of an event A are also contained in an event B, then A is called a **subevent** of B, and we write

$$A \subset B \qquad \text{or} \qquad B \supset A.$$

For instance, the event $D = \{4, 6\}$ is a subevent of A in Example 1. Clearly, if $A \subset B$, then if A occurs, B necessarily occurs.

The notions of union and intersection may be extended to more than two events, as follows.

Let $A_1, \cdots, A_m$ be several events in a sample space S. Then the event consisting of all elements contained in one or more of these m events is called the **union** of $A_1, \cdots, A_m$ and is denoted by

$$A_1 \cup A_2 \cup \cdots \cup A_m, \qquad \text{or more briefly} \qquad \bigcup_{j=1}^{m} A_j.$$

The event consisting of all elements contained in all those m events is called the **intersection** of $A_1, \cdots, A_m$ and is denoted by

$$A_1 \cap A_2 \cap \cdots \cap A_m, \qquad \text{or more briefly} \qquad \bigcap_{j=1}^{m} A_j.$$

More generally, let $A_1, A_2, \cdots, A_m, \cdots$ be infinitely many elements in S. Then the *union*

$$A_1 \cup A_2 \cup \cdots, \qquad \text{or more briefly} \qquad \bigcup_{j=1}^{\infty} A_j$$

is defined to be the event consisting of all the elements contained in at least one of those events, and the *intersection*

$$A_1 \cap A_2 \cap \cdots, \qquad \text{or more briefly} \qquad \bigcap_{j=1}^{\infty} A_j$$

is defined to be the event consisting of all the elements contained in all those events.

If events $A_1, A_2, \cdots, A_m, \cdots$ are such that the occurrence of any of them makes the simultaneous occurrence of any other of them impossible, then $A_j \cap A_k = \phi$ for any j and $k \neq j$, and the events are called **mutually exclusive events** or *disjoint events*.

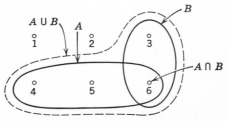

Fig. 4.2.2. Venn diagram in Ex. 1

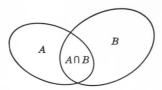

Fig. 4.2.3. Illustration of formula (1)

For instance, in throwing a die once the events

$$A: \text{ An even number turns up}$$

and

$$B: \text{ An odd number turns up}$$

are mutually exclusive.

Suppose that we perform a random experiment n times and obtain a sample consisting of n values. Let A and B be events whose relative frequencies in those n trials are $\tilde{f}(A)$ and $\tilde{f}(B)$, respectively. We shall prove that in this case the event $A \cup B$ has the relative frequency

(1) $$\tilde{f}(A \cup B) = \tilde{f}(A) + \tilde{f}(B) - \tilde{f}(A \cap B).$$

If A and B are mutually exclusive, then $\tilde{f}(A \cap B) = 0$, and

(2) $$\tilde{f}(A \cup B) = \tilde{f}(A) + \tilde{f}(B);$$

that is, *the relative frequency of the sum of two mutually exclusive events equals the sum of the relative frequencies of those events.*

We shall now prove (1). With respect to the outcomes we may distinguish among four cases as follows.

(C1) Both A and B have occurred.
(C2) A has occurred, and B has not.
(C3) B has occurred, and A has not.
(C4) Neither A nor B has occurred.

Let n_1, n_2, n_3, n_4 be the number of occurrence of (C1), (C2), (C3), (C4), respectively. These four cases are mutually exclusive. Hence the total numbers of occurrence of A, B, $A \cap B$, and $A \cup B$ are

$$n_1 + n_2, \quad n_1 + n_3, \quad n_1, \quad n_1 + n_2 + n_3,$$

respectively. Since we performed the experiment n times, we thus obtain the relative frequencies

(3)
$$\tilde{f}(A) = \frac{n_1 + n_2}{n}, \qquad \tilde{f}(B) = \frac{n_1 + n_3}{n}$$
$$\tilde{f}(A \cap B) = \frac{n_1}{n}, \qquad \tilde{f}(A \cup B) = \frac{n_1 + n_2 + n_3}{n}.$$

From this, (1) follows.

Problems

1. What is $A \cup B$, $B \cup C$, $A \cap B$, and $A \cup B \cup C$ in Example 1 of Sec. 4.1?

2. In the experiment of throwing a die once, graph the events
   A: Even number,
   B: Number divisible by 3,
   C: One.
   What is $A \cup B$, $A \cap B$, and $A \cap C$?

3. To inspect a lot of 1000 screws, 50 screws are drawn at random. It is found that 1 of the latter has a defective head as well as a defective thread, 3 have a defective head only, and 2 have a defective thread only. Find the relative frequencies of the events
   A: Defective thread,
   B: Defective head,
   $A \cap B$, and $A \cup B$.

4. Formula (3) gives relative frequencies that correspond to *all n* trials. Let $\tilde{f}(B \mid A)$ denote the relative frequency of B in those of the n trials in which A happens. Similarly, let $\tilde{f}(A \mid B)$ be the relative frequency of A in those trials in which B happens. Show that

   (4) $$\tilde{f}(B \mid A) = \frac{n_1}{n_1 + n_2}, \qquad \tilde{f}(A \mid B) = \frac{n_1}{n_1 + n_3}.$$

   Using (3), show that this implies

   (5) $$\tilde{f}(A)\tilde{f}(B \mid A) = \tilde{f}(A \cap B), \qquad \tilde{f}(B)\tilde{f}(A \mid B) = \tilde{f}(A \cap B).$$

5. Find $\tilde{f}(A \mid B)$ and $\tilde{f}(B \mid A)$ in Problem 3.

6. Galton observed the following frequencies of eye colors in a group of fathers and sons (data from K. Pearson, *Phil. Trans.*, A, 1900, 138; condensed).

Son's Eye Color	Father's Eye Color	
	Light	Dark
Light	471	148
Dark	151	230

   Find the relative frequency of the events
   A: Father's eye-color light,
   B: Son's eye-color light,
   $A \cap B$, and $A \cup B$. Find $\tilde{f}(B \mid A)$.

7. A box of 20 fountain pens contains 10 nondefective pens, 8 with type A defects, 5 with type B defects, and 3 with both types of defects. Suppose that 1 pen is drawn at random. Graph a Venn diagram of the corresponding sample space S showing the events E_A of getting a type A defective, E_B of getting a type B defective, $E_A \cap E_B$, $E_A \cap E_B^c$, $E_A^c \cap E_B$, $E_A^c \cap E_B^c$, $E_A \cup E_B$, $E_A^c \cup E_A$, $E_A \cup E_B^c$ and $E_A^c \cup E_B^c$. How many elements (outcomes) are in each event?

8. Set up a sample space for the single toss of 3 distinguishable coins. In how many of the outcomes do we obtain at least 2 heads?

9. Set up a sample space for the single throw of 2 dice. Using this space, find the number of outcomes such that the sum on both faces that show up will be 6 or larger.

10. How can (1) be made plausible by means of Fig. 4.2.3?

11. Applying (1), show that

$$\tilde{f}(A \cup B \cup C)$$
$$= \tilde{f}(A) + \tilde{f}(B) + \tilde{f}(C) - \tilde{f}(A \cap B) - \tilde{f}(B \cap C) - \tilde{f}(C \cap A) + \tilde{f}(A \cap B \cap C).$$

12. Using Venn diagrams, graph and check the following rules. ($A, B, \cdots$ are subsets of S, A^c is the complement of A with respect to S, and ϕ is the empty set.)

$$A \cup A = A \qquad\qquad A \cap A = A$$
$$A \cup A^c = S \qquad\qquad A \cap A^c = \phi$$
$$(A \cup B)^c = A^c \cap B^c \qquad (A \cap B)^c = A^c \cup B^c$$
$$A \cup (B \cap C) = (A \cup B) \cap (A \cup C)$$
$$A \cap (B \cup C) = (A \cap B) \cup (A \cap C)$$

(The formulas in the third line are called **De Morgan's laws**.)

4.3   Classical Concept of Mathematical Probability

Probability theory had its origins in the study of games of chance, and although the corresponding classical concept of mathematical probability is of limited direct use in statistics, we introduce it here and consider the nature of its limitations, thus motivating the ideas in the subsequent section.

If we toss a die, then one of the six numbers

$$1 \quad 2 \quad 3 \quad 4 \quad 5 \quad 6$$

will occur. These events are mutually exclusive. If the die is **fair,** that is, if it is of homogeneous material and strictly cubical in form, then we may assume that for reasons of symmetry, each of these six events is equally likely. We say that in this experiment there are six *equally likely* or *equally probable cases*.

Similarly, in other experiments we may distinguish among a certain number of **equally likely cases,** that is, mutually exclusive events that are equally likely and exhaust all possibilities.

If in a certain game there are m equally likely cases, then a player T may subdivide these cases in two classes, namely, the cases in which he wins the game and the cases in which he does not win. If there are w cases in which he wins, then, obviously, the fraction w/m is a measure for the player's chance to win the game. This suggests the following definition.

Laplace's classical definition of mathematical probability.   *The probability $P(A)$ of an event A in a random experiment is*

(1)
$$P(A) = \frac{w}{m},$$

where w is the number of cases in which A occurs and m is the number of all equally likely cases in the experiment.

Example 1. In tossing a fair die, there are six equally likely cases. Hence the outcome "*six*" has probability $P = 1/6$, and the event "*even number*" has probability 1/2 because there are $w = 3$ cases in which the event occurs.

If in our further consideration we use the terms **"drawing from a deck of cards"** and **"drawing from an urn"** (or a box, etc.), we shall always assume that each card in the deck or each object in the urn has the same probability of being drawn.

Example 2. An urn contains three red and seven black balls. One ball is drawn. Find the probability P of obtaining a red ball.

There are ten equally likely cases. In three cases the event under consideration happens. Hence $P = 3/10 = 30\%$.

Example 3. Two fair dice are thrown simultaneously. Find the probability P that both numbers which turn up are even.

We may distinguish among 36 cases

$$
\begin{array}{cccc}
(1,1) & (1,2) & \cdots & (1,6) \\
(2,1) & (2,2) & \cdots & (2,6) \\
\cdot & \cdot & \cdots & \cdot \\
(6,1) & (6,2) & \cdots & (6,6)
\end{array}
$$

where the first number in the parentheses is the number on the first die which turns up and the second number refers to the other die. There are nine cases in which the event under consideration happens, namely, the cases

$$(2,2) \quad (2,4) \quad (2,6) \quad (4,2) \quad (4,4) \quad (4,6) \quad (6,2) \quad (6,4) \quad (6,6).$$

Hence $P = 9/36 = 1/4$.

We see that Laplace defines the concept of probability in terms of the notion of equally likely cases. It follows that Laplace's definition can only be applied to experiments in which there are finitely many equally likely cases, whose definition is suggested by the nature of the experiment. Unfortunately, most practical problems are not of this type, and Laplace's definition cannot be applied. For example, if we ask for the probability of a patient being cured by a certain medical treatment, or the probability of a certain machine producing defective items, then there is no way of introducing equally likely cases.

Hence we need a more general concept of mathematical probability. In deriving that concept we shall use some of the ideas of A. N. Kolmogorov (1956); cf. Appendix 3.

Problems

1.–9. In each case describe a sample space for the given random experiment and assign probabilities to the outcomes as well as to the given event A.

    1. Tossing a fair coin.

    2. Tossing a dime and a nickel. *A: At least one head.*

    3. Drawing a rivet from a box containing 3 large and 2 small rivets which are numbered.

    4. Same as in Problem 3, but rivets of like size are not distinguishable.

5. Tossing 3 distinguishable fair dice. *A: Sum* 17 *or* 18.
6. Single toss of 3 distinguishable fair coins. *A: At least* 2 *heads.*
7. Tossing 2 distinguishable fair dice. *A: Sum greater than or equal to* 6.
8. Tossing 2 distinguishable fair dice. *A: Different faces.*
9. Drawing a chip from a box that contains 20 chips numbered from 1 to 20. *A: Number drawn is divisible by* 3 *or* 4.

10. Compare the chances of obtaining a 3 with 1 fair die and obtaining a total of 6 with 2 fair dice.

4.4   Probability Concept in Statistics

With a pencil and a ruler, we can draw things that we call "straight lines." We may then determine and describe properties of these "straight lines" and relations between them in an empirical fashion. The transition from the resulting "empirical geometry" to a geometry in the sense of mathematics requires two steps.

Step 1. We postulate the existence of mathematical concepts (such as point and straight line) that correspond to empirical concepts.

Step 2. We select the empirical properties and relations that we regard as most fundamental, and we state them in an idealized fashion, for example:

Two distinct points always completely determine a straight line.

Any two distinct points of a straight line completely determine that line.

etc. These statements are called *axioms*, and their totality is called a *system of axioms*. This is the basis of geometry in the sense that all the theorems of geometry must be derived from that set of axioms. The axioms must be chosen so that the resulting geometry is a useful mathematical model of the observable geometrical facts and therefore agrees with our geometrical intuition.

In the theory of mathematical probability we proceed quite similarly, as follows.

Experience shows that if we perform a random experiment very often, then the occurrence of events obeys certain laws. In particular the relative frequency of an event tends to become a constant. By this we mean that if we perform several long sequences of the experiment, the corresponding relative frequencies will be almost the same. We say that the experiment shows *statistical regularity* or *stability of the relative frequencies.* This is illustrated by Table 4.4.1, which needs no further explanation, and Fig. 4.4.1. In Fig. 4.4.1

Table 4.4.1. Coin Tossing

Experiments by	Number of Throws	Number of Heads	Relative Frequency of Heads
BUFFON	4,040	2,048	0.5069
K. PEARSON	12,000	6,019	0.5016
K. PEARSON	24,000	12,012	0.5005

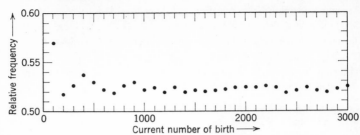

Fig. 4.4.1. Relative frequency of the event "birth of a boy" (data from Graz, Austria, 1962)

the point is that with increasing number of births the percentage of boys seems to fluctuate less and less. A similar behavior will be seen in the percentage of defective items in a production under reasonably constant conditions, and other examples can easily be found.

The great majority of random experiments having practical importance exhibit this stability. We may therefore conjecture that it will be practically certain that the relative frequency of an event E in a great number of performances of such a random experiment is approximately equal to a certain number $P(E)$.

For this reason we now postulate the existence of a number $P(E)$ which is called the *probability of occurrence* of that event E or, briefly, the **probability** of E in that random experiment. Note that this number is not an absolute property of E but refers to a certain sample space S, that is, to a certain random experiment.

The statement "E has the probability $P(E)$" then means that if we perform the experiment very often, it is practically certain that the relative frequency $\tilde{f}(E)$ is approximately equal to $P(E)$. (Here the term "approximately equal" must be made precise. This we have to postpone until Sec. 8.5.)

The probability thus introduced is the counterpart of the empirical relative frequency. It is therefore natural to require that it should have certain basic properties which the relative frequency has. These properties are suggested by Theorems 1 and 2, Sec. 2.1, and formula (2), Sec. 4.2, and may be formulated as follows.

Axioms of mathematical probability

1. *If E is any event in a sample space S, then*

(1) $$0 \leqq P(E) \leqq 1.$$

2. *To the entire sample space S there corresponds*

(2) $$P(S) = 1.$$

3. *If A and B are mutually exclusive events* (cf. Sec. 4.2), *then*

(3) $$P(A \cup B) = P(A) + P(B).$$

If the sample space is infinite, we must replace Axiom 3 by

3*. *If E_1, E_2, $\cdots$ are mutually exclusive events, then*

(3*) $$P(E_1 \cup E_2 \cup \cdots) = P(E_1) + P(E_2) + \cdots.$$

4.5   Practical Determination of Probabilities

How can we assign probabilities to the various events in a sample space S? This is a natural and important question, and although the "practical" determination of probabilities is not a matter of probability theory, but is in the realm of statistics, we shall include some relevant remarks in the present section.

We first note that *the classical concept of probability is a special case of the concept of probability defined in Section* 4.4. In fact, the classical probability concept satisfies Axioms 1-3.

Hence, if S is finite, consisting of k elements, and if the nature of the experiment shows that these k outcomes are equally likely to occur, then we may assign the same probability to each outcome. Now, because of Axiom 2, this probability must equal $1/k$. Consequently, in this case the computation of probabilities of events reduces to that of counting the elements that make up the events.

The situation is different if the nature of the experiment does not show that the finitely many outcomes are equally likely to occur, or if the sample space is not finite and the nature of the experiment does not indicate how to subdivide the sample space into finitely many equally likely events. Then we must assign probabilities by using relative frequencies observed in long sequences of trials. This must be done so that the axioms of probability are satisfied.

In this way we obtain only approximate values, but this does not matter. The situation is analogous to that in classical physics, where we postulate that each body has a certain mass but cannot determine that mass exactly. However, this is no hindrance in developing the physical theory.

Moreover, we should note that in the classical case the situation is no better. For example, the probability 0.5 of *heads* in tossing a coin is an approximate value only, since a coin is not completely symmetric and, for a definite coin, 0.499 or 0.5001, for example, may perhaps be a better approximation of the unknown probability.

The assignment of probabilities should be tested by a suitable statistical procedure. Such statistical tests will be considered in Part III.

4.6   Some Further Remarks

We shall now discuss some important consequences of the axioms of probability.

From Axiom 3 we obtain by induction the following theorem.

Theorem 1 (Addition rule for mutually exclusive events).   *If $E_1, \cdots, E_m$ are mutually exclusive events, then*

(1) $P(E_1 \cup E_2 \cup \cdots \cup E_m) = P(E_1) + P(E_2) + \cdots + P(E_m).$

Example 1.   We throw a fair die (cf. Sec. 4.3) once. In this experiment there are 6 equally likely cases corresponding to the 6 elements of the sample space $S = \{1, 2, 3, 4, 5, 6\}$. Thus $P(1) = 1/6$, $P(2) = 1/6, \cdots, P(6) = 1/6$. From this and Theorem 1 we see that, for instance, the event

$$A: \quad An \ even \ number \ turns \ up$$

has the probability $P(A) = P(2) + P(4) + P(6) = 1/2$, the event

$$B: \quad A \ number \ greater \ than \ 4 \ turns \ up$$

has the probability $P(B) = P(5) + P(6) = 1/3$, etc. More complicated cases and examples will be considered in the further sections of this chapter.

For two *arbitrary* events the following theorem holds.

Theorem 2 (Addition rule for arbitrary events).   *If A and B are any events in a sample space S, then*

(2) $P(A \cup B) = P(A) + P(B) - P(A \cap B).$

Proof. $A \cup B$ occurs if and only if $A \cap B$ or $A \cap B^c$ or $A^c \cap B$ occurs. Here A^c is the complement of A in S (cf. Sec. 4.1). The latter three events are mutually exclusive. Hence, by Theorem 1,

(3) $P(A \cup B) = P(A \cap B) + P(A \cap B^c) + P(A^c \cap B).$

Similarly, from Axiom 3 we obtain

$$P(A) = P(A \cap B) + P(A \cap B^c)$$

$$P(B) = P(A \cap B) + P(A^c \cap B).$$

By addition we find that

$$P(A) + P(B) = 2P(A \cap B) + P(A \cap B^c) + P(A^c \cap B).$$

Comparing this and (3), we see that

$$P(A) + P(B) = P(A \cup B) + P(A \cap B).$$

From this, formula (2) follows, and the theorem is proved.

Example 2. A fair die is thrown twice. What is the probability of obtaining at least one "*six*?"

The events

$$A: \text{ "Six" in the first trial,}$$
$$B: \text{ "Six" in the second trial}$$

have the probabilities $P(A) = 1/6$ and $P(B) = 1/6$. The event

$$A \cap B: \text{ "Six" in both trials}$$

has the probability $P(A \cap B) = 1/36$. From this and Theorem 2 we obtain

$$P(A \cup B) = \frac{1}{6} + \frac{1}{6} - \frac{1}{36} = \frac{11}{36} \approx 30\%.$$

To derive another important result, we take any event E in a random experiment and its complement E^c (cf. Sec. 4.1). E and E^c are mutually exclusive, and $E \cup E^c = S$, the sample space of the experiment. Using Axioms 3 and 2, we thus have

$$P(E \cup E^c) = P(E) + P(E^c) = 1.$$

This yields

Theorem 3 (Complementation rule). *The probabilities of an event E and its complement E^c in a sample space S are related by the formula*

(4) $$P(E) = 1 - P(E^c).$$

This formula may be used if the computation of $P(E^c)$ is simpler than that of $P(E)$.

Example 3. Five coins are tossed simultaneously. Find the probability of the event A: *At least 1 head turns up*. Since each coin can turn up heads or tails, the sample space consists of $2^5 = 32$ elements. Assuming that the coins are fair, we may assign the same probability $(1/32)$ to each outcome. Then the event A^c (*no heads turn up*) consists of only 1 outcome. Hence $P(A^c) = 1/32$, and the answer is $P(A) = 1 - P(A^c) = 31/32$.

Problems

1. Prove Theorem 1.
2. Show that if B is a subevent of A (cf. Sec. 4.2), then $P(B) \leq P(A)$.
3. Suppose that three fair dice are thrown simultaneously. Find the probability of the event E that at least two of the three numbers obtained are different.
4. Extend Theorem 2 to three events.
5. Obtain the result in Ex. 2 by means of Theorem 3.
6. Does the argument in Ex. 2 remain valid for any other number 1, 2, 3, 4, or 5?
7. Find the probability of obtaining at least one head if ten fair coins are tossed.
8. Consider the experiment of throwing a fair die twice and find the probability of the event E: *The sum of the 2 faces does not exceed* 10.
9. Two fair dice are thrown. Using (4), find the probability of the event E: *The faces that turn up are different*.
10. Three urns contain 5 chips each, numbered from 1 to 5, and 1 chip is drawn from each urn. Find the probability of the event E that the sum of the numbers on the drawn chips is greater than 3.

4.7   Conditional Probability. Multiplication Rule

Often we are required to find the probability of an event B if it is known that an event A has occurred. This probability is called the **conditional probability** *of B given A* and is denoted by $P(B \mid A)$. In this case A serves as a new (reduced) sample space, and that probability is the fraction of $P(A)$ which corresponds to $A \cap B$. Thus

(1) $$P(B \mid A) = \frac{P(A \cap B)}{P(A)} \qquad [P(A) \neq 0].$$

Similarly, the *conditional probability of A given B* is

(2) $$P(A \mid B) = \frac{P(A \cap B)}{P(B)} \qquad [P(B) \neq 0].$$

Example 1. We consider a random experiment in which we may distinguish between n equally likely cases. We assume that A and B are events that happen in k and l of these cases, respectively, and $A \cap B$ happens in m cases. Then the classical definition of probability gives

$$P(A) = \frac{k}{n}, \qquad P(B) = \frac{l}{n}, \qquad P(A \cap B) = \frac{m}{n}.$$

The conditional probability of B given A is the probability of B under the hypothesis that A has occurred. We see that there are k cases which satisfy the hypothesis, and in m of these cases the event B occurs. Thus

$$P(B \mid A) = \frac{m}{k}.$$

We may now easily verify that (1) holds. In fact,

$$P(B \mid A) = \frac{m}{k} = \frac{m/n}{k/n} = \frac{P(A \cap B)}{P(A)}.$$

Solving (1) and (2) for $P(A \cap B)$, we obtain the following result.

Theorem 1 (Multiplication rule). *If A and B are events in a sample space S and $P(A) > 0$, $P(B) > 0$, then*

(3) $$P(A \cap B) = P(A)P(B \mid A) = P(B)P(A \mid B).$$

Formula (3) is the analogue of (5) in the problem set of Sec. 4.2. It is useful if the computation of the conditional probability is simpler than the immediate computation of $P(A \cap B)$.

In preparing to discuss an illustrative example, we first note that there are two ways of drawing objects to obtain a sample from a given set of objects, briefly referred to as **sampling from a population**; these are as follows.

1. Sampling with replacement means that the object which was drawn at random is placed back into the given set and the set is mixed thoroughly. Then the next object is drawn at random.

2. Sampling without replacement means that the object which was drawn is put aside.

Example 2 (Sampling without replacement). A box contains 10 screws, 3 of which are defective. Two screws are drawn at random. Find the probability of the event that neither of the 2 screws is defective. We consider the events

$$A: \text{ First screw drawn is nondefective,}$$

$$B: \text{ Second screw drawn is nondefective.}$$

Clearly, $P(A) = 7/10$ because 7 of the 10 screws are nondefective and we sample at random so that each screw has the same probability $(1/10)$ of being picked.

If A has occurred, then there are 9 screws left in the box, 3 of which are defective. Thus

$$P(B \mid A) = \frac{6}{9} = \frac{2}{3},$$

and by Theorem 1 the answer is

$$P(A \cap B) = \frac{7}{10} \cdot \frac{2}{3} \approx 47\%.$$

Alternatively these ideas may be formulated as follows. In the first drawing we have 10 equally likely outcomes, and A consists of 7 of them. Thus $P(A) = 7/10$. In the second drawing we have 9 equally likely outcomes, and, if A has happened, B consists of 6 of them. Thus $P(B \mid A) = 6/9$, etc.

The multiplication rule (3) can be extended. In the case of m events we obtain

$$(4) \quad P(A_1 \cap A_2 \cap \cdots \cap A_m)$$

$$= P(A_1)P(A_2 \mid A_1)P(A_3 \mid A_1 \cap A_2) \cdots P(A_m \mid A_1 \cap A_2 \cap \cdots \cap A_{m-1}).$$

We shall now derive another interesting formula which is called Bayes's rule. For this purpose we consider an event B in a sample space S with $P(B) \neq 0$ and mutually exclusive events $A_1, A_2, \cdots$ (cf. Sec. 4.2) that exhaust S; that is, every point in S belongs to precisely one among the A_k. We want to obtain a formula for the conditional probability

$$(5) \qquad\qquad P(A_k \mid B) = \frac{P(B \cap A_k)}{P(B)}.$$

From (3) we see that the numerator is

$$(6) \qquad\qquad P(B \cap A_k) = P(B \mid A_k)P(A_k).$$

The event B happens if and only if one of the events $B \cap A_1, B \cap A_2, \cdots$ happens. These events are mutually exclusive. Thus, by (6),

$$P(B) = P(B \mid A_1)P(A_1) + P(B \mid A_2)P(A_2) + \cdots.$$

By substituting this and (6) in (5) we obtain

(7) $$P(A_k \mid B) = \frac{P(B \mid A_k)P(A_k)}{\sum_j P(B \mid A_j)P(A_j)}.$$

This is called **Bayes's rule.**

If the events A_j are called "*causes*," then (7) can be regarded as a formula for the probability that the event B, which has occurred, is the result of the "cause" A_k, that is, for the probability that the cause A_k is acting, calculated under the hypothesis that we have observed B. Hence this is a method of computing the probability of a cause given the effect. The difficulty with this interpretation may be that we may not know the probabilities on the right-hand side of (7).

Example 3 (*Bayes's rule*). An urn contains three coins C_1, C_2, C_3 with probabilities of falling head 0.4, 0.5, 0.6, respectively. A coin is drawn at random and tossed 20 times. Heads comes up 11 times. Find the probability that the chosen coin is fair.

Without information the probability of drawing the fair coin is 1/3. This is called the **prior probability** or **a-priori probability.**

With the given information we may proceed as follows. Let A_j be the event that coin C_j is drawn, and let B be the event of obtaining 11 heads in 20 trials. Then in (7), $P(A_j) = 1/3$ ($j = 1, 2, 3$) and

$$P(B \mid A_2) = \binom{20}{11}0.5^{11}0.5^9 = \binom{20}{11}0.5^{20} = 0.160\ 179$$

$$\sum_{j=1}^{3} P(B \mid A_j)P(A_j) = \binom{20}{11}(0.4^{11}0.6^9 + 0.5^{20} + 0.6^{11}0.4^9)\cdot\frac{1}{3} = 0.390\ 912 \cdot \frac{1}{3}$$

and the answer is

$$P(A_2 \mid B) = \frac{0.160\ 179 \cdot (1/3)}{0.390\ 912 \cdot (1/3)} = 0.41,$$

which is greater than the prior probability. This is called the **posterior probability** or **a-posteriori probability.** It is a conditional probability that is of interest to us only if it is known that the conditioning event B has occurred.

Problems

1. Suppose that in Example 2 three screws are drawn without replacement. Find probability of the event A: *The 3 screws drawn are nondefective.*

2. Suppose that in Example 2 we draw 4 screws without replacement. Find the probability of the event A: *At least 3 of the screws drawn are nondefective.*

3. A box contains 2 black, 3 white, and 4 red balls. Two balls are drawn without replacement. What is the probability that the first will be black and the second will be white?

4. In Problem 3, what is the probability of obtaining a black and a white ball?

5. What is the probability that in throwing 2 fair dice the sum of the faces exceeds 10, given that one of the faces is a 6?

6. Extending Theorem 1, show that

$$P(A \cap B \cap C) = P(A)P(B \mid A)P(C \mid A \cap B).$$

7. A box of 100 gaskets contains 10 gaskets with type *A* defects, 5 gaskets with type *B* defects, and 2 gaskets with both types of defects. What is the probability that in drawing 1 gasket, we obtain a gasket with type *B* defect assuming that it has a type *A* defect?

8. Three screws are drawn at random from a lot of 100 screws, 10 of which are defective. Find the probability of the event that all 3 screws are nondefective assuming that the drawing is (a) with replacement, (b) without replacement.

9. Find the posterior probability in Example 3 when *B* is the event of obtaining 10 heads in 20 trials and the other conditions are as before.

10. Urn I contains 1 white and 3 black balls. Urn II contains 3 white and 2 black balls. An urn is selected at random, and a ball is drawn from it. Given that the ball drawn is black, what is the probability that urn I was chosen?

4.8　Independent Events

The notion of stochastically independent events is fundamental in probability theory because it occurs in many various situations. We start with the case of two events.

If two events *A* and *B* in a random experiment are such that

(1)　　　　　　　　　　$P(A \cap B) = P(A)P(B),$

and $P(A) > 0$, $P(B) > 0$, then the multiplication rule (3) in the last section takes the form

(2)　　　$P(A \cap B) = P(A)P(B) = P(A)P(B \mid A) = P(B)P(A \mid B).$

It follows that

(3)　　　**(a)** $P(A \mid B) = P(A)$　　and　　**(b)** $P(B \mid A) = P(B).$

Now (3*a*) shows that from the information whether *B* has occurred or not, we are not permitted to make any inference about the occurrence of *A*. Similarly, (3*b*) shows that from the information whether *A* has occurred or not, we are not permitted to make any inference about the occurrence of *B*. Conversely, starting from (3) and using (2), we obtain (1). Events for which (1) holds are therefore called *statistically* or *stochastically independent events* or, more briefly, **independent events.**

This definition is accepted also if $P(A) = 0$ or $P(B) = 0$, in which case $P(B \mid A)$ and $P(A \mid B)$, respectively, are not defined.

We note that *statistically* independent is synonymous with *stochastically* independent, and *stochastic* means *connected with random experiments and probabilities*.

Example 1.　What is the probability of obtaining 2 aces in drawing 2 cards from a bridge deck, assuming drawing with replacement?
We consider the events
　　　　　　　　　A: The first card drawn is an ace,
　　　　　　　　　B: The second card drawn is an ace.

Since the deck consists of 52 cards, 4 of which are aces, $P(A) = 4/52 = 1/13$. Since we draw with replacement, A and B are independent, $P(B) = 1/13$, and the answer is

$$P(A \cap B) = P(A)P(B) = \frac{1}{13} \cdot \frac{1}{13} = \frac{1}{169} = 0.6\%.$$

Example 2 (*Sampling with and without replacement*). A box contains 10 screws, 3 of which are defective. Two screws are drawn at random. Find the probability that neither of the 2 screws is defective.

We consider the events

> A: *First screw drawn is nondefective,*
>
> B: *Second screw drawn is nondefective.*

We see that $P(A) = 0.7$ because 7 of the 10 screws are nondefective, and we sample at random so that each screw has the same probability (1/10) of being picked. If we sample with replacement, the situation before the second drawing is the same as at the beginning, and $P(B) = 0.7$. The events are independent, and the answer is

$$P(A \cap B) = P(A)P(B) = 0.7 \cdot 0.7 = 0.49 = 49\%.$$

If we sample without replacement, then (cf. Example 2 in Sec. 4.7) $P(A) = 7/10$, $P(B \mid A) = 6/9 = 2/3$, and

$$P(A \cap B) = P(A)P(B \mid A) = \frac{7}{10} \cdot \frac{2}{3} \approx 47\%.$$

In the case of games of chance, it will generally be quite simple to decide whether two events are independent or not. In the case of other random experiments we must be careful. Events should be regarded as being independent if and only if we know the nature of the experiment so well that we are certain that there cannot be a relationship between those events.

We shall now indicate how the definition of independence can be extended to more than two events.

From the definition [cf. (1)] it follows that three events A, B, C are *pairwise independent* if

$$\begin{align} P(A \cap B) &= P(A)P(B) \\ (4) \qquad P(B \cap C) &= P(B)P(C) \\ P(C \cap A) &= P(C)P(A). \end{align}$$

Three events A, B, C are said to be **independent,** if (4) and

$$(5) \qquad\qquad P(A \cap B \cap C) = P(A)P(B)P(C)$$

hold.

This definition is motivated by the fact that it implies the independence of the pairs

$$(6) \qquad\qquad A \text{ and } B, \quad B \text{ and } C, \quad C \text{ and } A$$

as well as the independence of the pairs

$$(7) \qquad \begin{align} &A \text{ and } B \cap C, \quad B \text{ and } C \cap A, \quad C \text{ and } A \cap B, \\ &A \text{ and } B \cup C, \quad B \text{ and } C \cup A, \quad C \text{ and } A \cup B. \end{align}$$

We mention that (4) does not imply (5), so that pairwise independence does not imply independence, and independence of the pairs in (7) does not necessarily follow from (4).

To illustrate this, suppose that an urn contains 4 chips numbered 000, 011, 101, 110, and 1 chip is drawn. Let A, B, C be the events that the first, second, third digit, respectively, on the drawn chip is 1. Then

$$P(A) = 2/4 = 1/2, \qquad P(B) = 1/2, \qquad P(C) = 1/2$$

and

$$P(A \cap B) = 1/4, \qquad P(B \cap C) = 1/4, \qquad P(C \cap A) = 1/4,$$

which shows independence in pairs. However, $P(A \cap B \cap C) = 0$ because there is no chip numbered 111; hence

$$P(A \cap B \cap C) \neq P(A)P(B)P(C) = 1/8,$$

which shows that A, B, C are not independent.

m events $A_1, \cdots, A_m$ are said to be **independent** if for any k events $A_{j_1}, \cdots, A_{j_k}$,

(8) $$P(A_{j_1} \cap A_{j_2} \cap \cdots \cap A_{j_k}) = P(A_{j_1})P(A_{j_2}) \cdots P(A_{j_k})$$

where $1 \leqq j_1 < j_2 < \cdots < j_k \leqq m$ and $k = 2, 3, \cdots, m$.

Problems

1. Show that for independent events A and B,

$$P(A \cup B) = 1 - P(A^c)P(B^c)$$

   where A^c is the complement of A in the sample space.

2. Show that in drawing with replacement the outcome of a trial does not influence the further trials.

3. A fair coin is tossed 4 times. Find the probability of obtaining at first 2 heads and then 2 tails.

4. A fair coin is tossed 4 times. Find the probability of obtaining 2 heads and 2 tails.

5. Two fair dice are thrown. Find the probability of the event E: *An even number on the first die and an odd number on the second.*

6. In Problem 5 find the probability of obtaining an even number on one die and an odd number on the other. What is the complementary event?

7. Assuming that the events *birth of a boy* and *birth of a girl* are equally likely and independent, find the probability that in a family of 5 children all children will be of the same sex.

8. Making the same assumptions as in Problem 7, find the probability that in a family of 4 children, 2 will be boys and 2 will be girls.

9. Find the probabilities of boys and girls in families with 3 children under the assumption stated in Problem 7.

10. Show that if A, B, C are independent, then $A \cup B$ and C are independent.

4.9   Permutations and Combinations

The sample space S corresponding to simple games of chance, to sampling methods, or to order and occupancy problems is finite, in general, and the same probability is assigned to all its points (outcomes). From Sec. 4.3 we know that this probability is $1/m$ where m is the number of points of S, and the probability of an event A is obtained by counting the number of the outcomes of which A consists. Clearly, if this number is w, then $P(A) = w/m$. Hence the assignment of probabilities to the various events in S amounts to counting points. This task can be facilitated by the use of some basic notions and results from elementary combinatorial analysis which we shall now consider. In this way we shall obtain effective counting methods, which prevent the counting of sample points from becoming tedious in more complicated cases.

Suppose that n things (**elements** or *objects*) are given. We may arrange them in a row *in any order*. Each such arrangement is called a **permutation** of these things.

For example, there are 6 permutations of the 3 letters a, b, c, namely,

$$abc \quad bac \quad cab$$
$$acb \quad bca \quad cba.$$

Theorem 1.   *The number of permutations of n different things taken all at a time is equal to*

(1) $n! = 1 \cdot 2 \cdot 3 \cdots n$ (*read n* factorial).

This can be proved by induction or simply by noting that there are n possibilities for filling the first place in the row; then $n - 1$ things are still available for filling the second place in the row, etc.

A table of $n!$ is included in Appendix 4. For a larger table, see Fisher and Yates (1957); cf. Appendix 3. Some properties of $n!$ will be discussed in the next section.

If some of the n given things are alike, then the total number of permutations will be smaller than before. In fact, the following theorem holds.

Theorem 2.   *If n given things can be divided into c classes such that things belonging to the same class are alike while things belonging to different classes are different, then the number of permutations of these things taken all at a time is*

(2) $$\frac{n!}{n_1! \, n_2! \cdots n_c!}$$ $(n_1 + n_2 + \cdots + n_c = n)$

where n_j is the number of things in the jth class.

The simple proof is left to the reader (Problem 1 in Sec. 4.10).

A **permutation of *n* things taken *k* at a time** is a permutation containing only *k* of the *n* given things. Two such permutations consisting of the same *k* elements, in a different order, are different, by definition. For example, there are 6 different permutations of the 3 letters *a*, *b*, *c*, taken 2 letters at a time, namely *ab, ac, bc, ba, ca, cb*.

A **permutation of *n* things taken *k* at a time with repetitions** is an arrangement obtained by putting any given thing in the first position, any given thing, including a repetition of the one just used, in the second, and continuing until *k* positions are filled. For example, there are $3^2 = 9$ different such permutations of *a*, *b*, *c*, taken 2 letters at a time, namely, the preceding 6 permutations and *aa, bb, cc*.

Theorem 3. *The number of different permutations of n different things taken k at a time without repetitions is*

(3a) $$n(n - 1)(n - 2) \cdots (n - k + 1) = \frac{n!}{(n - k)!}$$

and with repetitions is

(3b) $$n^k.$$

The ideas of the proof is the same as that of Theorem 1, but instead of filling *n* places we now have to fill only *k* places. Without repetitions, we then have *n* possibilities for filling the first place, $n - 1$ for the second, $\cdots$, $n - k + 1$ for the *k*th place. This yields (3a). With repetitions, we have *n* possibilities for filling each of the *k* places and we obtain (3b).

There is no standard notation for the number of permutations of *n* things taken *k* at a time [cf. (3a)]; we may write

$$P_{n,k} = n(n - 1) \cdots (n - k + 1);$$

other notations are $P_k{}^n$, $_nP_k$, etc.

In the case of a permutation not only are the things themselves important but so also is their order. A **combination** of given things is any selection of one or more of the things *without regard to order*. There are two types of combinations, as follows.

The number of **combinations of *n* different things, *k* at a time, without repetitions** is the number of sets that can be made up from the *n* things, each set containing *k* different things and no two sets containing exactly the same *k* things.

The number of **combinations of *n* different things, *k* at a time, with repetitions** is the number of sets that can be made up of *k* things chosen from the given *n*, each being used as often as desired.

For example, there are 3 combinations of the 3 letters *a*, *b*, *c*, taken 2 letters at a time, without repetitions, namely, *ab, ac, bc*, and 6 such combinations with repetitions, namely, *ab, ac, bc, aa, bb, cc*.

Theorem 4.   *The number of different combinations of n different things, k at a time, without repetitions, is*

(4a) $$\binom{n}{k} = \frac{n!}{k!\,(n-k)!} = \frac{n(n-1)\cdots(n-k+1)}{1\cdot 2\cdots k},$$

and the number of combinations with repetitions is

(4b) $$\binom{n+k-1}{k}.$$

The statement involving (4a) follows from the first part of Theorem 3 by noting that there are $k!$ permutations of k things from the given n things which differ only in the order of the elements (cf. Theorem 1), but there is only a single combination of those k things of the type characterized in the first statement of Theorem 4. The last statement of Theorem 4 can be proved by induction (cf. Problem 2 in Sec. 4.10).

Example 1.   Suppose that 10 different screws are put in an empty box and the screws are needed in a certain order for assembling a kit. Find the probability that in random drawing without replacement, we obtain the screws in the desired order.
  There are $10! = 3,628,800$ equally likely cases because there are $10!$ ways (different orders) in which the screws can be drawn (cf. Theorem 1), and the answer is

$$P = \frac{1}{10!} = \frac{1}{3,628,800} \approx 0.000\,03\,\%.$$

This is surprisingly small because $n!$ increases so rapidly as n increases.
  Suppose that a box contains 6 identical right-handed screws and 4 identical left-handed screws. If the 6 right-handed ones are needed first and the 4 left-handed ones are needed later, the probability P that random drawing yields the screws in the desired order is (cf. Theorem 2)

$$P = \frac{6!\,4!}{10!} = \frac{1}{210} \approx 0.5\,\%.$$

Example 2.   In a coded telegram the letters are arranged in groups of 5 letters, called *words*. From (3b) we see that there are

$$26^5 = 11,881,376$$

different such words. From (3a) it follows that there are

$$\frac{26!}{(26-5)!} = 26\cdot 25\cdot 24\cdot 23\cdot 22 = 7,893,600$$

different such words which contain each letter at most once.

Example 3.   The number of samples of 5 light bulbs which can be selected from a lot of 500 bulbs is [cf. (4a)]

$$\binom{500}{5} = \frac{500!}{5!\,495!} = \frac{500\cdot 499\cdot 498\cdot 497\cdot 496}{1\cdot 2\cdot 3\cdot 4\cdot 5} = 255,244,687,600.$$

Problems will be included at the end of the next section.

4.10   Remarks About the Factorial Function and Binomial Coefficients

Let us include some formulas in connection with the *factorial function* and *binomial coefficients*. We define

(1) $$0! = 1$$

and may compute further values by the relation

(2) $$(n + 1)! = (n + 1)n! \, .$$

For large n the values of the function are very large (cf. Table 1*a* in Appendix 4). A convenient approximation for large n is **Stirling's formula**

(3) $$n! \sim \sqrt{2\pi n} \left(\frac{n}{e}\right)^n \qquad\qquad (e = 2.718\cdots),$$

where $\sim$ means that the ratio of the two sides of (3) approaches 1 as n approaches infinity. A derivation of this formula can be found in the book by Cramér (1961) listed in Appendix 3.

It can be shown that, as n approaches infinity, the relative error of the approximation (3) *approaches zero, but the absolute error approaches infinity.* This should be kept in mind when Stirling's formula is applied. An illustration of the accuracy of (3) is given in Table 4.10.1.

The **binomial coefficients** are defined by the formula

(4) $$\binom{a}{k} = \frac{a(a-1)(a-2)\cdots(a-k+1)}{k!}$$

where k is a nonnegative integer and a is any real number. We see that the numerator has k factors. Furthermore, we define

(5) $$\binom{a}{0} = 1, \quad \text{in particular } \binom{0}{0} = 1.$$

These quantities are the coefficients of the **binomial series**

(6) $$(b + c)^a = \sum_k \binom{a}{k} b^{a-k} c^k \qquad\qquad (|c| < |b|).$$

Here we sum over all nonnegative integers k for which $\binom{a}{k}$ is not zero.

Table 4.10.1. Illustration of Accuracy of Formula (3)

n	Approximation (3)	Exact Value of $n!$	Error Absolute	Error Relative
4	23.5	24	0.5	2%
6	710	720	10	1.4%
8	39,902	40,320	400	1%
10	3,598,696	3,628,800	30,000	0.8%

From (4) we obtain

(7)
$$\binom{a}{k} = \binom{a}{a-k} \qquad (a \geqq 0, 0 \leqq k \leqq a; k, a \text{ integral}),$$

(8)
$$\binom{a}{k} + \binom{a}{k+1} = \binom{a+1}{k+1} \qquad (k \geqq 0, \text{ integral}),$$

(9)
$$\binom{r}{k} = 0 \qquad (k > r \geqq 0; k, r \text{ integral}).$$

Formula (8) is a recursion formula for computing the binomial coefficients. For nonnegative integral a, the computation may be facilitated by arranging the binomial coefficients in the form of the well-known Pascal triangle:

$$
\begin{array}{ccccccccc}
 & & & & 1 & & & & \\
 & & & 1 & & 1 & & & \\
 & & 1 & & 2 & & 1 & & \\
 & 1 & & 3 & & 3 & & 1 & \\
1 & & 4 & & 6 & & 4 & & 1 \\
\end{array}
$$

$$\cdot \quad \cdot \quad \cdot \quad \cdot \quad \cdot \quad \cdot \quad \cdot \quad \cdot \quad \cdot$$

Numerical values of the binomial coefficients are included in Table 1c; cf. Appendix 4.

For any positive m we obtain from (4)

$$\binom{-m}{k} = \frac{-m(-m-1)(-m-2)\cdots(-m-k+1)}{k!}$$

$$= (-1)^k \frac{m(m+1)\cdots(m+k-1)}{k!}.$$

This may be written

(10)
$$\binom{-m}{k} = (-1)^k \binom{m+k-1}{k} \qquad (m > 0).$$

There is a surprisingly large number of relations between binomial coefficients. We mention

(11)
$$\sum_{k=0}^{r} \binom{p}{k}\binom{q}{r-k} = \binom{p+q}{r},$$

(12)
$$\sum_{k=0}^{p} \binom{p}{k}^2 = \binom{p}{0}^2 + \binom{p}{1}^2 + \cdots + \binom{p}{p}^2 = \binom{2p}{p},$$

(13)
$$\sum_{s=0}^{n-1} \binom{k+s}{k} = \binom{n+k}{k+1} \qquad (k \geqq 0, n \geqq 1, \text{ both integral}).$$

Problems

1. Prove Theorem 2, Sec. 4.9.

2. Prove the last statement of Theorem 4 in Sec. 4.9. *Hint.* Use induction with respect to k and apply (13).

3. Using (3), compute an approximate value of 4! and determine the absolute and relative errors, thus confirming the values given in Table 4.10.1.

4. Derive (7) from (4).

5. Find the number of samples of 10 objects which can be drawn from a lot of 100 objects.

6. How many different license plates showing 5 symbols, namely, 2 letters followed by 3 digits, could be made?

7. An urn contains 2 black, 3 white, and 4 red balls. We draw 1 ball at random and put it aside. Then we draw the next ball, and so on. Find the probability of drawing at first the two black balls, then the 3 white ones, and finally the red ones.

8. Suppose that 3 letters addressed to 3 different persons are inserted into 3 addressed envelopes at random. What is the probability that at least 1 letter is inserted into its own envelope?

9. List all permutations of 4 letters a, b, c, d taken all at a time.

10. List all permutations of the five numbers 1, 2, 3, 4, 5 taken 3 at a time.

11. Suppose that 6 fair dice are tossed. Find the probability that each of the numbers 1 through 6 will occur.

12. If a four-volume set of books is placed on a shelf in random order, what is the probability that the books will be in the correct order?

13. In how many ways can a committee of 3 be chosen from 10 persons?

14. How many diagonals are there in an eight-sided polygon?

15. An urn contains 6 chips numbered from 1 to 6. What is the probability of obtaining them in their natural order if they are drawn without replacement?

16. Jack is supposed to draw 3 chips without replacement from an urn containing 5 chips numbered 1 to 5. If he obtains 1, 2, 3, in this order, he wins and gets 5 dollars. Otherwise he loses the game and has to pay 10 cents. Can Jack expect to make money in the long run?

17. How does the situation in Problem 16 change if Jack wins in case he draws 1, 2, 3 in any order?

18. What is the probability that a family of 4 children will have exactly x boys ($x = 0$, $1, \cdots$, 4) if we assume equal probability for boys and girls and independence of births?

19. In the game of bridge a well-shuffled deck of 52 playing cards is distributed card by card to the 4 players successively. Each player thus receives 13 cards, called a *hand*, the order in which the cards are received being immaterial. Find the number of different hands.

20. What is the probability that 5 cards drawn (without replacement) from a bridge deck will all belong to the same suit?

CHAPTER **5**

Probability Distributions

The notion of probability distribution arises if we consider a random experiment and ask for the possible events and corresponding probabilities. There are two types of distributions that are important in practical applications, namely, the discrete and the continuous distribution. A discrete distribution will arise if we *count* (for example, the number of defective items in a given lot, the number of cars on a road, or the number of cases of illness). A continuous distribution will appear if we *measure* (for example, lengths, or temperatures).

In the present chapter we discuss probability distributions of a single random variable. Two-dimensional and more general distributions will be considered in Chap. 9.

Here in Part II we study theoretical models for populations and, therefore, the notions under discussion will be of a theoretical nature. The names of these concepts will be similar to those of their empirical analogues in Part I.

5.1   Random Variables

If we throw two dice, we know that the sum X of the two numbers which turn up must be an integer between 2 and 12, but we cannot predict which value of X will occur in the next trial, and we may say that X depends on "chance." Similarly, if we plan to draw 5 bolts from a lot of bolts and measure their diameters, we cannot predict how many will be defective, that is, will not meet given requirements; hence $X = $ *number of defective bolts* is again a function which depends on "chance." The lifetime X of a light bulb to be drawn at random from a lot of bulbs also depends on "chance," and so does the volume X of lemonade in a bottle filled by a filling machine and selected at random from a given lot.

If the outcomes are not immediately given in terms of numbers, we may assign numbers and reduce such *qualitative observations* to the quantitative case. For example, to the events *blue eyes, brown eyes, other color eyes,* we may assign the numbers 1, 2, 3. To the events *heads* and *tails* in coin tossing we may assign the numbers 0 and 1, etc.

Roughly speaking, a **random variable** X (also called **stochastic variable** or **variate**) is a function whose values are real numbers and depend on "chance"; more precisely, it is a function X which is associated with a random experiment and has the following properties.

1. *X is defined on the sample space S of the experiment, and its values are real numbers.*

2. *Let a be any real number, and let I be any interval* (cf. Appendix 1). *Then the set of all the outcomes in S for which $X = a$ has a well-defined probability, and the same is true for the set of all the outcomes in S for which the values of X are in I. These probabilities are in agreement with the axioms in Sec. 4.4.*

The set of numbers that X can take is called the *sample space of X*, and any subset of that space is called an *event*.

For instance, let

$X =$ *total number of heads obtained in independent tossing of a dime and a nickel.*

Here S consists of the 4 points (outcomes)

$$(H, H) \qquad (H, T) \qquad (T, H) \qquad (T, T)$$

($H =$ *head*, $T =$ *tail;* the first letter refers to the dime and the second to the nickel). The corresponding values of X are

$$2 \qquad\qquad 1 \qquad\qquad 1 \qquad\qquad 0,$$

respectively. If the coins are fair, then to $X = 0$ there corresponds the probability 0.25, to $X = 1$ the probability 0.5, and to $X = 2$ the probability 0.25. From this we may obtain probabilities corresponding to intervals; for instance, to the interval $0 \leq X \leq 1.5$ there corresponds the probability $0.25 + 0.50 = 0.75$, etc.

Although the definition of a random variable is quite general and includes many functions, we shall see that in practice the number of important types of random variables and corresponding "probability distributions" is rather small.

Let X be a random variable associated with a random experiment. Suppose that to the outcome of a performance of the experiment there corresponds a value a of X. Then we say that in this trial the random variable X has **assumed** the value a. We also say that we have **observed** the value $X = a$. Instead of "the event corresponding to a number a," we say, more briefly, "the event $X = a$." The corresponding probability is denoted by

$$P(X = a).$$

Similarly, the probability of the event

X assumes any value in the interval $a < X < b$

is denoted by
$$P(a < X < b).$$
The probability of the event

$$X \leqq c \qquad (X \text{ assumes any value smaller than } c \text{ or equal to } c)$$

is denoted by
$$P(X \leqq c),$$
and the probability of the event

$$X > c \qquad (X \text{ assumes any value greater than } c)$$
is denoted by
$$P(X > c).$$

The last two events are mutually exclusive. From Axiom 3, Sec. 4.4, we thus obtain

$$P(X \leqq c) + P(X > c) = P(-\infty < X < \infty).$$

From Axiom 2 we see that the right side equals 1, because $-\infty < X < \infty$ includes the whole sample space of X. This yields the important formula

(1) $$P(X > c) = 1 - P(X \leqq c) \qquad (c \text{ arbitrary, real}).$$

For example, if X is the number that turns up in throwing a fair die, $P(X = 1) = 1/6, P(X = 2) = 1/6$, etc., $P(1 < X < 2) = 0, P(1 \leqq X \leqq 2) = 1/3, P(0.3 \leqq X \leqq 3.2) = 1/2, P(X > 4) = 1/3, P(X \leqq 0.5) = 0$, etc.

Problems

1. Let $X = $ *number of heads in tossing a fair coin twice.* Find the probabilities $P(X = 0), P(X = 1), P(X = 2), P(1 < X < 2), P(X \leqq 1), P(X \geqq 1), P(X > 1)$, and $P(0.5 < X < 10)$.

2. A box contains 4 right-handed and 6 left-handed screws. Two screws are drawn at random without replacement. Let X be the number of left-handed screws drawn. Find the probabilities $P(X = 0), P(X = 1)$, etc., as in Problem 1.

3. Show that $b < c$ implies $P(X \leqq b) \leqq P(X \leqq c)$.

4. Graph the sample space corresponding to the experiment of throwing two dice. Let $X_1 = $ *number the first die turns up*, $X_2 = $ *number the second die turns up.* Indicate the events (a) $X_1 + X_2 > 3$, (b) $X_1/X_2 = 2$, (c) $X_1^2 + X_2^2 \leqq 20$, (d) $X_1 - X_2 = 2$ and find the corresponding probabilities, assuming that the dice are fair.

5. Obtain (1) from Theorem 3 in Sec. 4.6.

6. Let X be a random variable that can assume any real value. What are the complements of the events $X \leqq b, X < b, X \geqq c, X > c, b \leqq X \leqq c, b < X \leqq c$?

5.2 Discrete Distribution. Probability Function

In most practical cases the random variables are either *discrete* or *continuous*. These two important notions will now be considered in turn.

A random variable X and the corresponding distribution are said to be **discrete,** if X has the following properties.

1. The number of values for which X has a positive probability is finite or at most countably infinite.

2. Each finite interval on the real number scale contains at most finitely many of those values. If an interval $a < X \leq b$ does not contain such a value, then $P(a < X \leq b) = 0$.

Let

$$x_1, \qquad x_2, \qquad x_3, \qquad \cdots$$

be the values for which X has a positive probability, and let

$$p_1, \qquad p_2, \qquad p_3, \qquad \cdots$$

be the corresponding probabilities. Then $P(X = x_1) = p_1$, etc., and the set $x_1, x_2, \cdots$ is called the *sample space of X*. We now introduce the function

(1)
$$f(x) = \begin{cases} p_j & \text{when } x = x_j \qquad (j = 1, 2, \cdots) \\ 0 & \text{otherwise.} \end{cases}$$

$f(x)$ is called the **probability function** of X. Some simple examples will be considered in the next section.

Since $P(S) = 1$ (cf. Axiom 2 in Sec. 4.4), we must have

(2)
$$\sum_{j=1}^{\infty} f(x_j) = 1.$$

If we know the probability function of a discrete random variable X, then we may readily compute the probability $P(a < X \leq b)$ corresponding to any interval $a < X \leq b$. In fact,

(3)
$$P(a < X \leq b) = \sum_{a < x_j \leq b} f(x_j) = \sum_{a < x_j \leq b} p_j.$$

This is the sum of all the probabilities $f(x_j) = p_j$ for which the x_j lie in that interval. For a closed, open, or infinite interval the situation is quite similar. We express this by saying that the probability function $f(x)$ determines the **probability distribution** or, briefly, the **distribution** of the random variable X in a unique fashion.

5.3 Some Simple Examples

Example 1. Let X be the number obtained in throwing a fair die. The corresponding probability function is (cf. Fig. 5.3.1.)

$$f(x) = 1/6 \qquad\qquad \text{when } x = 1, 2, \cdots, 6$$

and $f = 0$ otherwise.

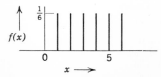

Fig. 5.3.1. Probability function in Example 1

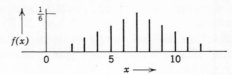

Fig. 5.3.2. Probability function in Example 2

Example 2.   Let X be the sum of the two numbers obtained in throwing two fair dice. The corresponding probability function $f(x)$ has the following values (cf. Fig. 5.3.2):

x	2	3	4	5	6	7	8	9	10	11	12
$f(x)$	1/36	2/36	3/36	4/36	5/36	6/36	5/36	4/36	3/36	2/36	1/36

In fact, there are $6 \cdot 6 = 36$ equally likely cases which we may denote by $(1, 1), (1, 2), \cdots$, $(6, 6)$. Here the first number refers to the first die and the second number to the other die. In the case $(1, 1)$ we have $X = 2$, and $P(X = 2) = 1/36$. In the cases $(1, 2)$ and $(2, 1)$ we have $X = 3$, and therefore $P(X = 3) = 2/36$, etc.

Example 3.   We toss a fair coin and denote by X the number of trials until a head appears for the first time (including the trial in which the head appears). Then the corresponding sample space is infinite because there are countably many outcomes, namely, $1, 2, 3, \cdots$. In fact, $X = 1$ means that a head appears in the first throw. $X = 2$ means that we first obtain a tail and then a head, etc. Since heads and tails are equally likely and the trials are independent, we have

$$P(X = 1) = \frac{1}{2}, \qquad P(X = 2) = \frac{1}{2} \cdot \frac{1}{2} = \frac{1}{4}, \qquad P(X = 3) = \frac{1}{8}$$

etc. We thus obtain the probability function

$$f(x) = \frac{1}{2^x} \qquad\qquad \text{when } x = 1, 2, 3, \cdots$$

and $f = 0$ otherwise. We see that X is a discrete random variable which has a positive probability for countably infinitely many values.

Problems

1. Plot a line graph of the probability function in Example 3.

2. Show that $f(x)$ in Example 3 satisfies (2), Sec. 5.2.

3. Find and graph the probability function of the random variable $X = $ *sum of the 3 numbers obtained in throwing 3 fair dice.*

4. Find and graph the probability function of the random variable $X = $ *number of heads in tossing 4 fair coins.*

5. Find the probability function of the random variable $X = $ *number of times a fair die is thrown until 6 appears* (including the trial in which 6 appears).

6. Show that the probability function in Problem 5 satisfies (2), Sec. 5.2.

7. Find and graph the probability function of the random variable $X = $ *product of the 2 numbers obtained in throwing 2 fair dice.*

8. Find and graph the probability function of the random variable $X = $ *number of boys in 3 single births*, assuming that the outcomes *boy* and *girl* are equally likely and the outcome of a particular birth does not affect the further outcomes.

9. A box contains 5 defective and 5 nondefective screws. Two screws are drawn at random without replacement. Find and graph the probability function of the random variable $X = $ *number of nondefective screws obtained*.

10. Perform the same task as in Problem 9, assuming that the box contains 3 defective and 7 nondefective screws.

5.4 Distribution Function of a Random Variable

If X is any random variable, then for any real number x there exists the probability $P(X \leq x)$ of the event

$$X \leq x \qquad (X \text{ assumes any value smaller than } x \text{ or equal to } x).$$

Clearly, $P(X \leq x)$ depends on the choice of x; it is a function of x, which is called the **distribution function**[1] of X and is denoted by $F(x)$. Thus

(1)
$$F(x) = P(X \leq x).$$

Example 1. Find the distribution function $F(x)$ of the random variable

$$X = \textit{number of heads in a single toss of a fair coin.}$$

Clearly, X can only assume the values 0 and 1, the corresponding probabilities being 0.5. Thus $F(x) = 0$ when $x < 0$, $P(X = 0) = 0.5$ and

$$F(0) = P(X \leq 0) = 0.5.$$

With increasing x the function $F(x)$ retains this value until x reaches the next value which X can assume. This is $x = 1$. Then

$$F(1) = P(X \leq 1) = P(X = 0) + P(X = 1) = 0.5 + 0.5 = 1,$$

and $F(x) = 1$ when $x > 1$. Altogether (cf. Fig. 5.4.1),

x	$x < 0$	$0 \leq x < 1$	$x \geq 1$
$F(x)$	0	0.5	1

We shall now prove that the probability $P(a < X \leq b)$ of an event $a < X \leq b$ can be expressed in terms of the distribution function $F(x)$. Here a and b are any real numbers, and $b > a$. We say, briefly, that $F(x)$ uniquely

---

[1] We note that some authors call $F(x)$ the *cumulative distribution function*, in particular those who use the term *distribution function* for the probability function $f(x)$.

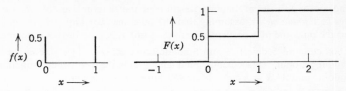

Fig. 5.4.1. Probability function $f(x)$ and distribution function $F(x)$ in Example 1

determines the **probability distribution** or the **distribution** of the corresponding random variable.

To prove the statement, we first note that

$$X \leqq a \qquad \text{and} \qquad a < X \leqq b$$

are mutually exclusive events. Their union is the event $X \leqq b$. According to Axiom 3 in Sec. 4.4 we thus obtain

$$P(X \leqq b) = P(X \leqq a) + P(a < X \leqq b).$$

This can be written

(2) $$P(a < X \leqq b) = P(X \leqq b) - P(X \leqq a).$$

In this formula,

$$P(X \leqq b) = F(b) \qquad \text{and} \qquad P(X \leqq a) = F(a).$$

This yields the basic relation

(3) $$P(a < X \leqq b) = F(b) - F(a),$$

and our statement is proved.

5.5   Distribution Function of a Discrete Distribution

From Sec. 5.2 we know that if $f(x)$ is the probability function of a discrete random variable X, then the probability corresponding to an interval is obtained as the sum of suitable values of $f(x)$. In particular, for the interval $-\infty < X \leqq x$ or, more briefly, $X \leqq x$, we have [cf. (1) in Sec. 5.2]

$$P(X \leqq x) = \sum_{x_j \leqq x} f(x_j).$$

This is the sum of all $f(x_j)$ for which x_j is smaller than x or equal to x. Now, by definition, the left side equals $F(x)$. This means that

(1) $$F(x) = \sum_{x_j \leqq x} f(x_j).$$

Figures 5.5.1 and 5.5.2 show simple illustrative examples.

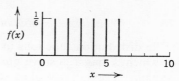

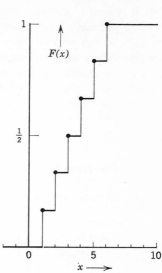

Fig. 5.5.1. Probability function $f(x)$ and distribution function $F(x)$ in Example 1, Sec. 5.3. [The dots at the left ends of the segments indicate the value of $F(x)$ at those values of x.]

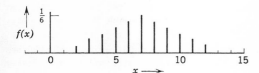

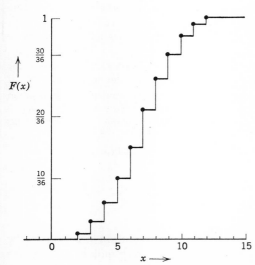

Fig. 5.5.2. Probability function $f(x)$ and distribution function $F(x)$ of the random variable in Example 2, Sec. 5.3

The distribution functions in Figs. 5.5.1 and 5.5.2 have jumps at those x for which X has a positive probability. Between two such values they are constant. They are so-called **step functions** or **piecewise constant functions.** This is typical of discrete distributions.

More precisely, the values x_1, x_2, x_3, $\cdots$ for which a discrete random variable X has positive probability (and only these values) are called the **possible values** of X. From Sec. 5.2 we know that these are the points (outcomes) of the sample space of X. In each interval that contains no possible value, the distribution function $F(x)$ is constant. Hence $F(x)$ is a step function which has an upward jump of magnitude $p_j = P(X = x_j)$ at $x = x_j$ and is constant between two subsequent possible values.

Problems

1.–3. In each case graph the given probability function and the corresponding distribution function.

   1. $f(x) = 1/n$ when $x = 1, 2, \cdots, n$ and $f(x) = 0$ otherwise.

   2. $f(x) = 0.1x$ when $x = 1, 2, 3, 4$ and $f(x) = 0$ otherwise.

   3. $f(x) = 1/2^x$ when $x = 1, 2, \cdots$ and $f(x) = 0$ otherwise.

   4. Suppose that in a single birth the outcomes *boy* and *girl* are equally likely and the births are independent (exclude twins, etc.). Graph the probability function $f(x)$ and the distribution function $F(x)$ of the random variable $X = $ *number of boys in 3 single births.*

   5. Two screws are drawn without replacement from a set of 10 screws, 4 of which are defective. Find and graph the probability function $f(x)$ and the distribution function $F(x)$ of the random variable $X = $ *number of defective screws drawn.*

   6. Perform the same task as in Problem 5 when 3 screws (instead of 2 screws) are drawn without replacement.

   7. Find and graph the distribution function of the random variable $X = $ *number of heads in tossing* 4 *fair coins.*

   8. Find and graph the probability function and the distribution function of the random variable $X = $ *product of the 2 numbers obtained in throwing 2 fair dice.*

   9. An urn contains 8 balls, 3 of which are red. Graph and compare the distribution functions of the random variables $X_1 = $ *number of red balls obtained in drawing* 2 *balls without replacement* and $X_2 = $ *number of red balls obtained in drawing 2 balls with replacement.*

   10. Graph the distribution function of the random variable in Problem 9, Sec. 5.3.

5.6 Continuous Distributions

A random variable X and the corresponding distribution are said to be *of continuous type* or, briefly, **continuous** if the corresponding distribution function

$$F(x) = P(X \leq x)$$

can be represented by an integral in the form

(1)
$$F(x) = \int_{-\infty}^{x} f(v)\, dv,$$

where the integrand is continuous, possibly except for at most finitely many values of v.

Of course, $F(x)$ is continuous for every x. We have used v to denote the variable of integration because x is used to denote the right endpoint of the interval of integration.

The integrand f is called the *probability density* or, briefly, the **density** of the distribution under consideration.

Differentiating (1), we see that

$$F'(x) = f(x)$$

for every x for which $f(x)$ is continuous. In this sense *the density is the derivative of the distribution function.*[2]

From (1) and Axiom 2 in Sec. 4.4 we also have

(2)
$$\int_{-\infty}^{\infty} f(v)\, dv = 1.$$

Furthermore, from (3), Sec. 5.4, and (1) we obtain

(3)
$$P(a < X \leq b) = F(b) - F(a) = \int_{a}^{b} f(v)\, dv.$$

This means that the probability of the event $a < X \leq b$ equals the area under the curve of the density $f(x)$ between $x = a$ and $x = b$, as illustrated in Fig. 5.6.1.

It follows that for a short interval of length Δx with midpoint $x = c$, the corresponding probability (3) is approximately equal to

$$f(c)\, \Delta x$$

because this is the area of a rectangle of width Δx and height $f(c)$.

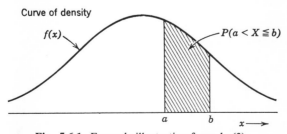

Fig. 5.6.1. Example illustrating formula (3)

[2] Continuity of $F(x)$ does not imply the existence of a representation of the form (1). However, random variables with continuous $F(x)$ not satisfying (1) are rare in practice, so that the above widely accepted terms "continuous random variable" and "continuous distribution" (instead of the terms "random variable of continuous type" and "distribution of continuous type") do not lead to confusion.

We see that if we let Δx approach 0, then, since $F(x)$ is continuous,

$$P(X = c) = 0,$$

and this holds for any number c because c was arbitrary. Of course this does *not* mean that the event $X = c$ can never happen because then none of these events could.

Furthermore, since $F(x)$ is continuous, we see that the probabilities corresponding to the intervals

$$a < X \leqq b, \qquad a < X < b, \qquad a \leqq X < b, \qquad a \leqq X \leqq b$$

(with arbitrary fixed a and b where $b > a$) are all the same. This is different from the situation in the case of a discrete distribution.

Since probabilities are nonnegative and (3) holds for every interval, we may assume that

$$f(x) \geqq 0 \qquad \qquad \text{for all } x.$$

The distribution function of a continuous distribution determines the distribution uniquely (and so does the density function).

We conclude this section with a simple example. Further important continuous distributions are discussed later (in Chap. 8, etc.).

***Example 1** (**Uniform distribution**).* Let X be the angle between a fixed direction and the direction of the pointer of a spinner (cf. Fig. 5.6.2). If the spinner works properly, we may assume that for each x between 0 and 2π the probability $P(X \leqq x)$ is equal to the ratio of the angle x and the total angle 2π. This yields the distribution function

$$F(x) = \begin{cases} 0 & \text{when } x \leqq 0 \\ x/2\pi & \text{when } 0 < x \leqq 2\pi \\ 1 & \text{when } x > 2\pi. \end{cases}$$

By differentiation we obtain the corresponding density

$$f(x) = \begin{cases} 1/2\pi & \text{when } 0 < x < 2\pi \\ 0 & \text{otherwise.} \end{cases}$$

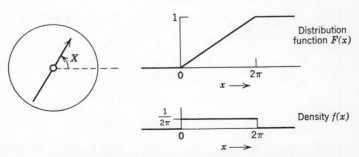

Fig. 5.6.2. Distribution function and density in Example 1

A distribution with density

(4)
$$f(x) = \begin{cases} \dfrac{1}{b-a} & \text{when } a < x < b \\ 0 & \text{otherwise} \end{cases}$$

is called a **uniform distribution** (or sometimes a *rectangular distribution*) on the interval $a < x < b$. We see that our problem led to a particular case of this distribution.

Problems

1. Show that any distribution function $F(x)$ has the properties

$$F(b) \geq F(a) \text{ when } b > a, \qquad \lim_{x \to \infty} F(x) = 1.$$

2. Suppose that X has a uniform distribution on the interval $-1 \leq x \leq 1$. Find the density function $f(x)$ and the distribution function $F(x)$. Find $P(X \geq 0)$, $P(0 \leq X \leq 0.3)$, and $P(X = 0.5)$.

3. What value must the constant k have in order that

$$f(x) = kx \qquad \text{when } 0 \leq x \leq 2, \qquad f(x) = 0 \qquad \text{otherwise}$$

be the density of a continuous distribution? Find and graph the corresponding distribution function.

4. Consider the distribution with the density

$$f(x) = 0 \ (x < 0), \qquad f(x) = ce^{-\alpha x} \ (x \geq 0).$$

Show that the parameter α must be positive. Determine c as a function of α. Graph $f(x)$ and $F(x)$ in the cases $\alpha = 0.5$ and $\alpha = 1$.

5. Find and graph the distribution function corresponding to (4) in Example 1.

6. Consider (4) in Example 1. Find $P(c \leq X \leq c + \Delta x)$ where c is any value between a and b and $c + \Delta x \leq b$. Let $\Delta x \to 0$ and show that this gives $P(X = c) = 0$.

7. Let X have the density $f(x) = 6x(1 - x)$ when $0 < x < 1$ and zero otherwise. Check that $f(x)$ is a density. Find $P(0 < X < 0.75)$.

8. Let X have the density $f(x) = kx$ when $0 < x < 4$ and zero otherwise. Find k. Find $F(x)$. Determine c so that $P(X \leq c) = 81\%$.

9. Determine the probability of obtaining a sample of 2 values from a population with the density $f(x) = 2x \ (0 < x < 1)$, $f(x) = 0$ otherwise, so that both sample values are greater than $1/2$.

10. Find the probability that none of 3 bulbs in a signal-light will have to be replaced during the first 1200 hours of operation if the lifetime X of a bulb is a random variable with the density

$$f(x) = 6[0.25 - (x - 1.5)^2] \qquad \text{when} \qquad 1 \leq x \leq 2,$$

$f(x) = 0$ otherwise, where x is measured in multiples of 1000 hours.

11. Find the density $f(x)$ and the distribution function $F(x)$ of a random variable X that has a uniform distribution on the interval $0 \leq x \leq 1$. Find the distribution function $F(z)$ and the density $f(z)$ of the corresponding random variable $Z = X^2$.

12. Suppose that a random variable X has the density $f(x) = 1$ when $0 < x < 1$ and zero otherwise. Determine c so that the probability is 90% that a sample of 3 observed values of X will contain at least 1 value greater than c.

13. Show that if X has the density $f(x) = 2x$ when $0 < x < 1$ and zero otherwise, then $Z = X^2$ has the density $g(z) = 1$ when $0 < z < 1$ and zero otherwise.

14. If X has the distribution function $F(x)$, show that $Z = F(X)$ is uniformly distributed on $0 < z < 1$.

15. Using direct calculation, verify the result in Problem 14 in the case of the distribution with the density $f(x) = 3x^2$ when $0 \leqq x \leqq 1$ and zero otherwise.

16. Let X be uniformly distributed on an interval $0 < x < \theta$. Find the distribution function and density of the random variable X_3 for which the largest value, x_3, of 3 independent observed values x_1, x_2, x_3 of the random variable X is an observed value.

5.7   Analogy Between Probability Distributions and Mass Distributions

There is a strictly quantitative analogy between probability distributions of a single variable and mass distributions of total mass 1 along a straight line.

In fact, the analogue of a discrete probability distribution with probability function (1), Sec. 5.2, is a distribution consisting of n masses $p_1, p_2, p_3, \cdots$ located at the points $x_1, x_2, x_3, \cdots$ of the x-axis. The mass located at a point x or to its left is given by the function

$$F(x) = \sum_{x_j \leqq x} f(x_j) = \sum_{x_j \leqq x} p_j.$$

This function corresponds to the distribution function $F(x)$ of the probability distribution.

The mechanical analogue of a continuous probability distribution with probability density $f(x)$ is a continuous mass distribution of total mass 1 with mass density $f(x)$. Then the mass located between $-\infty$ and a value x is

$$F(x) = \int_{-\infty}^{x} f(v) \, dv$$

and the mass in an interval $a < x \leqq b$ is

$$F(b) - F(a) = \int_{a}^{b} f(v) \, dv.$$

This function $F(x)$ corresponds to the distribution function of the probability distribution.

By way of illustration we may thus say that any distribution function defines a *distribution of mass* on the x-axis, and talk of a *probability mass* which is distributed according to $F(x)$.

Problems

1.–3. Describe the mass distributions corresponding to the following probability distributions.

1. The distribution in Example 1, Sec. 5.3.
2. The distribution in Example 2, Sec. 5.3.
3. The distribution in Example 1, Sec. 5.6.

CHAPTER **6**

Mean, Variance, and Skewness of a Distribution

Instead of using the complete characterization of a distribution given by its distribution function, it is often sufficient to describe the distribution usefully (although incompletely) in terms of certain quantities that can be obtained from the distribution function and characterize certain general properties of that distribution. The two most important such quantities are the *mean value* or *mean* μ (Sec. 6.1) and the *variance* σ^2 (Sec. 6.2). We shall also consider the *skewness* γ (Sec. 6.5). μ and σ^2 are particular cases of the *moments* of a distribution (Sec. 6.4).

6.1 Mean Value of a Distribution

The *mean value* or **mean** *of a distribution* is denoted by μ. In the case of a discrete distribution it is defined by

(1a) $$\mu = \sum_j x_j f(x_j)$$

and in the case of a continuous distribution by[1]

(1b) $$\mu = \int_{-\infty}^{\infty} x f(x)\, dx.$$

Here $f(x)$ is the probability function or the density, respectively, of the random variable X under consideration.

Another, generally less important, measure of central tendency, the *median*, will be considered in the set of problems for this section.

---

[1] In this definition, it is assumed that the series in (1a) converges absolutely and the integral

$$\int_{-\infty}^{\infty} |x| f(x)\, dx$$

exists. If this does not hold for a distribution, we say that the distribution does not have a mean; this case will rarely occur in applications.

Fig. 6.1.1. Probability function $f(x)$ and mean in Example 1

Example 1.   Let the random variable X denote the number that shows up in throwing a fair die. The corresponding probability function is

$$f(x) = 1/6 \qquad \text{when} \qquad x = 1, 2, \cdots, 6$$

and $f = 0$ otherwise. From (1a) we thus obtain the mean (cf. Fig. 6.1.1)

$$\mu = 1 \cdot \frac{1}{6} + 2 \cdot \frac{1}{6} + 3 \cdot \frac{1}{6} + 4 \cdot \frac{1}{6} + 5 \cdot \frac{1}{6} + 6 \cdot \frac{1}{6} = 3.5.$$

This is the average number to be expected in the sense that the sum of the numbers obtained, for example, in 1000 performances of the experiment will *approximately* be equal to $1000 \cdot 3.5 = 3500$.

Example 2.   The uniform distribution with density (4), Sec. 5.6, has the mean

$$\mu = \int_{-\infty}^{\infty} x f(x)\, dx = \int_{a}^{b} \frac{x}{b-a}\, dx = \frac{1}{b-a} \left(\frac{b^2}{2} - \frac{a^2}{2} \right) = \frac{a+b}{2}.$$

Further important examples will be considered in Chaps. 7 and 8.

We mention that the mean μ is also known as the *mathematical expectation* or, briefly, the **expectation** *of* X and is sometimes denoted by $E(X)$. Further details will follow in Sec. 6.3.

The mean value corresponds to the center of gravity of the analogous mass distribution.

In fact, (1) is the analogue of the well-known formula for that center of gravity.

A distribution is said to be **symmetric** *with respect to a number* $x = c$ if for every x,

(2) $$f(c + x) = f(c - x).$$

Theorem 1.   *If a distribution is symmetric with respect to* $x = c$ *and has a mean value* μ, *then*

(3) $$\mu = c.$$

The proof is simple. From this theorem, the results in Exs. 1 and 2 now follow without any calculation.

Problems

1. Find the mean of the distribution in Example 2, Sec. 5.3.
2. What total sum can you expect in throwing a fair die 20 times? Perform the experiment.

3. Find the mean of the distribution with the density $f(x) = xe^{-x}$ when $x > 0$, $f(x) = 0$ otherwise. Graph $f(x)$ and μ.

4. Prove Theorem 1 for a continuous distribution.

5. Find the mean of the distribution in Example 3, Sec. 5.3.

6. Find the mean of the distribution in Problem 5, Sec. 5.3.

7. Let X be any random variable and $F(x)$ its distribution function. Then any solution x of the equation

$$F(x) = 0.5$$

is called a **median** of the random variable X (or of the distribution). Give illustrative examples of distributions (a) for which the median is not unique, (b) for which the median coincides with the mean, (c) for which the median does not coincide with the mean. (In the case of highly skewed distributions like those of income per family, annual sales of business firms, etc., the median may give valuable additional information not obvious from the mean. For example, a very rich family moving into a small community may increase the mean income considerably without changing the median of the incomes.)

8. Show that if a distribution is symmetric and has a mean, the median (or a median) coincides with the mean.

9. Find the median $\tilde{\mu}$ and the mean μ of the random variable X with the density $f(x) = \theta e^{-\theta x}$ $(x > 0, \theta > 0$ and fixed) and zero otherwise; here, θ is a parameter. Graph $f(x)$ for some θ. Why is it intuitively clear that in this case, $\tilde{\mu} < \mu$?

10. The distribution with the density $f(x) = 1/\pi(1 + x^2)$ is called the **Cauchy distribution**; it was introduced by Cauchy (1853) (cf. Appendix 3). Show that this distribution does not have a mean, but has a median.

11. Show that $f(x)$ in Problem 10 satisfies (2), Sec. 5.6, and the distribution function is

$$F(x) = \frac{1}{2} + \frac{1}{\pi} \arctan x.$$

12. Show that for a discrete random variable which has only finitely many possible values, and for a continuous variable which can only assume values in a finite interval, the mean always exists.

13. Show that if a random variable can only assume values in a finite interval, then μ must lie in that interval.

14. A value x for which the probability function or density $f(x)$ of a random variable X has a maximum is called a **mode** of the distribution of X. Find the modes, median, and mean of the distribution of $X = $ *product of the 2 numbers obtained in throwing 2 fair dice*.

15. Give an example of a distribution for which the mode and the mean coincide.

6.2　Variance of a Distribution

The **variance** *of a distribution* is denoted by σ^2. In the discrete case it is defined by the formula

$$\sigma^2 = \sum_j (x_j - \mu)^2 f(x_j)$$

(1a)

and in the continuous case by the formula[2]

(1b) $$\sigma^2 = \int_{-\infty}^{\infty} (x - \mu)^2 f(x)\, dx.$$

Here $f(x)$ is the probability function or the density, respectively, of the distribution under consideration.

In the case of a discrete distribution with $f(x) = 1$ at a point and $f = 0$ otherwise we have $\sigma^2 = 0$. This case is of no practical interest. In any other case

(2) $$\sigma^2 > 0.$$

The positive square root of the variance is called the **standard deviation** and is denoted by σ.

Roughly speaking, *the variance is a measure of the spread or dispersion of the values which the corresponding variable X can assume.*

In fact, if in the discrete case σ^2 is small, then each term in (1a) must be small. Hence values x_j that lie far away from μ must have a small probability. Large deviations of X from μ are therefore unlikely to occur. Conversely, if σ^2 is large, not all x_j can lie close to μ. For a continuous distribution the conclusions are similar.

From (1) we see that *the mechanical analogue of the variance is the moment of inertia with respect to the center of gravity of the corresponding mass distribution.*

Example 1. The random variable

$$X = number\ of\ heads\ in\ a\ single\ toss\ of\ a\ fair\ coin$$

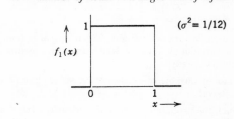

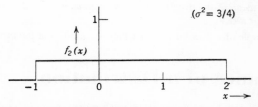

Fig. 6.2.1. Example of uniform distributions having the same mean (1/2) but different values of the variance

[2] In this definition it is assumed that the series in (1a) converges absolutely and the integral in (1b) exists.

has the possible values $X = 0$ and $X = 1$ with probabilities $P(X = 0) = 1/2$ and $P(X = 1) = 1/2$. The mean value is

$$\mu = 0 \cdot \frac{1}{2} + 1 \cdot \frac{1}{2} = \frac{1}{2}.$$

From (1a) we thus obtain the variance

$$\sigma^2 = \left(0 - \frac{1}{2}\right)^2 \cdot \frac{1}{2} + \left(1 - \frac{1}{2}\right)^2 \cdot \frac{1}{2} = \frac{1}{4}.$$

Example 2. The uniform distribution (4), Sec. 5.6, has the mean $\mu = (a + b)/2$. From (1b) we thus obtain the variance

$$\sigma^2 = \int_a^b \left(x - \frac{a + b}{2}\right)^2 \frac{1}{b - a}\, dx = \frac{(b - a)^2}{12}.$$

The particular cases with densities

$$f_1 = \begin{cases} 1 \text{ when } 0 \leq x \leq 1 \\ 0 \text{ otherwise} \end{cases} \quad \text{and} \quad f_2 = \begin{cases} 1/3 \text{ when } -1 \leq x \leq 2 \\ 0 \text{ otherwise} \end{cases}$$

have the same mean (1/2), but the variance of the first distribution is much smaller than that of the last (1/12 and 3/4, respectively; cf. Fig. 6.2.1).

Problems

1. Find the mean and the variance of the distribution with the density $f(x) = 0.5x$ when $0 \leq x \leq 2$, $f(x) = 0$ otherwise.

2. Give simple examples of a discrete and a continuous distribution whose variance is (*i*) very large ($\sigma^2 > 1000$), (*ii*) very small ($\sigma^2 < 1/1000$).

3. Mass produced items always show random variation, caused by small unpredictable and uncontrollable disturbing influences. Hence in the production of bolts the diameter X (in.) of the bolts must be regarded as a random variable. Suppose that the distribution of X has the density $f(x) = k(x - 0.9)(1.1 - x)$ when $0.9 < x < 1.1$ and $f(x) = 0$ otherwise. Determine k from (2), Sec. 5.6, graph $f(x)$, and find μ and σ^2.

4. Suppose that in Problem 3 a bolt is regarded as being defective if its diameter deviates from 1 by more than 0.06. What percent of defective bolts should we then expect?

5. For what choice of the maximum possible deviation from 1 in Problem 3 shall we obtain 10% defective bolts?

6. Suppose that a small filling station is supplied with gasoline every Saturday afternoon. Its volume X of sales in thousands of gallons is a random variable, and we assume that the density function of X is $f(x) = 6x(1 - x)$ when $0 \leq x \leq 1$ and $f(x) = 0$ otherwise. Determine the mean and the variance.

7. What must be the capacity of the tank in Problem 6 in order that the probability that the tank will be emptied in a given week be 10%?

8. Suppose that X is a discrete random variable and can assume $2n + 1$ equally spaced values, each with the same probability, the smallest value being -0.5 and the largest 0.5. Using $1^2 + 2^2 + \cdots + n^2 = n(n + 1)(2n + 1)/6$, find the variance σ^2 of X and show that $\sigma^2 \to 1/12$ (the variance of the uniform distribution on an interval of length 1) as $n \to \infty$.

9. Let X be uniformly distributed on the interval $0 \leqq x \leqq 1$. Find the probability that X assumes any value whose distance from the mean does not exceed σ.

10. Find the probability that a random variable X, which is uniformly distributed on $a \leqq x \leqq b$, will assume any value whose distance from the mean is (*i*) less than σ, (*ii*) less than 2σ.

6.3   Mathematical Expectation

To introduce the notion of mathematical expectation, let us start with a simple example.

Example 1. Two persons, S and T, play the following game. S throws a fair die. T has to pay him

> 10 cents if a *one* or *two* occurs,
> 20 cents if a *three* or *four* occurs,
> 40 cents if a *five* occurs, and
> 80 cents if a *six* occurs.

How much should S pay to T before each game in order that the game be fair?

The answer is that the payment of S should be equal to the average amount that S can expect to win in a game. This amount equals

(1) $$10 \cdot \frac{1}{6} + 10 \cdot \frac{1}{6} + 20 \cdot \frac{1}{6} + 20 \cdot \frac{1}{6} + 40 \cdot \frac{1}{6} + 80 \cdot \frac{1}{6} = 30 \text{ (cents)}$$

because the probability of "one" equals $1/6$, and then S gets 10 cents, etc.

In (1) with each possible value of the random variable

$$X = number\ obtained\ in\ throwing\ a\ fair\ die$$

we have associated a number, namely, the gain of S. This gain is a function of X and we denote it by $g(X)$. Its values are:

X	1	2	3	4	5	6
$g(X)$	10	10	20	20	40	80

Since the values of X depend on chance, the same is true for the value that $g(X)$ will assume in a certain game. Hence $g(X)$ itself is a random variable.

The expression (1) is the (average) expectation (expected gain) of S per game. It depends on the choice of the function g and we therefore denote it by $E(g(X))$. Obviously it has the form

(2a) $$E(g(X)) = \sum_j g(x_j) f(x_j).$$

Here $f(x)$ is the probability function corresponding to X, and we sum over all possible values x_j (cf. Sec. 5.5).

If X is any discrete random variable with probability function $f(x)$ and if $g(x)$ is any real-valued function that is defined for all possible values of X, then we may form the expression (2a). This expression is called the **expectation** *of the function $g(X)$.*

Similarly, in the case of a continuous distribution with density $f(x)$, the expectation of a function $g(X)$ is defined by the formula[3]

(2b)
$$E(g(X)) = \int_{-\infty}^{\infty} g(x)f(x)\,dx.$$

Of course, we must require that $g(x)$ be defined for all real x for which $f(x)$ is not zero.

The expectation of a function

$$ag(X) + bh(X) \qquad\qquad (a,\, b \text{ constant})$$

can be computed from the expectations of $g(X)$ and $h(X)$ by the formula

(3)
$$E(ag(X) + bh(X)) = aE(g(X)) + bE(h(X)).$$

The simple proof of this useful formula is left to the reader.

Problems

1. Prove (3).
2. James and Harry play the following game. James throws 2 fair dice, and Harry pays k cents to James where k is the product of the 2 faces that show on the dice. How much should James pay to Harry for each game to make the game fair?
3. Suppose that in a lottery 10,000 tickets are sold at 1 dollar each. The winner will get a car whose value is \$5000. If someone buys 3 tickets, what is his expectation?
4. What is a fair price to pay to enter a game in which one can win \$100 with probability 0.1, \$5 with probability 0.4, and nothing with probability 0.5?
5. Find the expectation of $g(X) = X^2$ where X is uniformly distributed on the interval $-1 \leq x \leq 1$.
6. Find the expectation of $g(X) = aX + b$ where X is uniformly distributed on the interval $0 \leq x \leq 1$.
7. Show that when $g(x) = x$, then $E(g(X)) = \mu$, the mean of X.
8. Find the expectation of $g(X) = X^3$, where X is a discrete random variable with probability function $f(0) = 1/8$, $f(1) = 3/8$, $f(2) = 3/8$, and $f(3) = 1/8$.

6.4   Moments of a Distribution

We shall now see that the mean and the variance are particular cases of more general quantities that are known as *moments*.

---

[3] In this definition it is assumed that the series in (2a) converges absolutely or, in (2b), the integral

$$\int_{-\infty}^{\infty} |g(x)|\, f(x)\, dx$$

exists. A sufficient condition is that $|g|$ be bounded. We mention without proof that (2) is the mean of the random variable $Y = g(X)$, so that our notation is consistent with that in Sec. 6.1.

If in (2), Sec. 6.3, we choose $g(X) = X^k$, where $k = 1, 2, \cdots$, then we obtain

(1) $$E(X^k) = \begin{cases} \sum_j x_j^k f(x_j) & \text{(Discrete distribution)} \\ \int_{-\infty}^{\infty} x^k f(x) \, dx & \text{(Continuous distribution).} \end{cases}$$

This quantity is called the **kth moment** of the random variable X or of the corresponding distribution under consideration.

The first moment is the mean,

(2) $$\mu = E(X).$$

This follows by comparing (1) with $k = 1$ and (1) in Sec. 6.1.

If in (2) we choose $g(X) = (X - \mu)^k$, then we obtain

(3) $$E([X - \mu]^k) = \begin{cases} \sum_j (x_j - \mu)^k f(x_j) & \text{(Discrete distribution)} \\ \int_{-\infty}^{\infty} (x - \mu)^k f(x) \, dx & \text{(Continuous distribution).} \end{cases}$$

This quantity is called the **kth central moment** of the random variable X or of the corresponding distribution.

If the first central moment exists, it is zero.

Mechanical analogue: the first moment with respect to the center of gravity is zero.

The second central moment is the variance,

(4) $$\sigma^2 = E([X - \mu]^2).$$

The central moments can be represented in terms of the moments $E(X)$, $E(X^2)$, $\cdots$

For example, if we use (3) in Sec. 6.3 and

$$E(1) = \sum_j f(x_j) = 1, \qquad E(1) = \int_{-\infty}^{\infty} f(x) \, dx = 1,$$

it follows that

$$\sigma^2 = E([X - \mu]^2) = E(X^2 - 2\mu X + \mu^2) = E(X^2) - 2\mu E(X) + \mu^2.$$

On the right, $E(X) = \mu$. Therefore

(5) $$\sigma^2 = E(X^2) - \mu^2.$$

In a similar fashion it can be shown that

(6) $$E([X - \mu]^3) = E(X^3) - 3\mu E(X^2) + 2\mu^3$$

etc.

Example 1. If X is the number obtained in throwing a fair die, then

$$\mu = E(X) = \frac{1}{6}(1 + 2 + \cdots + 6) = \frac{7}{2},$$

$$E(X^2) = \frac{1}{6}(1^2 + 2^2 + \cdots + 6^2) = \frac{91}{6}.$$

From (5) we thus obtain

$$\sigma^2 = \frac{91}{6} - \frac{49}{4} = \frac{35}{12}.$$

Problems

1. Show that if the first central moment exists, it is zero.
2. Derive (6).
3. The expression

$$E([X - c]^2) \qquad\qquad (c \text{ any real number})$$

   is called the **second moment of X with respect to c**. Show that if this moment exists, it is minimum when $c = \mu$.
4. What is the mechanical analogue of the statement in Problem 3?
5. Show that
   (7) $$\sigma^2 = E(X[X - 1]) + \mu - \mu^2.$$

6. For a one-dimensional mass distribution of total mass M, **Steiner's theorem** may be written

$$I_P = I_G + a^2 M,$$

   where a is the distance of a point P from the center of gravity G, and I_P and I_G are the moments of inertia with respect to P and G, respectively. Show that (5) is an analogue of this theorem.
7. To get a feeling for the usefulness of (5), obtain σ^2 in Example 1 without using (5).
8. Find the third central moment in Example 1. Can you see without calculation that it must be zero?
9. Find the moments and central moments of the uniform distribution on the interval $0 \leq x \leq 1$ (cf. Sec. 5.6).
10. Find the moments of the uniform distribution on an arbitrary interval $a \leq x \leq b$.
11. A property concerning the minimum of the median (cf. Sec. 6.1) similar to that in Problem 3 is as follows. Show that $E(|X - c|)$ is minimum if and only if c is the median of X. (For simplicity, assume that X is continuous and the median is unique, but the statement also holds without these restrictions.)

6.5   Skewness of a Distribution

Theorem 1. *If a distribution is symmetric with respect to the mean $x = \mu$ (cf. Sec. 6.1) and its third central moment exists, this moment is zero.*

The proof is left to the reader.

Example 1. The distribution in Example 1, Sec. 6.4, is symmetric with respect to $x = \mu = 3.5$, and its third central moment exists. Hence it follows from Theorem 1 that this moment must be zero.

Example 2. Take a fair die and write 1 on three of its faces, -4 on two faces, and 5 on one face. Then the random variable $X = $ *number that shows up on the modified die* assumes the values 1, -4, and 5 with probabilities 1/2, 1/3, and 1/6, respectively. The mean is 0. The distribution is not symmetric, but a direct calculation shows that the third central moment is 0.

Example 2 shows that $E([X - \mu]^3) = 0$ does *not* imply that the distribution of X is symmetric. Nevertheless it is customary to introduce the quantity

$$\textbf{(1)} \qquad\qquad \gamma = \frac{1}{\sigma^3} E([X - \mu]^3)$$

and regard it as a measure of asymmetry of distributions that are important in applications, since γ is 0 for a symmetric distribution and is likely to be a large positive (negative) number for a distribution with a large right (left) tail; the cubes of the deviations corresponding to the tail will then generally outweigh the cubes on the other side of μ; cf. Ex. 3 and Fig. 6.5.1, which is typical. γ is called the **skewness** of X or of the corresponding distribution. The reason for using γ rather than the third central moment is that γ is independent of the units of measurement, whereas the third central moment is not.

Example 3. The distribution with the density

$$f(x) = xe^{-x} \quad \text{when} \quad x > 0, \quad f(x) = 0 \quad \text{otherwise}$$

(cf. Fig. 6.5.1) has the mean

$$\mu = E(X) = \int_0^\infty x^2 e^{-x}\, dx = 2,$$

as follows by integration by parts. Furthermore,

$$E(X^2) = \int_0^\infty x^3 e^{-x}\, dx = 6, \qquad E(X^3) = \int_0^\infty x^4 e^{-x}\, dx = 24.$$

From (5) in Sec. 6.4 we thus obtain the variance

$$\sigma^2 = 6 - 4 = 2$$

and from (6) in Sec. 6.4 the third central moment

$$E([X - \mu]^3) = 24 - 3 \cdot 2 \cdot 6 + 2 \cdot 8 = 4.$$

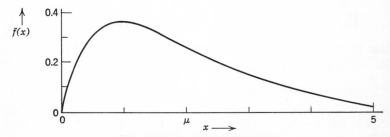

Fig. 6.5.1. Density in Example 3

Hence the distribution has the positive skewness

$$\gamma = \frac{4}{2\sqrt{2}} = \sqrt{2}.$$

For the sake of completeness we mention that the quantity

$$\gamma^* = \frac{1}{\sigma^4} E([X - \mu]^4)$$

is sometimes used as a measure of the **peakedness** of a distribution, but this interpretation is somewhat vague and of questionable value.

In fact, *all* measures of location, dispersion, and other similar properties are to a large extent arbitrary. This is quite natural because the properties to be measured by such quantities are only vaguely defined.

Problems

1. Prove Theorem 1.
2. Show that if a distribution is symmetric with respect to $x = \mu$, then all its existing central moments of odd order are zero.
3. Verify the statement in Example 1 by direct calculation.
4. Show that the third central moment of the nonsymmetric distribution in Example 2 is zero.
5. Show that Example 2 is the simplest possible example of a nonsymmetric distribution with $E([X - \mu]^3) = 0$ in the sense that any random variable X which assumes only 2 values and has the property $E([X - \mu]^3) = 0$ must have a symmetric distribution.
6. Suppose that X can assume the values 0 and 1 with probabilities $1 - p$ and p, respectively. Find all moments and central moments and γ.
7. Find the skewness of the distribution with density $f(x) = 2(1 - x)$ when $0 < x < 1$, $f(x) = 0$ otherwise.
8. Determine the kth moment of the distribution in Problem 7.
9. Using (6), Sec. 6.4, and the answer to Problem 8, check the answer to Problem 7.
10. Carry out the details of the integrations in Example 3.

6.6 Moment Generating Function. Characteristic Function

In some cases the moments may be computed directly from (1), Sec. 6.4. We shall see later that in other cases it is simpler to use an auxiliary function, namely, the expectation of e^{tX}. This function $E(e^{tX})$ is called the **moment generating function** of the distribution, and is denoted by $G(t)$. Thus

$$(1) \qquad G(t) = E(e^{tX}) = \begin{cases} \sum_j e^{tx_j} f(x_j) & \text{(Discrete distribution)} \\ \int_{-\infty}^{\infty} e^{tx} f(x)\, dx & \text{(Continuous distribution).} \end{cases}$$

Assuming that we may differentiate under the summation sign (or under the integral sign, respectively), we obtain

$$G'(t) = \begin{cases} \sum_j x_j e^{t x_j} f(x_j) \\ \int_{-\infty}^{\infty} x e^{tx} f(x) \, dx. \end{cases}$$

Differentiating k times, we find

$$\frac{d^k G}{dt^k} = \begin{cases} \sum_j x_j{}^k e^{t x_j} f(x_j) \\ \int_{-\infty}^{\infty} x^k e^{tx} f(x) \, dx. \end{cases}$$

When $t = 0$, the exponential function equals 1 and the expression on the right equals the kth moment. Thus

(2) $$E(X^k) = G^{(k)}(0) \qquad \left[G^{(k)}(0) = \frac{d^k G}{dt^k} \bigg|_{t=0} \right].$$

In particular, when $k = 1$,

(3) $$\mu = E(X) = G'(0).$$

Typical examples illustrating the method will be given in Chap. 7.

Of course, this method can only be applied to distributions for which the above series converge (or the integrals exist, respectively). We shall not discuss this convergence problem, but confine ourselves to the following remark.

If all the moments of a given distribution exist, then, because of (2), the corresponding moment generating function has the Taylor expansion

$$G(t) = \sum_{k=0}^{\infty} \frac{G^{(k)}(0)}{k!} t^k = \sum_{k=0}^{\infty} \frac{E(X^k)}{k!} t^k.$$

It can be shown that if the radius of convergence of this series is not zero, the distribution is uniquely determined by $G(t)$, that is, by the moments $E(X^k)$, where $k = 0, 1, \cdots$.

More details about generating and characteristic functions (cf. Problem 5) can be found in the books by Wilks (1962), Chap. 5, and Cramér (1961), Chap. 10, which are listed in Appendix 3.

Problems

1. Let p be the probability of hitting a target by firing once. Let the random variable X denote the number of shots that precede the first hit. Show that X has the probability function

$$f(x) = q^x p \qquad \text{where} \qquad q = 1 - p \qquad (x = 0, 1, \cdots)$$

and determine the corresponding moment generating function. (The distribution of X is called the **geometric distribution**.)

2. Find the mean and the variance of the geometric distribution in Problem 1.

3. Check the result in Example 1, Sec. 6.4, by the use of the moment generating function.

4. Find the moment generating function of the distribution in Example 3, Sec. 5.3.

5. Difficulties with respect to convergence can be avoided by the use of the complex function

$$(4) \qquad\qquad \Psi(t) = E(e^{itX}) \qquad\qquad (i = \sqrt{-1}),$$

which is called the **characteristic function** of the corresponding distribution. Show that in the case of any discrete or continuous distribution, this function exists for any real t.

6. Show that if $E(X^k)$ exists,

$$E(X^k) = i^{-k}\Psi^{(k)}(0).$$

7. Find the mean and the variance of the distribution with density

$$f(x) = \theta e^{-\theta x} \quad\text{when}\quad x \geq 0, \quad f(x) = 0 \quad\text{otherwise};$$

use (a) the defining formulas, (b) the moment generating function, (c) the characteristic function.

8. For what values of t does the moment generating function in Problem 7 exist?

6.7   Linear Transformation of Random Variables

It happens quite frequently that theoretical or practical considerations require the transition from a given random variable X to a new random variable

$$(1) \qquad\qquad X^* = c_1 X + c_2 \qquad\qquad (c_1 \neq 0).$$

We say that X^* is obtained from X by the **linear transformation** (1). We want to compute the mean μ^* and the variance σ^{*2} of X^* from the mean μ and the variance σ^2 of X.

From (3) in Sec. 6.3 we readily obtain

$$\mu^* = E(X^*) = E(c_1 X + c_2) = c_1 E(X) + c_2 E(1).$$

Since $E(X) = \mu$ and $E(1) = 1$, this gives

$$(2) \qquad\qquad \mu^* = c_1 \mu + c_2.$$

Consequently,

$$X^* - \mu^* = (c_1 X + c_2) - (c_1 \mu + c_2) = c_1(X - \mu).$$

Hence the kth central moments are related as follows.

$$(3) \qquad E([X^* - \mu^*]^k) = E(c_1^k [X - \mu]^k) = c_1^k E([X - \mu]^k).$$

In particular, when $k = 2$ this takes the form

$$(4) \qquad\qquad \sigma^{*2} = c_1^2 \sigma^2.$$

An immediate consequence of (4) is:

Theorem 1.   *The variance is invariant under a translation of the origin, that is, a transformation of the form*

$$X^* = X + c_2.$$

If we choose $c_1 = 1/\sigma$ and $c_2 = -\mu/\sigma$, then X^* in (1) takes the form $(X - \mu)/\sigma$. This variable will be denoted by Z. From (2) and (4) it follows that Z has mean 0 and variance 1. This proves the following theorem.

Theorem 2.   *If a random variable X has mean μ and variance σ^2, then the corresponding variable*

$$Z = \frac{X - \mu}{\sigma}$$

has mean 0 and variance 1.

Z is called the **standardized variable** corresponding to X.

Problems

1. Show that if X has the moment generating function $G(t)$, then $X^* = c_1 X + c_2$ has the moment generating function

   (5) $$G^*(t) = e^{c_2 t} G(c_1 t).$$

2. Suppose that X has the density

   $$f(x) = 0.75(1 - x^2) \quad \text{when} \quad -1 \leq x \leq 1, \qquad f(x) = 0 \quad \text{otherwise.}$$

   Find the mean and the variance of $Y = 2X - 2$.

3. Show that

   (6) $$\sigma^2 = \tilde{G}''(0) \quad \text{where} \quad \tilde{G}(t) = E(e^{(X-\mu)t}).$$

4. Show that in Problem 3,

   $$\tilde{G}(t) = e^{-\mu t} G(t).$$

   Using this formula and (2), Sec. 6.6, derive (5), Sec. 6.4.

5. Show that if the skewness γ of a random variable X is zero, then the same is true for $X^* = c_1 X + c_2$.

6. Applying the result of Problem 5 to Example 2 in Sec. 6.5, obtain further distributions which have skewness $\gamma = 0$ but are not symmetric.

7. Show that under the transformation $X^* = c_1 X + c_2$, the kth central moment is multiplied by c_1^k, that is,

   $$E([X^* - \mu^*]^k) = c_1^k E([X - \mu]^k),$$

   where μ^* is the mean of X^*. [Cf. (3).]

8. Let X be a continuous random variable with density $f(x)$. Let $y = g(x)$ be strictly monotone and let $x = h(y)$ be its inverse. Show that then $Y = g(X)$ has the density $f^*(y) = f(h(y)) |dh/dy|$.

9. Let X be uniformly distributed on the interval $0 \leq x \leq 1$. Applying the result of Problem 8, find and graph the distribution function and density of $Y = X^2$.

10. Find the standardized variable Z corresponding to a random variable X that is uniformly distributed on an interval $a \leq x \leq b$.

CHAPTER 7

Special Discrete Distributions

We shall now consider three discrete distributions that are particularly important in statistics. These are the binomial distribution (Secs. 7.1–7.3), the Poisson distribution (Secs. 7.4–7.6), and the hypergeometric distribution (Secs. 7.7, 7.8).

Let p be the probability of an event A in a random experiment. Suppose that the experiment is performed several times, say, n times. Then we may be interested in the number of times that A occurs in those n trials. This leads us to the binomial distribution if we assume that p is constant and the outcomes of the trials do not influence one another.

If n is large and p is small, then that distribution can be approximated by the Poisson distribution, which is somewhat simpler.

While the binominal distribution is important in experiments in which we draw *with* replacement, the hypergeometric distribution plays a similar role in experiments in which we draw *without* replacement; these experiments are slightly more complicated.

7.1 Binomial Distribution

The binomial distribution occurs if we are interested in the number of times an event A happens in n independent performances of a random experiment, assuming that A has probability

$$P(A) = p$$

in a single trial. Then $1 - p$ is the probability that in a single trial the event A does not occur, and we set

$$q = 1 - p.$$

Let us consider the random variable

$$X = \text{number of times the event } A \text{ happens}$$

and first assume that the experiment is performed only once. Then X may

91

Fig. 7.1.1. Probability function (1) with $p = 1/6$

have the values 0 or 1, depending on whether A does not happen or does happen. The corresponding probabilities are

$$P(X = 0) = q \qquad \text{and} \qquad P(X = 1) = p,$$

respectively. Hence the probability function of X has the values

$$f(0) = q, \qquad f(1) = p,$$

and $f(x) = 0$ otherwise. The reader may easily verify that the formulas $f(0) = q$ and $f(1) = p$ can be combined into the single formula

$$(1) \qquad\qquad f(x) = p^x q^{1-x} \qquad\qquad (x = 0, 1).$$

For example, if we throw a fair die and denote by A the event that 6 turns up, then $p = 1/6$, and we obtain the function in Fig. 7.1.1.

We now assume that the above experiment is performed several times, say, n times. Then X can assume the values $0, 1, \cdots, n$, and we want to determine the corresponding probabilities. For this purpose we consider the event $X = x$ which means that in x of the n trials A occurs and in the other $n - x$ trials A does not occur. This may look as follows:

$$(2) \qquad\qquad \underbrace{AA \cdots A}_{x \text{ times}} \underbrace{BB \cdots B}_{n-x \text{ times}}.$$

Here $B = A^c$, that is, A does not occur. We assume that the trials are *independent*, that is, do not influence each other. Then, since $P(A) = p$ and $P(B) = q$, we see that (2) has the probability

$$(3) \qquad\qquad \underbrace{pp \cdots p}_{x \text{ times}} \underbrace{qq \cdots q}_{n-x \text{ times}} = p^x q^{n-x}.$$

Clearly, (2) is merely *one* order of arranging x A's and $n - x$ B's, and the probability of $X = x$ thus equals $p^x q^{n-x}$ times the number of different arrangements of x A's and $n - x$ B's, as follows from Theorem 1 in Sec. 4.6. We may number the n trials from 1 to n and pick x of these numbers corresponding to those trials in which A happens. Since the order in which we pick the x numbers does not matter, we see from (4a) in Sec. 4.9 that there are $\binom{n}{x}$ different ways in which we can pick those x numbers from the n numbers. Hence the probability $P(X = x)$ of the event $X = x$ equals

$$(4) \qquad\qquad f(x) = \binom{n}{x} p^x q^{n-x} \qquad\qquad (x = 0, 1, \cdots, n)$$

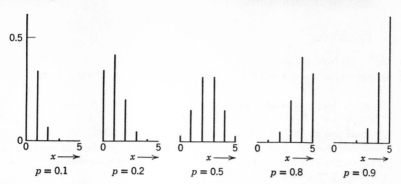

Fig. 7.1.2. Probability function (4) of the binomial distribution for $n = 5$ and various values of p

and $f(x) = 0$ for any other value of x. This is the probability that in n independent trials an event A occurs precisely x times, where p is the probability of A in a single trial and $q = 1 - p$. The distribution determined by the probability function (4) is called the **binomial distribution** or *Bernoulli distribution*. The occurrence of A is called **success**, and the nonoccurrence of A is called **failure.** p is called the *probability of success in a single trial.* Figure 7.1.2 shows illustrative examples of $f(x)$.

The name *binomial distribution* comes from the fact that the values of $f(x)$ are the terms of the binomial development

$$(p + q)^n = \sum_{x=0}^{n} \binom{n}{x} p^x q^{n-x} = q^n + \binom{n}{1} pq^{n-1} + \binom{n}{2} p^2 q^{n-2} + \cdots + p^n,$$

so that we may write

$$(p + q)^n = \sum_{x=0}^{n} f(x).$$

From the definition of the binomial coefficients it follows that

(5)
$$\binom{n}{x + 1} = \frac{n - x}{x + 1} \binom{n}{x}.$$

From this we obtain

(6)
$$f(x + 1) = \left(\frac{n - x}{x + 1}\right) \frac{p}{q} f(x) \qquad (x = 0, 1, \cdots, n - 1).$$

This formula is useful for computational purposes.

From (4) we see that the distribution function is $F(x) = 0$ when $x < 0$ and

(7)
$$F(x) = \sum_{k \leq x} \binom{n}{k} p^k q^{n-k} \qquad \text{when } x \geqq 0.$$

Numerical values are given in Appendix 4 (see Table 1*d*, which also includes references to more extended tables).

Problems

1. Derive (5) from (4), Sec. 4.10.
2. Graph $f(x)$ with $n = 8$ and $p = 0.2, 0.3, 0.4, 0.6, 0.7, 0.8$ (cf. Table 1d in Appendix 4).
3. Using (6), give a qualitative description of the behavior of $f(x)$ for fixed n and p. Where does $f(x)$ have a maximum (a mode; cf. Sec. 6.1)?
4. Compute and graph $f(x)$ and $F(x)$ when $n = 4$ and $p = 0.15$.
5. Show that the following formulas for probabilities of numbers of successes in n performances of a Bernoulli experiment hold; here p is the probability of success in a single performance, and $q = 1 - p$.

At most m successes:

$$P(X \leqq m) = \sum_{k=0}^{m} \binom{n}{k} p^k q^{n-k} = F(m).$$

At least l successes:

(8) $$P(X \geqq l) = \sum_{k=l}^{n} \binom{n}{k} p^k q^{n-k} = 1 - F(l-1).$$

At least 1 success:

(9) $$P(X \geqq 1) = 1 - F(0) = 1 - q^n.$$

At least l but at most m successes:

(10) $$P(l \leqq X \leqq m) = \sum_{k=l}^{m} \binom{n}{k} p^k q^{n-k} = F(m) - F(l-1).$$

7.2 Mean and Variance of the Binomial Distribution

Formulas for the mean and the variance of the binomial distribution may be obtained by direct calculation or by the use of the moment generating function $G(t)$. We shall choose the latter method. From (1), Sec. 6.6, and (4), Sec. 7.1, we have

(1) $$G(t) = \sum_{x=0}^{n} e^{tx} \binom{n}{x} p^x q^{n-x}.$$

This may be written

$$G(t) = \sum_{x=0}^{n} \binom{n}{x} (pe^t)^x q^{n-x}.$$

By applying the binomial formula (6), Sec. 4.10, we thus obtain

(2) $$G(t) = (pe^t + q)^n.$$

Differentiating and noting that $p + q = 1$, we find

$$G'(t) = n(pe^t + q)^{n-1}pe^t, \qquad G'(0) = np.$$

From this and (3), Sec. 6.6, it follows that the binomial distribution has the mean value

(3) $\mu = np.$

In a similar fashion we obtain the variance

(4) $\sigma^2 = npq.$

In fact, by differentiating $G'(t)$ we first have

$$G''(t) = n(n - 1)(pe^t + q)^{n-2}(pe^t)^2 + n(pe^t + q)^{n-1}pe^t.$$

Using (2), Sec. 6.6, we thus find

$$E(X^2) = G''(0) = n(n - 1)p^2 + np.$$

If we substitute this and (3) in (5), Sec. 6.4, formula (4) follows.

7.3 Some Applications of the Binomial Distribution

Suppose we have a box containing N things, for example, screws, M of which are defective. Then the probability of obtaining a defective screw in drawing one screw is

$$p = \frac{M}{N}.$$

If we draw n screws with replacement (cf. Sec. 4.7), the outcomes are independent. The probability of obtaining precisely x defective screws among the n screws to be drawn is [cf. (4), Sec. 7.1]

(1) $$f(x) = \binom{n}{x}\left(\frac{M}{N}\right)^x\left(1 - \frac{M}{N}\right)^{n-x}.$$

This shows that drawing with replacement leads to the binomial distribution. Drawing without replacement is more important, but leads to a more complicated distribution. In cases in which this distribution does not differ too much from the binomial distribution, the latter is preferable. Details will follow in Secs. 7.7 and 7.8.

Example 1. Six cards are drawn with replacement from a bridge deck. Find the probability P of obtaining at least 3 aces.

$M = 4$ among the $N = 52$ cards are aces. Hence $p = 4/52 = 1/13$, $q = 12/13$, and

$$P = \sum_{k=3}^{6}\binom{6}{k}\left(\frac{1}{13}\right)^k\left(\frac{12}{13}\right)^{6-k} = \frac{36{,}793}{4{,}826{,}809} \approx \frac{3}{4}\%.$$

Example 2. A fair die is thrown 3 times. What is the probability P that at least one 5 or 6 turns up?

In a single performance the event

$$A: 5 \text{ or } 6 \text{ turns up}$$

has the probability $p = 2/6 = 1/3$. Hence $q = 2/3$, and (9), Sec. 7.1, yields

$$P = 1 - \left(\frac{2}{3}\right)^3 = \frac{19}{27} \approx 70\%.$$

Example 3.   Suppose that under certain conditions the probability of hitting a target with a shot from a rifle is 0.1. Find the probability of hitting the target at least once if 10 shots are fired and the outcomes are assumed to be independent.

From (9), Sec. 7.1, with $n = 10$, $p = 0.1$, and $q = 0.9$ we obtain the answer

$$P = 1 - (0.9)^{10} \approx 65\%.$$

Some further applications are illustrated by the following problems.

Problems

1. If in the experiment *birth of a single child* the outcomes *birth of a boy* and *birth of a girl* are equally likely and we assume independence of repeated trials, what is the probability that a family with 4 children will have (a) 2 boys and 2 girls, (b) 3 boys and 1 girl, (c) 4 boys?

2. Show that for $p = 0.5$, formula (4), Sec. 7.1, takes the simple form

$$f(x) = \frac{1}{2^n}\binom{n}{x}.$$

   Find μ and σ^2 in this case.

3. A recently published article included a table of 15 measurements of pressures, and in 14 of them the last digit was odd. What is the probability of obtaining at most 1 even last digit in 15 measurements if even and odd last digits are equally likely?

4. Suppose that in a certain experiment positive and negative values are equally likely. Find the probability of obtaining at most 1 negative value in 9 performances of the experiment.

5. Five fair coins are tossed simultaneously. Find the probability function of the random variable $X = $ *number of heads* and compute the probabilities of obtaining no heads, heads precisely once, heads at least once, and heads not more than 4 times.

6. What number of heads has the maximum probability in each case if 2, 4, 10, and 100 fair coins are tossed simultaneously?

7. Draw 4 balls with replacement from a box containing balls, 1/3 of which are red. Perform the experiment 81 times and record the number of red balls in each trial. Compare the distribution thus obtained with the theoretical distribution.

8. Suppose that for a certain type of aircraft motor the probability of failure of a motor during a 100-hour period is p. Assume that a 4-motor plane can fly with at least 2 motors, whereas a 2-motor plane can fly with at least 1 motor. If the failure of one motor is independent of the failure of another and p is small, show that during an intended 100-hour flight the 2-motor plane is about $1/4p$ times more likely to be forced down by motor failure than the 4-motor plane.

9. Let $p = 1\%$ be the probability that a certain type of light bulb will fail in a 24-hour test. Find the probability that a sign consisting of 10 such bulbs will burn 24 hours with no bulb failures. (Assume independence.)

10. Suppose that each of 3 given cartons contains 20 fuses, 5 of which are defective. Find the probability of obtaining precisely x defective fuses in drawing 1 fuse from each carton.

11. If the probability of hitting a target is 20% and 5 shots are fired independently, what is the probability that the target will be hit at least once?

12. Suppose that the probability of hitting a target is p and n shots are fired independently. Compare the probabilities of hitting the target at least once in the two cases (a) $p = 1/2$ and $n = 2$ shots, (b) $p = 1/4$ and $n = 4$ shots. Which is larger? (First guess, then compute.)

13. Suppose that for a certain kind of flower bulb it is known that about 5% of the bulbs do not germinate. The bulbs are packaged and sold in boxes of 10 with the guarantee that at least 9 of the 10 bulbs will germinate. Find the probability that an arbitrary fixed box will not have the guaranteed property.

14. How does the situation in Problem 13 change if the guarantee is reduced from 9 to 8 bulbs per box?

15. Suppose that 5% of certain items produced are defective and the quality of each item is independent of the others. Find and graph the probability that in a sample of 10 items 0, 1, 2, $\cdots$ will be defective.

16. A process of manufacturing screws is checked every hour by inspecting n screws selected at random from that hour's production. If one or more screws are defective, the process is halted and carefully examined. How large should n be if the manufacturer wants the probability to be about 95% that the process will be halted when 10% of the screws being produced are defective? (Assume independence of the quality of any item of that of the other items.)

17. Let X have a binomial distribution with $p = 0.5$. Find the probability that X will assume a value in the interval $\mu - \sigma < X < \mu + \sigma$, assuming that (a) $n = 1$, (b) $n = 2$, (c) $n = 3$, (d) $n = 4$, and (e) $n = 5$.

18. For fixed n the variance σ^2 of the binomial distribution is a function of p. For what p is σ^2 maximum?

19. The distribution having the probability function

$$f(x) = \binom{k + x - 1}{x} p^k q^x, \qquad q = 1 - p, \qquad x = 0, 1, 2, \cdots$$

is called the **Pascal distribution**. Show that $f(x)$ is the probability of obtaining the kth success in the $(k + x)$th performance of a Bernoulli experiment; here k is given and p is the probability of success in a single trial. (This is a simple *waiting time problem*.)

20. Show that the geometric distribution (cf. Problem 1, Sec. 6.6) is a special Pascal distribution.

7.4   Poisson Distribution

The distribution with the probability function

(1) $$f(x) = \frac{\mu^x}{x!} e^{-\mu} \qquad\qquad (x = 0, 1, \cdots)$$

is called the **Poisson distribution,** named after S. D. Poisson who introduced it in 1837. Numerical values are included in Appendix 4 (Table 2). Figure 7.4.1 shows $f(x)$ for various μ. The parameter μ is the *mean* of the distribution. This will be shown below and confirmed in Sec. 7.6.

From (1) we see that the distribution function of the Poisson distribution is

$$(2) \qquad\qquad F(x) = e^{-\mu} \sum_{s \leqq x} \frac{\mu^s}{s!} \qquad\qquad \text{when } x \geqq 0$$

and $F(x) = 0$ when $x < 0$.

The Poisson distribution has important applications. In fact, this distribution is a convenient approximation of the binomial distribution in cases of a large number n of trials and a small probability p of success in a single trial. This is a consequence of the following proposition.

If in the binomial probability function (4), *Sec. 7.1, for fixed x, we let $n \to \infty$ and $p \to 0$ through sequences of values such that np equals a fixed number μ, then the limit of* (4), *Sec. 7.1, is* (1), *this section.*

To prove this, we start from $\mu = np$ and have

$$p = \frac{\mu}{n} \qquad \text{and} \qquad p^x = \frac{\mu^x}{n^x}.$$

Similarly,

$$q^{n-x} = (1 - p)^{n-x} = \left(1 - \frac{\mu}{n}\right)^{n-x} = \left[1 - \frac{\mu}{n}\right]^n \left\{1 - \frac{\mu}{n}\right\}^{-x}.$$

It follows that the right-hand side of (4), Sec. 7.1, can be written

$$\frac{\mu^x}{x!} \frac{n(n-1)\cdots(n-x+1)}{n^x} \left[1 - \frac{\mu}{n}\right]^n \left\{1 - \frac{\mu}{n}\right\}^{-x}.$$

As $n \to \infty$, the expression

$$\frac{n(n-1)\cdots(n-x+1)}{n^x} = \left(\frac{n}{n}\right)\left(\frac{n-1}{n}\right)\cdots\left(\frac{n-x+1}{n}\right)$$

approaches 1, and so does the expression in the braces, whereas the expression

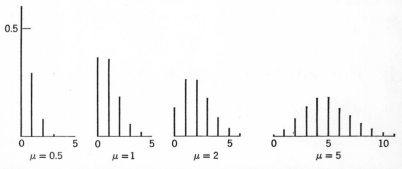

Fig. 7.4.1. Probability function (1) of the Poisson distribution for various values of μ

Table 7.4.1. Approximation of the Binomial Distribution by the Poisson Distribution

x	Binomial Distribution			Poisson Distribution with $\mu = 1$
	$n = 4, p = 1/4$	$n = 8, p = 1/8$	$n = 100, p = 1/100$	
0	0.316	0.344	0.366	0.368
1	0.422	0.393	0.370	0.368
2	0.211	0.196	0.185	0.184
3	0.047	0.056	0.061	0.061
4	0.004	0.010	0.015	0.015
5	—	0.001	0.003	0.003

in the brackets approaches $e^{-\mu}$. This completes the proof, which also shows that μ in (1) is the mean of the Poisson distribution.

Table 7.4.1 illustrates that even for relatively small n the approximation of the binomial distribution by the Poisson distribution is rather good. The approximation is of great practical importance because for large n the binomial coefficients are rather inconvenient.

7.5 Applications of the Poisson Distribution

The Poisson distribution has applications in various fields. Three typical examples are shown in Tables 7.5.1–7.5.3. In Table 7.5.1,

$$\bar{x} = \tfrac{1}{200}(1 \cdot 65 + 2 \cdot 22 + 3 \cdot 3 + 4 \cdot 1) = 0.61.$$

Using this value for μ in (1), Sec. 7.4, and multiplying by 200, the total number of years, we obtain the values in the last column of Table 7.5.1. The

Table 7.5.1. Number of Fatalities Caused by the Kick of a Horse in 10 Prussian Army Corps During a 20-Year Period (1875–1894) (L. v. Bortkiewicz, *Das Gesetz der kleinen Zahlen*. Leipzig, 1898)

x	Number of Years with x Deaths per Corps per Year	
	Observed	Theoretical (Rounded)
0	109	109
1	65	66
2	22	20
3	3	4
4	1	1
$\geqq 5$	0	0

Table 7.5.2. Number of Alpha Particles (E. Rutherford and H. Geiger, *Phil. Mag.* **(6) 20,** 1910, 698)

x	Number of Intervals of Time (Length 7.5 sec) with x Particles per Interval	
	Observed	Theoretical (Rounded)
0	57	54
1	203	210
2	383	407
3	525	526
4	532	509
5	408	394
6	273	254
7	139	140
8	45	68
9	27	29
10	10	11
11	4	4
12	2	1
$\geqq 13$	0	1

last column in the other two tables is obtained in a similar fashion.

Another example is the distribution of bombs in a target area, the area being divided into squares which play a role similar to that of the time intervals in Table 7.5.2. Further examples are the distributions of misprints in a book, raisins in a cake, pitch troubles in paper production, etc.

Table 7.5.3. Traffic Distribution on a Street in Graz, Austria, on September 9, 1963, 10:20–11:10 A.M.

x	Number of Intervals of Time (Length 30 sec) with x Cars per Interval	
	Observed	Theoretical (Rounded)
0	6	6
1	18	17
2	21	24
3	26	22
4	16	15
5	8	9
6	2	4
7	1	2
8	2	1
$\geqq 9$	0	0

Problems

1. Suppose that 3% of the bolts made by a machine are defective, the defective bolts occurring at random during production. If the bolts are packaged 50 per box, what is the Poisson approximation of the probability that a given box will contain x defective bolts?

2. Suppose that in the production of 50-ohm radio resistors, nondefective items are those that have a resistance between 45 and 55 ohms and the probability of a resistor's being defective is 0.2%. The resistors are sold in lots of 100, with the guarantee that all resistors are nondefective. What is the probability that a given lot will violate this guarantee?

3. A distributor sells bulbs of a certain variety of red tulip in packages of 1000, and he knows from previous experience that about 1% of a large batch of bulbs will not be of the desired variety. What is the probability that a given package will contain more than 1% bulbs of another variety?

4. Assuming that the birth rate is constant throughout the year (which is not quite true), find the probability that in a given village of 500 inhabitants, at least one person will have a birthday on December 25?

5. Show that the distribution function (2), Sec. 7.4, of the Poisson distribution satisfies $F(\infty) = 1$.

6. For what x does (1), Sec. 7.4, with given μ, assume its largest value (its mode; cf. Sec. 6.1)?

7. Suppose that a telephone switchboard handles 300 calls on the average during a rush hour, and that the board can make at most 10 connections per minute. Using the Poisson distribution, estimate the probability that the board will be overtaxed during a given minute.

8. Suppose that it is known that 0.005% of the population of a country dies from a certain kind of accident each year, and an insurance company has 10,000 among its customers that are insured against that accident. Find the probability that in a given year the company must pay off more than 3 risks.

9. If the probability that a person suffers a bad reaction from an injection of a certain serum is 0.001, what is the probability that out of 1000 persons, 2 or more will suffer a bad reaction?

10. If we examine under a microscope for red-blood-cell deficiency, choosing a small fixed volume that will contain on the average 5 red cells for a normal person, what is the probability that a specimen from a normal person will contain only 3 red cells or fewer?

7.6   Variance and Skewness of the Poisson Distribution

From (1), Sec. 6.6, and (1), Sec. 7.4, it follows that the Poisson distribution has the moment generating function

(1) $$G(t) = e^{-\mu}e^{\mu e^{t}}$$

(cf. Problem 1). We see that $G(0) = 1$. By repeated differentiation we obtain

$$
\begin{aligned}
&(a) \quad G'(t) = e^{-\mu}e^{\mu e^{t}}\mu e^{t} = \mu e^{t}G(t) \\
(2) \quad &(b) \quad G''(t) = \mu e^{t}[G(t) + G'(t)], \\
&(c) \quad G'''(t) = \mu e^{t}[G(t) + 2G'(t) + G''(t)].
\end{aligned}
$$

Hence $G'(0) = \mu$. Furthermore [cf. (2), Sec. 6.6]

$$E(X^2) = G''(0) = \mu + \mu^2.$$

From this and (5), Sec. 6.4, it follows that the Poisson distribution has the variance

$$(3) \qquad\qquad \sigma^2 = \mu.$$

We now use $(2c)$, (2) in Sec. 6.6, and (6) in Sec. 6.4. Then

$$(4) \qquad\qquad E([X - \mu]^3) = \mu,$$

as can readily be verified. Hence the Poisson distribution has the positive skewness [cf. (1), Sec. 6.5]

$$(5) \qquad\qquad \gamma = \frac{1}{\sqrt{\mu}}.$$

We see that $\gamma \to 0$ as $\mu \to \infty$. It follows that *for large μ the Poisson distribution is almost symmetric* (cf. Fig. 7.4.1).

Problems

1. Derive (1).
2. Using $(2a)$, show that the parameter μ is, in fact, the mean value of the Poisson distribution.
3. Using (5), Sec. 6.7, and (1), obtain the moment generating function $G^*(t)$ of the variable $X - \mu$ and then, using (6), Sec. 6.7, obtain (3).
4. Verify (4).

7.7 Hypergeometric Distribution

From Sec. 7.3 we know that the binomial distribution is important in **sampling with replacement.** In fact, if a box contains N things, for example, screws, M of which are defective, and we draw n screws *with replacement*, the probability that precisely x of the n screws are defective is [cf. (1) in Sec. 7.3]

$$(1) \qquad\qquad f(x) = \binom{n}{x}\left(\frac{M}{N}\right)^{x}\left(1 - \frac{M}{N}\right)^{n-x} \qquad (x = 0, 1, \cdots, n).$$

In **sampling without replacement** that probability is

$$
(2) \qquad f(x) = \frac{\binom{M}{x}\binom{N-M}{n-x}}{\binom{N}{n}} \qquad (x = 0, 1, \cdots, n).
$$

The distribution with the probability function (2) is called the **hypergeometric distribution.**[1] [Note that because of (9), Sec. 4.10, the function may be zero for some of the values $x = 0, 1, \cdots, n$.]

To verify our statement involving (2), we first note that, according to (4a) in Sec. 4.9, there are:

(a) $\binom{N}{n}$ different ways of picking n items from N,

(b) $\binom{M}{x}$ different ways of picking x defective items from M,

(c) $\binom{N-M}{n-x}$ different ways of picking $n - x$ nondefective items from $N - M$, and each way in (b) combined with each way in (c) gives the total number of mutually exclusive ways of obtaining x defective items in n drawings without replacement. Since (a) is the total number of outcomes and we draw at random, each such way has the probability $1 / \binom{N}{n}$. From this, (2) follows.

The hypergeometric distribution has the mean (cf. Problem 1)

$$
(3) \qquad \mu = n\frac{M}{N}
$$

and the variance

$$
(4) \qquad \sigma^2 = \frac{nM(N-M)(N-n)}{N^2(N-1)}.
$$

Problems

1. Obtain (3). *Hint.* Use (11), Sec. 4.10.
2. Calculate and graph $f(x)$, given by (2), when $N = 12$, $n = 8$, and M has various values, for example, $M = 3, 4, 6$ (cf. Table 1c in Appendix 4).
3. A distributor sells rubber bands in packages of 100 and guarantees that at most 10% are defective. A consumer controls each package by drawing 10 bands without replacement. If the sample contains no defective rubber bands, he accepts the package. Otherwise he rejects it. Find the probability that in this process any given package will be rejected although it still satisfies the guarantee.

---

[1] This name comes from the fact that the moment generating function of this distribution can be represented in terms of the hypergeometric function. An extensive table of numerical values has been computed by Lieberman and Owen (1961); cf. Appendix 3.

4. In Problem 3 find the probability that any given package is accepted although it contains 20 defective rubber bands.

5. Eight balls are drawn without replacement from an urn containing 9 blue and 3 black balls. Find the probability of obtaining precisely x blue balls.

6. **(French lottery.)** During the eighteenth century and earlier, the following lottery was commonly held in France. An urn contained 90 chips numbered from 1 to 90, and 5 chips were drawn without replacement. A participant was permitted to buy 1, 2, 3, 4, or 5 tickets each of which had a number $(1, 2, 3, \cdots,$ or 90). If the 1, 2, 3, 4, or 5 numbers, respectively, of the tickets were equal to the numbers on the 5 drawn chips, the participant obtained 15, 270, 5500, 75,000, and 1,000,000 times the amount he had to pay for one ticket. What is the probability of winning in each of these 5 cases?

7.8 Comparison of the Hypergeometric and the Binomial Distributions

If in the last section, n is small compared with N, M, and $N - M$, then we may expect that there will be little difference between drawing with and without replacement. To show this, we first note that for the probability function (2), Sec. 7.7, of the hypergeometric distribution we have

$$(1) \qquad \binom{n}{x}\left(p - \frac{x}{N}\right)^x \left(q - \frac{n-x}{N}\right)^{n-x} < f(x) < \binom{n}{x} p^x q^{n-x} \left(1 - \frac{n}{N}\right)^{-n}$$

(cf. Problems 3 and 4). Here,

$$(2) \qquad p = \frac{M}{N}$$

and $q = 1 - p$. We keep n and x fixed and let both N and M so approach infinity that (2) approaches a value between 0 and 1. Then both the first expression and the last expression in (1) approach the probability function (1), Sec. 7.3, of the binomial distribution. From the practical point of view this result may be formulated as follows.

If N, M, and $N - M$ are large compared with n, then it does not matter too much whether we sample with or without replacement, and in this case the hypergeometric distribution may be approximated by the binomial distribution (with $p = M/N$), *which is somewhat simpler.*

Hence in sampling from an indefinitely large population (**"infinite population"**) *we may use the binomial distribution, regardless of whether we sample with or without replacement.*

Table 7.8.1 gives an impression of the accuracy of the approximation for large N. Of course, for small values of N the approximation is not satisfactory; cf. Table 7.8.2. Corresponding graphical illustrations are given in Figs. 7.8.1 and 7.8.2.

Table 7.8.1. Values of the Probability Functions of the Hypergeometric Distribution with $M = 20$, $N = 1000$, $n = 100$ [cf. (1), Sec. 7.7] and the Binomial Distribution with $p = 0.02$, $n = 100$

x	Hypergeometric Distribution	Binomial Distribution
0	0.119	0.133
1	0.270	0.271
2	0.288	0.273
3	0.192	0.182
4	0.089	0.090
5	0.031	0.035
6	0.008	0.011
7	0.002	0.003
8	0.000	0.001

Table 7.8.2. Values of the Probability Functions of the Hypergeometric Distribution with $M = 8$, $N = 16$, $n = 8$ [cf. (1), Sec. 7.7] and the Binomial Distribution with $p = 0.5$, $n = 8$

x	Hypergeometric Distribution	Binomial Distribution
0	0.000	0.004
1	0.005	0.031
2	0.061	0.109
3	0.244	0.219
4	0.381	0.273
5	0.244	0.219
6	0.061	0.109
7	0.005	0.031
8	0.000	0.004

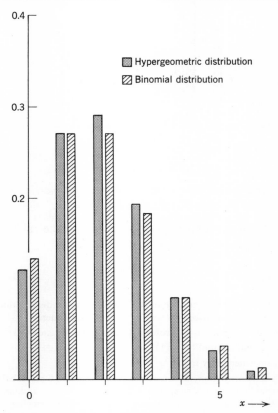

Fig. 7.8.1. Values in Table 7.8.1

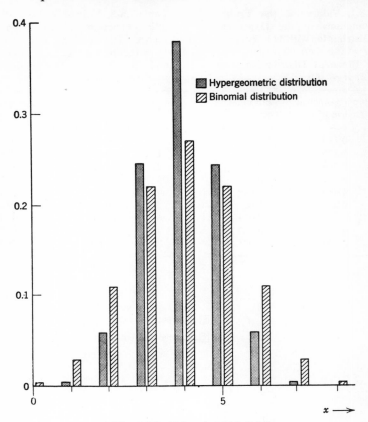

Fig. 7.8.2. Values in Table 7.8.2

For small p, large n, and very large N, the hypergeometric distribution can be approximated by the Poisson distribution with $\mu = np$.

This follows from the above approximation and the relation between the binomial distribution and the Poisson distribution.

Problems

1. Show that for $n > 1$ the variance of the hypergeometric distribution is smaller than that of the binomial distribution with $p = M/N$. Comment.

2. Show that the distributions in Problem 1 have the same mean.

3. Derive the second inequality in (1).

4. Derive the first inequality in (1).

5. Three balls are drawn from an urn containing 4 blue and 6 black balls. Consider the random variable $X = $ *number of blue balls drawn*, and find and compare the probability functions, means, and variances corresponding to drawing with and without replacement.

CHAPTER 8

Normal Distribution

The Gaussian distribution or normal distribution was introduced by C. F. Gauss in connection with the theory of errors of physical measurements. (An introduction to this theory will be given in Chap. 19.) The normal distribution is the most important continuous distribution, for the following reasons.

1. Many random variables that appear in connection with practical experiments or observations are normally distributed.
2. Other variables are approximately normally distributed.
3. Sometimes a variable is not normally distributed, not even approximately, but can be transformed into a normally distributed variable by a relatively simple transformation.
4. Certain more complicated distributions can be approximated by the normal distribution. This holds for the binomial distribution (cf. Sec. 8.4) and has important consequences, for example, the so-called law of large numbers (cf. Sec. 8.5).
5. Certain variables that are basic for justifying statistical tests are normally distributed. This we shall see in Part III.

The distribution function of the normal distribution is an integral that cannot be evaluated by elementary methods. However, it has been tabulated, cf. Table 3a in Appendix 4. The use of this table is explained in Sec. 8.3, and the reader should study that section with great care.

8.1 Gaussian or Normal Distribution

The continuous distribution having the density

(1)
$$f(x) = \frac{1}{\sigma\sqrt{2\pi}}\, e^{-\frac{1}{2}\left(\frac{x-\mu}{\sigma}\right)^2} \qquad (\sigma > 0)$$

is called the **normal distribution** or *Gaussian distribution*. A random variable having this distribution is said to be **normal** or *normally distributed*.

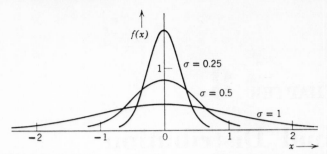

Fig. 8.1.1. Density (1) of the normal distribution with $\mu = 0$ for various values of σ

The curve of $f(x)$ is a **bell-shaped curve.** It is symmetric with respect to $x = \mu$. Since the integral of $|x| f(x)$ from $-\infty$ to ∞ exists, it follows from Theorem 1 in Sec. 6.1 that the parameter μ in (1) is the mean value of the distribution. Figure 8.1.1 shows $f(x)$ for $\mu = 0$. For $\mu > 0$ ($\mu < 0$) the curves have the same shape, but are shifted $|\mu|$ units to the right (to the left).

In Problem 3, Sec. 8.2, it will be shown that the parameter σ in (1) is the standard deviation of the distribution. The smaller σ^2 is, the higher will be the peak at $x = 0$ in Fig. 8.1.1 and the steeper will be the descent on both sides. This agrees with the meaning of σ^2.

8.2 Distribution Function of the Normal Distribution

From (1), Sec. 8.1, we see that the normal distribution has the distribution function

(1)
$$F(x) = \frac{1}{\sigma\sqrt{2\pi}} \int_{-\infty}^{x} e^{-\frac{1}{2}\left(\frac{v-\mu}{\sigma}\right)^2} dv.$$

If a random variable X is normally distributed, then the probability that X assumes any value in an interval $a < X \leqq b$ is [cf. (3) in Sec. 5.6]

(2)
$$P(a < X \leqq b) = F(b) - F(a) = \frac{1}{\sigma\sqrt{2\pi}} \int_{a}^{b} e^{-\frac{1}{2}\left(\frac{v-\mu}{\sigma}\right)^2} dv.$$

The integral in (1) cannot be evaluated by elementary methods, but can be expressed in terms of the integral

(3)
$$\Phi(z) = \frac{1}{\sqrt{2\pi}} \int_{-\infty}^{z} e^{-u^2/2} du$$

whose values are given in Table 3*a* of Appendix 4. Note that (3) is the distribution function of the normal distribution with mean 0 and variance 1 (cf. Fig. 8.2.1).

To express (1) in terms of (3) we set

$$\frac{v - \mu}{\sigma} = u.$$

Then $du/dv = 1/\sigma$ and $dv = \sigma \, du$. To the integration over v from $-\infty$ to x there corresponds the integration over u from $-\infty$ to

$$z = \frac{x - \mu}{\sigma}.$$

From (1) we thus obtain

$$F(x) = \frac{1}{\sigma\sqrt{2\pi}} \int_{-\infty}^{(x-\mu)/\sigma} e^{-u^2/2}\sigma \, du.$$

σ drops out, and the expression on the right equals (3) with $z = (x - \mu)/\sigma$. Hence we have the basic relationship

(4)
$$F(x) = \Phi\left(\frac{x - \mu}{\sigma}\right).$$

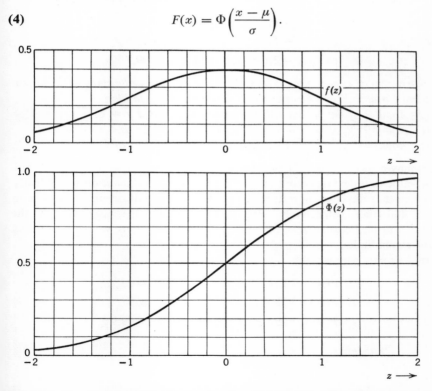

Fig. 8.2.1. Density $f(z)$ and distribution function $\Phi(z)$ [cf. (3)] of the normal distribution with mean 0 and variance 1

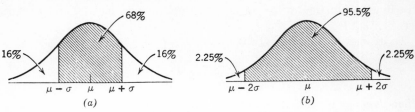

Fig. 8.2.2. Illustration of formula (6)

The practical application of this important formula will be explained in detail in the next section.

From (2) and (4) it follows that

(5) $P(a < X \leqq b) = F(b) - F(a) = \Phi\left(\dfrac{b - \mu}{\sigma}\right) - \Phi\left(\dfrac{a - \mu}{\sigma}\right).$

In particular, if $a = \mu - \sigma$ and $b = \mu + \sigma$, the right side of (5) is $\Phi(1) - \Phi(-1)$; if $a = \mu - 2\sigma$ and $b = \mu + 2\sigma$, the right side is $\Phi(2) - \Phi(-2)$, etc. Using Table 3a in Appendix 4, we thus obtain (cf. Fig. 8.2.2)

(6)
(a) $P(\mu - \sigma < X \leqq \mu + \sigma) \approx 68\%$
(b) $P(\mu - 2\sigma < X \leqq \mu + 2\sigma) \approx 95.5\%$
(c) $P(\mu - 3\sigma < X \leqq \mu + 3\sigma) \approx 99.7\%$

Hence we may expect that a large number of observed values of a normal random variable X will be distributed in the following fashion.
(a) *About $\frac{2}{3}$ of the values will lie between $\mu - \sigma$ and $\mu + \sigma$.*
(b) *About 95% of the values will lie between $\mu - 2\sigma$ and $\mu + 2\sigma$.*
(c) *About $99\frac{3}{4}\%$ of the values will lie between $\mu - 3\sigma$ and $\mu + 3\sigma$.*

This may also be expressed as follows.

A value that deviates more than σ from μ will occur *about* once in 3 trials. A value that deviates more than 2σ or 3σ from μ will occur *about* once in 20 or 400 trials, respectively. Practically speaking, this means that all the values will lie between $\mu - 3\sigma$ and $\mu + 3\sigma$; these two values are called **three-sigma limits.**

In a similar way we obtain

(7)
(a) $P(\mu - 1.96\sigma < X \leqq \mu + 1.96\sigma) = 95\%$
(b) $P(\mu - 2.58\sigma < X \leqq \mu + 2.58\sigma) = 99\%$
(c) $P(\mu - 3.29\sigma < X \leqq \mu + 3.29\sigma) = 99.9\%.$

Problems

1. Show that

(8) $$\Phi(\infty) = \frac{1}{\sqrt{2\pi}} \int_{-\infty}^{\infty} e^{-u^2/2} \, du = 1.$$

   Hint. Consider $\Phi^2(\infty)$ and introduce polar coordinates in the resulting double integral.

2. Show that the curve of the function (1), Sec. 8.1, has two points of inflection, which correspond to $x = \mu \pm \sigma$.

3. Using integration by parts and (8), show that the parameter σ in (1), Sec. 8.1, is the standard deviation of the distribution.

4. Show that

   (9) $$\Phi(-z) = 1 - \Phi(z).$$

5. If X is normal with mean 0 and variance 1, show that $P(-c \leq X \leq c) = \gamma$ is equivalent to $\Phi(c) = (1 + \gamma)/2$.

6. Let X be normal with mean μ and variance σ^2, and let a be a given positive number. Find the number c for which $P(c \leq X \leq c + a)$ is maximum.

7. Find the moment generating function (cf. Sec. 6.6) of the random variable $X - \mu$ where X is normal with mean μ and variance σ^2 and show that the peakedness γ^* of the distribution (cf. Sec. 6.5) equals 3, so that $\epsilon = \gamma^* - 3$ is 0 for the normal distribution. (ϵ is sometimes called the **excess** of a distribution.)

8. What are the probabilities in (6) if X is not a normal random variable but is uniformly distributed on some interval?

8.3   Use of Tables 3a and 3b in Appendix 4

   The following typical examples should help the reader to understand the practical use of Tables 3a and 3b in Appendix 4. This is quite important.

Example 1.   Determine the probabilities

(a) $P(X \leq 2.44)$	(b) $P(X \leq -1.16)$	(c) $P(X \leq 1.923)$
(d) $P(X \geq 1)$	(e) $P(X \geq -2.9)$	(f) $P(2 \leq X \leq 10)$

where X is assumed to be normal with mean 0 and variance 1.

   Since $\mu = 0$ and $\sigma^2 = 1$, we may obtain the desired values directly from Table 3a in Appendix 4. We find

   (a) 0.9927

   (b) 0.1230

   (c) 0.9728 (by linear interpolation)

   (d) $1 - P(X \leq 1) = 1 - 0.8413 = 0.1587$ [cf. (1), Sec. 5.1]

   (e) $1 - P(X \leq -2.9) = 1 - \Phi(-2.9) = 0.9981$

   (f) $\Phi(10) = 1.0000$ (why?), $\Phi(2) = 0.9772$, $\Phi(10) - \Phi(2) = 0.0228$.

Example 2.   Determine the probabilities in the previous example assuming that X is normal with mean 0.8 and variance 4.

   From (5), Sec. 8.2, and Table 3a in Appendix 4 we obtain

   (a) $F(2.44) = \Phi\left(\dfrac{2.44 - 0.80}{2}\right) = \Phi(0.82) = 0.7939$

   (b) $F(-1.16) = \Phi(-0.98) = 0.1635$

(*c*) $F(1.923) = \Phi(0.5615) = 0.7128$

(*d*) $1 - P(X \leqq 1) = 1 - F(1) = 1 - \Phi(0.1) = 0.4602$

(*e*) $1 - P(X \leqq -2.9) = 1 - \Phi\left(\dfrac{-2.9 - 0.8}{2}\right) = 1 - \Phi(-1.85) = 0.9678$

(*f*) $F(10) - F(2) = \Phi(4.6) - \Phi(0.6) = 1 - 0.7257 = 0.2743$.

Example 3. Let X be normal with mean 0 and variance 1. Determine the constant c such that:

(*a*) $P(X \geqq c) = 10\%$ (*b*) $P(X \leqq c) = 5\%$

(*c*) $P(0 \leqq X \leqq c) = 45\%$ (*d*) $P(-c \leqq X \leqq c) = 99\%$.

From Table 3*b* in Appendix 4 we obtain

(*a*) $1 - P(X \leqq c) = 1 - \Phi(c) = 0.1$, $\Phi(c) = 0.9$, $c = 1.282$

(*b*) $c = -1.645$

(*c*) $\Phi(c) - \Phi(0) = \Phi(c) - 0.5 = 0.45$, $\Phi(c) = 0.95$, $c = 1.645$

(*d*) $c = 2.576$.

Example 4. Let X be normal with mean -2 and variance 0.25. Determine the constant c such that:

(*a*) $P(X \geqq c) = 0.2$ (*b*) $P(-c \leqq X \leqq -1) = 0.5$

(*c*) $P(-2 - c \leqq X \leqq -2 + c) = 0.9$ (*d*) $P(-2 - c \leqq X \leqq -2 + c) = 99.6\%$.

Using Table 3*b* in Appendix 4, we obtain the following results.

(*a*) $1 - P(X \leqq c) = 1 - \Phi\left(\dfrac{c + 2}{0.5}\right) = 0.2$, $\Phi(2c + 4) = 0.8$, $2c + 4 = 0.842$,

$c = -1.579$

(*b*) $\Phi\left(\dfrac{-1 + 2}{0.5}\right) - \Phi\left(\dfrac{-c + 2}{0.5}\right) = 0.9772 - \Phi(4 - 2c) = 0.5$, $\Phi(4 - 2c) = 0.4772$,

$4 - 2c = -0.057$, $c = 2.03$

(*c*) $\Phi\left(\dfrac{-2 + c + 2}{0.5}\right) - \Phi\left(\dfrac{-2 - c + 2}{0.5}\right) = \Phi(2c) - \Phi(-2c) = 0.9$, $2c = 1.645$,

$c = 0.823$

(*d*) $\Phi(2c) - \Phi(-2c) = 99.6\%$, $2c = 2.878$, $c = 1.439$.

Example 5. Suppose that iron plates being produced by a shaper are required to have a certain thickness. All such industrial products will differ slightly from each other because the properties of the material and the behavior of the machines and tools used show slight random variations caused by small disturbances which we cannot predict. We may therefore regard the thickness X (in millimeters) of the plates as a random variable. We assume that for a certain setting of the shaper the variable X is normal with mean $\mu = 10$ mm and standard deviation $\sigma = 0.02$ mm. We want to determine the percentage of defective plates to be expected, assuming that defective plates are (*a*) plates thinner than 9.97 mm, (*b*) plates thicker than 10.05 mm, (*c*) plates that deviate more than 0.03 mm from 10 mm. (*d*) How should we choose numbers $10 - c$ and $10 + c$ in order that the expected percentage of defective plates be not greater than 5% (where *defective* means plates thinner than $10 - c$ or thicker than $10 + c$)? (*e*) How does the percentage of defective plates in part (*d*) change if μ is shifted from 10 mm to 10.01 mm?

Using Table 3*a*, Appendix 4, and (5) in Sec. 8.2, we obtain the following solutions.

(*a*) $P(X < 9.97) = \Phi\left(\dfrac{9.97 - 10.00}{0.02}\right) = \Phi(-1.5) = 0.0668 \approx 6.7\%$

(*b*) $P(X > 10.05) = 1 - P(X \leqq 10.05) = 1 - \Phi\left(\dfrac{10.05 - 10.00}{0.02}\right)$

$\qquad\qquad = 1 - \Phi(2.5) = 1 - 0.9938 \approx 0.6\%$

(*c*) $P(9.97 \leqq X \leqq 10.03) = \Phi\left(\dfrac{10.03 - 10.00}{0.02}\right) - \Phi\left(\dfrac{9.97 - 10.00}{0.02}\right)$

$\qquad\qquad = \Phi(1.5) - \Phi(-1.5) = 0.8664.$ *Answer*: $1 - 0.8664 \approx 13\%$

(*d*) From (7a) in Sec. 8.2 we obtain $c = 1.96\sigma = 0.039.$

$\qquad\qquad\qquad\qquad\qquad$ *Answer*: 9.961 mm and 10.039 mm.

(*e*) $P(9.961 \leqq X \leqq 10.039) = \Phi\left(\dfrac{10.039 - 10.010}{0.02}\right) - \Phi\left(\dfrac{9.961 - 10.010}{0.02}\right)$

$\qquad\qquad = \Phi(1.45) - \Phi(-2.45) = 0.9265 - 0.0071 \approx 92\%.$ *Answer*: 8%.

We see that this slight change of the adjustment of the tool bit yields a considerable increase in the percentage of defective plates.

We mention finally that under a linear transformation, a normal random variable transforms into a normal random variable, as follows.

Theorem 1. *If X is normal with mean μ and variance σ^2, then $X^* = c_1 X + c_2$ ($c_1 \neq 0$) is normal with mean $\mu^* = c_1\mu + c_2$ and variance $\sigma^{*2} = c_1^2\sigma^2$.*

Proof. Setting $x = (x^* - c_2)/c_1$, we obtain $(x - \mu)/\sigma = (x^* - \mu^*)/\sigma^*$ where μ^* and σ^* are the expressions in the theorem. X^* has the distribution function

$$F(x^*) = P(X^* \leqq x^*) = P(c_1 X + c_2 \leqq x^*) = P(X \leqq x)$$

$$= \Phi\left(\frac{x - \mu}{\sigma}\right) = \Phi\left(\frac{x^* - \mu^*}{\sigma^*}\right),$$

where we made use of (5), Sec. 8.2. This completes the proof.

The property of the normal distribution expressed in Theorem 1 will have important applications in Part III (Sec. 12.2, etc.).

Problems

1. Let X be normal with mean 100 and variance 36. Find $P(X > 110)$, $P(X < 105)$, and $P(90 < X < 110)$.

2. Let X be normal with mean 10 and variance 4. Determine c such that $P(X < c) = 5\%$, $P(X > c) = 1\%$, and $P(10 - c < X < 10 + c) = 50\%$.

3. A manufacturer knows from experience that the resistance of resistors he produces is normal with mean $\mu = 100$ ohms and standard deviation $\sigma = 2$ ohms. What percentage of resistors will have resistance between 98 ohms and 102 ohms? Between 95 ohms and 105 ohms?

4. In Problem 3, find c such that 95% of the resistors produced lie between $100 - c$ and $100 + c$. Find c^* such that 90% of the resistors produced lie between $100 - c^*$ and $100 + c^*$.

5. If the height of a population is a normal random variable with mean 68 in. and standard deviation 2.5 in. and we want to select 200 of these persons at random, how many of them can we expect to be (a) 68 in., (b) greater than 70 in., assuming that the measurements are recorded to the nearest inch?

6. What percentage of observations of a normal random variable is expected to lie (a) between $\mu - \sigma/4$ and $\mu + \sigma/4$, (b) between $\mu - \sigma/2$ and $\mu + \sigma/2$?

7. Using Fig. 8.2.1, give approximate answers to question (b) in Example 1 and question (a) in Example 3.

8. Give a graphical illustration of the result of question (e) in Example 5 by plotting the curves of the densities in questions (d) and (e) on the same axes.

9. Obtain the answer to question (d) in Example 5 from Table 3b, Appendix 4.

10. What will the percentage of defective iron plates in question (c) of Example 5 be if we use a better shaper so that $\sigma = 0.01$ mm?

11. Determine σ so that the percentage of defective plates in question (c) of Example 5 equals 1%.

12. Let X be normal with mean 10 and σ so that the probability that X will assume any value $x \geq 15$ is not greater than 5%. Find the largest σ for which this condition still holds.

13. In Problem 12, replace 15 by 11 and find the corresponding σ.

14. A producer of air mail envelopes knows from experience that the weight of the envelopes is normally distributed with mean $\mu = 1.95$ grams and standard deviation $\sigma = 0.05$ grams. About how many envelopes weighing 2 grams or more can then be expected in a given package of 100 envelopes?

15. In Problem 14, about how many envelopes weighing 2.05 grams or more can be expected in a given package of 100 envelopes?

16. Let X_0 and X_1 be normal with means $\mu_0 = 10$, $\mu_1 = 20$ and equal variance $\sigma^2 = 36$. Determine c such that the probability α that X_0 will assume any value greater than c is only 5%. Then find the probability β that X_1 will assume any value smaller than that c. Graph both densities on the same coordinate system and interpret α and β as areas under those curves. What will happen to c and β if we let α decrease?

17. How does the situation in Problem 16 change if the variance is smaller, say, $\sigma^2 = 9$?

18. Let Y be normal with mean κ and variance λ^2. Set $Y = \ln X$ and show that X has the density

(1) $$f(x) = \frac{1}{x\lambda\sqrt{2\pi}} e^{-\frac{1}{2}\left(\frac{\ln x - \kappa}{\lambda}\right)^2} \qquad \text{when } x > 0$$

and $f(x) = 0$ when $x < 0$. This distribution is called the **logarithmic normal distribution**.

19. Graph the density of the logarithmic normal distribution with $\kappa = 0$ and $\lambda = 1$.

20. Show that the logarithmic normal distribution has the mean

$$\mu = e^{\kappa + 0.5\lambda^2}.$$

8.4 Approximation of the Binomial Distribution by the Normal Distribution

We shall now see that the normal distribution also yields a useful approximation of the binomial distribution when n is large. From Secs. 7.1 and 7.2 we know that the binomial distribution has the probability function

$$f(x) = \binom{n}{x} p^x q^{n-x} \qquad (x = 0, 1, \cdots, n), \tag{1}$$

the mean

$$\mu = np, \tag{2}$$

and the variance

$$\sigma^2 = npq. \tag{3}$$

Theorem 1. *Let* $0 < p < 1$. *Then for large n the binomial distribution can be approximated by the normal distribution with mean* (2) *and variance* (3), *that is,*

$$f(x) \sim f^*(x) \qquad (x = 0, 1, \cdots, n),$$

where

$$f^*(x) = \frac{1}{\sqrt{2\pi}\sqrt{npq}} e^{-z^2/2}, \qquad z = \frac{x - np}{\sqrt{npq}} \tag{4}$$

is the density of that normal distribution and the symbol $\sim$ *(read* **asymptotically equal**) *means that the ratio of both sides approaches* 1 *as n approaches* ∞. *Furthermore,*

$$P(a \leqq X \leqq b) = \sum_{x=a}^{b} \binom{n}{x} p^x q^{n-x} \sim \Phi(\beta) - \Phi(\alpha),$$

$$\alpha = \frac{a - np - 0.5}{\sqrt{npq}}, \qquad \beta = \frac{b - np + 0.5}{\sqrt{npq}}. \tag{5}$$

This is called the **limit theorem of De Moivre and Laplace**; cf. the books by De Moivre (1718) and Laplace (1812) listed in Appendix 3. A proof is included in Appendix 1; it shows that the term 0.5 in α and β is a correction caused by the change from a discrete to a continuous distribution.

The practical importance of such an approximation is obvious because for large n the binomial coefficients and powers in (1) become very inconvenient. Table 8.4.1 and Fig. 8.4.1 illustrate that even for relatively small n the approximation is rather good, provided p is close to 1/2. We shall not present a theoretical consideration of the error. Experience indicates that the approximation is fairly good as long as $np > 5$ when $p \leqq 0.5$ and $nq > 5$ when $p > 0.5$.

Table 8.4.1. Probability Function (1) and Approximation (4) for Some n and p

x	$n = 8, p = 0.2$		$n = 8, p = 0.5$		$n = 25, p = 0.2$	
	Approximation	Exact	Approximation	Exact	Approximation	Exact
0	0.130	0.168	0.005	0.004	0.009	0.004
1	0.306	0.336	0.030	0.031	0.027	0.024
2	0.331	0.294	0.104	0.109	0.065	0.071
3	0.164	0.147	0.220	0.219	0.121	0.136
4	0.037	0.046	0.282	0.273	0.176	0.187
5	0.004	0.009	0.220	0.219	0.199	0.196
6	0.000	0.001	0.104	0.109	0.176	0.163
7	0.000	0.000	0.030	0.031	0.121	0.111
8	0.000	0.000	0.005	0.004	0.065	0.062
9					0.027	0.029
10					0.009	0.012
11					0.002	0.004

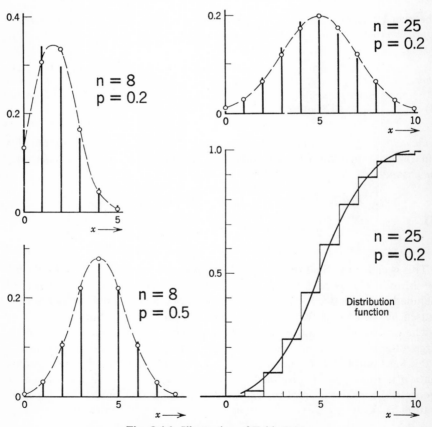

Fig. 8.4.1. Illustration of Table 8.4.1

Problems

1. A producer sells fluorescent bulbs in cartons of 1000 bulbs. What is the probability that any given carton contains not more than 1 % defective bulbs if we regard the production process as a Bernoulli experiment with $p = 1\%$ ($=$ probability that any given bulb will be defective)?

2. Using (5), compute the probability of obtaining at least 4 heads and at most 6 heads in tossing 10 fair coins, and compare the result with the exact value obtained from Table 1d in Appendix 4.

3. Using (5), compute the probability of obtaining at least 4 red balls and at most 6 red balls in 8 drawings with replacement from an urn containing 1 red ball and 4 white balls, and compare the result with the exact value obtained from Table 1d in Appendix 4.

4. In marriages between unrelated individuals the probability of the birth of a girl is about $p = 0.48$. In 299 marriages of which 287 were between cousins and the remaining 12 were between uncles and nieces, 386 of 709 children were girls. Find the probability that there should be 386 or more girls in 709 births under the assumption that p is also 0.48 in marriages between those relatives.

5. What is the probability of obtaining at least 2048 heads in tossing a fair coin 4040 times (cf. Table 4.4.1 in Sec. 4.4)?

6. Characterize the relationship between Problem 3, Sec. 7.5, and Problem 1, this section.

7. Of the first 3000 births in 1962 in Graz, Austria, 1578 were boys. What is the probability of obtaining 1578 or more boys in 3000 births, assuming that the events *birth of a boy* and *birth of a girl* are equally likely and the outcome of any birth is independent of the outcomes of the other births?

8. Obtain the approximate values (5) for the distribution function of the binomial distribution with $n = 9$ and $p = 0.5$. Compare these values with those in Table 1d, Appendix 4. Show that the absolute error is small over the whole range $x = 0$, $1, \cdots, 9$, whereas the relative error is large at $x = 0$ and $x = 1$. (Use Φ (3.33) $=$ 0.9996.)

8.5 Law of Large Numbers

The statement that the probability of success in a Bernoulli trial equals a certain number p means that the relative frequency of successes in a large number of trials is approximately equal to p; cf. Sec. 4.4. This statement can be made precise, as follows. The theorem and its generalizations are some of the most important theorems in the theory of probability.

Theorem 1. (Bernoulli's law of large numbers). *Let p $(0 < p < 1)$ be the probability of an event A ("success") in a random experiment. Let the random variable X denote the number of successes in n independent trials. Then, a positive number ϵ being given (no matter how small, but not zero),*

$$P\left(\left|\frac{X}{n} - p\right| \leqq \epsilon\right) \to 1 \qquad\qquad \text{as } n \to \infty.$$

Hence the probability that the average number of successes differs from p by more than a given positive ε approaches zero as n approaches infinity.

Proof. The inequality

$$\left|\frac{X}{n} - p\right| \le \epsilon$$

may be written

$$-\epsilon \le \frac{X}{n} - p \le \epsilon.$$

If we add p then we have

$$p - \epsilon \le \frac{X}{n} \le p + \epsilon.$$

We now multiply by n, finding

$$[p - \epsilon]n \le X \le [p + \epsilon]n.$$

Consequently,

(1) $$P\left(\left|\frac{X}{n} - p\right| \le \epsilon\right) = P([p - \epsilon]n \le X \le [p + \epsilon]n).$$

We now apply Theorem 1, Sec. 8.4, choosing

$$a = [p - \epsilon]n \quad \text{and} \quad b = [p + \epsilon]n.$$

Then in (5), Sec. 8.4,

(2) $$\alpha = -(\epsilon n + 0.5)/\sqrt{npq}, \qquad \beta = (\epsilon n + 0.5)/\sqrt{npq}.$$

We see that $\alpha \to -\infty$ and $\beta \to \infty$ as $n \to \infty$. Hence the probability in (1) approaches

$$\Phi(\infty) - \Phi(-\infty) = 1 - 0 = 1.$$

This proves Theorem 1.

Example 1. In tossing a fair coin, $p = 0.5$, and (2) becomes

$$\alpha = -2\epsilon\sqrt{n} - \frac{1}{\sqrt{n}}, \qquad \beta = 2\epsilon\sqrt{n} + \frac{1}{\sqrt{n}}.$$

Hence by Theorem 1, Sec. 8.4, the probability in (1) is approximately equal to

(3) $$\Phi\left(2\epsilon\sqrt{n} + \frac{1}{\sqrt{n}}\right) - \Phi\left(-2\epsilon\sqrt{n} - \frac{1}{\sqrt{n}}\right).$$

The relative frequency 0.5069 in Table 4.4.1 deviates by the amount $\epsilon = 0.0069$ from $p = 0.5$. Since $n = 4040$ and $\sqrt{n} = 63.561$, we obtain from (3) and Table 3a in Appendix

4 the value

$$P\left(\left|\frac{X}{4040} - 0.5\right| \leqq 0.0069\right) = \Phi(0.893) - \Phi(-0.893) = 63\%.$$

This value is large. The observed value seems to justify the assumption that $p = 0.5$. A very small value of P, for example, $P = 1\%$, would be a reason to doubt whether the assumption is right. Conclusions of this type and their applications will be considered extensively in Part III.

CHAPTER **9**

Probability Distributions of Several Random Variables

Probability distributions of several random variables are important for the following reasons.

First, in various random experiments we observe several quantities at the same time. Examples are the observation of several racial features (such as weight, height, and color of eyes and hair), the observation of several properties of a raw material (for instance, hardness and carbon content of steel), etc.

Furthermore, probability distributions of several random variables play an important role in the theoretical justification of various tests to be considered in Part III. Of course, we can apply those tests to practical problems without knowing the details of the underlying theory. However, the reader should make every effort to become familiar with that theory, too. This will lead to a deeper understanding of the entire field.

We start with two variables. This is the simplest case. It has the advantage that we shall be able to interpret various concepts and relationships in a geometrical fashion and illustrate them by figures.

Further facts about distributions of several random variables will be presented later (in Chaps. 17 and 18), after we have gained some knowledge of the nature of statistical tests.

9.1 Two-Dimensional Distributions

If in a random experiment we observe a single quantity, we have to associate with that experiment a single random variable, call it X. A single performance of the experiment yields a number $X = x$, which may be plotted as a point on the x-axis. If for each interval $a < X \leqq b$ we know the probability

$$P(a < X \leqq b),$$

then the probability distribution of X is known. It is uniquely determined by the distribution function

$$F(x) = P(X \leqq x).$$

In fact, for any a and b ($b > a$) we have

$$P(a < X \leqq b) = F(b) - F(a)$$

(cf. Sec. 5.4).

If in a random experiment we observe two quantities, we have to associate with the experiment two random variables, say X and Y. For example, X may correspond to the Rockwell hardness and Y to the carbon content of steel, if we measure these two quantities. Each performance of the experiment yields a pair of numbers $X = x$, $Y = y$, briefly (x, y), which may be plotted as a point in the XY-plane, having the abscissa x and the ordinate y.

We may now consider an event

$$a_1 < X \leqq b_1, \qquad a_2 < Y \leqq b_2$$

(cf. Fig. 9.1.1), consisting of all the outcomes that lie in this rectangle. If for each such event we know the corresponding probability

$$P(a_1 < X \leqq b_1, a_2 < Y \leqq b_2),$$

then we say that the **two-dimensional probability distribution** of the random variables X and Y or of the **two-dimensional random variable** (X, Y) is known. Clearly that probability is the probability with which (X, Y) assumes any value corresponding to a point in that rectangle.

The function

(1) $$F(x, y) = P(X \leqq x, Y \leqq y)$$

is called the **distribution function** of that two-dimensional distribution or of that two-dimensional random variable (X, Y). We see that for every (x, y) this is the probability with which X assumes any value not greater than x and Y simultaneously assumes any value not greater than y.

The distribution function (1) determines the corresponding distribution uniquely. In fact, for any rectangle $a_1 < X \leqq b_1, a_2 < Y \leqq b_2$ we have

(2) $$P(a_1 < X \leqq b_1, a_2 < Y \leqq b_2)$$
$$= F(b_1, b_2) - F(a_1, b_2) - F(b_1, a_2) + F(a_1, a_2).$$

This is the analogue of the above formula for intervals. The proof is left to the reader (cf. Problem 1).

The **mechanical analogue** of a two-dimensional probability distribution is the distribution of mass of total amount 1 in the XY-plane. The mass in a

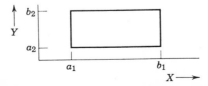

Fig. 9.1.1. Concept of a two-dimensional distribution

rectangle R corresponds to the probability with which (X, Y) assumes any value (x, y) in R.

As in the case of a single variable, there are two important types of two-dimensional distributions, namely, the discrete and the continuous distributions. We shall first consider some basic properties of discrete distributions.

Problems

1. Interpret each term on the right-hand side of (2) and prove (2).
2. Generalizing (1), define the distribution function $F(x, y, z)$ of a three-dimensional random variable (X, Y, Z) and find the analogue of (2).

9.2   Discrete Two-Dimensional Distribution

A two-dimensional random variable (X, Y) and its probability distribution are said to be **discrete** if (X, Y) has the following properties.

There are only finitely many or at most countably infinitely many pairs of values (x, y) that (X, Y) can assume, the corresponding probabilities being positive. Each bounded[1] domain in the XY-plane contains only finitely many of those pairs of values, and to any domain containing no such pairs, there corresponds the probability 0.

Let p_{ij} denote the probability corresponding to such a pair (x_i, y_j), that is,

$$P(X = x_i, Y = y_j) = p_{ij},$$

(where we admit that for certain pairs of subscripts i, j the corresponding p_{ij} may be zero). Then we may characterize the distribution by the function

(1)
$$f(x, y) = \begin{cases} p_{ij} & \text{when } x = x_i, y = y_j \\ 0 & \text{otherwise.} \end{cases}$$

Here $i = 0, 1, 2, \cdots$ and $j = 0, 1, 2, \cdots$, independently. This function is called the **probability function** of the distribution. It is the analogue of the probability function in the one-dimensional case (cf. Sec. 5.2).

The probability function and the distribution function are related by the formula

(2)
$$F(x, y) = \sum_{x_i \leq x} \sum_{y_j \leq y} f(x_i, y_j).$$

This is the analogue of (1) in Sec. 5.5. Instead of (2), Sec. 5.2, we now have

$$\sum_i \sum_j f(x_i, y_j) = 1.$$

Here we sum over all pairs of values for which $f(x, y)$ is not zero.

---

[1] That is, a domain which can be enclosed in a circle of sufficiently large radius.

Table 9.2.1. Values of the Probability Function $f(x, y)$ in Example 1

	$y = 0$	$y = 1$
$x = 0$	1/4	1/4
$x = 1$	1/4	1/4

Table 9.2.2. Values of the Distribution Function $F(x, y)$ in Example 1

	$y < 0$	$0 \leq y < 1$	$y \geq 1$
$x < 0$	0	0	0
$0 \leq x < 1$	0	1/4	1/2
$x \geq 1$	0	1/2	1

Example 1. Suppose a dime and a nickel are tossed with H and T denoting head and tail for the dime and h and t denoting head and tail for the nickel. Then there are the four outcomes

$$Tt \quad Th \quad Ht \quad Hh.$$

We may now consider the random variables

$$X = number\ of\ heads\ on\ the\ dime,$$
$$Y = number\ of\ heads\ on\ the\ nickel.$$

Then $X = 0$ means that the dime turns up a tail, $X = 1$ means that it turns up a head, etc. The above four outcomes correspond to the four ordered pairs

$$(0, 0) \quad (0, 1) \quad (1, 0) \quad (1, 1).$$

If we assume the coins to be fair, these outcomes are equally likely; hence each of them has probability 1/4. We thus obtain Table 9.2.1 and, from it, Table 9.2.2. Fig. 9.2.1 shows $f(x, y)$, and Fig. 9.2.2 shows $F(x, y)$, graphically represented as a surface over the xy-plane.

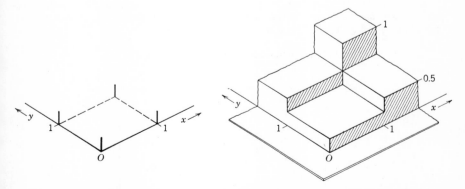

Fig. 9.2.1. Probability function $f(x, y)$ in Ex. 1 (cf. Table 9.2.1)

Fig. 9.2.2. Distribution function $F(x, y)$ in Ex. 1 (cf. Table 9.2.2)

Problems

1. Consider the experiment of drawing 3 cards with replacement from an ordinary deck. Show that the probability function $f(x, y)$ of the random variables

$$X = \textit{number of queens drawn}$$
$$Y = \textit{number of aces and kings drawn}$$

is

$$f(x, y) = \frac{3!}{x!\, y!(3 - x - y)!} \left(\frac{1}{13}\right)^{x} \left(\frac{2}{13}\right)^{y} \left(\frac{10}{13}\right)^{3-x-y} \qquad (x + y \leq 3),$$

$f(x, y) = 0$ for all other pairs (x, y),

and has the values given in Table 9.2.3.

2. Graph the probability function and the distribution function in Problem 1.

3. The distribution having the probability function

$$f(x_1, x_2, \cdots, x_r) = \frac{n!}{x_1!\, x_2! \cdots x_r!} p_1{}^{x_1} p_2{}^{x_2} \cdots p_r{}^{x_r}$$

(where $n = x_1 + x_2 + \cdots + x_r$), is called the **multinomial distribution.** Show that $f(x_1, \cdots, x_r)$ is the probability that in n independent trials we obtain precisely x_j times an event $E_j, j = 1, \cdots, r$, provided that in a single trial precisely one of the E_j's happens, the corresponding probability being p_j.

4. Show that the binomial distribution and the distribution in Problem 1 are special cases of the multinomial distribution.

5. Suppose that in producing axle shafts, the probability that any of the shafts to be produced will be too small or too big is $p_1 = 3\%$ and $p_2 = 5\%$, respectively. What is the probability that a sample of 20 shafts will contain precisely x_1 shafts that are too small and precisely x_2 shafts that are too big?

6. In throwing a fair die twice consider the random variables

$$X = \textit{number of times 6 turns up}$$
$$Y = \textit{number of times 5 turns up}$$

and determine and graph the probability function of the (X, Y)-distribution.

7. In throwing two fair dice, let $X = \textit{number the first die turns up}$, $Y = \textit{number the second die turns up}$. Find the probabilities $P(X + Y = 6)$, $P(X - Y = 2)$, $P(X^2 + Y^2 \leq 20)$, $P(X + Y > 9)$, and $P(XY < 10)$.

Table 9.2.3. Numerical Values in Problem 1

x	$y = 0$	$y = 1$	$y = 2$	$y = 3$
0	$\frac{1000}{2197}$	$\frac{600}{2197}$	$\frac{120}{2197}$	$\frac{8}{2197}$
1	$\frac{300}{2197}$	$\frac{120}{2197}$	$\frac{12}{2197}$	0
2	$\frac{30}{2197}$	$\frac{6}{2197}$	0	0
3	$\frac{1}{2197}$	0	0	0

9.3 Continuous Two-Dimensional Distribution

A two-dimensional random variable (X, Y) and its probability distribution are said to be **continuous**[2] if the corresponding distribution function $F(x, y)$ can be represented by a double integral

(1)
$$F(x, y) = \int_{-\infty}^{y} \int_{-\infty}^{x} f(x^*, y^*)\, dx^*\, dy^*$$

where $f(x, y)$ is defined, nonnegative, and bounded in the entire plane and is continuous, possibly except for finitely many continuously differentiable curves. $f(x, y)$ is called the **probability density** of the distribution.

It follows that to a rectangle $R\colon a_1 < X \leq b_1,\ a_2 < Y \leq b_2$ there corresponds the probability

(2)
$$P(a_1 < X \leq b_1, a_2 < Y \leq b_2) = \int_{a_2}^{b_2} \int_{a_1}^{b_1} f(x, y)\, dx\, dy.$$

Of course this probability can be expressed in terms of the distribution function; cf. (2), Sec. 9.1.

Furthermore,

(3)
$$\int_{-\infty}^{\infty} \int_{-\infty}^{\infty} f(x, y)\, dx\, dy = 1.$$

Example 1 (Uniform distribution). The two-dimensional analogue of the uniform distribution in an interval (cf. Example 1, Sec. 5.6) is the uniform distribution in a rectangle $R\colon$ $\alpha_1 < X \leq \beta_1,\ \alpha_2 < Y \leq \beta_2$. It has the probability density

$$f(x, y) = \begin{cases} 1/k & \text{when } (x, y) \text{ is in } R \\ 0 & \text{otherwise.} \end{cases}$$

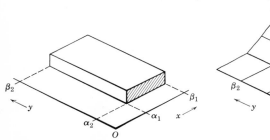
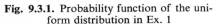
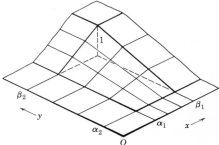

Fig. 9.3.1. Probability function of the uniform distribution in Ex. 1

Fig. 9.3.2. Distribution function of the uniform distribution in Ex. 1

[2] An obvious modification of the remark in the footnote in Sec. 5.6 also applies to the present use of the term *continuous*.

The constant $k = (\beta_1 - \alpha_1)(\beta_2 - \alpha_2)$ is the area of R (cf. Fig. 9.3.1). The value of the distribution function $F(x, y)$ at a point (x, y) equals the area of the portion of R in the region $X \leq x,\ Y \leq y$ of the XY-plane (cf. Fig. 9.3.2).

Problems

1. Represent the distribution function in Example 1 by a formula.
2. Graph the level curves $F(x, y) = const$ of the distribution function in Example 1.
3. Graph the density and the distribution function of the uniform distribution in the square $0 < x < 1, 0 < y < 1$.
4. Let $f(x, y) = 2$ when $x > 0,\ y > 0,\ x + y < 1$ and outside of this region let $f(x, y) = 0$. Graph $f(x, y)$ and the corresponding distribution function.
5. Graph the density $f(x, y) = e^{-(x+y)}$ when $x \geq 0,\ y \geq 0,\ f(x, y) = 0$ otherwise. Show that (3) is satisfied. Find the corresponding distribution function. Find the probability $P(a_1 < X \leq b_1, a_2 < Y \leq b_2)$ where $a_1 > 0, a_2 > 0$.
6. In Problem 5, find the probability that (a) $X < 1$, (b) $X > Y$.
7. Let $f(x, y) = 1$ when $0 \leq x \leq 1, 0 \leq y \leq 1$ and $f(x, y) = 0$ otherwise. Find the probability that (a) $X > 0.4$ and $Y > 0.8$, (b) $X < 0.4$, (c) $X < Y$, (d) $X = Y$.
8. Let $f(x, y) = 0.5$ when $0 < x < 2,\ 0 < y < x$. Graph $f(x, y)$. Find the probability that $X + Y < 1$.
9. Let (X, Y) have density $f(x, y) = h(x)h(y)$ when $x > 0, y > 0$ and zero otherwise. Find $P(X > Y)$.
10. If (X, Y) has density $f(x, y)$ when $x > 0, y > 0$ and zero otherwise, and $f(x, y) = f(y, x)$, what is $P(X > Y)$?

9.4 Marginal Distributions

With any two-dimensional distribution we may associate two one-dimensional distributions which are called *marginal distributions*. To introduce this notion, let us start with an illustrative example.

Example 1. In Problem 1, Sec. 9.2, we considered the distribution of the random variables

$$X = number\ of\ queens$$

$$Y = number\ of\ kings\ and\ aces$$

in the random experiment of drawing three cards with replacement from a bridge deck.
  We shall now ask for the probability of the event

$$X = x,\ Y\ arbitrary,$$

that is, we ask for the probability of obtaining precisely x queens and any number of kings and aces, paying no attention to that number. This probability is a function of x, say,

$$f_1(x) = P(X = x,\ Y\ arbitrary).$$

Since the events whose probabilities are listed in Problem 1, Sec. 9.2, are independent, Axiom 3 in Sec. 4.4 yields

$$f_1(x) = \sum_y f(x, y).$$

Table 9.4.1. Values of the Probability Functions f_1 and f_2 of the Marginal Distributions in Example 1

	$y = 0$	$y = 1$	$y = 2$	$y = 3$	$f_1(x)$
$x = 0$	1000/2197	600/2197	120/2197	8/2197	1728/2197
$x = 1$	300/2197	120/2197	12/2197	0	432/2197
$x = 2$	30/2197	6/2197	0	0	36/2197
$x = 3$	1/2197	0	0	0	1/2197
$f_2(y)$	1331/2197	726/2197	132/2197	8/2197	

For each x we obtain $f_1(x)$ by summing the values in the corresponding *row* of Table 9.2.3. For example,

$$f_1(0) = f(0, 0) + f(0, 1) + f(0, 2) + f(0, 3)$$

$$= \frac{1000}{2197} + \frac{600}{2197} + \frac{120}{2197} + \frac{8}{2197} = \frac{1728}{2197},$$

and so on.

On the other hand, we may ask for the probability

$$P(X \text{ arbitrary}, \ Y = y)$$

of obtaining precisely y kings and aces and any number of queens. This probability is a function of y, say, $f_2(y)$, and

$$f_2(y) = \sum_x f(x, y)$$

where we now sum the values in the *columns* of Table 9.2.3. Inserting the values of $f_1(x)$ and $f_2(y)$ on the margin of Table 9.2.3, we obtain Table 9.4.1.

From this example we see that in the case of a two-dimensional discrete random variable (X, Y) with probability function $f(x, y)$, we may ask for the probability

$$P(X = x, \ Y \text{ arbitrary}).$$

This is the probability that X assumes a certain value x while Y assumes any value whatsoever. Then

(1) $f_1(x) = P(X = x, \ Y \text{ arbitrary}) = \sum_y f(x, y).$

Here we sum all values of $f(x, y)$ which, for the x under consideration, are not zero. $f_1(x)$ determines a one-dimensional probability distribution, which is called the **marginal distribution** *of X with respect to the given two-dimensional distribution*. $f_1(x)$ is called the *probability function* of that marginal distribution. The corresponding distribution function is obtained by summing, that is,

(2) $F_1(x) = P(X \leqq x, \ Y \text{ arbitrary}) = \sum_{x^* \leqq x} f_1(x^*).$

Similarly, the probability function

(3) $$f_2(y) = P(X \text{ arbitrary}, Y = y) = \sum_x f(x, y)$$

determines the so-called **marginal distribution** *of Y with respect to the given two-dimensional distribution*. The corresponding distribution function is

(4) $$F_2(y) = P(X \text{ arbitrary}, Y \leq y) = \sum_{y^* \leq y} f_2(y^*).$$

We see that the marginal distributions of a discrete distribution are discrete.

In the case of a *continuous* distribution the considerations are quite similar. Instead of summations we then have integrations. Let $f(x, y)$ be the probability density of a continuous distribution, and let us consider the event

$$(X \leq x, \; Y \text{ arbitrary}).$$

This event may also be written

$$(X \leq x, \; -\infty < Y < \infty).$$

Clearly it has the probability

$$F_1(x) = P(X \leq x, \; -\infty < Y < \infty) = \int_{-\infty}^{x} \left[\int_{-\infty}^{\infty} f(x^*, y) \, dy \right] dx^*.$$

We set

(5) $$f_1(x) = \int_{-\infty}^{\infty} f(x, y) \, dy.$$

Then we simply have

(6) $$F_1(x) = \int_{-\infty}^{x} f_1(x^*) \, dx^*.$$

$f_1(x)$ is called the *probability density* of the **marginal distribution** *of X with respect to the given two-dimensional distribution*. $F_1(x)$ is called the *distribution function* of that marginal distribution.

Similarly, the function

(7) $$f_2(y) = \int_{-\infty}^{\infty} f(x, y) \, dx$$

is the *probability density*, and

(8) $$F_2(y) = \int_{-\infty}^{y} f_2(y^*) \, dy^* = \int_{-\infty}^{y} \int_{-\infty}^{\infty} f(x, y^*) \, dx \, dy^*$$

is the *distribution function* of the **marginal distribution** *of Y with respect to the given continuous two-dimensional distribution*.

We see that the two marginal distributions of a continuous distribution are continuous.

Furthermore, our results show that from the distribution function of a two-dimensional distribution we may readily obtain the distribution functions of each of the two random variables involved.

Let a two-dimensional (X, Y)-distribution be given and consider the mechanical analogue, which is a certain mass distribution in the XY-plane. We now shift each particle parallel to the Y-axis until it reaches the X-axis. The result is a one-dimensional mass distribution on the X-axis. This distribution is the analogue of the marginal distribution of X with respect to that (X, Y)-distribution. The shifting process is called an *orthogonal projection*.

Similarly, the analogue of the marginal distribution of Y is obtained by projecting those mass particles orthogonally onto the Y-axis.

If in (2), Sec. 9.2, we let $x \to \infty$ and $y \to \infty$, respectively, and use (1)–(4), we obtain

$$F_1(x) = F(x, \infty) \qquad \text{and} \qquad F_2(y) = F(\infty, y).$$

For a continuous distribution these formulas also hold; in fact, they are obtained by letting $x \to \infty$ and $y \to \infty$, respectively, in (1), Sec. 9.3, and applying (5)–(8).

Similarly, in the case of an n-dimensional random variable $(X_1, \cdots, X_n)$ *with distribution function* $F(x_1, \cdots, x_n)$ *there are precisely n marginal distributions, namely, the marginal distributions of the variables* $X_1, X_2, \cdots, X_n$ *which, by definition, have the distribution functions*

$$F_1(x_1) = F(x_1, \infty, \cdots, \infty), \cdots, F_n(x_n) = F(\infty, \cdots, \infty, x_n),$$

respectively.

We see that

$$F_j(x_j) = P(X_j \leqq x_j, X_k \; [k \neq j] \text{ arbitrary}).$$

Problems

1. Graph the two marginal distributions in Example 1.

2.–5. Find the probability functions or densities of the marginal distributions of the following distributions.

   2. The distribution in Example 1, Sec. 9.2.

   3. The distribution in Example 1, Sec. 9.3.

   4. The distribution in Problem 4, Sec. 9.3.

   5. The distribution in Problem 8, Sec. 9.3.

6. Let (X, Y) have the probability function

$$f(x, y) = p^{x+y} q^{2-x-y}, \qquad q = 1 - p \qquad (x = 0, 1; \; y = 0, 1).$$

Find the probability function of (Z, Y) where $Z = X + Y$ and the probability functions of the corresponding marginal distributions.

7. Show that the random variables with densities $f(x, y) = x + y$ and $g(x, y) = (x + \frac{1}{2})(y + \frac{1}{2})$ when $0 \leqq x \leqq 1, 0 \leqq y \leqq 1$, have the same marginal distributions.

8. Give an example of two different discrete distributions that have the same marginal distributions.

9. Let (X, Y) have density $f(x, y) = k$ when $x^2 + y^2 < 1$ and zero otherwise. Determine k. Find the densities of the marginal distributions. Find $P(X^2 + Y^2 < 1/2)$.

10. Same tasks as in Problem 9, when $f(x, y) = k(1 - x^2 - y^2)$.

9.5   Independent Random Variables

The two random variables X and Y of a two-dimensional (X, Y)-distribution with distribution function $F(x, y)$ are said to be **independent** if

(1) $$F(x, y) = F_1(x)F_2(y)$$

for all (x, y). Here F_1 and F_2 are the distribution functions of the marginal distributions of X and Y, respectively, with respect to the (X, Y)-distribution, that is (cf. Sec. 9.4)

$$F_1(x) = P(X \leq x, \ Y \text{ arbitrary}),$$
$$F_2(y) = P(X \text{ arbitrary}, \ Y \leq y).$$

If X and Y are not independent they are said to be **dependent.**

Suppose that those variables are either both discrete or both continuous. Then they are independent if and only if

(2) $$f(x, y) = f_1(x)f_2(y)$$

for all (x, y). Here f, f_1, and f_2 are the probability functions (or the densities) of (X, Y) and the marginal distributions of X and Y, respectively.

In the continuous case (2) follows from (1) by differentiation, and (1) follows from (2) by integration. In the discrete case our statement is a consequence of the following theorem.

Theorem 1.   *Two random variables X and Y are independent if and only if for every pair of events*

$$a_1 < X \leq b_1 \quad \text{and} \quad a_2 < Y \leq b_2$$

the relation

(3) $$P(a_1 < X \leq b_1, a_2 < Y \leq b_2) = P(a_1 < X \leq b_1)P(a_2 < Y \leq b_2)$$

holds, that is, if and only if these events are independent.

The proof is left to the reader (cf. Problem 1).

The reader may also show that the variables in Example 1, Sec. 9.2, are independent.

Example 1.   A box contains 10 drill bits, 4 of which are dull. We draw 2 of the bits without replacement and consider the random variables

$$X = \textit{number of dull bits in the first drawing},$$
$$Y = \textit{number of dull bits in the last drawing}.$$

These variables may assume the values 0 or 1. Since 4 of the 10 bits are dull and 6 are sharp, the probability function $f(x, y)$ of the two-dimensional variable (X, Y) has the values

$$f(0, 0) = \frac{6}{10} \cdot \frac{5}{9} = \frac{1}{3}, \qquad f(0, 1) = \frac{6}{10} \cdot \frac{4}{9} = \frac{4}{15},$$

$$f(1, 0) = \frac{4}{10} \cdot \frac{6}{9} = \frac{4}{15}, \qquad f(1, 1) = \frac{4}{10} \cdot \frac{3}{9} = \frac{2}{15}.$$

The probability functions of the marginal distributions of X and Y have the values

$$f_1(0) = f(0, 0) + f(0, 1) = \frac{1}{3} + \frac{4}{15} = 0.6,$$

$$f_2(0) = f(0, 0) + f(1, 0) = \frac{1}{3} + \frac{4}{15} = 0.6,$$

etc. We see that the variables are dependent because

$$f(0, 0) = 1/3 \qquad \text{but} \qquad f_1(0)f_2(0) = 0.36.$$

Our above definition may be extended, as follows.

The n random variables $X_1, \cdots, X_n$ of an n-dimensional $(X_1, \cdots, X_n)$-distribution with distribution function

$$F(x_1, \cdots, x_n) = P(X_1 \leq x_1, \cdots, X_n \leq x_n)$$

are said to be **independent** if

(4) $$F(x_1, \cdots, x_n) = F_1(x_1)F_2(x_2) \cdots F_n(x_n)$$

for all $(x_1, \cdots, x_n)$. Here $F_1, \cdots, F_n$ are the distribution functions of the *marginal distributions of* $X_1, \cdots, X_n$, respectively, that is,

$$F_1(x_1) = P(X_1 \leq x_1; \; X_2 \cdots, X_n \text{ arbitrary}),$$

$$F_2(x_2) = P(X_2 \leq x_2; \; X_1, X_3, \cdots, X_n \text{ arbitrary}),$$

etc.

If those variables are not independent they are said to be **dependent.**

Suppose that those variables are either all discrete or all continuous. Then they are independent if and only if

(5) $$f(x_1, \cdots, x_n) = f_1(x_1) \cdots f_n(x_n)$$

for all $(x_1, \cdots, x_n)$. Here $f, f_1, \cdots$, and f_n are the probability functions (or the densities) of $(X_1, \cdots, X_n)$ and the marginal distributions of $X_1, \cdots$, and X_n, respectively.

Problems

1. Prove Theorem 1.
2. Show that the variables X and Y in Example 1, Sec. 9.2, are independent

3. A box contains N spark plugs, M of which are defective, where $M > 0$, and we draw without replacement. Show that the corresponding random variables

$$X = \text{number of defective plugs obtained in the first drawing}$$

$$Y = \text{number of defective plugs obtained in the second drawing}$$

are dependent.

4. Show that the variables X and Y in Problem 5, Sec. 9.3, are independent.

5. Let (X, Y) have the probability function $f(x, y)$, where

$$f(0, 0) = 3/8, \qquad f(0, 1) = 1/8, \qquad f(1, 0) = 1/8, \qquad f(1, 1) = 3/8.$$

Are X and Y dependent or independent?

6. Same question as in Problem 5, when

$$f(0, 0) = f(1, 1) = 1/2, \qquad f(0, 1) = f(1, 0) = 0.$$

7. If X and Y are dependent random variables, X^2 and Y^2 may be independent. To illustrate this, consider the experiment of drawing chips from an urn containing 8 chips, each labeled with an ordered pair of numbers, namely, $(0, 1)$, $(1, 1)$, $(-1, 0)$, $(0, 0)$, $(0, 0)$, $(1, 0)$, $(-1, -1)$, $(0, -1)$. Show that the random variables

$$X = \text{first number on the chip drawn}$$

$$Y = \text{second number on the chip drawn}$$

are dependent, but X^2 and Y^2 are independent.

8. Determine the constant c in the density $f(x, y) = xy + ce^x$ $(0 < x < 1, 0 < y < 1)$, $f(x, y) = 0$ otherwise. Are the corresponding random variables dependent or independent?

9. Determine the constant c in the density $f(x, y) = c(x^2 + y^2)$ $(x^2 + y^2 < 1)$, $f(x, y) = 0$ otherwise. Are the corresponding random variables dependent or independent?

10. Let $f(x, y) = 0.5xy$ when $0 \leqq x \leqq 2, 0 \leqq y \leqq x$ and $f(x, y) = 0$ otherwise. Show that the corresponding random variables X and Y are dependent.

9.6 Functions of Several Random Variables

The considerations in Sec. 6.3 may be extended to several variables. For the sake of simplicity we shall consider the two-dimensional case.

Let (X, Y) be a given two-dimensional random variable with distribution function $F(x, y)$ and probability function (or density) $f(x, y)$. Furthermore, let $g(x, y)$ be a function that is defined and continuous in the entire plane and is not constant. Then

$$Z = g(X, Y)$$

is a random variable, and we may ask for the corresponding distribution function or for the probability function (or density).

Similarly, in the *n*-dimensional case we need a function $g(x_1, \cdots, x_n)$ and obtain a random variable

$$Z = g(X_1, X_2, \cdots, X_n).$$

Example 1.   We throw two distinguishable fair dice and consider the random variables

$$X = \textit{number the first die turns up},$$
$$Y = \textit{number the second die turns up}.$$

The two-dimensional (X, Y)-distribution has the distribution function

$$f(x, y) = \frac{1}{36} \qquad \text{when } x = 1, \cdots, 6 \text{ and } y = 1, \cdots, 6.$$

We take the function $g(x, y) = x + y$ and consider the random variable

$$Z = g(X, Y) = X + Y,$$

that is, the sum of the two numbers obtained from both dice. Clearly the corresponding probability function $f(z)$ is obtained as follows. For each possible value of z $(= 2, 3, \cdots, 12)$ we sum all those values of $f(x, y)$ for which $x + y$ equals the value of z under consideration. In formulas,

$$f(z) = \sum_{x+y=z} \sum f(x, y).$$

This leads to the values in Example 2, Sec. 5.3.

Our example is typical because in the discrete case the values of the probability function $f(z)$ of a random variable $Z = g(X, Y)$ are obtained from the probability function $f(x, y)$ of (X, Y) by suitable summations,

(1) $$f(z) = P(Z = z) = \sum_{g(x,y)=z} \sum f(x, y).$$

For each z we sum those values of $f(x, y)$ for which

$$g(x, y) = z.$$

From (1) we see that the random variable $Z = g(X, Y)$ has the distribution function

(2) $$F(z) = P(Z \leqq z) = \sum_{g(x,y)\leqq z} \sum f(x, y).$$

For each z the sum consists of all those values $f(x, y)$ for which

$$g(x, y) \leqq z.$$

In the case of a *continuous* two-dimensional distribution the situation is quite similar. Instead of summations we then have integrations and obtain

(3) $$F(z) = P(Z \leqq z) = \iint\limits_{g(x,y)\leqq z} f(x, y) \, dx \, dy.$$

The region of integration in the xy-plane is determined by

$$g(x, y) \leqq z.$$

The probability density $f(z)$ of Z is obtained by differentiation,

$$f(z) = F'(z).$$

Problems

1. Let the random variable (X, Y) be uniformly distributed in the square S: $0 < X \leqq 1, 0 < Y \leqq 1$. Find the distribution function $F(z)$ and the density $f(z)$ of the random variable $Z = X + Y$.

2. Find the means and the variances of the marginal distributions of the (X, Y)-distribution in Problem 1.

3. In Problem 1, find the distribution function of the random variable $Z = X^2$.

4. In Problem 1, find the distribution function and the density of the random variable $Z = X - Y$.

5. If X and Y in (X, Y) are *independent* continuous random variables, show that the random variable $Z = g(X, Y) = X + Y$ has the distribution function

$$(4) \qquad F(z) = \int_{-\infty}^{\infty} f_2(y) \left[\int_{-\infty}^{z-y} f_1(x) \, dx \right] dy$$

and, if $f_1(x)$ is continuous, the density

$$(5a) \qquad f(z) = \int_{-\infty}^{\infty} f_1(z - y) f_2(y) \, dy.$$

6. Show that, in addition to (5a),

$$(5b) \qquad f(z) = \int_{-\infty}^{\infty} f_2(z - x) f_1(x) \, dx.$$

7. Let (X, Y) have the density $f(x, y) = e^{-(x+y)}$ when $x \geqq 0, y \geqq 0$ and otherwise $f(x, y) = 0$. Find the distribution function $F(z)$ of $Z = X + Y$ by direct integration. Differentiate $F(z)$ to get the density $f(z)$ of Z.

8. Show that the random variables in Problem 7 are independent and obtain $F(z)$ from (4).

9. Let X have a binomial distribution with $p = 0.5$ and $n = 3$, and let Y have a binomial distribution with $p = 0.75$ and $n = 2$. Assume that X and Y are independent. Find the probability functions of (a) (X, Y), (b) $X + 2Y$, and (c) $X^2 + Y^2$.

10. Let X and Y be independent random variables with probability functions:

x	1	2	3	4	5	y	0	1	2	3
$f(x)$	0.1	0.2	0.4	0.2	0.1	$g(y)$	0.1	0.4	0.3	0.2

Find the values of the probability functions of (a) (X, Y), (b) $X + Y$, (c) $X - Y$, (d) XY, and (e) Y/X.

9.7   Mathematical Expectation. Mean Value

In the two-dimensional case the mathematical expectation of a given function $g(X, Y)$ is denoted by $E(g(X, Y))$ and is defined by the formula[3]

$$
\textbf{(1)} \qquad E(g(X, Y)) =
\begin{cases}
\displaystyle\sum_x \sum_y g(x, y) f(x, y) & \text{(Discrete case)} \\[2ex]
\displaystyle\int_{-\infty}^{\infty} \int_{-\infty}^{\infty} g(x, y) f(x, y)\, dx\, dy & \text{(Continuous case)}
\end{cases}
$$

where $f(x, y)$ is the probability function or the density, respectively, of the random variable (X, Y).

The analogue of (3) in Sec. 6.3 is

$$
\textbf{(2)} \qquad E(ag(X, Y) + bh(X, Y)) = aE(g(X, Y)) + bE(h(X, Y)),
$$

and the proof is quite similar.

If g depends on one variable only, for example, on X, then in the discrete case we obtain from (1)

$$
E(g(X)) = \sum_x g(x) \sum_y f(x, y) = \sum_x g(x) f_1(x).
$$

Here $f_1(x)$ is the probability function of the marginal distribution of X with respect to the variable (X, Y). This means that the definition above is in agreement with that in the one-dimensional case. For a continuous distribution the situation is similar.

In particular, it follows that

$$
\textbf{(3)} \qquad E(X + Y) = E(X) + E(Y).
$$

Replacing Y by a sum of two variables, we obtain the corresponding formula for three random variables, etc. By repeated application of this process we have the following result.

Theorem 1 (Addition rule for mean values). *The mean value of a sum of random variables (whose mean values exist) equals the sum of the mean values of the variables, that is,*

$$
\textbf{(4)} \qquad E(X_1 + X_2 + \cdots + X_n) = E(X_1) + E(X_2) + \cdots + E(X_n).
$$

---

[3] In this definition it is assumed that the double series converges absolutely and the integral

$$
\int_{-\infty}^{\infty} \int_{-\infty}^{\infty} |g(x, y)|\, f(x, y)\, dx\, dy
$$

exists.

Example 1. Consider a Bernoulli experiment with probability of success p and suppose that the experiment is performed n times. Let the random variable X_j denote the number of successes in the jth performance. Then the corresponding probability function has the values [cf. (1), Sec. 7.1]

$$f_j(0) = 1 - p \quad \text{and} \quad f_j(1) = p.$$

Hence the mean is

(5) $$E(X_j) = 0 \cdot (1 - p) + 1 \cdot p = p.$$

The total number of successes in n trials is

$$Z = X_1 + X_2 + \cdots + X_n.$$

From (4) and (5) it follows that Z has the mean

$$E(Z) = E(X_1) + \cdots + E(X_n) = np,$$

in agreement with (3), Sec. 7.2.

The case of the mean value of a *product* of random variables is more complicated. In general, $E(X^2)$ will be different from $[E(X)]^2$. For example, in the case of the variable

$$X = \textit{number obtained in tossing a fair die}$$

we have $E(X) = 7/2$, but

$$E(X^2) = 1^2 \cdot \frac{1}{6} + 2^2 \cdot \frac{1}{6} + \cdots + 6^2 \cdot \frac{1}{6} = \frac{91}{6} \neq \left(\frac{7}{2}\right)^2.$$

However, if two random variables X and Y are *independent* (and both discrete or both continuous) and their mean values exist, then

(6) $$E(XY) = E(X)E(Y).$$

In fact, from (2), Sec. 9.5, we obtain in the discrete case

$$E(XY) = \sum_x \sum_y xy f(x, y) = \sum_x x f_1(x) \sum_y y f_2(y),$$

and the last expression is equal to $E(X)E(Y)$. Note that the rearrangement of the double series is justified because we assumed absolute convergence. In the continuous case the proof is quite similar.

Formula (6) may be extended, as follows.

Theorem 2 (Multiplication rule for mean values). *If $X_1, \ldots, X_n$ are **independent** random variables which are all discrete or all continuous and whose mean values exist, then*

(7) $$E(X_1 X_2 \cdots X_n) = E(X_1)E(X_2) \cdots E(X_n).$$

Problems

1. Show that the moment generating function of a sum of independent random variables equals the product of the moment generating functions of those variables.
2. Prove (2).
3. n balls are drawn with replacement from an urn containing r red and b black balls. Find the mean of the random variable $Z = \textit{number of red balls drawn}$.

4. Does the mean in Problem 3 change if one draws without replacement?

5. Show that the mean μ of a linear combination $Z = c_1 X_1 + c_2 X_2 + \cdots + c_n X_n$ of random variables $X_1, \cdots, X_n$ whose means $\mu_1, \cdots, \mu_n$ exist equals the corresponding linear combination of the means, $\mu = c_1\mu_1 + c_2\mu_2 + \cdots + c_n\mu_n$.

6. A box contains 10 fuses, 3 of which are defective. Two fuses are drawn without replacement. Let $X =$ *number of defective fuses in the first drawing* and $Y =$ *number of defective fuses in the second drawing*. Find the probability functions of (X, Y) and of the marginal distributions. Find $E(X), E(Y), E(X + Y)$, and $E(XY)$. Use the values to illustrate that (4) holds but (7) does not. (Why?).

9.8   Variance

We shall now derive relations between the variances $\sigma_X{}^2$ and $\sigma_Y{}^2$ of two random variables X and Y and the variance σ^2 of the sum

(1) $$Z = X + Y.$$

According to (5), Sec. 6.4, we first have

(2) $$\sigma^2 = E(Z^2) - [E(Z)]^2.$$

From (1) and Sec. 6.3, formula (3), it follows that

(3) $$E(Z^2) = E(X^2 + 2XY + Y^2) = E(X^2) + 2E(XY) + E(Y^2).$$

Furthermore, by (3), Sec. 9.7,

$$[E(Z)]^2 = [E(X + Y)]^2 = [E(X) + E(Y)]^2$$
$$= [E(X)]^2 + 2E(X)E(Y) + [E(Y)]^2.$$

By substituting this together with (3) in (2) we have

$$\sigma^2 = E(X^2) - [E(X)]^2 + E(Y^2) - [E(Y)]^2$$
$$+ 2[E(XY) - E(X)E(Y)].$$

The first line on the right is the sum of the variances of X and Y. We set

(4) $$\sigma_{XY} = E(XY) - E(X)E(Y).$$

Then our formula becomes

(5) $$\sigma^2 = \sigma_X{}^2 + \sigma_Y{}^2 + 2\sigma_{XY}.$$

The quantity σ_{XY} is called the **covariance** of the random variables X and Y. Its importance will be explained later (in Sec. 18.2).

If X and Y are independent, it follows from (6) in Sec. 9.7 that the covariance is zero. Then (5) reduces to the form

(6) $$\sigma^2 = \sigma_X{}^2 + \sigma_Y{}^2.$$

This result can be extended to more than two variables, as follows.

Theorem 1 (Addition rule for variances). *The variance of the sum of* **independent** *random variables whose variances exist equals the sum of these variances.*

Combining this theorem with (4), Sec. 6.7, we obtain a result that will be basic in Part III.

Theorem 2. *If X_1, $X_2, \cdots, X_n$ are independent random variables with common variance σ^2, then the random variable*

$$\bar{X} = \frac{1}{n}(X_1 + X_2 + \cdots + X_n)$$

has the variance

$$\sigma_{\bar{X}}^{\;2} = \frac{\sigma^2}{n}.$$

Finally, let us consider two examples.

Example 1.   Each of the two variables in Example 1, Sec. 9.6, has the mean value 7/2 and the variance 35/12; (cf. Example 1 in Sec. 6.4). Hence the sum of the variables has mean value 7 (cf. Fig. 5.3.2) and variance 35/6. In fact, the variables are independent so that we may apply Theorem 1.

Example 2 (A Bernoulli trial with variable probability of success).   Suppose that we perform a Bernoulli trial n times. Consider the random variable

$$X_j = \text{number of successes in the jth performance,}$$

and let p_j denote the probability of success in this performance.
X_j has mean $E(X_j) = p_j$. A simple calculation shows that

$$E(X_j{}^2) = p_j.$$

From (5) in Sec. 6.4 it follows that X_j has variance

$$\sigma_j{}^2 = E(X_j{}^2) - [E(X_j)]^2 = p_j - p_j{}^2.$$

The variables $X_1, \cdots, X_n$ are independent. Hence we may apply Theorem 1 to their sum

$$Z = X_1 + \cdots + X_n = \text{number of successes in the n performances}$$

and conclude that Z has the variance

(7)
$$\sigma^2 = \sum_{j=1}^{n}(p_j - p_j{}^2) = \sum_{j=1}^{n}p_j - \sum_{j=1}^{n}p_j{}^2.$$

We now introduce the "average probability of success"

(8)
$$p = \frac{1}{n}\sum_{j=1}^{n}p_j = \frac{1}{n}(p_1 + p_2 + \cdots + p_n).$$

Then (7) may be written

$$\sigma^2 = np - \sum_{j=1}^{n}p_j{}^2.$$

If n and p are fixed, then σ^2 is a function of $p_1, \cdots, p_n$. σ^2 is maximum when $\sum p_j{}^2$ is minimum. Since (8) must be satisfied, this holds if and only if $p_1 = p_2 \cdots = p_n \, (= p)$. From this we can draw the surprising conclusion that if the probability of success is constant (say, p), the values to be expected vary more than in the case of variable probability of success with the average value p.

Problems

1. Find the mean and the variance of the random variable $X = $ *sum of the n numbers that turn up in throwing n fair dice.*

2. Give a simple example illustrating that Theorem 1 does not hold for *dependent* random variables.

3. Let $X_1, \cdots, X_k$ be independent random variables with variances $\sigma_1^2, \cdots, \sigma_k^2$. Show that the variance of $Z = (a_1 X_1 + \cdots + a_k X_k)/(a_1 + \cdots + a_k)$ is minimized if the weight a_j is chosen inversely proportional to σ_j^2.

4. In Problem 3, let $k = 3$ and $\sigma_1^2 = 1$, $\sigma_2^2 = 2$, $\sigma_3^2 = 4$. Calculate the variance σ^2 of Z, choosing (a) a_j inversely proportional to σ_j^2, (b) $a_j = 1$. Compare the results.

5. Prove Theorem 2.

6. Show that if $X_1, \cdots, X_n$ are independent random variables with variances $\sigma_1^2, \cdots, \sigma_n^2$, then $Z = c_1 X_1 + c_2 X_2 + \cdots + c_n X_n$ has the variance

$$\sigma^2 = c_1^2 \sigma_1^2 + c_2^2 \sigma_2^2 + \cdots + c_n^2 \sigma_n^2.$$

CHAPTER 10

Distributions Used in Tests

We shall now consider two special distributions, the chi-square distribution and the t-distribution, that play an important role in connection with the tests to be explained in Part III.

(The F-distribution will be defined in Sec. 13.6.)

10.1 Chi-Square Distribution. Gamma Function

Let $X_1, \cdots, X_n$ be independent normal random variables with mean 0 and variance 1. The sum of their squares is generally denoted by χ^2 (chi-squared), that is,

(1) $$\chi^2 = X_1{}^2 + X_2{}^2 + \cdots + X_n{}^2.$$

The corresponding distribution is called the **chi-square distribution.** It has the density

(2) $$f(x) = K_n x^{(n-2)/2} e^{-x/2} \qquad \text{when } x > 0$$

and $f(x) = 0$ when $x < 0$ (for the derivation, see Appendix 1). Here n is a positive integer and is called the *number of degrees of freedom* of the distribution. K_n is a constant (see below). Figure 10.1.1 shows $f(x)$ for various n. For $n = 1$ and 2 the curves are monotone. For $n > 2$ they have a maximum at $x = n - 2$. This is easily seen by setting $f'(x)$ equal to zero.

From (2) we obtain the distribution function

(3) $$F(x) = K_n \int_0^x u^{(n-2)/2} e^{-u/2} \, du \qquad \text{when } x \geqq 0$$

and $F(x) = 0$ when x is negative.

The chi-square distribution was introduced by F. R. Helmert (1876) (cf. Appendix 3) and constitutes the basis of an important test to be discussed in Sec. 15.1.

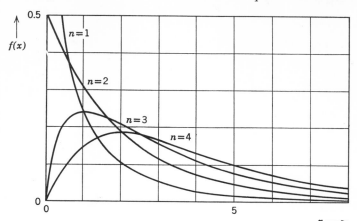

Fig. 10.1.1. Density of the chi-square distribution

The constant K_n in (2) and (3) must be chosen so that $F(\infty) = 1$. It follows that (cf. Problem 4)

$$(4) \qquad K_n = \frac{1}{2^{n/2}\Gamma\left(\dfrac{n}{2}\right)}.$$

Here $\Gamma(\lambda)$ is the so-called **gamma function**, defined by the integral

$$(5) \qquad \Gamma(\lambda) = \int_0^\infty e^{-t}t^{\lambda-1}\,dt \qquad\qquad (\lambda > 0).$$

Replacing λ with $\lambda + 1$ and integrating by parts, we obtain the basic relation

$$(6) \qquad \Gamma(\lambda + 1) = \lambda\Gamma(\lambda).$$

When $\lambda = 1$ in (5), we may integrate, finding

$$\Gamma(1) = \int_0^\infty e^{-t}\,dt = 1.$$

From this and (6) we have

$$\Gamma(2) = 1 \cdot \Gamma(1) = 1! \qquad \Gamma(3) = 2 \cdot \Gamma(2) = 2!$$

and in general

$$(7) \qquad \Gamma(n + 1) = n! \qquad\qquad (n = 0, 1, \cdots).$$

Hence the gamma function generalizes the elementary factorial function.

If n is even, then in (4),

$$\Gamma\left(\frac{n}{2}\right) = \left(\frac{n}{2} - 1\right)! \qquad\qquad (n = 2, 4, \cdots).$$

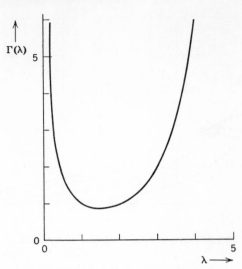

Fig. 10.1.2. Gamma function $\Gamma(\lambda)$ for positive λ

We turn to the case of odd n. When $n = 1$, then (cf. Problem 3)

(8) $\Gamma(\tfrac{1}{2}) = \sqrt{\pi}.$

By applying (6) we thus obtain

$$\Gamma(\tfrac{3}{2}) = \tfrac{1}{2}\Gamma(\tfrac{1}{2}) = \tfrac{1}{2}\sqrt{\pi}, \qquad \Gamma(\tfrac{5}{2}) = \tfrac{3}{2}\Gamma(\tfrac{3}{2}) = \tfrac{3}{4}\sqrt{\pi}$$

etc.

Numerical values of the gamma function are included in Appendix 4 (cf. Table 1f). Fig. 10.1.2 shows the graph of the gamma function for positive values of λ. Table 6 in Appendix 4 contains values of x for given values of (3).

Problems

1. Obtain (6) from (5).

2. Using (6) and Table 1f, Appendix 4, compute $\Gamma(2.18)$, $\Gamma(3.99)$, and $\Gamma(4.61)$.

3. Derive (8) from (8) in Problem 1, Sec. 8.2.

4. The chi-square distribution is a special case of the **gamma distribution**, whose density is

(9) $f(x) = e^{-x}x^{\lambda-1}/\Gamma(\lambda)$ when $x > 0$,

$f(x) = 0$ when $x < 0$, where $\lambda > 0$. Show that the corresponding distribution function approaches 1 as $x \to \infty$.

5. The distribution with density

(10) $f(x) = x^{\alpha-1}(1-x)^{\beta-1}/B(\alpha, \beta)$ $(0 < x < 1, \alpha > 0, \beta > 0)$,

$f(x) = 0$ otherwise,

is called the **beta distribution**, here $B(\alpha, \beta) = \Gamma(\alpha)\Gamma(\beta)/\Gamma(\alpha + \beta)$ is the beta function. Graph $f(x)$ with $\alpha = 2$, $\beta = 2$.

6. Let Y_1, Y_2, Y_3 be Cartesian coordinates of the point in space at which an anti-aircraft shell is supposed to burst, and assume that Y_1, Y_2, Y_3 are independent normal random variables with a common standard deviation of 100 ft. Find the probability that the shell will have a radial error of at most 250 ft.

7. Show that the distribution function of the chi-square distribution with 2 degrees of freedom is $F(x) = 1 - e^{-x/2}$. Using this result and a table of the exponential function, check the values in the second column of Table 6 in Appendix 4.

8. The functions

$$\Gamma(x, \lambda) = \int_0^x e^{-v} v^{\lambda-1}\, dv, \qquad \gamma(x, \lambda) = \int_x^\infty e^{-v} v^{\lambda-1}\, dv$$

are called the **incomplete gamma functions**. Show that in (3),

$$F(x) = \Gamma\left(\frac{x}{2}, \frac{n}{2}\right) \Big/ \Gamma\left(\frac{n}{2}\right).$$

Using this result, show that $F(x) \to 1$ as $x \to \infty$.

9. Integrate (3) with $n = 4$ and use a table of the exponential function for checking the value corresponding to $F = 95\%$ given in Table 6, Appendix 4.

10. Show that for even values of n, the distribution function $F(x)$ in (3) can be expressed in terms of finitely many elementary functions (exponential functions and powers of x).

10.2 Further Properties of the Chi-Square Distribution

The chi-square distribution has mean value

$$(1) \qquad\qquad \mu = n$$

and variance

$$(2) \qquad\qquad \sigma^2 = 2n.$$

Formula (1) is obtained from (1*b*), Sec. 6.1, by expressing the integral in terms of the gamma function (cf. Problem 1). Formula (2) is obtained in a similar fashion by using (5), Sec. 6.4, and (6), Sec. 10.1.

It can be shown that for large n the chi-square distribution may be approximated by the normal distribution, as follows.

(I) The random variable χ^2 is asymptotically normal with mean (1) and variance (2), that is,

$$(3) \qquad\qquad F(x) \sim \Phi\left(\frac{x - n}{\sqrt{2n}}\right)$$

where F is given by (3), Sec. 10.1, Φ is given by (3), Sec. 8.2, and $\sim$ is defined as in Sec. 8.4, so that (3) yields a useful approximation for $F(x)$ when n is large.

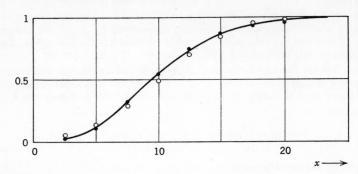

Fig. 10.2.1. Curve of the distribution function of the chi-square distribution with $n = 10$ degrees of freedom and approximations (3) (circles) and (4) (dots)

(II) The random variable $\sqrt{2\chi^2}$ is asymptotically normal with mean $\sqrt{2n - 1}$ and variance 1, so that

(4) $$F(x) \sim \Phi(\sqrt{2x} - \sqrt{2n - 1}).$$

This gives another approximation for $F(x)$, which is even better than (3); cf. Fig. 10.2.1. It also yields the approximation in the last column of Table 6 in Appendix 4.

Problems

1. Derive (1).
2. Obtain (2) from (5), Sec. 6.4, by representing the integral for $E(X^2)$ in terms of the gamma function.
3. Compare the exact values and the approximations (3) and (4) when $n = 100$ and x equals some of the values in Table 6, Appendix 4.
4. How can the approximation formulas in Table 6, Appendix 4, be obtained from (4)?
5. Show that the density of the chi-square distribution with $n \geqq 3$ degrees of freedom has a maximum at $x = n - 2$.
6. Using Table 6 in Appendix 4, graph the distribution function of the chi-square distribution with $n = 1, 2, 3, 4$ degrees of freedom, using common axes. In what way do these curves and the curves in Fig. 10.1.1 illustrate that the mean and the variance increase as n increases?

10.3   Student's *t*-Distribution

The so-called *t*-distribution was introduced by W. S. Gosset who published under the name of "Student" (1908); cf. also Pearson and Wishart (1942). It constitutes the basis of important tests to be considered in Secs. 12.3, 13.3, and 13.4.

The *t*-distribution is the distribution of the random variable

$$\textbf{(1)} \qquad\qquad\qquad T = \frac{X}{\sqrt{Y/n}}$$

under the following assumptions. n is a positive integer and is called the *number of degrees of freedom* of the *t*-distribution. X and Y are independent random variables. X is normal with mean 0 and variance 1, and Y has a chi-square distribution with n degrees of freedom.

The variable T is often denoted by t. We shall not adopt this notation because all our random variables are uniformly denoted by capital letters.

The *t*-distribution has the density (cf. Fig. 10.3.1)

$$\textbf{(2)} \qquad\qquad f(z) = \frac{\Gamma\left(\dfrac{n+1}{2}\right)}{\sqrt{n\pi}\,\Gamma\left(\dfrac{n}{2}\right)} \cdot \frac{1}{\left(1 + \dfrac{z^2}{n}\right)^{(n+1)/2}}$$

(for the derivation, see Appendix 1). Hence the distribution function is

$$\textbf{(3)} \qquad\qquad F(z) = \frac{\Gamma\left(\dfrac{n+1}{2}\right)}{\sqrt{n\pi}\,\Gamma\left(\dfrac{n}{2}\right)} \int_{-\infty}^{z} \frac{du}{\left(1 + \dfrac{u^2}{n}\right)^{(n+1)/2}}.$$

For $n = 1$ this is the Cauchy distribution (cf. Problem 10, Sec. 6.1), which has no mean value. For $n = 2, 3, \cdots$ the mean value of the *t*-distribution is

$$\textbf{(4)} \qquad\qquad\qquad \mu = 0.$$

This follows from Theorem 1 in Sec. 6.1 and the fact that $f(z)$ is an even function.

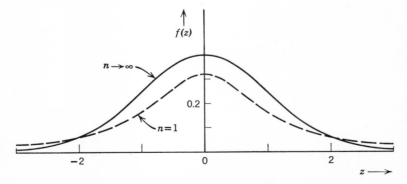

Fig. 10.3.1. Density of the *t*-distribution

For $n = 1$ and 2 the t-distribution has no variance. For $n = 3, 4, \cdots$ we obtain (cf. Problem 1)

$$(5) \qquad\qquad \sigma^2 = \frac{n}{n-2}.$$

As n increases the distribution function of the t-distribution approaches the distribution function of the normal distribution with mean value 0 and variance 1.

In Part III we shall need values of z for given values of the distribution function (3) of the t-distribution. A corresponding table is included in Appendix 4 (Table 8).

Problems

1. Prove (5). *Hint.* Transform the integral in (1b), Sec. 6.2, into an integral from 0 to ∞, set $1 + \dfrac{z^2}{n} = \dfrac{1}{t}$, and use (11) in that part of Appendix 1 which corresponds to Sec. 10.1.

2. Show that the distribution function in (3) approaches 1 as $z \to \infty$.

3. For the normal distribution with mean 0 and variance 1, 99% of the area under the bell-shaped curve lies between -2.58 and 2.58. What are the corresponding values $-x$ and x in the case of the t-distribution with (a) 2, (b) 5, (c) 20, (d) 100 degrees of freedom?

PART III

STATISTICAL INFERENCE

In Part I we discussed methods for arranging statistical data in suitable tables and representing them in graphical form. In Part II we considered important mathematical models of populations.

Now, in Part III we shall obtain relations between the theory and the observable reality. We shall ask what conclusions we can draw about a population from a given sample and how reliable such conclusions are. These conclusions will be quantitative. Some typical corresponding situations and problems of practical interest are shown in the table on pp. 149–150.

We recall that the importance of mathematical models is rather obvious and was stressed before. The present methods will be helpful in selecting, setting up, or modifying models and in testing their agreement with the real world.

In these methods we have to use samples. So far it has been sufficient to know that a **sample from a population** is a selection taken from a population, but now it is necessary to formulate this concept in a precise fashion. By definition, a sample must have certain properties, as follows.

Samples are supposed to yield information about the corresponding population, since it is generally too expensive or too time-consuming or even impossible to observe or measure all the individuals corresponding to the population. Illustrative examples were given in Sec. 1.2. In order that such information can be obtained, the sample must be a **random selection.** By this we mean that each element of the population must have a known probability of being drawn, that is, of being taken into the sample; the simplest and most common case is that this probability is the same for all elements of the population. If and only if this requirement is satisfied (at least approximately), the statistical methods to be considered will yield sensible and useful results.

Furthermore we require that the n performances of the random experiment by which we obtain the n sample values be **independent,** that is, the result of a performance does not influence the other performances. This is equivalent to saying that the probability that any member of the population will appear in a sample does not depend on the appearance or nonappearance of the other members of the population in the sample.

The theory of sampling based on this assumption is called sampling from an **infinite population,** for the following reason. We may regard the sample values $x_1, \cdots, x_n$ as results of drawing from a population which must remain unaltered to guarantee that independence.

Now if we draw *with* replacement this certainly holds because before each drawing we first restore the original situation. For example, if we throw a die *n* times, the sample consists of *n* numbers that turn up, and the population is infinite, consisting of the infinitely many one's, two's, $\cdots$, six's to be obtained in throwing the die infinitely many times. Of course, this population is hypothetical.

In the case of drawing without replacement, that independence is guaranteed if and only if the population is infinite. In practice we regard the population as being infinite if it is "very large" compared with the size of the sample (example: the heights of 1000 persons selected from the population of a big city). Then we may assume that the sample values are independent even if we draw without replacement.

It is not so easy to satisfy the requirement that a sample be a random selection, because there are many subtle factors of various types that can bias results of sampling. For example, if an interested purchaser wants to draw and inspect a sample of 10 items from a lot of 800 items before he decides whether to purchase the lot, how should he physically select those 10 items so that he can be reasonably sure that all possible $\binom{800}{10}$ samples of size 10 would be equally probable?

Methods to solve the problem of selecting at random have been developed, and we shall now describe such a procedure, which is frequently used.

Suppose that 800 items are given, and we want to select 10 of them at random. For this purpose we number the given items from 1 to 800. The selection is made by the use of Table 5 in Appendix 4, which is a **table for random selection.** We first choose any two integers, for example, 1728 and 219. We divide the first number by 100 and the last by 10. The remainders 28 and 9 are the numbers of the row and column, respectively, from which we start in Table 5. In row 28 and column 9 of Table 5 we find the number 83814. We read downward, finding

$$83814 \qquad 87802 \qquad 67056 \qquad 61340 \qquad \text{etc.}$$

We omit the last two figures of each number. There remains

$$838 \qquad 878 \qquad 670 \qquad 613 \qquad \text{etc.}$$

We omit the numbers that are greater than 800 or occur for the second time. We then obtain the 10 numbers

$$670 \quad 613 \quad 783 \quad 528 \quad 90 \quad 658 \quad 765 \quad 242 \quad 324 \quad 600.$$

The 10 items having these numbers represent the desired random selection.

Some Basic Statistical Problems

Situation, Problem	Where Discussed
Estimation of unknown parameters in a distribution How to obtain approximate values of the parameters? How to judge the accuracy of such approximations? How to test whether such a parameter has a certain numerical value?	Chap. 11 Chap. 12, in particular: Normal distribution Secs. 12.1, 12.3, 12.5 Binomial distribution Sec. 12.6 Arbitrary distributions Sec. 12.7 Chap. 13
Quality control. Acceptance How to test whether a process of production is running properly? How to test whether a lot meets specified quality requirements?	Sec. 14.1 Secs. 14.2–14.5
Problems involving several normally distributed populations with possibly different means or variances How to test whether the means are equal? How to test whether the variances are equal?	Sec. 13.4, Chap. 16 Sec. 13.6
Test on medians How to test whether the median has a certain value?	Sec. 20.1
Test on distribution functions How to test whether a population has a certain type of distribution? How to test whether two populations have the same distribution?	Chap. 15 Sec. 20.4
Randomness How to test randomness of sample values? How to select things at random?	Sec. 20.3 Page 148
Physical measurements How to judge the accuracy of physical measurements?	Chap. 19

Situation, Problem	Where Discussed
Problems involving an ordinary variable x and a random variable Y possibly depending on x	
How to test the assumption that Y depends linearly on x?	Sec. 17.10
How to determine the corresponding regression line?	Sec. 17.1
How to judge the accuracy of the slope of that line?	Sec. 17.5
How to test whether that slope has a certain numerical value?	Secs. 17.7, 17.9
How to determine a regression parabola?	Sec. 17.11
How to test whether the regression curve is of a certain type?	Sec. 17.12
How to test whether the Y-values exhibit trend?	Secs. 17.7, 17.9, 20.2
Problems involving two random variables which are possibly related	
How to compute the correlation coefficient?	Sec. 18.1
How to judge the accuracy of the value of the correlation coefficient?	Sec. 18.4
How to test whether that population has correlation coefficient 0?	Sec. 18.4

CHAPTER 11

Estimation of Parameters

Quantities appearing in distribution functions, such as p in the binomial distribution and μ and σ in the normal distribution, are called *parameters*. We shall now explain how to obtain *estimates* of parameters from a given sample. This is an important practical problem.

Two kinds of such estimates are in common use. One is called a *point estimate* because it is a number (point on the real line), which is computed from a given sample and serves as an approximation of the unknown exact value of the parameter. This kind of estimate is discussed in the present chapter. The other kind is called an *interval estimate* because it is an interval; it will be studied in Chap. 12.

11.1 Mean Value. Variance. Method of Moments

It is natural to regard the mean $\bar{x}$ of a sample as an approximation of the mean μ of the corresponding population. In this way we have the estimate $\hat{\mu} = \bar{x}$ for μ, that is,

$$(1) \qquad \hat{\mu} = \bar{x} = \frac{1}{n}(x_1 + \cdots + x_n),$$

where n is the size of the sample.

Similarly, the variance s^2 of a sample may be regarded as an approximation of the variance σ^2 of the population. We thus have the estimate $\hat{\sigma}^2 = s^2$ for σ^2, that is,

$$(2) \qquad \hat{\sigma}^2 = s^2 = \frac{1}{n-1}\sum_{j=1}^{n}(x_j - \bar{x})^2.$$

In certain distributions μ appears explicitly as a parameter, and (1) is then an estimate of a parameter. Examples are the normal and the Poisson distributions.

151

In the case of the binomial distribution we have $p = \mu/n$ [cf. (3), Sec. 7.2]. In this case, x_j in (1) is 1 if the event whose probability is p occurred in the jth performance of the experiment, and is 0 if it did not occur in that trial. From (1) we thus obtain the following estimate $\hat{p}$ for p:

$$\text{binomial} \qquad \hat{p} = \frac{\bar{x}}{n}.$$

We mention that (1) is a very special case of a method which is called the **method of moments.** In this method one represents the parameters to be estimated in terms of the moments of the distribution. In the resulting formulas those moments are then replaced by the corresponding moments of the sample. This yields the desired estimates. Here the **kth moment of a sample** $x_1, \cdots, x_n$ is defined by the formula

$$(3) \qquad\qquad m_k = \frac{1}{n} \sum_{j=1}^{n} x_j{}^k \qquad\qquad (k = 1, 2, \cdots).$$

Grouping will affect the values of the moments of the sample. This effect can be corrected to some extent by the use of the **Sheppard correction,** introduced by Sheppard (1898) (cf. Appendix 3). For m_1 this correction is zero. m_2 must be replaced by

$$m_2 - \frac{l^2}{12} \qquad (l = \text{length of the class intervals}).$$

For details, see Cramér (1961) and Wold (1934).

In the case of the Poisson distribution, $\mu = \sigma^2$. Hence (1) as well as (2) is an estimate of the parameter of that distribution. This is not an unusual situation because in various branches of mathematics there often are several approximation formulas for a certain quantity. However, we should try to find out what properties are essential in characterizing the "goodness" of such an approximation formula. This will be done in the next section.

11.2 Estimators. Unbiased Estimators. Efficient Estimators

We consider a distribution involving a single unknown parameter θ, and we assume that we know a formula for computing an approximate value $\hat{\theta}$ of θ from a given sample $x_1, \cdots, x_n$. Clearly, $\hat{\theta}$ depends on the sample values, that is, it is a function of those values. Let us denote this function by g. Then our formula has the form

$$(1) \qquad\qquad \hat{\theta} = g(x_1, \cdots, x_n).$$

Examples are (1) and (2) in the previous section.

To given sample values $x_1, \cdots, x_n$ there corresponds a certain numerical value of g. This number is called an **estimate** of the parameter θ.

We shall now use the following simple but very important idea.

So far we have regarded the values $x_1, \cdots, x_n$ of a sample as n observed values of a single random variable X. We may equally well regard these n values as single observations of n random variables $X_1, \cdots, X_n$ which have the same distribution (the distribution of X) and are independent because the sample values are assumed to be independent.

Then we may regard $\theta = g(x_1, \cdots, x_n)$ as a single observation of the random variable

$$(2) \qquad \hat{\Theta} = g(X_1, \cdots, X_n).$$

This random variable $\hat{\Theta}$ is called an **estimator** for the parameter θ.

In this connection we remember that a nonconstant function of random variables is a random variable (cf. Sec. 9.6). A nonconstant function of those random variables $X_1, \cdots, X_n$ is called a **statistic.**

Note that in (2) we use a capital theta because (2) is a random variable, whereas the observed value (1) of (2) is denoted by a lowercase theta.

Example 1. Suppose that we throw a die twice and obtain $x_1 = 5$ and $x_2 = 3$. Then we may regard each of these numbers as an observed value of the random variables

$$X_1 = number\ obtained\ in\ the\ first\ trial$$

and

$$X_2 = number\ obtained\ in\ the\ second\ trial.$$

The sum

$$z = g(x_1, x_2) = x_1 + x_2 = 8$$

is then an observed value of the random variable

$$Z = X_1 + X_2 = sum\ of\ the\ numbers\ obtained\ in\ both\ trials.$$

Z has the probability function shown in Fig. 5.3.2. (Why?). Similarly, the mean value

$$\bar{x} = \tfrac{1}{2}(x_1 + x_2) = 4$$

is an observed value of the random variable

$$\bar{X} = \tfrac{1}{2}(X_1 + X_2).$$

The expression

$$\bar{x} = g(x_1, \cdots, x_n) = \frac{1}{n}(x_1 + \cdots + x_n)$$

in (1), Sec. 11.1, can now be regarded as an observed value of the random variable

$$(3) \qquad \bar{X} = g(X_1, \cdots, X_n) = \frac{1}{n}(X_1 + \cdots + X_n).$$

Since X_j has the mean $E(X_j) = \mu$, it follows from Theorem 1 in Sec. 9.7 that the sum $X_1 + \cdots + X_n$ has the mean $n\mu$. From this and (2) in Sec. 6.7 we conclude that $\bar{X}$ has the mean

(4)
$$E(\bar{X}) = \frac{1}{n} n\mu = \mu.$$

An estimator $g(X_1, \cdots, X_n)$ for a parameter θ is said to be **unbiased** if

$$E(g(X_1, \cdots, X_n)) = \theta,$$

and a corresponding value $g(x_1, \cdots, x_n)$ obtained from a sample $x_1, \cdots, x_n$ is called an **unbiased estimate.**

Note that it is the mean value rather than, say, the median of $g(X_1, \cdots, X_n)$ which is set equal to θ in this definition, which rests largely on mathematical convenience.

Example 2. From (4) we see that the estimator corresponding to (1), Sec. 11.1, is an unbiased estimator for the mean μ of a distribution.

Example 3. The estimator corresponding to (2) in Sec. 11.1 is an unbiased estimator for the variance σ^2 because this estimator

(5)
$$S^2 = \frac{1}{n-1} \sum_{j=1}^{n} (X_j - \bar{X})^2$$

has the expectation

(6)
$$E(S^2) = \sigma^2,$$

as the reader may show (cf. Problem 3).

If we replace the denominator $n - 1$ in (2), Sec. 11.1, with n, then the corresponding estimator is not unbiased. This is another reason for the choice of that denominator in (3), Sec. 3.1.

An unbiased estimator $\hat{\Theta} = g(X_1, \cdots, X_n)$ for a parameter θ is said to be **efficient** if it has a finite variance

(7)
$$E([\hat{\Theta} - \theta]^2)$$

and if there does not exist another estimator $\hat{\Theta}^* = g^*(X_1, \cdots, X_n)$ for θ whose variance is smaller than that of $\hat{\Theta}$.

If the variance of $\hat{\Theta}$ is small, this means that $\hat{\Theta}$ assumes values which lie close to $E(\hat{\Theta}) = \theta$ and therefore is a good estimator.

The *efficiency* of any other unbiased estimator is defined as the ratio of the variance of the efficient estimator(s) to the variance of the other estimator. We may also define the *efficiency of an unbiased estimator* $\hat{\Theta}_1$ *of* θ *with respect to another unbiased estimator* $\hat{\Theta}_2$ *of* θ to be the ratio σ_2^2/σ_1^2 of the variances σ_2^2 of $\hat{\Theta}_2$ and σ_1^2 of $\hat{\Theta}_1$.

Unbiasedness is desirable; however, if an estimator has a small bias and a small second moment about θ, it may be better than an unbiased estimator with a relatively large variance.

The concept of efficiency was introduced by Fisher (1922, 1925) (cf. Appendix 3).

a biased estimator can have a smaller variance t in cases of interval estimating it may be more accurate

Problems

1. Determine the values of the probability function of the random variable $\bar{X}$ in Example 1.
2. Why does Z in Example 1 have the probability function shown in Fig. 5.3.2? How can we obtain from this function the probability function of $\bar{X}$ in Example 1?
3. Prove (6). *Hint.* Use

$$(8) \qquad\qquad E([\bar{X} - \mu]^2) = \frac{\sigma^2}{n} \qquad\qquad \text{(cf. Theorem 2, Sec. 9.8).}$$

4. Given three samples (from the same population) of size $n_1 = 4$, $n_2 = 10$, $n_3 = 50$ with variances $s_1{}^2 = 3$, $s_2{}^2 = 4$, $s_3{}^2 = 2$, respectively, combine these three variances to obtain an unbiased estimate of σ^2.
5. Consider the distribution with density $f(x) = 1/\theta$ when $0 \leq x \leq \theta$ and $f(x) = 0$ elsewhere. Show that $2\bar{X}$ is an unbiased estimator of θ.
6. Show that $E([\bar{X} - k\mu]^2)$ is minimum if and only if $k = 1$.
7. Let $\hat{\theta}_1$ and $\hat{\theta}_2$ be estimates of the same parameter θ resulting from independent experiments. If the estimates are unbiased, show that any linear combination $\hat{\theta} = c_1\hat{\theta}_1 + c_2\hat{\theta}_2$ with $c_1 + c_2 = 1$ is an unbiased estimate of θ.
8. Let $x_1, \cdots, x_n$ be a sample from a population which is uniformly distributed on an interval $0 \leq x \leq \theta$. Show that the largest sample value, call it y, may be regarded as an observed value of a random variable Y with distribution function $F(y) = P(Y \leq y) = y^n/\theta^n$. Hence show that $(1 + n^{-1})y$ is an unbiased estimate of θ.
9. Show that the variance σ^2 of $\hat{\Theta} = c_1\hat{\Theta}_1 + c_2\hat{\Theta}_2$ in Problem 7 is minimum if and only if the weights c_1 and c_2 are proportional to the reciprocals of the variances $\sigma_1{}^2$ of $\hat{\Theta}_1$ and $\sigma_2{}^2$ of $\hat{\Theta}_2$, that is, $c_1/c_2 = \sigma_2{}^2/\sigma_1{}^2$.
10. Show that the difference of the means of two independent random samples from two populations is an unbiased estimate of the difference of the population means, provided the latter exist.
11. In Sec. 12.4 we shall see that if $X_1, \cdots, X_n$ are independent normal random variables with mean μ and variance σ^2, then $(n-1)S^2/\sigma^2$ has a chi-square distribution with $n-1$ degrees of freedom, where S^2 is defined by (5). Using this information, show that under the present assumption an unbiased estimate of σ is

$$\sqrt{\frac{n-1}{2}}\, s\Gamma\left(\frac{n-1}{2}\right) \Big/ \Gamma\left(\frac{n}{2}\right).$$

(From this and Example 3 we see that if $\hat{\theta}$ is an unbiased estimate of a parameter θ, then $\hat{\theta}^2$ need not be an unbiased estimate of θ^2.)
12. Using (4) and Theorem 2, Sec. 9.8, show that although $\bar{x}$ is an unbiased estimate of μ, the square $\bar{x}^2$ is not an unbiased estimate of μ^2.

11.3 Consistent Estimators

From (8) in Problem 3, Sec. 11.2, we see that the variance of the random variable (3), Sec. 11.2, becomes smaller as n increases. Hence we can expect that (1), Sec. 11.1, yields values which are the more accurate the larger n is. In fact, we may use this conjecture to motivate a more general discussion, which is based upon the following theorem.

Theorem 1.   *Let c be any real number and let X be any random variable for which* $E([X - c]^2)$ *is finite. Then for every* $\epsilon > 0$ *the following* **inequality of Tchebichef** *holds:*

$$(1) \qquad\qquad P(|X - c| \geqq \epsilon) \leqq \frac{1}{\epsilon^2} E([X - c]^2).$$

The proof will follow at the end of this section.

If c is the mean μ of X, then (1) becomes

$$(2) \qquad\qquad P(|X - \mu| \geqq \epsilon) \leqq \sigma^2/\epsilon^2$$

where σ^2 is the variance of X.

Let $\hat{\Theta} = g(X_1, \cdots, X_n)$ be an estimator for a parameter θ, and suppose that g is defined even for arbitrarily large n. Then, setting $c = \theta$ and $X = \hat{\Theta}$ in (1), we have

$$(3) \qquad\qquad P(|\hat{\Theta} - \theta| \geqq \epsilon) \leqq \frac{1}{\epsilon^2} E([\hat{\Theta} - \theta]^2).$$

If the estimator has the property

$$(4) \qquad\qquad E([\hat{\Theta} - \theta]^2) \to 0 \qquad\qquad \text{as } n \to \infty,$$

then for each fixed $\epsilon > 0$ the probability in (3) approaches 0 as n approaches infinity. For each fixed $\epsilon > 0$ we thus obtain

$$P(|\hat{\Theta} - \theta| < \epsilon) = 1 - P(|\hat{\Theta} - \theta| \geqq \epsilon) \to 1 \qquad\qquad \text{as } n \to \infty.$$

This means that for each fixed $\epsilon > 0$ (no matter how small) the probability that the approximation for θ will differ from θ by less than ϵ approaches 1 as the sample size approaches infinity. An estimator that has this property is called a **consistent estimator.** This concept was introduced by Fisher (1922, 1925) (cf. Appendix 3).

Example 1.   The estimator corresponding to (1), Sec. 11.1, is consistent for any distribution whose variance is finite. In fact, using

$$\hat{\Theta} = \bar{X} = \frac{1}{n} (X_1 + \cdots + X_n)$$

and (8) in Problem 3, Sec. 11.2, we immediately have

$$E([\hat{\Theta} - \theta]^2) = E([\bar{X} - \mu]^2) = \frac{\sigma^2}{n} \to 0 \qquad \text{as } n \to \infty.$$

We shall now prove Theorem 1.

Let X be a continuous variable with density $f(x)$. Then

$$P(|X - c| \geqq \epsilon) = \int_{|x-c| \geqq \epsilon} f(x)\, dx$$

where we integrate from $-\infty$ to $c - \epsilon$ and from $c + \epsilon$ to ∞. In these two intervals of integration,

$$|x - c| \geq \epsilon \qquad \text{and} \qquad \frac{(x - c)^2}{\epsilon^2} \geq 1.$$

Hence the value of our integral cannot exceed that of the integral

$$\int_{|x-c|\geq\epsilon} \frac{(x - c)^2}{\epsilon^2} f(x) \, dx.$$

Since the integrand is nonnegative and we integrate in the positive direction, the value of this integral cannot be greater than that of the integral

$$\frac{1}{\epsilon^2} \int_{-\infty}^{\infty} (x - c)^2 f(x) \, dx = \frac{1}{\epsilon^2} E([X - c]^2)$$

because the latter is obtained from the former by increasing the range of integration. This proves Theorem 1 for a continuous random variable. In the discrete case the proof is similar.

Problems

1. Suppose that a random variable X has variance σ^2. How large a sample must be taken in order that the probability be at least 95% that $\bar{X}$ will assume a value that deviates from the population mean by less than (a) σ, (b) $\sigma/2$, (c) $\sigma/4$? *Hint.* Use (2) and Theorem 2, Sec. 9.8.

2. How many times must a fair coin be tossed in order that the probability be at least 90% that $\bar{X}$ will assume a value between 0.4 and 0.6? Here $X = $ *number of heads in a single trial*. *Hint.* Use (2) and Theorem 2, Sec. 9.8.

3. Using the Tchebichef inequality, show that for any random variable X (whose mean and variance exist) the probability is at least 75% (88.8%) that X will assume any value between the *two-sigma limits* $\mu - 2\sigma$ and $\mu + 2\sigma$ (the *three-sigma limits* $\mu - 3\sigma$ and $\mu + 3\sigma$).

4. From (2) with $\epsilon = \sigma$ we have $P(|X - \mu| \geq \sigma) \leq 1$. Find a distribution illustrating that in the last inequality the equality sign may hold.

5. The value 75% in Problem 3 is rather conservative for most practical cases; in fact, for the normal distribution, $P(|X - \mu| < 2\sigma) = 95.5\%$, cf. Sec. 8.2. Show that, however, there are distributions for which 75% is the exact value (give an example of a discrete distribution).

6. Show that if $\hat{\Theta}$ is a consistent estimator of θ, then $k\hat{\Theta}$ ($k \neq 0$) is a consistent estimator of $k\theta$.

11.4   Probability Paper

In the case of the normal distribution we may obtain estimates of μ and σ by a graphical method, using so-called **normal probability paper.** This paper has the property that in it the s-shaped graph of the distribution function of the normal distribution becomes a straight line. The basic idea is similar to that of the logarithmic paper, with which the reader is, no doubt, familiar.

Figure 11.4.1 illustrates how the probability paper is obtained from the usual graph paper by an appropriate stretching of the scale of ordinates. That new scale is constructed by using the inverse

(1)
$$w = \Psi(y)$$

of the distribution function $y = \Phi(w)$ defined by (3), Sec. 8.2. Since the normal distribution with mean μ and standard deviation σ has the distribution function (cf. (4) in Sec. 8.2)

$$y = F(x) = \Phi\left(\frac{x - \mu}{\sigma}\right),$$

we obtain from (1) a representation of a straight line, namely,

(2)
$$w = \Psi(y) = \frac{x - \mu}{\sigma}.$$

$x = \mu$ corresponds to $w = 0$. Since $\Phi(w) = \frac{1}{2}$ when $w = 0$, we thus have the following result.

The mean μ is the abscissa of the point of intersection of the straight line (2) *and the 50%-line.*

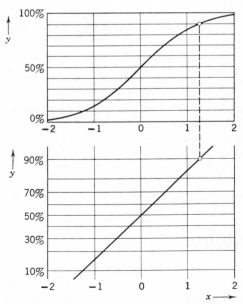

Fig. 11.4.1. Curve of the distribution function $y = \Phi(x)$ of the normal distribution with mean 0 and standard deviation 1 and corresponding straight line graphed on probability paper

Furthermore, $\Phi(1) \approx 0.84$ (cf. Table 3*a* in Appendix 4). Consequently,

$$\Phi\left(\frac{x - \mu}{\sigma}\right) \approx 0.84 \quad \text{when} \quad \frac{x - \mu}{\sigma} = 1, \quad \text{that is,} \quad x = \mu + \sigma.$$

Hence the straight line (2) *intersects the* 84%-*line approximately at the point with the abscissa* $x = \mu + \sigma$.

To determine approximate values (estimates) of μ and σ by the use of a given sample from a normal population we graph the distribution function of the sample as a step curve on probability paper. Then we draw a straight line which approximates the curve as closely as possible. This line intersects the 50%-line at a point with abscissa $x \approx \bar{x}$. This is an approximation for μ. Furthermore the standard deviation s of the sample is approximately equal to the difference of the x-values of the points of intersection with the 50%- and the 84%-lines. This is an approximation for σ.

An example is shown in Fig. 11.4.2, where $\bar{x} \approx 1.944$ and $s \approx 0.054$ (computed 0.053).

If the sample values are equally spaced (as in Table 11.4.1), we may save work by plotting merely the values of the cumulative relative frequencies as points on probability paper and fitting a straight line as best we can "by eye." From Fig. 11.4.2 it is obvious that if we would plot each value above the

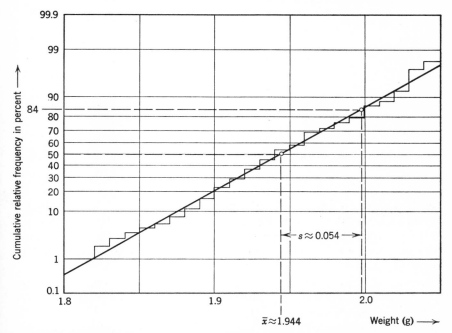

Fig. 11.4.2. Distribution function of the sample in Table 11.4.1 (see next page) graphed on probability paper

Table 11.4.1. Weight of Airmail Envelopes
(Sample of 100 Values)

Weight (in Grams)	Frequency	Cumulative Relative Frequency
1.80	1	0.01
1.81	0	0.01
1.82	1	0.02
1.83	1	0.03
1.84	1	0.04
1.85	1	0.05
1.86	1	0.06
1.87	2	0.08
1.88	3	0.11
1.89	5	0.16
1.90	7	0.23
1.91	6	0.29
1.92	8	0.37
1.93	8	0.45
1.94	9	0.54
1.95	4	0.58
1.96	11	0.69
1.97	3	0.72
1.98	4	0.76
1.99	3	0.79
2.00	7	0.86
2.01	2	0.88
2.02	4	0.92
2.03	5	0.97
2.04	1	0.98
2.05	2	1.00

corresponding x-value, we would make a systematic error because the line would lie higher than that in Fig. 11.4.2. To compensate for this effect, we plot each value above the corresponding x-value augmented by $\frac{1}{2}$ the distance between consecutive x-values. (In Table 11.4.1 this distance is 0.01.) This yields Fig. 11.4.3.

Similarly, if the sample is grouped, we graph the cumulative relative frequencies as points vertically above the right endpoints of the class intervals (not above the class marks). Then we fit a straight line to these points "by eye." An example is shown in Fig. 11.4.4, which corresponds to the grouped sample in Table 11.4.2.

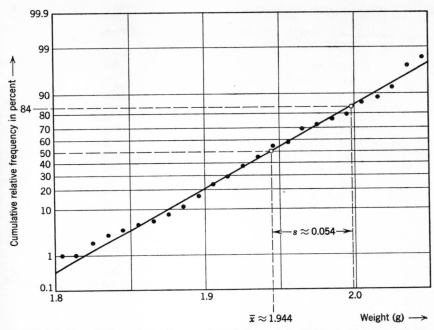

Fig. 11.4.3. Cumulative relative frequencies of the sample in Table 11.4.1 graphed on probability paper

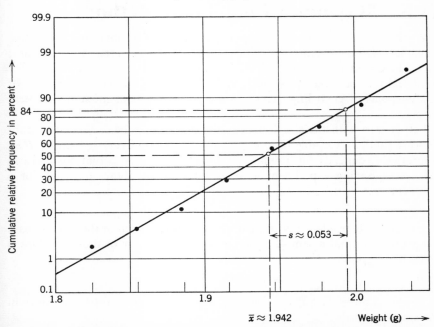

Fig. 11.4.4. Cumulative relative frequencies of the grouped sample in Table 11.4.2; note that the abscissa shows the class boundaries, not the class marks

Table 11.4.2. Sample of Table 11.4.1 in Grouped Form

Class Interval (Weight in Grams)	Class Mark	Class Frequency	Cumulative Relative Class Frequency
1.795–1.825	1.81	2	0.02
1.825–1.855	1.84	3	0.05
1.855–1.885	1.87	6	0.11
1.885–1.915	1.90	18	0.29
1.915–1.945	1.93	25	0.54
1.945–1.975	1.96	18	0.72
1.975–2.005	1.99	14	0.86
2.005–2.035	2.02	11	0.97
2.035–2.065	2.05	3	1.00

Problems

1.–3. In each case determine the sample mean and the sample variance by means of probability paper, assuming that the corresponding populations are normally distributed.

1. The sample in Problem 5, Sec. 2.1.
2. The sample in Problem 2, Sec. 2.1.
3. The sample in Problem 6, Sec. 3.3.

11.5   Maximum Likelihood Method

We shall now consider an important method for obtaining estimates, which is called the maximum likelihood method. It was used in special cases by C. F. Gauss (cf. Werke vol. 4, Göttingen, 1880). Its general form for statistical purposes was introduced by R. A. Fisher (1922) (cf. Appendix 3); this idea was of great importance to the development of modern statistical theory.

Let us start with the simplest possible case. Let X be a discrete or continuous random variable whose probability function $f(x)$ or density $f(x)$, respectively, depends on a single parameter θ. Suppose that we perform the corresponding experiment n times, so that we obtain a sample of n numbers

$$x_1, x_2, \cdots, x_n.$$

We assume independence of the n trials, as before. Then in the discrete case the probability that a sample of size n consists precisely of those n values is given by the product

(1) $$l = f(x_1)f(x_2) \cdots f(x_n).$$

In the continuous case the probability that the sample consists of values in the small intervals

$$x_1 \leqq x \leqq x_1 + \Delta x, \quad x_2 \leqq x \leqq x_2 + \Delta x, \cdots, \quad x_n \leqq x \leqq x_n + \Delta x$$

is given by the expression

(2) $$f(x_1)\, \Delta x \; f(x_2)\, \Delta x \cdots f(x_n)\, \Delta x = l(\Delta x)^n.$$

The values $f(x_1), \cdots, f(x_n)$ depend on the parameter θ. It follows that l depends on $x_1, \cdots, x_n$ and θ. We imagine that the values $x_1, \cdots, x_n$ are given and fixed. Then l is a function of θ, which is called the **likelihood function.**

The basic idea of the maximum likelihood method is very simple. We choose that approximation for the unknown value of θ for which the value of l is as large as possible. If l is a differentiable function of θ, then a necessary condition for l to have a maximum (not on the boundary) is that the first derivative with respect to θ is zero,

(3) $$\frac{\partial l}{\partial \theta} = 0.$$

Here we write *partial* derivatives because l depends also on the quantities $x_1, \cdots, x_n$ that are kept constant in our present discussion. A solution of (3) that depends on $x_1, \cdots, x_n$ is called a **maximum likelihood estimate** for the parameter θ. If in the solution we replace $x_1, \cdots, x_n$ by independent random variables $X_1, \cdots, X_n$, each of which has the distribution of X, we obtain a random variable which is called a **maximum likelihood estimator** for θ.

If the distribution involves several unknown parameters $\theta_1, \cdots, \theta_r$, then instead of the single equation (3) we have the r equations

(4) $$\frac{\partial l}{\partial \theta_1} = 0, \quad \cdots, \quad \frac{\partial l}{\partial \theta_r} = 0$$

from which we may derive estimates for those parameters.

Since $f(x)$ is nonnegative, a maximum value of l will, in general, be positive. Since the natural logarithm $\ln l$ is a monotone increasing function of l, it has a maximum precisely at the points at which l has a maximum. We may therefore use $\ln l$ instead of l and replace (3) with

(5) $$\frac{\partial \ln l}{\partial \theta} = 0$$

and (4) with

(6) $$\frac{\partial \ln l}{\partial \theta_1} = 0, \quad \cdots, \quad \frac{\partial \ln l}{\partial \theta_r} = 0.$$

This is a technical matter. The advantage is that differentiation of products is now replaced by differentiation of sums.

Nevertheless it may still be difficult to solve the resulting equation (or equations). In some practical cases the method of moments (cf. Sec. 11.1) is simpler and is then preferable.

If for a parameter there exists an efficient estimator, then it can be obtained from (5). A corresponding proof and other details about maximum likelihood estimators can be found in the book by Cramér (1961) (cf. Appendix 3), Sec. 33.2.

We should note that a maximum likelihood estimator may be biased; an illustrative example is given in the next section.

11.6   Examples of Maximum Likelihood Estimators

Example 1 (Poisson distribution).   Using a sample $x_1, \cdots, x_n$, find a maximum likelihood estimate of the parameter μ of the Poisson distribution.

From (1), Sec. 7.4, and (1), Sec. 11.5, we obtain the likelihood function

$$l = \frac{\mu^{x_1}}{x_1!} e^{-\mu} \frac{\mu^{x_2}}{x_2!} e^{-\mu} \cdots \frac{\mu^{x_n}}{x_n!} e^{-\mu}.$$

Simplifying and using (1) in Sec. 3.1, we have

$$l = \frac{1}{x_1! \cdots x_n!} \mu^{x_1 + \cdots + x_n} e^{-n\mu} = \frac{1}{x_1! \cdots x_n!} \mu^{n\bar{x}} e^{-n\mu}.$$

The natural logarithm of this function is

$$\ln l = -\ln (x_1! \cdots x_n!) + n\bar{x} \ln \mu - n\mu.$$

It follows that (5), Sec. 11.5, is of the form

$$\frac{\partial \ln l}{\partial \mu} = \frac{n\bar{x}}{\mu} - n = 0.$$

Solving for μ, we obtain the estimate

$$\hat{\mu} = \bar{x} = \frac{1}{n} (x_1 + \cdots + x_n).$$

Example 2 (Binomial distribution).   Suppose that in a certain experiment an event A has probability p which is unknown. Suppose that in 100 independent performances of the experiment the event A happened 63 times. Estimate p.

We consider the random variable

$X =$ *number of occurrences of A in a single performance of that experiment.*

Clearly X can assume the values

$$X = 0 \ (A \ does \ not \ happen) \qquad \text{and} \qquad X = 1 \ (A \ happens).$$

Hence the corresponding probability function $f(x)$ has the values

$$f(0) = P(X = 0) = 1 - p \qquad \text{and} \qquad f(1) = P(X = 1) = p.$$

In our sample of $n = 100$ values, the event A occurred $k = 63$ times whereas in the other $n - k = 37$ trials it did not occur. Consequently the likelihood function is

$$l = p^k (1 - p)^{n-k}.$$

The natural logarithm is

$$\ln l = k \ln p + (n - k) \ln (1 - p).$$

Equation (5), Sec. 11.5, thus takes the form

$$\frac{\partial \ln l}{\partial p} = \frac{k}{p} - \frac{n - k}{1 - p} = 0.$$

Solving for p, we obtain the estimate

$$\hat{p} = \frac{k}{n}.$$

This is the relative frequency of A in our series of experiments. The numerical result is $p \approx \hat{p} = 0.63$.

Example 3 (Normal distribution). Apply the maximum likelihood method to a normal random variable X with unknown mean μ and unknown variance σ^2.

X has the density (1), Sec. 8.1. From (1), Sec. 11.5, we thus obtain the likelihood function

$$l = \frac{1}{\sqrt{2\pi}\,\sigma} e^{-(x_1-\mu)^2/2\sigma^2} \cdots \frac{1}{\sqrt{2\pi}\,\sigma} e^{-(x_n-\mu)^2/2\sigma^2}$$

This can be written

$$l = \left(\frac{1}{\sqrt{2\pi}}\right)^n \left(\frac{1}{\sigma}\right)^n e^{-h}$$

where the exponent is

(1) $$h = \frac{1}{2\sigma^2} \sum_{k=1}^{n} (x_k - \mu)^2.$$

Taking logarithms, we have

(2) $$\ln l = -n \ln \sqrt{2\pi} - n \ln \sigma - h.$$

We must estimate two parameters. The corresponding two equations (6), Sec. 11.5, are obtained by differentiating (2). The first equation is $\partial \ln l/\partial \mu = 0$. Taking (1) into account, we obtain

(3) $$\frac{\partial \ln l}{\partial \mu} = -\frac{\partial h}{\partial \mu} = \frac{1}{\sigma^2} \sum_{k=1}^{n} (x_k - \mu) = 0.$$

The second equation is $\partial \ln l/\partial \sigma = 0$, written out

(4) $$\frac{\partial \ln l}{\partial \sigma} = -\frac{n}{\sigma} - \frac{\partial h}{\partial \sigma} = -\frac{n}{\sigma} + \frac{1}{\sigma^3} \sum_{k=1}^{n} (x_k - \mu)^2 = 0.$$

From (3) we obtain the equation

$$\sum_{k=1}^{n} (x_k - \mu) = \sum_{k=1}^{n} x_k - n\mu = 0.$$

We solve for μ and denote the solution by $\hat{\mu}$. This gives the estimate

(5) $$\hat{\mu} = \frac{1}{n} \sum_{k=1}^{n} x_k = \bar{x}.$$

for μ. By substituting this in (4) we readily have

$$-\frac{n}{\sigma} + \frac{1}{\sigma^3} \sum_{k=1}^{n} (x_k - \bar{x})^2 = 0.$$

Solving for σ^2 and denoting the solution by $\tilde{\sigma}^2$ [to distinguish it from (2) in Sec. 11.1], we obtain the estimate

(6) $$\tilde{\sigma}^2 = \frac{1}{n} \sum_{k=1}^{n} (x_k - \bar{x})^2.$$

Note that the corresponding estimator is not unbiased, since it differs from the unbiased estimator (5) in Sec. 11.2.

Our example shows that a maximum likelihood estimator may be biased. Nevertheless, our result is of practical interest, in particular if n is large.

Problems

1. Show that in the case of the parameters a and b of the uniform distribution (4), Sec. 5.6, the maximum of the likelihood function cannot be obtained by equating the first derivative to zero. How can we obtain the maximum in this case?

2. Find the maximum likelihood estimate for the parameter μ of a normal distribution with known variance $\sigma^2 = \sigma_0^2$.

3. If $\hat{\theta}$ is the maximum likelihood estimate of a parameter θ and $\varphi(\theta)$ is a (single-valued) monotone increasing function of θ, show that $\varphi(\hat{\theta})$ is the maximum likelihood estimate of $\varphi(\theta)$.

4. The fourth central moment of the normal distribution equals $3\sigma^4$. Using Problem 3, find the maximum likelihood estimate of that moment.

5. Let p be the probability of an event A in a random experiment and consider the random variable $X = $ *number of independent trials until A occurs*. Show that X has the probability function

$$f(x) = pq^{x-1}, \qquad q = 1 - p \qquad\qquad (x = 1, 2, \cdots)$$

and find the maximum likelihood estimate of p corresponding to a single observed value x of X.

6. Suppose that in Problem 5 a sample of n values $x_1, \cdots, x_n$ is available. Show that then the maximum likelihood estimate is

$$\hat{p} = \frac{1}{\bar{x}},$$

where $\bar{x}$ is the mean of the sample.

7. Apply the maximum likelihood method to the normal distribution with mean $\mu = 0$.

8. In Example 3, regard μ and $\tau = \sigma^2$ as the parameters. Show that the maximum likelihood estimate $\hat{\tau}$ of τ satisfies $\hat{\tau} = \hat{\sigma}^2$, so that the present result is in agreement with that in Example 3.

9. Suppose that a box contains ten balls, and let p be the proportion of balls that are red. Two balls are drawn with replacement. Find the probability function $f(x)$ of the random variable $X = $ *number of red balls drawn*. For each x that X can assume determine the value of p that maximizes $f(x)$.

10. Extend Example 2 as follows. Suppose that m times n trials were made and in the first n trials A happened k_1 times, in the second n trials A happened k_2 times, $\cdots$,

in the mth n trials A happened k_m times. Find a maximum likelihood estimate of p based on this information.

11. Consider the continuous distribution with the density $f(x) = ke^{-\theta x}$ when $x \geq 0$ and $f(x) = 0$ when $x < 0$. Determine k and find the maximum likelihood estimate of θ based on a sample of n values.

12. In Problem 11, find the mean μ, substitute it in $f(x)$, find the maximum likelihood estimate of μ, and show that it is identical with the estimate for μ which can be obtained from that for θ in Problem 11.

CHAPTER 12

Confidence Intervals

In the last chapter we have obtained formulas for approximating parameters in probability distributions. A numerical value obtained from such a formula by the use of a sample from the population is called a **point estimate** of the corresponding parameter.

For example, the sample in Table 11.4.1 has the mean $\bar{x} = 1.944$, and this is a point estimate for the mean μ of the corresponding population.

There is another type of estimate, called an **interval estimate**, which we shall now consider, starting with its general motivation.

Whenever we use mathematical approximation formulas, we should try to find out how much the approximate value can at most deviate from the unknown true value.

For example, in the case of numerical integration methods there exist "error formulas" from which we can compute the maximum possible error (that is, the difference between the approximate and the true value). Suppose that in a certain case we obtain 2.47 as an approximate value of a given integral and ± 0.02 as the maximum possible deviation of 2.47 from the unknown exact value. Then we are sure that the values

$$2.47 - 0.02 = 2.45 \qquad \text{and} \qquad 2.47 + 0.02 = 2.49$$

"*include*" the unknown exact value, that is, 2.45 is smaller than or equal to that value while 2.49 is larger than or equal to that value.

In estimating a parameter θ, the corresponding problem would be the determination of two numerical quantities that depend on the sample values and include the unknown value of the parameter with certainty. However, we already know that from a sample we cannot draw conclusions about the corresponding population that are 100% certain. So we have to be more modest and modify our problem, as follows.

Choose a probability γ close to 1 (for example, $\gamma = 95\%$, 99%, or the like). Then determine two quantities Θ_1 and Θ_2 such that the probability that Θ_1 and Θ_2 include the exact unknown value of the parameter θ is equal to γ.

Here the idea is that we replace the impossible requirement "with certainty" by the attainable requirement "with a preassigned probability close to 1."

Numerical values of those two quantities should be computed from a given sample $x_1, \cdots, x_n$. The n sample values may be regarded as observed values of n random variables $X_1, \cdots, X_n$. Then Θ_1 and Θ_2 are functions of these random variables and therefore random variables, too. Our above requirement may thus be written

$$P(\Theta_1 \leqq \theta \leqq \Theta_2) = \gamma.$$

If we know such functions Θ_1 and Θ_2 and a sample is given, we may compute a numerical value θ_1 of Θ_1 and a numerical value θ_2 of Θ_2. The interval with endpoints θ_1 and θ_2 is called a **confidence interval**[1] or *interval estimate* for the unknown parameter θ, and we shall denote it by

$$\text{CONF } \{\theta_1 \leqq \theta \leqq \theta_2\}.$$

The values θ_1 and θ_2 are called **lower** and **upper confidence limits** for θ. The number γ is called the **confidence level**. One chooses $\gamma = 95\%$, 99%, sometimes 99.9%.

Clearly, if we intend to obtain a sample and determine a corresponding confidence interval, then γ is the probability of getting an interval that will include the unknown exact value of the parameter.

For example, if we choose $\gamma = 95\%$, then we may expect that *about* 95% of the samples that we may obtain will yield confidence intervals that do include the value θ, whereas the remaining 5% do not. Hence the statement "the confidence interval includes θ" will be correct in *about* 19 out of 20 cases, while in the remaining case it will be false.

Choosing $\gamma = 99\%$ instead of 95%, we may expect that statement to be correct even in *about* 99 out of 100 cases. But we shall see later that the intervals corresponding to $\gamma = 99\%$ are longer than those corresponding to $\gamma = 95\%$. This is the disadvantage of increasing γ.

What value of γ should we choose in a concrete case? This is not a mathematical question, but one that must be answered from the viewpoint of the application, taking into account what risk of making a false statement we can afford.

It is clear that the uncertainty involved in the present method as well as in the methods yet to be discussed comes from the sampling process, so that the statistician should be prepared for his share of mistakes. However, he is no worse off than a judge or a banker, who is subject to the laws of chance. Quite the contrary, he has the advantage that he can *measure* his chances of making a mistake.

---

[1] The modern theory and terminology of confidence intervals were developed by J. Neyman (1935, 1937). For earlier results, see Wilson (1927).

In mathematics, $\theta_1 \leqq \theta \leqq \theta_2$ means that θ lies between θ_1 and θ_2, and, to avoid misunderstandings, it seems worthwhile to characterize a confidence interval by a special symbol, such as CONF.

Furthermore, we should emphasize that a confidence statement is a statement about the population under consideration, *not* about further samples to be drawn. Moreover the statement refers to the population that is actually sampled, and any claim that it applies to a more extended population rests on the judgment of the investigator or on additional information that he has.

12.1   Confidence Intervals for the Mean of a Normal Distribution Whose Variance Is Known

Let $x_1, \cdots, x_n$ be a given sample from a normally distributed population whose variance σ^2 is known. We assume that the mean μ is unknown, and we want to determine a confidence interval for μ.

This problem is of practical interest. For example, the normally distributed quantity may be a length or a diameter (of screws, bolts, or the like). Then μ depends on the particular adjustment of the machine that makes the screws, while σ depends on the precision of the machine (but not on the adjustment) and may therefore be known from previous experience. We shall return to this point in Sec. 12.3.

The steps necessary for determining a confidence interval under the above assumptions are shown in Table 12.1.1. Corresponding motivations and a mathematical justification will be given in the next section. For the time being, let us note that c in (1) is an increasing function of the confidence level γ. Hence the closer to 1 we choose γ, the longer confidence intervals we have to expect. Similarly, the sample size n appears in the denominator of k. This implies that, generally speaking, larger samples will yield shorter

Table 12.1.1. Determination of a Confidence Interval for the Mean μ of a Normal Distribution with Known Variance σ^2

1st step. Choose a confidence level γ (95%, 99%, or the like).
2nd step. Determine the corresponding c:

γ	0.90	0.95	0.99	0.999
c	1.645	1.960	2.576	3.291

3rd step. Compute the mean $\bar{x}$ of the sample $x_1, \cdots, x_n$.
4th step. Compute

(1) $$k = c\sigma/\sqrt{n}.$$

The confidence interval for the mean μ of the population is

(2)   CONF $\{\bar{x} - k \leqq \mu \leqq \bar{x} + k\}.$

[handwritten in margin:] $\alpha = 1 - \gamma$
$c = Z_{\alpha/2}$

[handwritten at bottom:] $c = .95(.1) =$

parts calc of n for γ=.99
.95

confidence intervals, that is, more precise information. This is under-standable. *Sy, b*

A simple application of the method in Table 12.1.1 is given in the following example.

Example 1. Determine a 95%-confidence interval for the mean of a normal distribution with variance $\sigma^2 = 9$, using a sample of $n = 100$ values with mean $\bar{x} = 5$.

1st step. $\gamma = 0.95$ is required.

2nd step. The corresponding c equals 1.960.   *why? (see p. 178*

3rd step. $\bar{x} = 5$ is given.

4th step.. We need

$$k = 1.960 \cdot 3/\sqrt{100} = 0.588.$$

Hence $\bar{x} - k = 4.412$ and $\bar{x} + k = 5.588$. The confidence interval is

$$\text{CONF } \{4.412 \leqq \mu \leqq 5.588\}.$$

This is sometimes written

$$\mu = 5 \pm 0.588,$$

but we shall not use this notation, which may be misleading.

We want to emphasize that, according to the explanation given in the introduction to this chapter, our result means that 4.412 and 5.588 are "observed" values of the random endpoints of an interval that includes μ with probability 0.95.

In connection with practical problems the question frequently arises of how large we should choose the sample size to obtain a certain desired precision. Too large n may mean a waste of time and money, whereas too small n may prevent us from attaining this precision; hence the question is important. The following example illustrates how to proceed.

Example 2 (*Determination of the sample size necessary for obtaining a confidence interval of prescribed length*). How large must n be in the last example if we want to obtain a 95%-confidence interval of length $L = 0.4$?

The confidence interval in Table 12.1.1 has the length

$$(3) \qquad\qquad L = 2k = 2c\sigma/\sqrt{n}.$$

Solving for n, we obtain

$$n = (2c\sigma/L)^2 = 4c^2\sigma^2/L^2.$$

Important particular cases are

$$n = \frac{15.4\sigma^2}{L^2} \qquad \text{when} \qquad \gamma = 95\%$$

and

$$n = \frac{26.5\sigma^2}{L^2} \qquad \text{when} \qquad \gamma = 99\%.$$

Since in our case, $\gamma = 95\%$, we thus calculate the numerical answer

$$n = 15.4 \cdot 9/0.16 \approx 870.$$

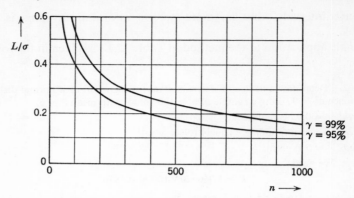

Fig. 12.1.1. Length of the confidence interval (2) (measured in multiples of σ) as a function of the sample size n

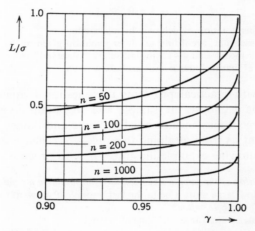

Fig. 12.1.2. Length of the confidence interval (2) (measured in multiples of σ) as a function of the confidence level γ for constant n

Figure 12.1.1 shows how L decreases as n increases. The shorter we want the confidence intervals to be, the larger the sample size n we must choose, as we mentioned before.

Figure 12.1.2 shows how L increases with increasing γ (and constant n). Clearly $L \to \infty$ as $\gamma \to 1$.

Problems

1. What 95%-confidence interval would we obtain in Example 1 if (a) $n = 10$, (b) $n = 1000$?

2. Using a sample of size $n = 36$ with mean $\bar{x} = 18.4$, determine a 99%-confidence interval for the mean of a normal distribution with variance $\sigma^2 = 1.69$.

3. Make the same determination as in Problem 2, when $\sigma^2 = 5.76$, $\bar{x} = 7.26$, and $n = 225$.

4. Use Fig. 12.1.1 or 12.1.2 for obtaining the answer to Problem 3.

5. What sample size should we choose in Example 1 if we want to obtain a 99%-confidence interval of length $L = 0.2$? *ex 2 for method*

6. Answer the same question as in Problem 5, with $L = 0.2$ replaced by $L = 0.4$.

7. What sample size would be needed to produce a 95%-confidence interval (2) of length (a) 2σ, (b) σ, (c) 0.2σ, (d) 0.02σ?

8. Let X be normal with variance $\sigma^2 = 1$. Using a sample of size 100 with mean $\bar{x} = 10$, determine a 90%-confidence interval (a) using Table 12.1.1, (b) using Tchebichef's inequality in Sec. 11.3 and Theorem 2 in Sec. 9.8. Compare the results. Give reasons why the interval in (b) is longer than that in (a).

9. Show that the ratio of the lengths of the two confidence intervals in Problem 8 is independent of σ and n but depends only on the confidence level γ. Find and graph the ratio for $\gamma = 0.9, 0.95, 0.99$, and 0.999.

10. Suppose that in a standard process of making string, the breaking strength is a normal random variable with mean 100 lb and standard deviation 5 lb. Suppose that we shall introduce a proposed new process provided the mean breaking strength will be higher by at least 10%. Assuming that in the new process the breaking strength is normal with about the same standard deviation as in the old process, what sample size should we choose in the examination of the new process if we want the probability to be only 5% that we shall not adopt the new process although it produces string with mean breaking strength 111 lb?

11. Using a single observed value x_1, find a 99%-confidence interval for the mean μ of a normally distributed population with variance σ^2 and explain the relation between the result and formula (7b) in Sec. 8.2.

12. Why are interval estimates in most cases more useful than point estimates?

12.2 ~~omit~~ Sum of Normal Random Variables. Theory Corresponding to Sec. 12.1

We shall first prove some general theorems about properties of normal random variables and then derive from these theorems a justification of the method for obtaining confidence intervals given in Table 12.1.1.

Theorem 1 (Sum of independent normal random variables).　*Let $X_1, X_2, \cdots, X_n$ be independent normal random variables with means $\mu_1, \mu_2, \cdots, \mu_n$ and variances $\sigma_1^2, \sigma_2^2, \cdots, \sigma_n^2$, respectively. Then the random variable*

$$X = X_1 + X_2 + \cdots + X_n$$

is normal with mean

$$\mu = \mu_1 + \mu_2 + \cdots + \mu_n$$

and variance

$$\sigma^2 = \sigma_1^2 + \sigma_2^2 + \cdots + \sigma_n^2.$$

Proof.　The formulas for μ and σ^2 follow immediately from Theorem 1, Sec. 9.7, and Theorem 1, Sec. 9.8. We show that X is normal, proceeding by induction, as follows.

Let $n = 2$. Then $X = X_1 + X_2$. By assumption, X_1 has the density

$$f_1(x) = \frac{1}{\sqrt{2\pi}\,\sigma_1} \exp\left[-\frac{1}{2}\left(\frac{x-\mu_1}{\sigma_1}\right)^2\right],$$

where exp z means e^z, and X_2 has the density

$$f_2(x) = \frac{1}{\sqrt{2\pi}\,\sigma_2} \exp\left[-\frac{1}{2}\left(\frac{x-\mu_2}{\sigma_2}\right)^2\right].$$

From this and (5a) in the problem set of Sec. 9.6 it follows that $X = X_1 + X_2$ has the density

$$f(x) = \int_{-\infty}^{\infty} f_1(x-y)f_2(y)\,dy = \frac{1}{2\pi\sigma_1\sigma_2}\int_{-\infty}^{\infty} e^{-V/2}\,dy,$$

where

$$V = \left(\frac{x-y-\mu_1}{\sigma_1}\right)^2 + \left(\frac{y-\mu_2}{\sigma_2}\right)^2.$$

The reader may verify by straightforward calculation that V can be written $V = V_1^2 + V_2^2$ where

(1) $V_1 = \dfrac{\sigma}{\sigma_1\sigma_2}\left(y - \dfrac{\sigma_1^2\mu_2 + \sigma_2^2(x-\mu_1)}{\sigma^2}\right)$ and $V_2 = \dfrac{x-\mu}{\sigma}$

and

$$\mu = \mu_1 + \mu_2, \qquad \sigma^2 = \sigma_1^2 + \sigma_2^2.$$

Since V_2 does not depend on y, we may take a factor out from under the integral sign, finding

$$f(x) = \frac{1}{2\pi\sigma_1\sigma_2} e^{-V_2^2/2}\int_{-\infty}^{\infty} e^{-V_1^2/2}\,dy.$$

We now introduce $\tau = V_1$ as a new variable of integration. From (1) we see that $d\tau/dy = \sigma/\sigma_1\sigma_2$ and $dy = (\sigma_1\sigma_2/\sigma)\,d\tau$. Thus

$$f(x) = \frac{1}{2\pi\sigma} e^{-V_2^2/2}\int_{-\infty}^{\infty} e^{-\tau^2/2}\,d\tau.$$

From the formulas (3) and (8) in Sec. 8.2 it follows that the remaining integral has the value $\sqrt{2\pi}$. If we write out V_2, our result is

$$f(x) = \frac{1}{\sqrt{2\pi}\,\sigma} \exp\left[-\frac{1}{2}\left(\frac{x-\mu}{\sigma}\right)^2\right].$$

This completes the proof when $n = 2$.

We now make the induction hypothesis that X with any $n = k\ (\geq 2)$ is normal, that is,

$$Y_1 = X_1 + \cdots + X_k$$

is normal. Then from what we proved it follows that $X = Y_1 + Y_2$, where $Y_2 = X_{k+1}$, is normal. This completes the proof of Theorem 1.

Theorem 2.   *If $X_1, \cdots, X_n$ are independent normal random variables each of which has mean μ and variance σ^2, then*

$$(2) \qquad \bar{X} = \frac{1}{n}(X_1 + \cdots + X_n)$$

is normal with mean μ and variance σ^2/n.

Proof.   From Theorem 1 we see that under our present assumptions the random variable $X = X_1 + X_2 + \cdots + X_n$ is normal. Hence, by Theorem 1 in Sec. 8.3, the random variable $\bar{X} = X/n$ is normal. The statement about the mean of $\bar{X}$ follows from Theorem 1, this section, and (2) in Sec. 6.7. The expression for the variance of $\bar{X}$ follows from Theorem 2 in Sec. 9.8. This proves Theorem 2.

Theorem 3.   *Under the assumptions of Theorem 2 the random variable*

$$(3) \qquad Z = \sqrt{n}\,\frac{\bar{X} - \mu}{\sigma}$$

is normal with mean 0 and variance 1.

Proof.   We see that Z is of the form

$$Z = c_1\bar{X} + c_2 \qquad \text{where} \qquad c_1 = \frac{\sqrt{n}}{\sigma}, \qquad c_2 = -\frac{\sqrt{n}\,\mu}{\sigma}.$$

Since $\bar{X}$ is normal with mean μ and variance $\sigma_{\bar{X}}^2 = \sigma^2/n$ (cf. Theorem 2), it follows from Theorem 1 in Sec. 8.3 that Z is normal with mean

$$c_1\mu + c_2 = \frac{\sqrt{n}}{\sigma}\mu - \frac{\sqrt{n}\,\mu}{\sigma} = 0$$

and variance

$$c_1^2\sigma_{\bar{X}}^2 = \left(\frac{\sqrt{n}}{\sigma}\right)^2\frac{\sigma^2}{n} = 1.$$

This completes the proof.

We shall now apply these theorems to give theoretical support to the steps in Table 12.1.1. The motivation for confidence intervals was given in the introduction to this chapter (see p. 168), and the student is advised to read once more those general ideas before continuing this discussion.

Let us now explain how we can derive the procedure in Table 12.1.1. Suppose that $x_1, \cdots, x_n$ is a sample from a normally distributed population with mean μ and variance σ^2. We may regard[2] the n sample values as n single observations of n random variables $X_1, \cdots, X_n$ which are independent

---

[2] Cf. also Sec. 11.2, where a similar idea was first used.

and have the same distribution, namely, the normal distribution with mean μ and variance σ^2. Hence these variables satisfy the assumptions in Theorems 2 and 3, so that $\bar{X}$ is normal with mean μ and variance σ^2/n, and Z in (3) is normal with mean 0 and variance 1. Clearly the sample mean $\bar{x}$ is an observed value of $\bar{X}$. Our goal is to find two random variables Θ_1 and Θ_2 such that

$$(4) \qquad\qquad P(\Theta_1 \leqq \mu \leqq \Theta_2) = \gamma,$$

where γ is chosen, and the sample gives observed values θ_1 and θ_2 of Θ_1 and Θ_2, respectively, which then yield a confidence interval

$$\text{CONF } \{\theta_1 \leqq \mu \leqq \theta_2\}.$$

In the present situation (4) will be obtained as follows. Using Theorem 3, we may first determine c from Table 3b in Appendix 4 so that

$$(5) \qquad\qquad P(-c \leqq Z \leqq c) = \gamma,$$

where Z is given by (3). (When $\gamma = 0.90, 0.95$, etc., we obtain the values c in Table 12.1.1.) The inequality $-c \leqq Z \leqq c$ in (5), when written out, is

$$-c \leqq \sqrt{n}\,\frac{\bar{X} - \mu}{\sigma} \leqq c.$$

We convert it into an inequality for μ. Multiplying by the positive number $\sigma/\sqrt{n}$, we have

$$(6) \qquad\qquad -k \leqq \bar{X} - \mu \leqq k \qquad \text{where} \qquad k = c\sigma/\sqrt{n}.$$

Multiplication by the negative number -1 reverses the inequality signs. Thus

$$k \geqq \mu - \bar{X} \geqq -k.$$

Adding $\bar{X}$, we obtain finally

$$(7) \qquad\qquad \bar{X} + k \geqq \mu \geqq \bar{X} - k.$$

Consequently, we may write (5) in the form

$$P(\bar{X} - k \leqq \mu \leqq \bar{X} + k) = \gamma.$$

This is of the form (4) with $\Theta_1 = \bar{X} - k$, $\Theta_2 = \bar{X} + k$. Under our assumptions it means that with probability γ the random variables $\bar{X} - k$ and $\bar{X} + k$ will assume values that include the unknown mean μ. Here $\bar{X}$ is given by (2), and k is given in (6). Hence by substituting the observed value $\bar{x}$ of $\bar{X}$ we obtain the desired confidence interval

$$\text{CONF } \{\bar{x} - k \leqq \mu \leqq \bar{x} + k\},$$

and we see that this is identical with (2) in Table 12.1.1.

This result may be summarized as follows.

Theorem 4.   *If $\bar{x}$ is the mean of a sample of size n from a normally distributed population with (unknown) mean μ and known variance σ^2, then (2) in Table 12.1.1 with k given by (1) in that table is a $100\gamma\%$-confidence interval for μ.*

Problems

1. If X is normal with mean 4 and variance 25, what distributions do $2X$, $-X$, and $3X - 12$ have?

2. If X_1 and X_2 are normal with mean 6 and -2 and variance 1 and 16, respectively, and are independent, what distributions do $X_1 + X_2$, $X_1 - X_2$, and $4X_1 - X_2$ have?

3. A machine fills boxes weighing Y lb with X lb of salt, where X and Y are normal with mean 100 lb and 5 lb and standard deviation 1 lb and 0.5 lb, respectively. What percent of filled boxes weighing between 104 lb and 106 lb are to be expected?

4. The filled boxes in Problem 3 are delivered in containers of 100 boxes each. If the weight of the empty containers is normal with mean 500 lb and standard deviation 10 lb, what is the distribution of the weight of the packed containers?

5. Suppose that certain elements in an electric network are protected against excess voltage by means of two relays R_1 and R_2 which are adjusted to be released X_1 and X_2 seconds, respectively, after the beginning of excess voltage. These release periods vary because of small uncontrollable factors, and we assume that X_1 and X_2 are independent normal random variables with means $\mu_1 = 1$ sec and μ_2 (*mean release times*) and variance $\sigma_1{}^2 = \sigma_2{}^2 = 0.1$ sec^2. How must we choose μ_2 in order that μ_2 be as small as possible, but so that R_2 is released earlier than R_1 in at most 1 of 1000 cases?

6. What is the distribution of the thickness of the core of a transformer consisting of 50 layers of sheet metal and 49 insulating paper layers if the thickness X of a single metal sheet is normal with mean 0.5 mm and standard deviation 0.05 mm and the thickness Y of a paper layer is normal with mean 0.05 mm and standard deviation 0.02 mm?

7. The confidence interval (2) in Sec. 12.1 may be regarded as a special case of a more general confidence interval which is obtained if we replace (5) by

   (8) $$P(-c_1 \leqq Z \leqq c_2) = \gamma.$$

   Show that this more general confidence interval is of the form

   (9) $$\text{CONF}\left\{\bar{x} - c_2 \frac{\sigma}{\sqrt{n}} \leqq \mu \leqq \bar{x} + c_1 \frac{\sigma}{\sqrt{n}}\right\};$$

   here c_1 is chosen and the corresponding c_2 is then determined from Table 3b in Appendix 4.

8. If we choose c_1 in (8) too small, we do not obtain a corresponding c_2. Why? What is the smallest possible c_1 if $\gamma = 0.99$?

9. Using the sample in Example 1, Sec. 12.1, determine a confidence interval (9) with $\gamma = 0.95$ and $c_1 = 2.5$.

10. Using the sample in Example 1, Sec. 12.1, determine a 90%-confidence interval (9) with the right endpoint 7.7.

11. Show that (2), Sec. 12.1, is the interval of minimum length among all the intervals (9) with the same γ, σ, and n.

12. Show that (5) is equivalent to $\Phi(c) = (1 + \gamma)/2$.

13. In fitting bushings to shafts, suppose we know that the diameter X of shafts is normal with mean 1.00 in. and standard deviation 0.01 in., and the inner diameter Y of bushings is normal with mean 1.01 in. and standard deviation 0.01 in. Suppose that a bushing fits a shaft satisfactorily if its diameter exceeds that of the shaft by

at least 0.002 in. but at most 0.018 in. Assuming that X and Y are independent, find the probability that a randomly chosen shaft and bushing will fit satisfactorily.

14. Let X have the density $f(x) = \theta e^{-\theta x}$ when $x > 0$ and zero elsewhere. Set up a $100\gamma\%$-confidence interval for θ based on a single observed value of X.

15. An analogue of Theorem 1 for the Poisson distribution is that if X_1 and X_2 are independent and have a Poisson distribution with parameters μ_1 and μ_2, respectively, then $Y = X_1 + X_2$ has a Poisson distribution with the parameter $\mu = \mu_1 + \mu_2$. Prove this theorem. Using induction, extend it to n independent variables $X_1, \cdots, X_n$.

12.3 Confidence Intervals for the Mean of a Normal Distribution with Unknown Variance

From Sec. 12.1 we know how to obtain a confidence interval for the mean μ of a normal distribution if the variance σ^2 of the distribution is known. However, if σ^2 is not known, the situation changes, and we can no longer

Table 12.3.1. Determination of a Confidence Interval for the Mean μ of a Normal Distribution with Unknown Variance

1st step. Choose a confidence level γ (95%, 99%, or the like).
2nd step. Determine the solution c of the equation

(1) $$F(c) = \tfrac{1}{2}(1 + \gamma)$$

from the table of the t-distribution with $n - 1$ degrees of freedom (Table 8 in Appendix 4; $n =$ sample size). Compute $c/\sqrt{n}$. For $\gamma = 0.95$ and 0.99 and some values of n the values of $c/\sqrt{n}$ are as follows.

n	$c/\sqrt{n}$ when $\gamma=0.95$	$\gamma=0.99$	n	$c/\sqrt{n}$ when $\gamma=0.95$	$\gamma=0.99$	n	$c/\sqrt{n}$ when $\gamma=0.95$	$\gamma=0.99$
2	8.99	45.0	8	0.836	1.24	30	0.373	0.503
3	2.48	5.73	9	0.769	1.12	40	0.320	0.428
4	1.59	2.92	10	0.715	1.03	50	0.284	0.379
5	1.24	2.06	15	0.554	0.769	100	0.198	0.263
6	1.05	1.65	20	0.468	0.640	200	0.139	0.184
7	0.925	1.40	25	0.413	0.559	500	0.088	0.116

3rd step. Compute the mean $\bar{x}$ and the variance s^2 of the sample $x_1, \cdots, x_n$.
4th step. Compute

(2) $$k = sc/\sqrt{n}.$$

The confidence interval is

(3) $$\text{CONF}\ \{\bar{x} - k \leq \mu \leq \bar{x} + k\}.$$

apply the method given in Table 12.1.1. The procedure in this case is shown in Table 12.3.1. The corresponding theoretical derivation will be presented in the next section. Since we now use less information than in Sec. 12.1, we should expect slightly longer confidence intervals, whose length depends on the sample size (cf. Fig. 12.3.1). We shall return to this point later in this section.

Example 1. Using the sample in Table 11.4.1, determine a 99%-confidence interval for the mean μ of the corresponding population. Assume that the population is normally distributed. (This assumption will be justified later, in Problem 1, Sec. 15.4.)

1st step. $\gamma = 0.99$ is required.

2nd step. Since $n = 100$, we have $c/\sqrt{n} = 0.263$. $.995$

3rd step. We compute

$$\bar{x} = 1.944, \quad s^2 = 0.00282, \quad s = 0.053.$$

(Note that the values in Fig. 11.4.2 are rather accurate.)

4th step. We finally obtain

$$k = 0.053 \cdot 0.263 = 0.014.$$

Since $1.944 - 0.014 = 1.930$ and $1.944 + 0.014 = 1.958$, the confidence interval is

$$\text{CONF}\,\{1.930 \leqq \mu \leqq 1.958\}.$$

To $n = 100$ there correspond $c/\sqrt{n} = 0.198$ and 0.263 in Table 12.3.1. Hence $c = 1.98$ and 2.63. These values differ very little from the values $c = 1.96$ and 2.58, respectively, corresponding to $n \to \infty$. The latter also appear in Table 12.1.1 because, as n approaches infinity, the distribution function of the t-distribution approaches the distribution function of the normal distribution with mean 0 and variance 1. This has a practical consequence, as follows.

If the sample size is large, then s differs so little from σ that we obtain practically the same confidence interval for μ no matter whether we use

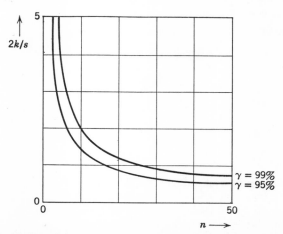

Fig. 12.3.1. Length of the confidence interval (3) measured in multiples of s

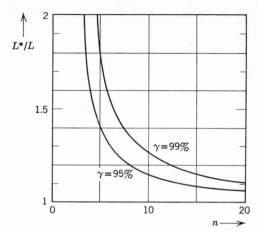

Fig. 12.3.2. Ratio of the lengths L^* and L of the confidence intervals (3), this section, and (2), Sec. 12.1, as a function of the sample size n for equal s and σ

Table 12.3.1 or whether we use Table 12.1.1 and assume σ to be known and equal to s. However, for small n the situation is quite different. In fact, Fig. 12.3.2 shows that the intervals obtained from Table 12.3.1 are then much longer than those obtained from Table 12.1.1 with s used in place of the unknown σ, and (1) in Sec. 12.1 is no longer a useful approximation of (2) in the present section.

Problems

1.–7. Assuming that the populations corresponding to the following samples are normally distributed, determine a 95%-confidence interval for the mean μ.

1. Content of nitrogen of steel (in percent)

$$0.74 \quad 0.75 \quad 0.73 \quad 0.75 \quad 0.74 \quad 0.72$$

2. Density of coke (in grams/centimeter^3)

$$1.40 \quad 1.45 \quad 1.39 \quad 1.44 \quad 1.38$$

3. Weight of duplicating paper (in grams)

$$4.3 \quad 4.5 \quad 4.2 \quad 4.3 \quad 4.3 \quad 4.7 \quad 4.4 \quad 4.2 \quad 4.3 \quad 4.5$$

4. Length of matches (in millimeters)

$$44.3 \quad 44.2 \quad 44.3 \quad 44.2 \quad 44.6 \quad 44.4 \quad 44.7 \quad 44.3 \quad 44.5 \quad 43.9$$

5. The sample in Table 3.3.3.

6. The sample in Problem 2, Sec. 2.3.

7. The sample in Table 12.3.2.

8. The confidence interval in Problem 3 has length 0.24. What sample size should we choose (approximately) if we want to obtain an interval of length 0.10?

9. For what n is the 95%-confidence interval (3) with $s = s_0$ 20% longer than the 95% confidence interval (2), Sec. 12.1, with $\sigma = s_0$?

Table 12.3.2. Weight x (in Grams) of Brain of Female White Mice [$A(x)$ = Frequency]

x	$A(x)$	x	$A(x)$	x	$A(x)$	x	$A(x)$
0.36	1	0.41	6	0.46	9	0.51	2
0.37	1	0.42	12	0.47	7	0.52	1
0.38	1	0.43	12	0.48	6	0.53	0
0.39	3	0.44	14	0.49	5	0.54	2
0.40	4	0.45	9	0.50	3	0.55	0

10. The variance (5), Sec. 10.3, of the t-distribution is greater than 1. Does this imply that for any finite n the interval (3) with $s = s_0$ must be longer than the interval (2), Sec. 12.1, with the same n, γ, and $\sigma = s_0$?

11. Find a 95%-confidence interval for the mean of a normal random variable, using a sample of 4 values with mean $\bar{x} = 10$ and standard deviation $s = 2$. To see the effect of the small sample size, compare the result with that obtained from Table 12.1.1 in the case $\bar{x} = 10$, $n = 4$, and known standard deviation $\sigma = 2$.

12. For what sample size in Problem 11 will the lengths of the two intervals differ by (a) 10%, (b) 1% of the length of the interval obtained from Table 12.1.1?

13. Are there sample sizes for which the 95%- and 99%-confidence intervals (3) are twice as long, for the same $s/\sqrt{n}$, as with very large samples?

14. Find a 95%-confidence interval for the breaking strength of cables, assuming normality and using a sample of 200 values of breaking strength with mean 452 lb and standard deviation 21 lb.

15. In a sample of a day's work for each of 25 men engaged in repetitive work, the average number of errors was 2.42 with a sample variance of 0.25. Assuming normality, determine a 95%-confidence interval for the corresponding population mean.

16. A sample of diameters of 20 ball bearings has mean 0.800 in. and standard deviation 0.002 in. Assuming normality, find a 95%-confidence interval for the mean μ of the corresponding population.

12.4 Derivation of the Confidence Interval (3) in Sec. 12.3

The theory underlying Table 12.3.1 results from the following theorem.

Theorem 1. *Let $X_1, \cdots, X_n$ be independent normal random variables with the same mean μ and the same variance σ^2. Then the variables*

(1) $$Z = \sqrt{n}\,\frac{\bar{X} - \mu}{\sigma} \qquad where \qquad \bar{X} = \frac{1}{n}(X_1 + \cdots + X_n)$$

and

(2) $$Y = \frac{1}{\sigma^2}\sum_{j=1}^{n}(X_j - \bar{X})^2$$

are independent, and Y has a chi-square distribution with n − 1 degrees of freedom.

The proof of this theorem is included in Appendix 1.

We consider the variable

$$(3) \qquad\qquad T = \frac{Z}{\sqrt{Y/(n-1)}}$$

where Y and Z are the variables in Theorem 1. The variable T is of the same form as (1) in Sec. 10.3 with Z instead of X and $n - 1$ instead of n. From Theorems 3, Sec. 12.2, and 1, this section, we see that Z and Y satisfy the assumptions made in connection with (1), Sec. 10.3. We thus obtain the following result.

Theorem 2.   *Under the assumptions in Theorem 1 the random variable* (3) *has a t-distribution with n − 1 degrees of freedom.*

We shall now derive the confidence interval (3) in the previous section. Our reasoning will be similar to that in the second half of Sec. 12.2.

We first note that if we substitute (1) and (2) in (3), then σ drops out and T takes the form

$$(4) \qquad\qquad T = \sqrt{n}\,\frac{\bar{X} - \mu}{S}$$

where

$$(5) \qquad\qquad S^2 = \frac{1}{n-1}\sum_{j=1}^{n}(X_j - \bar{X})^2.$$

As in Sec. 12.2, we may regard the n values of a sample $x_1, \cdots, x_n$ from a normally distributed population with mean μ and variance σ^2 as n single observed values of n independent random variables $X_1, \cdots, X_n$ each of which is normal with mean μ and variance σ^2. Then the sample mean $\bar{x}$ may be regarded as an observed value of $\bar{X}$ in (4) and the sample variance s^2 may be regarded as an observed value of S^2, cf. (5).

As in Sec. 12.2, we have to find two random variables Θ_1 and Θ_2 such that

$$(6) \qquad\qquad P(\Theta_1 \leqq \mu \leqq \Theta_2) = \gamma,$$

where γ is chosen, and the sample gives observed values θ_1 and θ_2 of Θ_1 and Θ_2, respectively, which then yield a confidence interval

$$\mathrm{CONF}\ \{\theta_1 \leqq \mu \leqq \theta_2\}.$$

For this purpose it is natural to consider T given by (4), because T involves $\bar{X}$ and S, for which we have observed values, and μ, the quantity for which we want to obtain a confidence interval. Since under our assumptions T has a t-distribution with $n - 1$ degrees of freedom, we may use the table of the t-distribution (Table 8 in Appendix 4) with $n - 1$ degrees of freedom and determine a number c such that

(7) $$P(-c \leq T \leq c) = F(c) - F(-c) = \gamma.$$

Since the t-distribution is symmetric, $F(-c) = 1 - F(c)$, and (7) takes the form

$$P(-c \leq T \leq c) = 2F(c) - 1 = \gamma.$$

Hence

$$F(c) = \tfrac{1}{2}(1 + \gamma),$$

which is identical with (1) in the previous section. We may now write out the inequality $-c \leq T \leq c$ in (7); using (4), we have

$$-c \leq \sqrt{n}\,\frac{\bar{X} - \mu}{S} \leq c.$$

Converting this into an inequality for μ, we obtain

$$\bar{X} - K \leq \mu \leq \bar{X} + K \qquad \text{where} \qquad K = cS/\sqrt{n}.$$

Consequently, we may write (7) in the form

$$P(\bar{X} - K \leq \mu \leq \bar{X} + K) = \gamma.$$

This is of the form (6) with $\Theta_1 = \bar{X} - K$ and $\Theta_2 = \bar{X} + K$ and means that, under our assumptions, with probability γ the random variables $\bar{X} - K$ and $\bar{X} + K$ will assume values that include the unknown μ. An observed value of $\bar{X}$ is $\bar{x}$, and an observed value of $K = cS/\sqrt{n}$ is $k = cs/\sqrt{n}$, and by substituting these values we obtain the desired confidence interval

$$\text{CONF } \{\bar{x} - k \leq \mu \leq \bar{x} + k\} \qquad\qquad (k = sc/\sqrt{n}).$$

We see that this is identical with (3) in the previous section. This completes the derivation, and we may summarize our result as follows.

Theorem 3. *If $\bar{x}$ and s are the mean and standard deviation of a sample of size n from a normally distributed population with (unknown) mean μ and (unknown) variance σ^2, then (3) in Table 12.3.1 with k given by (2) and c given by (1) in that table is a $100\gamma\%$-confidence interval for μ.*

The reader will note that the present derivation parallels that in Sec. 12.2 and the role of T corresponds to that of Z in that section. The derivation of other confidence intervals in the next sections will also be rather similar to the present one.

Problems

1. Find the probability that samples of size 20 from a normally distributed population will have a value of $t = \sqrt{20}\,(\bar{x} - \mu)/s$ between -2.09 and 2.09.

2. Find the probability that samples of size 5 from a normally distributed population will have a value of $t = \sqrt{5}\,(\bar{x} - \mu)/s$ smaller than -2.13.

3. What size of sample would have $|t| = \sqrt{n}\,|\bar{x} - \mu|/s > 2.10$ in 5% of all samples from a normal population?

4. What value of $t = \sqrt{n}\,(\bar{x} - \mu)/s$ would be exceeded in 5% of all samples of size 200 from a normal population?

5. Let $X_1, \cdots, X_n$ be independent normal random variables with the same mean and the same variance. Using Theorem 1, show that $S = \sqrt{S^2}$ [cf. (5)] has the distribution function

$$F(s) = 2^{-(n-1)/2}\left(\Gamma\left(\frac{n-1}{2}\right)\right)^{-1}\int_0^a u^{(n-3)/2}e^{-u/2}\,du,$$

where $a = (n-1)s^2/\sigma^2$, and the density

$$f(s) = 2\left(\frac{n-1}{2\sigma^2}\right)^{(n-1)/2}\left(\Gamma\left(\frac{n-1}{2}\right)\right)^{-1}s^{n-2}e^{-a/2}$$

6. Using $f(s)$ in Problem 5, show that if $X_1, \cdots, X_n$ are independent normal random variables with variance σ^2, then S has the mean

$$E(S) = \sqrt{\frac{2}{n-1}}\,\sigma\,\Gamma\left(\frac{n}{2}\right)\Big/\Gamma\left(\frac{n-1}{2}\right).$$

12.5   Confidence Intervals for the Variance of the Normal Distribution

In the preceding sections we presented methods for determining confidence intervals for the mean μ of the normal distribution, distinguishing between the case when the variance σ^2 is known (Sec. 12.1) and the case when σ^2 is not known (Sec. 12.3). Let us now turn to confidence intervals for the variance σ^2 of the normal distribution. Table 12.5.1 shows how to proceed. The mean μ of the distribution need not be known. We shall first give an application and then a derivation of the method.

Fig. 12.5.1 shows the length of the confidence interval (3), measured in multiples of the variance of the sample. It illustrates that large samples tend to produce short intervals.

Example 1. Using the sample in Table 11.4.1, determine a 95%-confidence interval of the variance of the corresponding population, assuming that the population is normally distributed. (This assumption will be justified later, in Problem 1 of Sec. 15.4.)

1st step. $\gamma = 0.95$ is required.

2nd step. Since $n = 100$, we have $c_1 = 73.4$ and $c_2 = 128$.

3rd step. From Table 11.4.1 we compute

$$(n-1)s^2 = 99s^2 = 0.2794.$$

4th step. The confidence interval is

$$\text{CONF } \{0.0021 \leq \sigma^2 \leq 0.0039\}.$$

We shall now justify the method in Table 12.5.1. This will be similar to

Table 12.5.1. Determination of a Confidence Interval for the Variance σ^2 of the Normal Distribution

---

1st step. Choose a confidence level γ (95%, 99%, or the like).

2nd step. Determine solutions c_1 and c_2 of the equations

(1) $$F(c_1) = \tfrac{1}{2}(1 - \gamma), \qquad F(c_2) = \tfrac{1}{2}(1 + \gamma)$$

from the table of the chi-square distribution with $n - 1$ degrees of freedom (Table 6 in Appendix 4, $n =$ size of sample). For $\gamma = 0.95$ and 0.99 and some values of n, the values of c_1 and c_2 are as follows.

n	$\gamma = 0.95$		$\gamma = 0.99$		n	$\gamma = 0.95$		$\gamma = 0.99$	
	c_1	c_2	c_1	c_2		c_1	c_2	c_1	c_2
2	0.00	5.02	0.00	7.88	10	2.70	19.0	1.73	23.6
3	0.05	7.38	0.01	10.6	15	5.63	26.1	4.07	31.3
4	0.22	9.35	0.07	12.8	20	8.91	32.9	6.84	38.6
5	0.48	11.1	0.21	14.9	25	12.4	39.4	9.89	45.6
6	0.83	12.8	0.41	16.7	30	16.0	45.7	13.1	52.3
7	1.24	14.4	0.68	18.5	40	23.7	58.1	20.0	65.5
8	1.69	16.0	0.99	20.3	50	31.6	70.2	27.2	78.2
9	2.18	17.5	1.34	22.0	100	73.4	128	66.5	139

3rd step. Compute $(n - 1)s^2$ where s^2 is the variance of the sample $x_1, \cdots, x_n$.

4th step. Compute

(2) $$k_1 = (n - 1)s^2/c_1 \qquad \text{and} \qquad k_2 = (n - 1)s^2/c_2.$$

The confidence interval is

(3) $$\text{CONF } \{k_2 \leqq \sigma^2 \leqq k_1\}.$$

---

the derivations in Secs. 12.2 and 12.4. As in those sections, we may regard the n values of a sample $x_1, \cdots, x_n$ from a normally distributed population with mean μ and variance σ^2 as n single observed values of n independent random variables $X_1, \cdots, X_n$ each of which is normal with mean μ and variance σ^2. Then the sample variance s^2 may be regarded as an observed value of the random variable

(4) $$S^2 = \frac{1}{n - 1} \sum_{j=1}^{n}(X_j - \bar{X})^2 \qquad \left[\bar{X} = \frac{1}{n}(X_1 + \cdots + X_n) \right],$$

which was already used in the preceding section. To obtain a confidence interval for the variance σ^2, we must find two random variables Θ_1 and Θ_2,

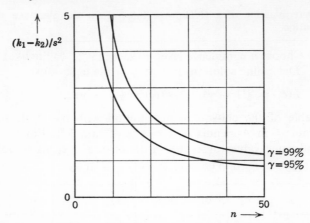

Fig. 12.5.1. Length of the confidence interval (3) for the variance σ^2, measured in multiples of s^2, as a function of the sample size n

so that

(5) $$P(\Theta_1 \leq \sigma^2 \leq \Theta_2) = \gamma,$$

where γ is chosen, and the sample gives observed values θ_1 and θ_2 of Θ_1 and Θ_2, respectively, which then yield a confidence interval

$$\text{CONF } \{\theta_1 \leq \sigma^2 \leq \theta_2\}.$$

For this purpose it is natural to consider the random variable

$$Y = \frac{1}{\sigma^2} \sum_{j=1}^{n} (X_j - \bar{X})^2$$

appearing in Theorem 1 of the preceding section. In fact, using (4), we may write

(6) $$Y = (n-1)\frac{S^2}{\sigma^2}$$

and we see that Y involves S^2, for which we have available the observed value s^2, and σ^2, for which we want to find a confidence interval. Moreover, Theorem 1 in Sec. 12.4 implies that under our present assumptions, Y has a chi-square distribution with $n-1$ degrees of freedom. Hence from the table of the chi-square distribution (Table 6 in Appendix 4) with $n-1$ degrees of freedom we may determine two numbers c_1 and c_2 so that

(7)
(a) $P(Y \leq c_1) = F(c_1) = \frac{1}{2}(1 - \gamma)$
(b) $P(Y \leq c_2) = F(c_2) = \frac{1}{2}(1 + \gamma).$

Subtraction gives

(8) $$P(c_1 \leq Y \leq c_2) = P(Y \leq c_2) - P(Y \leq c_1) = \gamma.$$

By inserting (6) into the inequality $c_1 \leq Y \leq c_2$ we first have

$$c_1 \leq (n-1)\frac{S^2}{\sigma^2} \leq c_2,$$

and we may convert this into an inequality for σ^2, finding

$$\frac{n-1}{c_2} S^2 \leq \sigma^2 \leq \frac{n-1}{c_1} S^2.$$

Hence (8) may be written

$$P\left(\frac{n-1}{c_2} S^2 \leq \sigma^2 \leq \frac{n-1}{c_1} S^2\right) = \gamma.$$

This is of the form (5) with

(9) $\Theta_1 = \dfrac{n-1}{c_2} S^2$ and $\Theta_2 = \dfrac{n-1}{c_1} S^2$

and means that, under our assumptions, with probability γ these two random variables (9) will assume values that include the unknown variance σ^2. An observed value of S^2 is s^2, and by inserting it we obtain the desired confidence interval

$$\mathrm{CONF}\left\{\frac{n-1}{c_2} s^2 \leq \sigma^2 \leq \frac{n-1}{c_1} s^2\right\}.$$

We see that this is identical with (3), and we may summarize our result as follows.

Theorem 1.   *If s^2 is the variance of a sample of size n from a normally distributed population with (unknown) variance σ^2, then (3) with k_1 and k_2 given by (2) is a $100\gamma\%$-confidence interval for σ^2.*

Problems

1.–7. Assuming that the populations from which the following samples are taken are normally distributed, determine a 99%-confidence interval for the variance σ^2.

1. The sample in Problem 1, Sec. 12.3.

2. Rockwell hardness of lathe tools

$$64.9 \quad 64.1 \quad 63.8 \quad 64.0$$

3. A sample of 128 values (tensile strength of sheet steel, measured in kilograms/millimeters²) with variance $s^2 = 1.921$.

4. Circumference (in centimeters) of heads of male babies at the time of birth

$$37 \quad 39 \quad 40 \quad 41 \quad 38 \quad 39 \quad 39 \quad 40 \quad 38 \quad 37$$

5. Weight (in grams) of Theragran tablets

$$1.19 \quad 1.23 \quad 1.18 \quad 1.21 \quad 1.27 \quad 1.17 \quad 1.15 \quad 1.14 \quad 1.19 \quad 1.20$$

6. The sample in Problem 7, Sec. 12.3.

7. The sample in Table 3.3.3.

8. Compare the approximate values obtained from the last column in Table 6, Appendix 4, with $m = 100$, with the exact values given in the table.

9. Find a 95%-confidence interval for the variance of a certain anesthetic required to produce anesthesia suitable for surgery, assuming normality and using a sample of 50 values (from 50 different patients) with variance 100 mg².

10. Using Table 6 in Appendix 4, extend the curves in Fig. 12.5.1 to values of n from 50 to 100.

12.6   Confidence Intervals for the Parameter p of the Binomial Distribution

Suppose that we perform a Bernoulli trial n times and that we observe m successes. Then we may use this result for obtaining a confidence interval for the parameter p in (4), Sec. 7.1; this interval is of the form

(1) $\text{CONF } \{p_1 \leqq p \leqq p_2\}.$

For large n the confidence limits p_1 and p_2 are the roots of the equation

$$(2) \qquad (n + c^2)p^2 - (2m + c^2)p + \frac{m^2}{n} = 0.$$

Here c is obtained from Table 12.1.1 after a confidence level γ has been chosen. The theory which yields (2) will be presented later in this section, after the examples.

If not only n but also m and $n - m$ are large, it follows from the formula for the solutions of the quadratic equation (2) that, approximately,

(3) $\text{CONF } \left\{\dfrac{m}{n} - k \leqq p \leqq \dfrac{m}{n} + k\right\}$ where $k = \dfrac{c}{n}\sqrt{\dfrac{m(n-m)}{n}}.$

If n is small ($n \leqq 100$), then the confidence limits p_1 and p_2 in (1) may be obtained from Table 1e in Appendix 4. The corresponding theory was developed by C. J. Clopper and E. S. Pearson (1934); see also Wilks (1962) and Hald (1962) (cf. Appendix 3).

Example 1. Of the first 3000 babies born in 1962 in Graz (Austria), 1578 were boys. Assuming that the binomial model applies, determine a 99%-confidence interval for the probability p of the event "birth of a boy."
In (3) we have

$$\frac{m}{n} = \frac{1578}{3000} = 0.526 \quad \text{and} \quad k = \frac{2.576}{3000}\sqrt{\frac{1578 \cdot 1422}{3000}} = 0.0235.$$

We thus obtain the confidence interval

$$\text{CONF } \{0.502 \leqq p \leqq 0.550\}.$$

Example 2. E. W. Lindstrom (*Cornell Univ. Agr. Exp. Station Memoir 13*, 1918) observed that $m = 42$ of $n = 55$ small corn seedlings were green (dominant trait) while the remaining 13 were yellow (recessive trait). Determine a 95%-confidence interval for p.

We have $m/n = 42/55 = 76\%$. There is no curve for $n = 55$ in Table 1e. However, from the curves for $n = 50$ and 100 we may conclude that the desired interval must be

$$\text{CONF } \{0.63 \leq p \leq 0.86\},$$

approximately.

We shall now see how to derive equation (2), which gives confidence limits p_1 and p_2 in (1) when n is large.

For large n the random variable

$$X = \textit{number of successes in n Bernoulli trials}$$

is approximately normal with mean np and variance npq; cf. Sec. 8.4. Hence, by Theorem 1 in Sec. 8.3, for large n the random variable

$$(4) \qquad\qquad Z = \frac{X - np}{\sqrt{npq}} \qquad\qquad (q = 1 - p)$$

is approximately normal with mean 0 and variance 1. This we may use to obtain a confidence interval for p, as follows. We choose γ and determine from Table 3b in Appendix 4 a number c such that

$$(5) \qquad\qquad P(-c \leq Z \leq c) = \gamma.$$

(For $\gamma = 0.90, 0.95$, etc., these are the numbers given in Table 12.1.1.) The inequality $-c \leq Z \leq c$, that is,

$$-c \leq \frac{X - np}{\sqrt{npq}} \leq c \qquad\qquad (q = 1 - p),$$

is equivalent to

$$\frac{(X - np)^2}{np(1 - p)} \leq c^2.$$

Multiplying by the positive number $np(1 - p)$, we obtain

$$(X - np)^2 \leq c^2 np(1 - p).$$

Performing the indicated multiplication, collecting like powers of p, and dividing by n, we have

$$(6) \qquad\qquad (n + c^2)p^2 - (2X + c^2)p + \frac{X^2}{n} \leq 0.$$

Let $\Theta_1 = p_1(X)$ and $\Theta_2 = p_2(X)$ be the solutions of the quadratic equation in p

$$(7) \qquad\qquad (n + c^2)p^2 - (2X + c^2)p + \frac{X^2}{n} = 0$$

obtained by taking (6) with the equality sign. Since the coefficient $n + c^2$ is positive, the left-hand side of (6) will be negative when p lies between p_1 and

p_2. This shows that (5) is equivalent to

(8) $$P(\Theta_1 \leqq p \leqq \Theta_2) = \gamma \qquad\qquad [\Theta_j = p_j(X)].$$

Observed values θ_1 of Θ_1 and θ_2 of Θ_2 are obtained by using the observed value m of X; thus

$$\theta_1 = p_1(m), \qquad \theta_2 = p_2(m),$$

and this yields the confidence interval

$$\text{CONF } \{p_1(m) \leqq p \leqq p_2(m)\}.$$

Now $p_1(X)$ and $p_2(X)$ are the solutions of (7). Hence $p_1(m)$ and $p_2(m)$ are the solutions of (7) with $X = m$. Setting $X = m$, we see that (7) takes the form (2), and this completes our derivation.

For confidence intervals in the case of the Poisson distribution and the hypergeometric distribution, see Garwood (1936), Ricker (1937), and Chung and DeLury (1950) (cf. Appendix 3).

Problems

1. In one of his classical experiments, Weldon rolled a die 49,152 times and obtained 25,145 times a 4, 5, or 6. Using this information, determine a 95%-confidence interval for the probability of obtaining a 4, 5, or 6.

2. Roll a die 30 times, record the numbers that turn up, and use the sample for determining a confidence interval for the probability p of obtaining 5 or 6 in a single trial.

3. Using Buffon's and Pearson's results in Table 4.4.1, find 95%-confidence intervals for the probability p of obtaining a head in a single trial.

4. Compare the values p_1 and p_2 obtained from (3) with those obtained from Table 1e in Appendix 4 when $\gamma = 95\%$, $n = 50$, and $m = 10, 20, 30, 40$.

5. Graph the length of the confidence interval in Table 1e, Appendix 4, with $\gamma = 99\%$ and $n = 50$ as a function of m. What is the reason for the symmetry with respect to $m = 25$?

6. In a cross-breeding experiment of lank-haired and curly-haired mice, 32 litters of 8 mice each were observed; the numbers of litters containing precisely x lank-haired mice were as follows.

x	0	1	2	3	4	5	6	7	8
Number of litters with precisely x lank-haired mice	0	1	2	4	12	6	5	2	0

Assuming that the binomial distribution may serve as a model, determine a 95%-confidence interval for the probability of the event *birth of a lank-haired mouse*.

7. If we want to estimate the percentage p of persons who will vote for a certain party, what sample size should we take to obtain a 95%-confidence interval for p of length 0.04?

8. Find a 95% and a 99%-confidence interval for the probability p of obtaining heads in a single toss of a coin, using a sample of size 10 in which heads appeared

4 times. Compare the values obtained from the table with the approximate values obtained from (3).

9. In a public opinion poll 100 persons from a population of 10,000 adults were asked to express their preference between candidates A and B. Thirty persons preferred A. From this it was concluded that between 2100 and 3900 in the population preferred A. What confidence level γ was used in this statement?

10. Using the formula for the solutions of a quadratic equation, derive (3) from (2).

12.7 Confidence Intervals in the Case of an Arbitrary Distribution

The previous methods for obtaining confidence intervals refer to special distributions. It is natural to ask whether and how we can determine confidence intervals if the distribution is of another type or is unknown. In such a case we need a sample of large size n and may then apply an approximation method. We shall explain this method in the case of confidence intervals for the mean μ of a distribution.

We know that if $X_1, \cdots, X_n$ are independent variables with the same mean μ and the same variance σ^2, then their sum

$$X = X_1 + \cdots + X_n$$

has the following properties.

(A) X has mean $n\mu$ and variance $n\sigma^2$ (cf. Theorems 1, Sec. 9.7, and 1, Sec. 9.8).

(B) If those variables are normal, then X is normal (cf. Theorem 1, Sec. 12.2).

If those variables are not normal, then property (B) fails to hold, but if n is large, then X is *approximately* normal. This fact results from the following basic theorem.

Theorem 1 (Central limit theorem). *Let X_1, X_2, $X_3, \cdots$ be independent random variables that have the same distribution function and therefore the same mean μ and the same variance σ^2. Let $Y_n = X_1 + \cdots + X_n$. Then the random variable*

$$(1) \qquad\qquad Z_n = \frac{Y_n - n\mu}{\sigma\sqrt{n}}$$

is **"asymptotically normal"** *with mean 0 and variance 1, that is, the distribution function $F_n(x)$ of Z_n satisfies the relation [cf. (3) in Sec. 8.2]*

$$\lim_{n \to \infty} F_n(x) = \Phi(x) = \frac{1}{\sqrt{2\pi}} \int_{-\infty}^{x} e^{-u^2/2} \, du.$$

For a proof, see Cramér (1961) (cf. Appendix 3). The surprising fact about the theorem is that nothing is said about the form of the distribution function of the population. For generalizations of the theorem, see Lindeberg (1922), Feller (1935), Lévy (1935), and Gnedenko and Kolmogorov (1954) (cf. Appendix 3).

If Z_n has the property given in the theorem, then Y_n is asymptotically normal with mean μ and variance $n\sigma^2$. Hence for large n the random variable

$$\bar{X} = \frac{1}{n}(X_1 + \cdots + X_n)$$

is approximately normal with mean μ and variance σ^2/n. [Remember that the sample mean

$$\bar{x} = \frac{1}{n}(x_1 + \cdots + x_n)$$

of a sample $x_1, \cdots, x_n$ is an observed value of $\bar{X}$.]

It follows that the previous methods for obtaining confidence intervals for the mean of the normal distribution are useful approximation methods in the case of any distribution. The accuracy increases with increasing sample size n.

Hence for large n the interval (2) in Sec. 12.1 is approximately a confidence interval for the mean of any distribution with known variance, and (3) in Sec. 12.3 is such an interval if the variance is not known. For large n both formulas yield about the same interval because the distribution function of the t-distribution approaches that of the normal distribution as n approaches infinity.

Of course the central limit theorem is one of the main reasons for the great importance of the normal distribution in statistics.

The minimum sample size for obtaining useful results depends on the type of parameter. If the sample indicates that the distribution does not seem to be too skew, then in the case of the mean we should have at least 30 sample values and in the case of the variance at least 100 values.

Problems

1.–4. Using the given sample, find a 95%-confidence interval for the mean and the variance.

    1. The sample in Problem 3, Sec. 2.3.

    2. The sample in Problem 2, Sec. 2.3.

    3. Weight (in pounds) of male adults.

Weight (Class Mark)	Frequency	Weight (Class Mark)	Frequency	Weight (Class Mark)	Frequency
105	5	145	57	185	13
115	1	155	51	195	8
125	7	165	36	205	1
135	42	175	25	215	1

4. Weight (in grams) of Austrian shillings minted between 1959 and 1961.

Weight	Frequency	Weight	Frequency	Weight	Frequency
4.07	1	4.18	6	4.25	3
4.10	1	4.19	9	4.26	3
4.12	5	4.20	10	4.28	1
4.13	3	4.21	10	4.29	1
4.14	4	4.22	11	4.30	1
4.15	5	4.23	7	4.32	2
4.16	7	4.24	3	4.38	1
4.17	6				

5. Using Table 5 in Appendix 4, draw 100 samples of size 5 each from the population of random digits $0, 1, 2, \cdots, 9$, calculate the means, graph the frequency function and the distribution function of the means, and compare the latter with the normal approximation given by the central limit theorem.

6. What sample size should we choose in Problem 3 if we want to obtain a 95%-confidence interval for μ of length 1?

7. Find a 95%-confidence interval for the mean of a uniform distribution, using a sample of size 100 with mean 0.5 and standard deviation 0.3.

CHAPTER **13**

Testing of Hypotheses

A statistical **hypothesis** is an assumption about the distribution of a random variable, for example, that a certain distribution has mean 20.3, etc. A statistical **test** of a hypothesis is a procedure in which a sample is used to find out whether we may **"not reject" ("accept")** the hypothesis,[1] that is, act as though it is true, or whether we should **"reject"** it, that is, act as though it is false.

These tests are applied quite frequently, and we may ask why they are important. Often we have to make decisions in situations where chance variation plays a role. If we have a choice between, say, two possibilities, the decision between them might be based on the result of some statistical test. To get an idea of how this works, let us give a few typical examples.

For quality control in a factory, one takes a small sample every hour of products just made and measures whatever quantity is important. In the case of yarn production, this may be the strength or the weight per yard. In the case of screws it may be the length or the diameter. Such a quantity must be regarded as a random variable, since it varies because of a large number of small factors whose influence cannot be predicted. In most cases these factors cannot even be enumerated. Suppose that, for example, the diameter should be $\mu = 2$ (in.). Then we have to test the hypothesis $\mu = 2$. As long as the means of the samples we take do not deviate "too much" from the required value $\mu = 2$, we let the production continue. If the deviation is "too large," then we reject the hypothesis, stop the production, and start looking for the source of the trouble. But what does "too much" or "too large" mean? Where should we draw the line between small chance deviations and large deviations that must have another cause, besides the unavoidable effect of chance factors? Such deviations are called **significant deviations,** since they signify that some other theory is needed to explain the results of the experiments, and these deviations are in contrast to the small deviations that are caused solely by random factors. The answer to our question will result from the theory that we shall develop in this chapter.

---

[1] The term *to accept a hypothesis* needs a careful explanation, which we shall give in Sec. 13.2 when we shall know more about such tests.

194

hypoth. source (handwritten)

A bus company considers changing schedules, assuming that this will be advantageous for 75% of its customers. This is the hypothesis to be tested by the use of a sample. In this case the sample will consist of a number of opinions collected by asking randomly selected customers in a suitable fashion. Depending on the result of the test, the change will or will not be made.

In many cases we want to compare two things, for example, two different drugs, two methods of performing a certain work, the accuracy of two methods of measurement, or the quality of products produced by two different machines or tools. Depending on the result of a suitable test, we then decide to use one of the two drugs, to introduce the better method of working, etc.

Typical sources for hypotheses are as follows.

1. The hypothesis may come from a quality requirement. (Experience about attainable quality may be gained by producing a large number of items with special care.)
2. The hypothesis is based on values known from previous experience.
3. The hypothesis results from a theory which one wants to verify.
4. The hypothesis is a pure guess caused by occasional observations.

In each test we use a sample and draw a conclusion about the corresponding population. We know that such a conclusion can never be completely certain. It follows that each test must involve a risk of error. This fact will be discussed later.

The theory of testing hypotheses was created by Neyman and Pearson (1928, 1933). For recent generalizations and extensions, see Lehmann (1959) (cf. Appendix 3).

The tests considered in this chapter will involve samples of fixed size. Sequential methods (that is, methods in which the size of the sample is not determined in advance) for testing hypotheses will be discussed in the next chapter (see Sec. 14.6).

13.1   An Example

To illustrate the ideas explained in the introduction to the present chapter, let us consider a typical example.

The birth of a single child may be regarded as a random experiment with two possible outcomes, namely, B: *Birth of a boy* and G: *Birth of a girl*. Intuitively we should feel that both outcomes are about equally likely. However, in the literature it is often claimed that births of boys are somewhat more frequent than births of girls. On the basis of this situation we want to test the hypothesis that the two outcomes B and G have the same probability. If we let p denote the probability of the outcome B: *Birth of boy*, our hypothesis to be tested is

$$p = 50\% = 0.5.$$

Because of those claims, another feasible possibility would be that the probability of B is greater than that of G; thus

$$p > 0.5.$$

Such an assumption in contrast to a hypothesis is called an *alternative hypothesis* or, briefly, an **alternative.** The original hypothesis is sometimes called the *null hypothesis*, to distinguish it from the alternative hypothesis.

For the test we use a sample of $n = 3000$ babies born in 1962 in Graz, Austria; 1578 of these babies were boys.

If the hypothesis is true, we expect that in a sample of $n = 3000$ births, *about* 1500 are boys. If the alternative holds, then we expect more than 1500 boys, on the average. Hence if the number of boys actually observed is much larger than 1500, we can use this as an indication that the hypothesis may be false, and we reject it.

To perform our test, we shall proceed as follows. We first determine a critical value c. Because of the alternative, c will be greater than 1500. (A method for determining c will be given below.) Then, if the observed number of boys is greater than c, we reject the hypothesis. If that number is not greater than c, we do not reject the hypothesis.

The basic question now is how we should choose c, that is, where we should draw the line between small random deviations and large significant deviations. Different people may have different opinions, and to answer the question we must use mathematical arguments. In the present case these are very simple, as will be seen in what follows.

We determine c such that if the hypothesis is true, the probability of observing more than c boys in a sample of 3000 single births is a very small number, call it α. It is customary to choose $\alpha = 1\%$ or 5%. Choosing $\alpha = 1\%$ (or 5%) we risk about once in 100 cases (in 20 cases, respectively) rejecting a hypothesis even though it is true. We shall return to this point later.

Let us choose $\alpha = 1\%$ and consider the random variable

$$X = \textit{number of boys in } 3000 \textit{ births}.$$

Assuming that the hypothesis is true, we obtain the critical value c from the equation

(1) $$P(X > c)_{p=0.5} = \alpha = 0.01.$$

c is negative confidence

(That assumption is indicated by the subscript $p = 0.5$.) If the observed value 1578 is greater than c, we reject the hypothesis. If $1578 \leqq c$, we do not reject the hypothesis.

To determine c from (1) we must know the distribution of X. For our

observ $x > c$ reject

ex. – binomial dist.
ϕ –Table 3b Apendix 4

purpose the binomial distribution is a sufficiently accurate model. Hence if the hypothesis is true, X has a binomial distribution with $p = 0.5$ and $n = 3000$. From Sec. 8.4 we know that this distribution can be approximated by the normal distribution with mean $\mu = np = 1500$ and variance $\sigma^2 = npq = 750$. (For the sake of simplicity we shall disregard the term 0.5 in (5), Sec. 8.4.) Using (1), we thus obtain

$$P(X > c) = 1 - P(X \le c) \approx 1 - \Phi\left(\frac{c - 1500}{\sqrt{750}}\right) = 0.01.$$

$= \alpha = 0.01$

Table 3b in Appendix 4 yields

look under 99 for $Z(\phi) \to 2.326$

$$\frac{c - 1500}{\sqrt{750}} = 2.326, \qquad c = 1564.$$

$c = 2.326 \cdot \sqrt{750} + 1500$

Since $1578 > c$, we reject the hypothesis and assert that

$1578 > 1564$

$$p > 0.5.$$

This completes the test. Figure 13.1.1 shows the critical value c and the density of the above random variable X under the assumption that the hypothesis is true.

Remark.   Let us note that for samples of 300 values, we obtain from (1) with

$$X = \text{number of boys in 300 births}$$

the critical value $c = 170$. If we had used a sample of 300 values for which $X = x = 158$ (the same percentage of boys as in the large sample), then $158 < c$, and we see that the hypothesis would not have been rejected. This is interesting because it illustrates that the usefulness of the test increases with increasing sample size n. We should choose n so large that the test will yield information about the question that is of interest in a concrete case. On

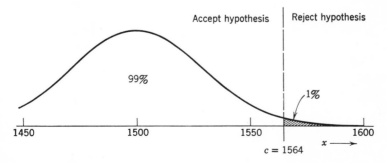

Accept hypothesis | Reject hypothesis

99%

1%

| 1450 | 1500 | 1550 | 1600 |

$c = 1564$

$x \longrightarrow$

Fig. 13.1.1. (Approximate) distribution of the random variable X used in the present test if the hypothesis is true. Critical value $c = 1564$

the other hand, n should not be larger than necessary, for reasons of time and money. In most cases an economical choice of n can be found from a small preliminary experiment.

In studying hypotheses it is convenient to classify them into one of two types by means of the following definition.

If a hypothesis completely specifies the distribution, that is, if it specifies its functional form as well as the values of all the parameters, it is called a **simple hypothesis;** otherwise it is called a **composite hypothesis.**

In our example, the form of the probability distribution is assumed known; hence the null hypothesis $p = 0.5$ is simple, whereas the alternative hypothesis $p > 0.5$ is composite because it does not specify the distribution completely.

In the case of a normal distribution, a hypothesis concerning the mean of the form $\mu = \mu_0$ (μ_0 a given number) is simple if the variance of the distribution is known, and is composite if the variance is unknown; in the latter case the variance remains unspecified so that infinitely many possibilities remain for the distribution of the population. More generally, if the form of a distribution is known, a simple hypothesis is one that specifies all the parameters of the distribution (that is, assigns a numerical value to each of them), whereas a composite hypothesis does not specify all these parameters.

13.2   Types of Alternatives. Types of Errors

We first recall from the preceding section that the hypothesis to be tested is sometimes called the *null hypothesis*, and a counter-assumption (like $p > 0.5$ in that section) is called an *alternative hypothesis* or, briefly, an **alternative.** The number α (or $100\alpha\%$) is called the **significance level** of the test and c is called the *critical value*. The region containing the values for which we reject the hypothesis is called the **rejection region** or **critical region.** The region of values for which we do not reject the hypothesis is called the **acceptance region.** A frequent choice for α is 5%.

In the preceding section we considered a random variable X whose distribution involved an unknown parameter p. If we write θ for p, we may write the hypothesis in that section in the form $\theta = \theta_0 = 0.5$. The alternative in that section was $p > 0.5$ or, in our more general notation,

(1) $$\theta > \theta_0.$$

In other random experiments the nature of the experiment may suggest the alternative

(2) $$\theta < \theta_0$$

or the alternative

(3) $$\theta \neq \theta_0.$$

(1)–(3) are three main types of alternatives. (1) and (2) are called **one-sided alternatives,** and (3) is called a **two-sided alternative.**

(1) is of the type considered in the preceding section (where $\theta_0 = p = 0.5$ and $\theta = p > 0.5$); c lies to the right of θ_0 and the rejection region extends from c to ∞ (Fig. 13.2.1, upper part). The test is called a **right-sided test.**

In the case of the alternative (2), the number c lies to the left of θ_0, the rejection region extends from c to $-\infty$ (Fig. 13.2.1, middle part), and the test is called a **left-sided test.**

This case may appear, for example, in connection with testing strength of material. θ_0 may then be the required strength, and the alternative characterizes an undesirable weakness. The case that the material may be stronger than required is acceptable, of course, and therefore needs no special attention.

Right-sided and left-sided tests are called **one-sided tests.**

In the case of alternative (3) we have two critical values c_1 and c_2 ($> c_1$), the rejection region extends from c_1 to $-\infty$ and from c_2 to ∞ (Fig. 13.2.1, lower part), and the test is called a **two-sided test.**

An alternative of type (3) may be important, for example, in connection with the diameter of an axle shaft. θ_0 then is the required diameter, and slimmer axle shafts are as bad as thicker ones, so that we have to watch for undesirable deviations from θ_0 in both directions.

We shall now consider the **risks of making false decisions in tests.**

Let the hypothesis be $\theta = \theta_0$. As an alternative we choose a single number

$$\theta = \theta_1,$$

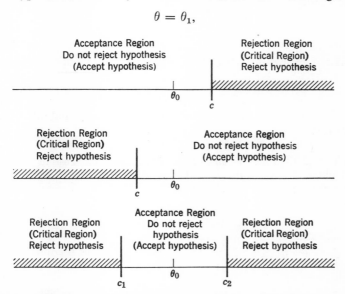

Fig. 13.2.1. Test in the case of alternative (1) (upper part of the figure), alternative (2) (middle part), and alternative (3)

for the sake of simplicity. We suppose that $\theta_1 > \theta_0$, so that we have a right-sided test, the consideration for a left-sided or a two-sided test being similar. Then both the critical value c and the rejection region lie to the right of θ_0, as in the upper part of Fig. 13.2.1. From a given sample $x_1, \cdots, x_n$, we compute a value

$$\hat{\theta} = g(x_1, \cdots, x_n).$$

If $\hat{\theta} > c$, the hypothesis is rejected (as in the previous section). If $\hat{\theta} \leq c$, the hypothesis is not rejected. $\hat{\theta}$ can be regarded as an observed value of the random variable

$$\hat{\Theta} = g(X_1, \cdots, X_n)$$

because x_j may be regarded as an observed value of X_j, where $j = 1, \cdots, n$.
In this test there are two possibilities of making an error, as follows.

Type I error (cf. Table 13.2.1). The hypothesis is true, but is rejected because $\hat{\Theta}$ assumes a value $\hat{\theta} > c$. Obviously, the probability of making such an error equals

(4) $P(\hat{\Theta} > c)_{\theta=\theta_0} = \alpha,$

the significance level of the test.

Type II error (cf. Table 13.2.1). The hypothesis is false, but is not rejected because $\hat{\Theta}$ assumes a value $\hat{\theta} \leq c$. The probability of making such an error is denoted by β; thus

(5) $P(\hat{\Theta} \leq c)_{\theta=\theta_1} = \beta.$

Note that this probability β depends on the alternative θ_1. The quantity

$$\eta = 1 - \beta$$

is called the **power** of the test. Obviously, this is the probability of avoiding a Type II error.

Table 13.2.1. Type I and Type II Errors in Testing a Hypothesis $\theta = \theta_0$ against an Alternative $\theta = \theta_1$

		Unknown Truth	
		$\theta = \theta_0$	$\theta = \theta_1$
Not rejected (Accepted)	$\theta = \theta_0$	True decision $P = 1 - \alpha$	Type II error $P = \beta$
	$\theta = \theta_1$	Type I error $P = \alpha$	True decision $P = 1 - \beta$

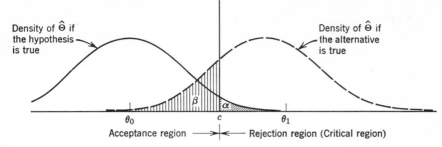

Density of $\hat{\Theta}$ if the hypothesis is true

Density of $\hat{\Theta}$ if the alternative is true

θ_0 c θ_1

Acceptance region $\longrightarrow$ $\vert$ $\longleftarrow$ Rejection region (Critical region)

Fig. 13.2.2. Illustration of Type I and II errors in testing a hypothesis $\theta = \theta_0$ against an alternative $\theta = \theta_1 \, (> \theta_0)$

For example, in acceptance inspection we take a sample and test the hypothesis that the entire lot satisfies the specified quality conditions. If in this process we reject the lot even though it satisfies those conditions, we make a Type I error. The corresponding probability α is therefore also called **Type I risk** or *producer's risk*. If we accept a lot although it does not satisfy those conditions, we make a Type II error. The corresponding probability β is therefore also called **Type II risk** or *consumer's risk*. The concepts of producer's risk and consumer's risk were introduced by Dodge and Romig around 1925; see Dodge and Romig (1929) (cf. Appendix 3). (Acceptance inspection will be studied in more detail in Chap. 14.)

Formulas (4) and (5) show that both α and β depend on c, and we would like to choose c so that these probabilities of making errors are as small as possible. But Fig. 13.2.2 indicates that these are conflicting requirements, since to let α decrease we must shift c to the right, but then β increases. In practice we first choose α (5%, sometimes 1%), then determine c, and finally compute β. If β is large so that the power $\eta = 1 - \beta$ is small, we should repeat the test, choosing a larger sample, for reasons that will appear shortly.

If the alternative is not a single number but is of the form (1)–(3), then β becomes a function of θ. This function $\beta(\theta)$ is called the **operating characteristic (OC)** of the test and its curve the **OC curve**. Clearly, in this case $\eta = 1 - \beta$ also depends on θ, and this function $\eta(\theta)$ is called the **power function** of the test.

Of course, from a test that leads to the acceptance of a certain hypothesis θ_0 it does *not* follow that this is the only possible hypothesis or the best possible hypothesis. Hence the terms **"not reject"** or **"fail to reject"** are perhaps better than the term **"accept."**

Of course, we should be particularly cautious as long as we do not know how large β is.

Often in practical applications, instead of a precise value θ_0 of a parameter θ to test, we only have available an approximate value $\tilde{\theta}_0$ based on experience. If we treat $\tilde{\theta}_0$ as the precise value to be tested and do not reject $\tilde{\theta}_0$ in the test, this does not mean that we believe that $\tilde{\theta}_0$ is the true value of θ, but that the true value of θ is probably close to $\tilde{\theta}_0$ and, from a practical point of view, it is safe to treat $\tilde{\theta}_0$ as the true value.

Using the knowledge gained in this section, the student may want to read again the paragraph after the end of the calculations in the preceding section. To that paragraph we can now add a few more remarks. Our discussions and examples show that if we use a small sample size, a deviation from the null hypothesis may be not significant, but it is clear that such a result gives only a weak confirmation of the null hypothesis, and it may be desirable to apply the test once more, using a larger sample size. On the other hand, a very large sample size may bring out differences that are too small to be of practical importance and are therefore ignored in the subsequent analysis.

Problems

1. Using Buffon's result in Table 4.4.1, test the hypothesis $p = 0.5$ (*fair coin*) against the alternative $p \neq 0.5$; here p is the probability of obtaining a head in a single trial. Use the significance level 5%.

2. Using Buffon's result in Table 4.4.1, test the hypothesis $q = 0.5$ (q = probability of obtaining a tail in a single trial) against the alternative $q \neq 0.5$.

3. Perform the test in Problem 1, using Pearson's data in Table 4.4.1.

4. Throw a die 100 times and record the number of times 5 or 6 turns up. Using this sample, test the hypothesis $p = 1/3$ (p = probability of obtaining 5 or 6) against the alternative $p > 1/3$.

5. Set up a test for the hypothesis $\theta = \theta_0 = 1$ against the alternative $\theta = \theta_1 > 1$ in the case of the continuous distribution with the density

$$f(x) = \frac{e^{-x/\theta}}{\theta} \text{ when } x \geq 0, \qquad f(x) = 0 \text{ when } x < 0,$$

that is, choose $\alpha = 5\%$, determine the corresponding c, the operating characteristic, and the power function $\eta = 1 - \beta$.

6. It should be noted that in the case of a discrete distribution it may not always be possible to choose precisely a desired value of α such as $\alpha = 5\%$ (a difficulty which rarely presents a problem in practical applications because then experiments are generally sufficiently large to permit many choices for α). To understand this, set up a test of the hypothesis $H_0: p = p_0 = 0.5$ against the alternative $H_1: p = p_1 > p_0$ in the case of the binomial distribution with the probability function

$$f(x) = \binom{3}{x} p^x q^{3-x}.$$

Show that a sensible critical region is $x = 3$ and corresponds to $\alpha = 12.5\%$, and the power function is $\eta = 1 - \beta = f(3)|_{p=p_1} = p_1{}^3$. Graph this function $\eta(p_1)$.

7. Set up a test for the hypothesis $\theta = \theta_0 = 1$ against the alternative $\theta = \theta_1 > 1$ in the case of the continuous distribution with the density

$$f(x) = \frac{1}{\theta} \text{ when } 0 \leq x \leq \theta, \qquad f(x) = 0 \text{ otherwise,}$$

that is, choose $\alpha = 5\%$, and determine the corresponding c and the power function $\eta = 1 - \beta$.

8. Set up a test for the hypothesis $\theta = \theta_0 = 2$ against the alternative $\theta = \theta_1 > 2$ in the case of the continuous distribution with the density

$$f(x) = \frac{2x}{\theta^2} \text{ when } 0 \leqq x \leqq \theta, \qquad f(x) = 0 \text{ otherwise,}$$

that is, choose $\alpha = 5\%$ and determine the corresponding c and the power function $\eta = 1 - \beta$.

9. Consider the continuous distribution with the density

$$f(x) = 1 \text{ when } \theta \leqq x \leqq \theta + 1, \qquad f(x) = 0 \text{ otherwise.}$$

Set up a test of the hypothesis $\theta = \theta_0 = 3$, choosing $\alpha = 10\%$, against the alternative $\theta = \theta_1 = 3.5$. What is the Type II error?

10. Suppose that X is a continuous random variable with the density

$$f(x) = kx^\theta \text{ when } 0 \leqq x \leqq 1, \qquad f(x) = 0 \text{ otherwise,}$$

where k is a constant. Show that we must have $k = \theta + 1$. If the hypothesis H_0: $\theta = \theta_0 = 1$ is to be tested, using the interval $x > 0.9$ as the rejection region, (a) calculate α, (b) calculate β in the case of the alternative H_1: $\theta = \theta_1 = 4$, (c) calculate β when H_1: $\theta = \theta_1 = 6$.

11. How does the situation in Problem 10 change if we take the interval $x \geqq 0.8$ as the rejection region? Calculate α and β.

12. Suppose that a bag is known to contain either 1 red ball and 4 white balls or, alternatively, 4 red balls and 1 white ball. One ball is drawn, and the hypothesis that 1 ball is red and 4 balls are white will not be rejected if and only if the ball drawn is white. Find α and β.

13. What are the values of α and β in Problem 12 if the alternative is 3 red balls and 2 white balls?

14. Suppose that a bag is known to contain either 2 red and 3 white balls (the hypothesis to be tested) or 3 red and 2 white balls (the alternative). Two balls are drawn without replacement, and the hypothesis is rejected if and only if both balls drawn are red. Find α and β.

15. A box contains 10 balls, and we want to test the hypothesis that 2 balls are red and 8 are white against the alternative that more than 2 balls are red. We draw 2 balls without replacement and reject the hypothesis if and only if both balls drawn are red. Find α. Find and graph the operating characteristic and the power function.

16. If a coin is tossed 5 times and comes up heads 5 times, can we conclude that the coin is not fair?

13.3 Application to the Normal Distribution

We shall now derive tests of hypotheses in the case of the normal distribution.

Example 1 (Mean of the normal distribution if the variance is known). Let X be a normal random variable with variance $\sigma^2 = 9$. Using a sample of size $n = 10$ with mean $\bar{x}$, test the hypothesis $\mu = \mu_0 = 24$ against the three types of alternatives

$$(a) \ \mu > \mu_0 \qquad (b) \ \mu < \mu_0 \qquad (c) \ \mu \neq \mu_0.$$

We choose the significance level $\alpha = 0.05$. As an estimator for the mean, we take

$$\bar{X} = \frac{1}{n}(X_1 + \cdots + X_n),$$

as before. If the hypothesis is true, it follows from Theorem 2, Sec. 12.2, that $\bar{X}$ is normal with mean $\mu = 24$ and variance $\sigma^2/n = 0.9$. Hence in each case we may obtain the critical value c from Table 3b in Appendix 4.

Case (a). We determine c from

$$P(\bar{X} > c)_{\mu=24} = \alpha = 0.05,$$

that is,

$$P(\bar{X} \leqq c)_{\mu=24} = \Phi\left(\frac{c-24}{\sqrt{0.9}}\right) = 1 - \alpha = 0.95.$$

The table yields

$$\frac{c-24}{\sqrt{0.9}} = 1.645. \qquad \text{Thus} \qquad c = 25.56.$$

c is greater than μ_0, as in the upper part of Fig. 13.2.1. If $\bar{x} \leqq 25.56$, the hypothesis is not rejected. If $\bar{x} > 25.56$, it is rejected. The power of the test is (cf. Fig. 13.3.1)

$$\eta(\mu) = P(\bar{X} > 25.56)_\mu = 1 - P(\bar{X} \leqq 25.56)_\mu$$

(1)

$$= 1 - \Phi\left(\frac{25.56 - \mu}{\sqrt{0.9}}\right) = 1 - \Phi(26.94 - 1.05\mu).$$

Case (b). The critical value c is now obtained from the equation

$$P(\bar{X} \leqq c)_{\mu=24} = \Phi\left(\frac{c-24}{\sqrt{0.9}}\right) = \alpha = 0.05.$$

Table 3b in Appendix 4 yields $c = 24 - 1.56 = 22.44$. If $\bar{x} \geqq 22.44$, we do not reject the hypothesis. If $\bar{x} < 22.44$, we reject it. The power of the test is

(2) $\qquad \eta(\mu) = P(\bar{X} \leqq 22.44)_\mu = \Phi\left(\frac{22.44 - \mu}{\sqrt{0.9}}\right) = \Phi(23.65 - 1.05\mu).$

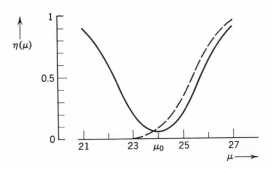

Fig. 13.3.1. Power $\eta(\mu)$ in Ex. 1, case (a) (dashed) and case (c)

Case (c). Since the normal distribution is symmetric, we choose c_1 and c_2 equidistant from $\mu = 24$, say, $c_1 = 24 - k$ and $c_2 = 24 + k$. We determine k from

$$P(24 - k \leqq \bar{X} \leqq 24 + k)_{\mu=24} = \Phi\left(\frac{k}{\sqrt{0.9}}\right) - \Phi\left(-\frac{k}{\sqrt{0.9}}\right) = 1 - \alpha = 0.95.$$

From this and Table 3*b* in Appendix 4 we obtain

$$k/\sqrt{0.9} = 1.960, \qquad k = 1.86.$$

Hence $c_1 = 24 - 1.86 = 22.14$ and $c_2 = 24 + 1.86 = 25.86$. If $\bar{x}$ is not smaller than c_1 and not greater than c_2, we do not reject the hypothesis. If $\bar{x}$ is smaller than c_1 or greater than c_2, we reject the hypothesis. The power of the test is (cf. Fig. 13.3.1)

$$\eta(\mu) = P(\bar{X} < 22.14)_\mu + P(\bar{X} > 25.86)_\mu.$$

The last term on the right is equal to

$$1 - P(\bar{X} \leqq 25.86)_\mu.$$

Hence we first obtain

$$\eta(\mu) = 1 + \Phi\left(\frac{22.14 - \mu}{\sqrt{0.9}}\right) - \Phi\left(\frac{25.86 - \mu}{\sqrt{0.9}}\right).$$

Carrying out the division, we have

(3) $$\eta(\mu) = 1 + \Phi(23.34 - 1.05\mu) - \Phi(27.26 - 1.05\mu).$$

From the last section we know that the function $\beta(\mu)$ is called the operating characteristic (OC) of the test, its curve is called the OC curve, and $\beta(\mu)$ is the probability of making a Type II error (cf. Table 13.2.1). In case (c) of our example we have (cf. Fig. 13.3.2)

$$\beta(\mu) = \Phi(27.26 - 1.05\mu) - \Phi(23.34 - 1.05\mu).$$

If we take a larger sample, say, of size $n = 100$ (instead of 10), then $\sigma^2/n = 0.09$ (instead of 0.9), and the critical values are $c_1 = 23.41$ and $c_2 = 24.59$, as can be verified by calculation. Then the operating characteristic of the test is

$$\beta(\mu) = \Phi\left(\frac{24.59 - \mu}{\sqrt{0.09}}\right) - \Phi\left(\frac{23.41 - \mu}{\sqrt{0.09}}\right).$$

By simplifying we obtain

$$\beta(\mu) = \Phi(81.97 - 3.33\mu) - \Phi(78.03 - 3.33\mu).$$

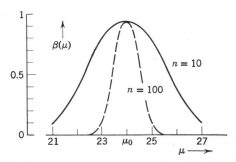

Fig. 13.3.2. Curves of the operating characteristic (OC curves) in Ex. 1, case (c), for two different sample sizes n

Figure 13.3.2 shows that the corresponding curve is steeper than that for $n = 10$. This means that the increase of n has led to an improvement of the test. In any practical case, n is chosen as small as possible but so large that the test brings out deviations between μ and μ_0 that are of practical interest. For instance, if in case (c) of our example, deviations of ± 2 units are of interest, we see from Fig. 13.3.2 that $n = 10$ is much too small because when $\mu = 24 - 2 = 22$ or $\mu = 24 + 2 = 26$, then β is almost 50%. On the other hand, we see that $n = 100$ will be sufficient for that purpose.

Example 2 (*Mean of the normal distribution with unknown variance*). The tensile strength of a sample of $n = 16$ manila ropes (diameter 3 in.) was measured. The sample mean was $\bar{x} = 4482$ kg, and the sample standard deviation was $s = 115$ kg (N. C. Wiley, 41st Annual Meeting of the Amer. Soc. for Test. Materials). Assuming that the tensile strength is a normal random variable, test the hypothesis $\mu_0 = 4500$ kg against the alternative $\mu_1 = 4400$ kg. Here μ_0 may be a value given by the manufacturer, while μ_1 may result from previous experience.

We choose the significance level $\alpha = 5\%$. If the hypothesis is true, it follows from Theorem 2, Sec. 12.4, that the random variable

$$T = \sqrt{n}\,\frac{\bar{X} - \mu_0}{S} = 4\,\frac{\bar{X} - 4500}{S}$$

has a t-distribution with $n - 1 = 15$ degrees of freedom. The critical value c is obtained from the equation

$$P(T < c)_{\mu_0} = \alpha = 0.05.$$

Table 8 in Appendix 4 yields $c = -1.75$. As an observed value of T, we obtain from the sample

$$t = 4\,\frac{\bar{x} - 4500}{s} = 4\,\frac{4482 - 4500}{115} = -0.626.$$

We see that $t > c$ and do not reject the hypothesis.

For obtaining numerical values of the power of the test, we would need tables called noncentral Student t-tables; we shall not discuss this question here.

Example 3 (*Variance of the normal distribution*). Using a sample of size $n = 15$ and sample variance $s^2 = 13$ from a normal population, test the hypothesis $\sigma^2 = \sigma_0^2 = 10$ against the alternative $\sigma^2 = \sigma_1^2 = 20$.

We choose the significance level $\alpha = 5\%$. If the hypothesis is true, then

$$Y = (n - 1)\,\frac{S^2}{\sigma_0^2} = 14\,\frac{S^2}{10} = 1.4 S^2$$

has a chi-square distribution with $n - 1 = 14$ degrees of freedom, cf. Theorem 1 in Sec. 12.4. From the equation

$$P(Y > c) = \alpha = 0.05, \qquad \text{that is,} \qquad P(Y \leqq c) = 0.95,$$

and Table 6 in Appendix 4 with 14 degrees of freedom, we obtain $c = 23.68$. This is the critical value of Y. Hence to

$$S^2 = \frac{\sigma_0^2 Y}{n - 1} = 0.714 Y$$

there corresponds the critical value

$$c^* = 0.714 \cdot 23.68 = 16.91.$$

Since $s^2 < c^*$, we do not reject the hypothesis.

If the alternative is true, the variable

$$Y_1 = 14 \frac{S^2}{\sigma_1^2} = 0.7 S^2$$

has a chi-square distribution with 14 degrees of freedom. Hence our test has the power

$$\eta = P(S^2 > c^*)_{\sigma^2=20} = P(Y_1 > 0.7c^*)_{\sigma^2=20}$$

$$= 1 - P(Y_1 \leqq 11.84)_{\sigma^2=20} \approx 62\%$$

and we see that the Type II risk is very large, namely, 38%. To make that risk smaller, we must increase the sample size.

Problems

General assumption. *In these problems assume that the populations from which the samples are taken are normally distributed.*

1. Using the sample in Example 1, Sec. 3.3, test the hypothesis $\mu = 0.80$ in. (the length indicated on the box) against the alternative $\mu \neq 0.80$ in.

2. Test the hypotheses that the population corresponding to the sample in Example 1, Sec. 3.1, has mean 80% and standard deviation 0.2% against the alternatives $\mu \neq 80\%$ and $\sigma \neq 0.2\%$, respectively. Choose $\alpha = 5\%$.

3. Using the sample in Problem 5, Sec. 12.5, test the hypothesis $\mu = 1.2$ against the alternative $\mu < 1.2$.

4. Perform the test in Problem 3, choosing (a) hypothesis $\mu = 1.25$, alternative $\mu < 1.25$, (b) hypothesis $\mu = 1.15$, alternative $\mu > 1.15$.

5. In the 143th revolution of the satellite Telstar on June 25/26, 1962, the azimuth showed the following deviations (measured in multiples of 0.01 radians):

$$1 \quad -1 \quad 1 \quad 3 \quad -8 \quad 6 \quad 0.$$

Using this sample, test the hypothesis $\mu = 0$ against the alternative $\mu > 0$.

6. Using the values in Table 13.3.1, test the hypothesis $\mu = 0$ against the alternative $\mu \neq 0$.

7. For comparing two methods of determining the starch content of potatoes, each of 16 potatoes was cut in halves and to each of the two halves one of the two methods was applied. The differences (measured in multiples of 0.1%) were

$$2 \quad 0 \quad 0 \quad 1 \quad 2 \quad 2 \quad 3 \quad -3 \quad 1 \quad 2 \quad 3 \quad 0 \quad -1 \quad 1 \quad -2 \quad 1.$$

Test the hypothesis that the difference between the methods is not significant.

8. Suppose that in a certain process of producing wire the breaking strength of the wire is a normal random variable with mean 200 lb. To reduce production costs, another process is tried. A corresponding sample of 100 values had the mean $\bar{x} = 188$ lb and the standard deviation $s = 6$ lb. Does the new process have a negative effect on the strength of the wire?

9. Suppose that from past experience it is known that when a certain automatic lathe is functioning properly, 3% of the produced parts are defective on the average.

Table 13.3.1. Relative Deviation (in Percent) of the Capacity of Certain Tantalum Capacitors from the Nominal Value

Deviation	Class Mark	Frequency
$-13.5 \cdots -10.5$	-12	1
$-10.5 \cdots -7.5$	-9	1
$-7.5 \cdots -4.5$	-6	4
$-4.5 \cdots -1.5$	-3	15
$-1.5 \cdots 1.5$	0	16
$1.5 \cdots 4.5$	3	5
$4.5 \cdots 7.5$	6	4
$7.5 \cdots 10.5$	9	2

The manufacturer wants to test the hypothesis H_0: $p = 0.03$, using a sample of 500 parts which was obtained during the course of a day's operation and contained 26 defective parts.

10. Suppose that in the past the standard deviation of weights of certain 25.0 oz packages filled by a machine was 0.4 oz. Test the hypothesis H_0: $\sigma = 0.4$ against the alternative H_1: $\sigma > 0.4$ (an undesirable increase), using a sample of 10 packages with standard deviation 0.5 oz.

11. If a standard drug cures about 70% of patients with a certain disease and a new drug cured 148 of the first 200 patients on whom it was tried, can we conclude that the new drug is more effective?

12. Suppose that is is known that spraying fields against corn borer effects does not decrease the corn yield. Test the hypothesis that spraying does not increase the yield against the alternative that it does. In the test use a sample of 10 values of differences of yield (yield of a sprayed strip minus yield of an unsprayed strip of the same field, measured in bushels/acre) with mean $\bar{x} = 6$ and variance $s^2 = 40$.

13. Suppose that in operating battery-powered electrical equipment, it is less expensive to replace all batteries at fixed intervals than to replace each battery individually when it breaks down, provided the standard deviation of the lifetime is less than a certain limit, say, less than 5 hours. Assuming normality and using a sample of 28 values of lifetimes with standard deviation $s = 3.5$ hours, test the hypothesis $\sigma^2 = \sigma_0^2 = 25$ against the alternative $\sigma^2 < 25$.

14. Graph the power function in Example 1, case (b).

15. Graph the power function for a two-sided test of the hypothesis H_0: $\mu = 0$ for a normal random variable with variance $\sigma^2 = 1$, assuming $\alpha = 5\%$ and sample sizes (a) 1, (b) 4, (c) 9, (d) 16.

16. Graph the operating characteristics in the cases (a) and (b) of Example 1.

17. Find the Type II error in a test of the hypothesis H_0: $\mu = 10.00$ against the alternative H_1: $\mu = 7.36$ for a normal distribution with variance $\sigma^2 = 9$ by means of a sample of size 9; choose the Type I error to be $\alpha = 5\%$ and use the proper critical region.

18. Graph the power function (by plotting a few points) of the test of H_0: $\mu_0 = 0$ against the hypothesis H_1: $\mu_1 \neq 0$ in the case of a normal random variable with $\sigma = 10$, assuming that $\alpha = 4.5\%$ and the sample used is of size (a) $n = 16$, (b) $n = 100$.

19. If in a test for the mean of the normal distribution a certain sample size leads to the detection of a deviation between μ and μ_0 of magnitude 0.5 unit, what sample size should we choose if we want the test to bring out deviations between μ and μ_0 oi magnitude 0.1 unit?

20. Let X be normal with known variance, and suppose we want to test the hypothesis H_0: $\mu = \mu_0$ against the alternative H_1: $\mu = \mu_1 > \mu_0$, choosing $\alpha = 5\%$. Find the smallest sample size necessary to reject H_0 in the case that μ is actually (a) σ units, (b) $\sigma/2$ units, (c) $\sigma/4$ units higher than μ_0.

21. Suppose we want to test the hypothesis H_0: $\mu_0 = 20$ against the alternative H_1: $\mu_1 = 26$ in the case of a normal distribution with variance $\sigma^2 = 100$. What sample size n should we choose in order that the Type I and Type II error will be 10% each?

22. Show that for a normal distribution the two types of errors in a test of a hypothesis H_0: $\mu = \mu_0$ against an alternative H_1: $\mu = \mu_1$ can be made as small as one pleases (not zero) by taking the sample size sufficiently large.

13.4   Comparison of the Means of Two Normal Distributions

We shall now consider the problem of testing whether the means μ_X and μ_Y of two normal random variables X and Y are equal or not. The variances of X and Y need not be known but are assumed to be equal. (How to test this assumption will be shown in Sec. 13.6. What to do if the variances are not equal will be discussed at the end of this section.)

Two samples will be needed in the test, one from each population. In practice there are two particularly important cases as follows.

Case A. *The samples have the same size. Furthermore, each value of the first sample corresponds to precisely one value of the other*, since corresponding values result from the same person or thing **(paired comparison)**; for example, two measurements of the same thing by two different methods, two measurements from the two eyes of the same animal, or measurements of the pulse of a person before and after heavy exercise); more generally they may result from pairs of *similar* individuals or things, for example, identical twins, two male rats from the same litter, two students of similar ability, or two front tires used on the same car.

Case B. *The two samples are independent and not necessarily of the same size.*

In Case A we should form the differences of corresponding values and test the hypothesis that the population corresponding to the differences has mean zero. This can be done by the method discussed in the previous section. For instance, Problem 7 in that section is of this type, and the differences are already given.

In Case B we can apply the test in Table 13.4.1. The underlying theory will be developed in the next section.

Table 13.4.1. Test of the Hypothesis $\mu_X = \mu_Y$ **against the Alternative** $\mu_X > \mu_Y$ **in the Case of Normal Distributions with the Same (Unknown) Variance Using Independent Samples**

1st step. Choose a significance level α (5%, 1%, or the like).
2nd step. Compute the means $\bar{x}$ and $\bar{y}$ of the samples

$$x_1, \cdots, x_{n_1} \quad \text{and} \quad y_1, \cdots, y_{n_2}.$$

Compute $(n_1 - 1)s_x^2$ and $(n_2 - 1)s_y^2$, where s_x^2 and s_y^2 are the variances of the samples.

3rd step. Determine a number c from the equation

(1) $$P(T \leq c) = 1 - \alpha$$

and Table 8 in Appendix 4 with $n_1 + n_2 - 2$ degrees of freedom.

4th step. Compute

(2) $$t_0 = \sqrt{\frac{n_1 n_2 (n_1 + n_2 - 2)}{n_1 + n_2}} \, \frac{\bar{x} - \bar{y}}{\sqrt{(n_1 - 1)s_x^2 + (n_2 - 1)s_y^2}}.$$

If $t_0 \leq c$, do not reject the hypothesis. If $t_0 > c$, reject it.

If in planning an experiment we have a choice, then Case A is generally preferable because it eliminates the variability between the experimental units (in the above examples between the products, the animals, etc.). To see this, we first note that as in Sec. 9.8 it follows that $Z = X - Y$ has the variance

$$\sigma_Z^2 = \sigma_X^2 + \sigma_Y^2 - 2\sigma_{XY},$$

where

$$\sigma_{XY} = E([X - \mu_X][Y - \mu_Y]) = E(XY) - E(X)E(Y)$$

is the covariance (cf. Sec. 9.8) and $\mu_X = E(X)$ and $\mu_Y = E(Y)$ are the means of X and Y, respectively. In successful pairing, high values of X will correspond to high values of Y, so that both $X - \mu_X$ and $Y - \mu_Y$ will be positive; also, low values of X will correspond to low values of Y, so that both $X - \mu_X$ and $Y - \mu_Y$ will be negative. Hence in successful pairing, σ_{XY} will be positive in both cases and $-2\sigma_{XY}$ in σ_Z^2 will make the variance σ_Z^2 of $X - Y$ less than the sum of the variances of X and Y, sometimes much less. However, if X and Y are poorly related, the pairing may not be effective.

Before considering an application of the test given in Table 13.4.1, let us add a few remarks about that table. We first note that for samples of equal size $n_1 = n_2 = n$, formula (2) reduces to the simple form

(3) $$t_0 = \sqrt{n} \, \frac{\bar{x} - \bar{y}}{\sqrt{s_x^2 + s_y^2}}.$$

Furthermore, if in Table 13.4.1 we replace the alternative by the alternative $\mu_X < \mu_Y$ or $\mu_X \neq \mu_Y$, then we have to replace (1) by

$$(4) \qquad P(T \leq c) = \alpha$$

or

$$(5) \qquad P(T \leq c_1) = \frac{\alpha}{2} \quad \text{and} \quad P(T \leq c_2) = 1 - \frac{\alpha}{2},$$

respectively.

Example 1. We consider the two samples

| 105 | 108 | 86 | 103 | 103 | 107 | 124 | 105 |

and

| 89 | 92 | 84 | 97 | 103 | 107 | 111 | 97 |

showing the relative output of tin plate workers under two different working conditions (J. J. B. Worth, *J. Indust. Eng.* **9**, 1958, 249–253). Using these samples, we want to test the hypothesis that the corresponding populations have the same mean value against the alternative that these mean values are different. We assume that those two populations are normally distributed and have the same variance. (The latter assumption will be tested and justified in Sec. 13.6.) Then we may apply the method given in Table 13.4.1. Our hypothesis is $\mu_X = \mu_Y$, and the alternative is $\mu_X \neq \mu_Y$.

1st step. We choose the significance level $\alpha = 5\%$.

2nd step. We compute the sample means and variances, finding

$$\bar{x} = 105.125, \qquad \bar{y} = 97.500,$$
$$s_x^2 = 106.125, \qquad s_y^2 = 84.000.$$

3rd step. Because of the two-sided alternative $\mu_X \neq \mu_Y$ we have to use (5) instead of (1), that is, determine c_1 and c_2 from

$$P(T \leq c_1) = 2.5\% \quad \text{and} \quad P(T \leq c_2) = 97.5\%$$

and Table 8 in Appendix 4 with $n_1 + n_2 - 2 = 8 + 8 - 2 = 14$ degrees of freedom. We find $c_1 = -2.15$ and $c_2 = 2.15$.

4th step. Since $n_1 = n_2 = 8$, we may use (3), finding

$$t_0 = \sqrt{8} \, \frac{105.125 - 97.500}{\sqrt{106.125 + 84.000}} = \sqrt{8} \, \frac{7.625}{\sqrt{190.125}} = 1.56.$$

We see that $c_1 \leq t_0 \leq c_2$ and do not reject the hypothesis $\mu_X = \mu_Y$ that under both conditions the mean output is the same.

We mention that Case A applies to our present example because the two first sample values corresponded to a certain type of work, the next two were obtained in another kind of work, etc. So we may use the differences

| 16 | 16 | 2 | 6 | 0 | 0 | 13 | 8 |

of corresponding sample values and the method in Example 2 in the previous section to test the hypothesis $\mu = 0$ where μ is the mean of the population corresponding to the differences. As a logical alternative we take $\mu \neq 0$.

We choose the significance level $\alpha = 5\%$, as before. The sample mean is $\bar{d} = 7.625$, and the sample variance is $s^2 = 45.696$. From this we compute, since $n_1 = n_2 = n = 8$,

$$t = \sqrt{8} \, \frac{7.625 - 0}{\sqrt{45.696}} = 3.19.$$

The critical values c_1 and c_2 are obtained from

$$P(T \leq c_1) = 2.5\%, \qquad P(T \leq c_2) = 97.5\%$$

and Table 8 with $n - 1 = 7$ degrees of freedom. We find $c_1 = -2.37$ and $c_2 = 2.37$. Since $t = 3.19$ does not lie in the interval $[c_1, c_2]$ but lies outside, in the rejection region, we reject the hypothesis. Hence our present test, in which we used more information (but the same samples), shows that the difference in output is significant.

If the test in Table 13.4.1 leads to the rejection of the hypothesis, we assert that the two population means differ. Of course, this does *not* imply that every member of one population is superior to every member of the other, since the two populations may overlap to a large extent.

If the random variables X and Y considered do not satisfy the assumption of equal variance made in Table 13.4.1, then for the test we should choose samples of equal size ($n_1 = n_2 = n$) and n large enough (at least equal to 30, practically speaking). Then (3) is an observed value of a random variable which, if the hypothesis is true, is approximately normal with mean 0 and variance 1. Using this information, we may then perform the test.

Problems

General assumption. *In each of the following problems assume that the populations from which the samples were taken are normally distributed and have the same variance.*

1. Three specimens of high quality concrete had the compressive strength (in kilograms/centimeter^2)

$$357 \quad 359 \quad 413.$$

   For three specimens of ordinary concrete, the values were

$$346 \quad 358 \quad 302.$$

   Test the hypothesis that the corresponding population means μ_X and μ_Y are equal against the alternative $\mu_X > \mu_Y$ suggested by the nature of the experiment.

2. Using two independent samples with $n_1 = 9$, $\bar{x} = 12$, $s_x = 2$, $n_2 = 9$, $\bar{y} = 15$, $s_y = 2$, test the hypothesis $H_0: \mu_X = \mu_Y$ against the alternative $H_1: \mu_X \neq \mu_Y$, choosing $\alpha = 5\%$.

3. To investigate the reliability of a method of measurement used in cooling experiments, the following two samples A and B (values of temperature) were taken.

A	106.9	106.3	107.0	106.0	104.9
B	106.5	106.7	106.8	106.1	105.6

   Is the difference between the means significant?

4. Using the following samples of oxygen consumption (in millimeters^3 per hour) of trout, test the hypothesis that the consumption is independent of the speed of the water against the alternative that it is higher in more rapidly flowing rivers.

Speed	Oxygen Consumption								
High	108	122	144	129	107	115	114	97	96	126
Low	85	152	83	69	95	87	71	94	83	94

5. In a study of the effectiveness of working methods, a firm wanted to compare two types of hand-picking methods (used in peanut and other industries). Nine participants in the test obtained the following results (numbers of speckled beans hand-sorted from white and speckled beans within a given interval of time).

Worker number	1	2	3	4	5	6	7	8	9
First method	214	253	276	215	238	221	210	229	269
Second method	281	279	260	230	267	253	205	265	299

Test the hypothesis that both methods yield equal results against the alternative that the second method is better.

6. Brand *A* gasoline was used in 9 similar automobiles under identical conditions. The corresponding sample of 9 values (miles per gallon) had mean 20.2 and standard deviation 0.5. Under the same conditions, high power brand *B* gasoline gave a sample of 10 values with mean 21.8 and standard deviation 0.6. Test the hypothesis that *A* and *B* are of equal quality with respect to mileage against the alternative that *B* is better.

7. A sample of 16 students from one area of a city had mean I. Q. (intelligence quotient) 110 with a standard deviation of 10, whereas a sample of 16 students from another area of that city had mean I. Q. 105 with a standard deviation of 8. Test the hypothesis that the corresponding population means are equal against the alternative that they are different.

8. Test the hypothesis that a new fertilizer for wheat production is as effective as an old fertilizer against the alternative that the new fertilizer is superior to the old one. For this purpose consider the number of bushels of wheat harvested and use two samples of size 25 each, obtained from 50 squares of equal area and equal quality of soil, sunlight exposure, rainfall, etc. To 25 of the squares the old fertilizer was applied; the mean number of bushels was 16.0 with a standard deviation of 0.5. To the other 25 squares the new fertilizer was applied; the mean number of bushels was 18.5 with a standard deviation 0.7.

9. Is the difference of increase in weight (pounds in two months) of two groups of hogs significant? The two groups were fed two different diets.

Group I	33	66	26	43	46	55	54
Group II	53	53	37	73	58	61	38

10. Somebody wanted to buy a large quantity of light bulbs and had a choice between two brands I and II. He bought 100 bulbs of each brand and found by testing that brand I had a mean lifetime of 1120 hours with a standard deviation of 75 hours, and brand II had a mean lifetime of 1064 hours with a standard deviation of 82 hours. Is the difference of the mean lifetimes significant?

11. In Problem 10 the hypothesis is rejected when $\alpha = 5\%$. Choosing a smaller sample size, we would obtain less information. For what sample size n would the hypothesis still be accepted when $\alpha = 5\%$ and means and standard deviations are as before?

12. Construct two simple samples, such that the hypothesis of equal population means is not rejected although the difference between the sample means is large.

13. Test the hypothesis that in a certain group of elementary schools the means of the spelling grades for boys and girls are equal against the alternative that the mean for girls is higher; use a sample of 26 grades for boys with mean 70 and standard deviation 5 and a sample of 30 grades for girls with mean 77 and standard deviation 6.

14. Show that $Z = X - Y$ has the variance

$$\sigma_Z^2 = \sigma_X^2 + \sigma_Y^2 - 2\sigma_{XY}$$

where σ_{XY} is the covariance defined in Sec. 9.8.

13.5 ᵒᵐⁱᵗ Derivation of the Test in Sec. 13.4

From the definition of the chi-square distribution we immediately obtain the following theorem.

Theorem 1. *Let Z_1 and Z_2 be independent random variables that have chi-square distributions with m and n degrees of freedom, respectively. Then their sum $Z_1 + Z_2$ has a chi-square distribution with $m + n$ degrees of freedom.*

The test in the last section is based on the following theorem.

Theorem 2. *Let $X_1, \cdots, X_{n_1}, Y_1, \cdots, Y_{n_2}$ be independent normal random variables with the same variance σ^2. Suppose that each of the X_j has mean μ_X and each of the Y_j has mean μ_Y. Let*

$$(1) \qquad \bar{X} = \frac{1}{n_1}(X_1 + \cdots + X_{n_1}), \qquad \bar{Y} = \frac{1}{n_2}(Y_1 + \cdots + Y_{n_2})$$

and furthermore

$$(2) \qquad S_X^2 = \frac{1}{n_1 - 1}\sum_{j=1}^{n_1}(X_j - \bar{X})^2, \qquad S_Y^2 = \frac{1}{n_2 - 1}\sum_{j=1}^{n_2}(Y_j - \bar{Y})^2.$$

Then the random variable

$$(3) \qquad T = \sqrt{\frac{n_1 n_2 (n_1 + n_2 - 2)}{n_1 + n_2}} \cdot \frac{\bar{X} - \bar{Y} - (\mu_X - \mu_Y)}{\sqrt{(n_1 - 1)S_X^2 + (n_2 - 1)S_Y^2}}$$

has a t-distribution with $n_1 + n_2 - 2$ degrees of freedom.

Proof. From Theorem 1 in Sec. 12.4 it follows that the random variables

$$V_1 = \frac{1}{\sigma^2}(n_1 - 1)S_X^2 \qquad \text{and} \qquad V_2 = \frac{1}{\sigma^2}(n_2 - 1)S_Y^2$$

have chi-square distributions with $n_1 - 1$ and $n_2 - 1$ degrees of freedom, respectively. These variables are independent because the X_j and Y_j are independent. From this and Theorem 1 it follows that their sum $V_1 + V_2$ has a chi-square distribution with $n_1 + n_2 - 2$ degrees of freedom. From Theorems 1 in Sec. 12.2 and 2 in Sec. 12.2 we see that $\bar{X} - \mu_X$ and $-(\bar{Y} - \mu_Y)$ are normal with mean 0 and variance σ^2/n_1 and σ^2/n_2, respectively. These variables are independent. Hence their sum

$$Z^* = \bar{X} - \mu_X - (\bar{Y} - \mu_Y) = \bar{X} - \bar{Y} - (\mu_X - \mu_Y)$$

is normal with mean 0 and variance

$$\sigma^{*2} = \frac{\sigma^2}{n_1} + \frac{\sigma^2}{n_2} = \frac{n_1 + n_2}{n_1 n_2} \sigma^2;$$

cf. Theorem 1 in Sec. 12.2. Consequently, $Z = Z^*/\sigma^*$ is normal with mean 0 and variance 1. Similarly, as in Sec. 12.4, it follows that Z and $V = V_1 + V_2$ are independent. This means that these variables correspond to the variables X and Y, respectively, in Sec. 10.3. We may thus conclude that

(4) $$T = \frac{Z}{\sqrt{V/(n_1 + n_2 - 2)}}$$

has a t-distribution with $n_1 + n_2 - 2$ degrees of freedom. If we substitute the expressions for V and Z, we readily see that (4) takes the form (3). This completes the proof of Theorem 2.

If the hypothesis $\mu_X = \mu_Y$ is true, then (3) looks somewhat simpler. If we insert the observed values $\bar{x}$, $\bar{y}$, s_x, and s_y of $\bar{X}$, $\bar{Y}$, S_X, and S_Y, respectively, we obtain (2) in Sec. 13.4. This means that t_0 is an observed value of T. Since α is small, the probability in (1), Sec. 13.4, is large. This is the probability that T assumes any value $t_0 \leq c$, and the probability that T assumes any value $t_0 > c$ is small. Hence, if such a value $t_0 > c$ is observed, we reject the hypothesis. This justifies the steps in Table 13.4.1.

If the hypothesis is rejected, we also say that the difference between the means is **significant.**

13.6 Comparison of Variances of Normal Distributions

Table 13.6.1 shows how to test the hypothesis that two normal distributions have the same variance. The means need not be known. This test is of practical importance because the variance may occur as a measure of uniformity and quality of production, etc.

Example 1. Using the two samples in Example 1, Sec. 13.4, test the hypothesis $\sigma_X^2 = \sigma_Y^2$, assuming that the corresponding populations are normal and the nature of the experiment suggests the alternative $\sigma_X^2 > \sigma_Y^2$.

1st step. We know that $s_x^2 = 106.125$ and $s_y^2 = 84.000$.

2nd step. We choose the significance level $\alpha = 5\%$.

3rd step. We determine c from

$$P(V \leq c) = 95\%$$

and Table 9a with $(n_1 - 1, n_2 - 1) = (7, 7)$ degrees of freedom, finding $c = 3.79$.

4th step. We compute $v_0 = s_x^2/s_y^2 = 1.26$. Since $v_0 = 1.26 \leq c = 3.79$, we do not reject the hypothesis.

Table 13.6.1. Test of the Hypothesis $\sigma_X{}^2 = \sigma_Y{}^2$ against the Alternative $\sigma_X{}^2 > \sigma_Y{}^2$ for Normal Distributions by Means of Independent Samples

> *1st step.* Compute the variances $s_x{}^2$ and $s_y{}^2$ of the samples
>
> $$x_1, \cdots, x_{n_1} \quad \text{and} \quad y_1, \cdots, y_{n_2}.$$
>
> *2nd step.* Choose a significance level α (5% or 1%).
> *3rd step.* Determine a number c from the equation
>
> (1) $$P(V \leqq c) = 1 - \alpha$$
>
> and Table 9a or 9b (cf. Appendix 4) of the F-distribution with $(n_1 - 1, n_2 - 1)$ degrees of freedom.
> *4th step.* Compute $v_0 = s_x{}^2/s_y{}^2$. If $v_0 \leqq c$, do not reject the hypothesis. If $v_0 > c$, reject it.

We shall now discuss the theoretical foundation of the test. It can be shown that the following theorem holds (proof in Cramér (1961), p. 241; cf. Appendix 3).

Theorem 1. *Let U_1 and U_2 be independent random variables that have chi-square distributions with m and n degrees of freedom, respectively. Then the random variable*

$$V = \frac{U_1/m}{U_2/n}$$

has the distribution function $F(x) = 0$ when $x < 0$ and

(2) $$F(x) = P(V \leqq x) = \frac{\Gamma\left(\dfrac{m+n}{2}\right)}{\Gamma\left(\dfrac{m}{2}\right)\Gamma\left(\dfrac{n}{2}\right)} m^{m/2} n^{n/2} \int_0^x \frac{t^{(m-2)/2}}{(mt+n)^{(m+n)/2}}\, dt$$

when $x > 0$. Here $\Gamma(\lambda)$ is the gamma function defined in Sec. 10.1.

The distribution given by (2) is called the **F-distribution** *with (m, n) degrees of freedom.* It was introduced by R. A. Fisher (Proc. Int. Math. Congress, Toronto, 1924). A typical graph of the corresponding density is shown in Fig. 13.6.1.

From Theorem 1 and Theorem 1, Sec. 12.4, we obtain the following result.

Theorem 2. *Let $X_1, \cdots, X_{n_1}, Y_1, \cdots, Y_{n_2}$ be independent normal random variables. Suppose that each of the X_i has variance $\sigma_X{}^2$ and each of the Y_j has variance $\sigma_Y{}^2$. Then the random variable*

(3) $$V = \left(\frac{S_X{}^2}{\sigma_X{}^2}\right)\Big/\left(\frac{S_Y{}^2}{\sigma_Y{}^2}\right),$$

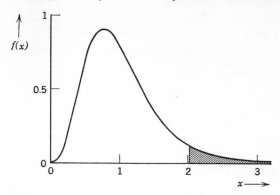

Fig. 13.6.1. Density $f(x)$ of the F-distribution with (10, 50) degrees of freedom. (The area of the shaded portion equals 0.05.)

where $S_X{}^2$ *and* $S_Y{}^2$ *are given by* (2), *Sec. 13.5, has an F-distribution with* $(n_1 - 1, n_2 - 1)$ *degrees of freedom.*

Proof.   From Theorem 1 in Sec. 12.4 it follows that the random variables

$$\frac{(n_1 - 1)S_X{}^2}{\sigma_X{}^2} = \frac{1}{\sigma_X{}^2} \sum_{j=1}^{n_1} (X_j - \bar{X})^2$$

and

$$\frac{(n_2 - 1)S_Y{}^2}{\sigma_Y{}^2} = \frac{1}{\sigma_Y{}^2} \sum_{j=1}^{n_2} (Y_j - \bar{Y})^2$$

have chi-square distributions with $n_1 - 1$ and $n_2 - 1$ degrees of freedom, respectively. From this and Theorem 1 we obtain Theorem 2, and the proof is complete.

If the hypothesis $\sigma_X{}^2 = \sigma_Y{}^2$ is true, then (3) reduces to the form

$$(4) \qquad\qquad V_0 = \frac{S_X{}^2}{S_Y{}^2}.$$

v_0 in Table 13.6.1 is an observed value of V_0. The probability in (1) is large because α is small. Hence if the hypothesis is true, it is very probable that V_0 assumes any value not exceeding c. If $v_0 \leqq c$, we therefore do not reject the hypothesis. On the other hand, if the hypothesis is true, the probability α that V_0 assumes a value $v_0 > c$ is small, and, if this happens, we reject the hypothesis.

It can be shown that our present test is rather sensitive to deviation from normality (in contrast to the test in Sec. 13.4). If a distribution shows considerable deviation from normality, the test may be replaced by the following one. Compute $x_i{}^* = |x_i - \bar{x}|$ and $y_j{}^* = |y_j - \bar{y}|$. It can be shown that the means of the corresponding random variables are proportional to σ_X and σ_Y, respectively. Hence we may test the hypothesis $\sigma_X = \sigma_Y$ by testing the hypothesis that those variables have the same mean. This can be done by the method in Sec. 13.4, which is not very sensitive to deviation from normality.

Problems

General assumption. *In the following problems, assume that the populations from which the samples are taken are normally distributed.*

1. Samples of sizes 10 and 5 had variances $s_x^2 = 50$ and $s_y^2 = 20$. Test the hypothesis $H_0: \sigma_X^2 = \sigma_Y^2$ against the alternative $\sigma_X^2 > \sigma_Y^2$, choosing the significance level 5%.

2. Same task as in Problem 2, when the last sample has size 20, the other data are as before, and the significance level is 5%.

3. In an investigation of the dust content of waste gas, it was conjectured that the weight of the dust (in milligrams) was more variable in a certain portion A of the systems of tubes than in another portion B. Two corresponding samples are

A	75	20	70	70	85	90	100	40	35	65	90	35

and

B	20	35	55	50	65	40

Test the hypothesis that the variances are equal against the alternative $\sigma_X^2 > \sigma_Y^2$, where σ_X corresponds to A and σ_Y corresponds to B.

4. The following sample was taken in an investigation about the design of office furniture (such as desks and chairs). Are the differences of the means and the variances significant? ($c = 1.16$ in (1).)

	Mean Values		Standard Deviations	
	500 Men	508 Women	Men	Women
Height (centimeters)	169.0	158.8	9.5	10.2
Lengths of arms (centimeters)	70.4	63.6	4.7	4.5
Breadth of shoulders (centimeters)	43.5	41.2	2.5	2.6

5. For performing the test in Problem 4, Sec. 13.4, it was necessary to assume that the difference between the variances is not significant. Test this assumption.

6. Does the variance of the tensile strength (in kilograms/centimeter^2) of a certain type of concrete depend on the type of sand used?

Coarse-grain sand	203	229	215	220	223	233	208	228	209
Fine-grain sand	181	207	181	173	165	190	185	184	182

7. Is the difference of the means in Problem 6 significant?

8. The data below are differences of temperatures (in °C) of iron at two stages of iron casting, taken from two different crucibles. Is the difference between the variances significant?

Crucible Number	Differences of Temperature						
1	50	90	100	90	110	80	
2	110	110	110	110	120	130	120

9. The following table shows numbers of breaks of thread (per 100 lb) corresponding to two different twists per inch. Is the difference between the variances significant?

Twist/Inch	Breaks/100 lb							
1.69	6.0	9.7	7.4	11.5	17.9	11.9	10.2	7.8
1.78	6.4	8.3	7.9	8.8	10.1	11.5	8.7	9.7

10. Screws may be produced by die cutting or by mill cutting. 16 of each of these two types of screws were randomly selected and the major diameter was measured. The means were $\bar{x} = 23.189$ mm and $\bar{y} = 23.277$ mm, respectively. The variances were $s_x^2 = 0.001382$ mm² and $s_y^2 = 0.000433$ mm², respectively. Using these values, test the hypothesis $\sigma_X^2 = \sigma_Y^2$ against the alternative $\sigma_X^2 > \sigma_Y^2$.

11. If T has a t-distribution with n degrees of freedom, show that T^2 has an F-distribution with $(1, n)$ degrees of freedom.

12. How can the result in Problem 11 be used to obtain the values in the first column of Table 9a (Appendix 4) from suitable values in Table 8?

13. Evaluating the integral in (2) with $m = 2$, $n = 2$, verify the values in Tables 9a and 9b (Appendix 4) corresponding to $m = 2$, $n = 2$.

14. Evaluate the integral in (2) when $m = 2$ and n is arbitrary.

15. Show that if the alternative $\sigma_X^2 > \sigma_Y^2$ in Table 13.6.1 is replaced by the alternative $\sigma_X^2 \neq \sigma_Y^2$, then (1) must be replaced by

$$P(V \leq c_1) = \frac{\alpha}{2}, \qquad P(V \leq c_2) = 1 - \frac{\alpha}{2}.$$

16. What formula should be used instead of (1) if the alternative is $\sigma_X^2 < \sigma_Y^2$?

13.7 Best Tests. Neyman-Pearson Lemma

In this section we shall discuss the problem of comparing the quality of tests of a given simple hypothesis against a given simple alternative.

In practice a statistician often determines in advance what size Type I error he will tolerate and decides what sample size n to use in a test. Then he may attempt to construct that test which minimizes the size of the Type II error. Hence in comparing the quality of tests of a given simple hypothesis, it will be natural to assume that α and n are determined. Then a **best test** (or **most powerful test**) is defined to be a test that minimizes β, the size of the Type II error, in the set of the tests corresponding to those values of α and n, and the critical region of a best test is called a **best critical region.**

Here a **critical region** of a test is a region in n-dimensional space consisting of all the *sample points* $(x_1, \cdots, x_n)$ (corresponding to samples $x_1, \cdots, x_n$)

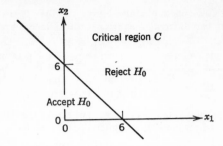

Fig. 13.7.1. Critical region C in a test of a hypothesis H_0: $\theta = \mu_0$ in which a sample of size 2 is used and H_0 is rejected if $\bar{x} > 3$, that is, $x_1 + x_2 > 6$

for which the test leads to the rejection of the hypothesis. A simple illustration is shown in Fig. 13.7.1; in this figure, the critical region C is the portion of the plane that lies above the line $x_1 + x_2 = 6$.

A test for which the size of the Type I error is α is briefly called a **test of size α** and the corresponding critical region is called a **critical region of size α** (or **rejection region of size α**).

Using this terminology, we may now state that a best test of size α is a test of size α for which β is minimum, and a best critical region of size α is a critical region that corresponds to a best test of size α.

In this connection we should note that a test specifies a critical region, as we know, but it can also be said that a choice of a critical region defines a test.

With this in mind, we may now state an important criterion for best tests by Neyman and Pearson (1933) (cf. Appendix 3), which is called the Neyman-Pearson lemma. This lemma will refer to tests of size α of a simple hypothesis H_0: $\theta = \theta_0$ against a simple alternative H_1: $\theta = \theta_1$; these tests are based on a sample $x_1, \cdots, x_n$ of fixed size n from a population with probability density function $f(x; \theta)$, and we shall use the notation (cf. Sec. 11.5)

$$(1) \qquad l(\theta) = f(x_1; \theta)f(x_2; \theta) \cdots f(x_n; \theta).$$

Neyman-Pearson lemma. *If C is a critical region of size α and there exists a constant k such that*

$$(2) \qquad \frac{l(\theta_1)}{l(\theta_0)} \geqq k \qquad when\ (x_1, \cdots, x_n)\ is\ in\ C$$

and

$$(3) \qquad \frac{l(\theta_1)}{l(\theta_0)} \leqq k \qquad when\ (x_1, \cdots, x_n)\ is\ outside\ C,$$

then C is a best critical region of size α for testing the hypothesis $\theta = \theta_0$ against the alternative $\theta = \theta_1$.

Remark. If for a sample $x_1, \cdots, x_n$ the sample point $(x_1, \cdots, x_n)$ is in the critical region C, the hypothesis is rejected; this is a correct decision when

$\theta = \theta_1$, but leads to a Type I error when $\theta = \theta_0$. Hence, intuitively speaking, it stands to reason that in this case, the quotient $q = l(\theta_1)/l(\theta_0)$ should be *large* [cf. (2)]. Similarly, q should be *small* [cf. (3)] when $(x_1, \cdots, x_n)$ is outside C, which leads to a correct decision when $\theta = \theta_0$ but to a Type II error when $\theta = \theta_1$.

Proof of the lemma. A sample value x_j may be regarded as an observed value of a random variable X_j with the density $f(x_j; \theta)$. Since these random variables $X_1, \cdots, X_n$ are independent, $l(\theta)$ is the density of the random variable $(X_1, \cdots, X_n)$. By definition of the critical region C, the probability that $(X_1, \cdots, X_n)$ will assume any value in C when $\theta = \theta_0$ equals α; thus

$$(4) \qquad \int_C l(\theta_0)\, dx = \alpha,$$

where $dx = dx_1 \cdots dx_n$. Let C^* be any other critical region of size α. Then

$$(5) \qquad \int_{C^*} l(\theta_0)\, dx = \alpha.$$

Let β and β^* be the sizes of the Type II error corresponding to C and C^*, respectively. Since β is the probability that $(X_1, \cdots, X_n)$ will assume any value outside the critical region C when $\theta = \theta_1$ is true, we have

$$(6) \qquad \beta = 1 - \int_C l(\theta_1)\, dx.$$

Similarly,

$$(7) \qquad \beta^* = 1 - \int_{C^*} l(\theta_1)\, dx.$$

Let $B = C \cap C^*$ be the intersection of C and C^*, and let $A = C - B$ and $A^* = C^* - B$ (cf. Fig. 13.7.2). Then from (4) and (5) we have

$$(8) \qquad \int_A l(\theta_0)\, dx = \int_{A^*} l(\theta_0)\, dx.$$

Similarly, (6) and (7) give

$$\beta^* - \beta = \int_A l(\theta_1)\, dx - \int_{A^*} l(\theta_1)\, dx.$$

Since A lies in C, we may apply (2), that is,

$$l(\theta_1) \geqq kl(\theta_0) \qquad\qquad [(x_1, \cdots, x_n) \text{ in } A]$$

and conclude that

$$\int_A l(\theta_1)\, dx \geqq k \int_A l(\theta_0)\, dx.$$

Since A^* lies outside C,

$$l(\theta_1) \leqq kl(\theta_0), \quad \text{thus} \qquad -l(\theta_1) \geqq -kl(\theta_0)$$

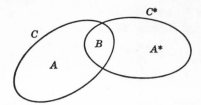

Fig. 13.7.2. Notations in the proof of the Neyman-Pearson lemma

and

$$-\int_{A^*} l(\theta_1)\,dx \geqq -k\int_{A^*} l(\theta_0)\,dx.$$

By addition,

$$\beta^* - \beta \geqq k\left(\int_A l(\theta_0)\,dx - \int_{A^*} l(\theta_0)\,dx\right).$$

The expression on the right is 0, as follows from (8). Hence $\beta^* - \beta \geqq 0$, $\beta^* \geqq \beta$, and the lemma is proved.

Example 1. Let us consider a normally distributed population with unknown mean μ and variance 1, and suppose we want to set up a test of a simple hypothesis H_0: $\mu = \mu_0$ against a simple alternative H_1: $\mu = \mu_1$. Then in the Neyman-Pearson lemma,

$$l(\mu) = (2\pi)^{-n/2}\exp\left[-\tfrac{1}{2}\sum (x_k - \mu)^2\right],$$

where $\exp z = e^z$ and we sum over k from 1 to n. The region C in that lemma is therefore the region in which

$$\frac{l(\mu_1)}{l(\mu_0)} = \frac{\exp\left[-\tfrac{1}{2}\sum (x_k - \mu_1)^2\right]}{\exp\left[-\tfrac{1}{2}\sum (x_k - \mu_0)^2\right]} \geqq k.$$

This may be written

$$\exp\left[-\tfrac{1}{2}\sum (x_k - \mu_1)^2 + \tfrac{1}{2}\sum (x_k - \mu_0)^2\right] \geqq k.$$

Taking logarithms, we have

$$\tfrac{1}{2}\sum (x_k - \mu_0)^2 - \tfrac{1}{2}\sum (x_k - \mu_1)^2 \geqq \ln k.$$

Simplifying on the left side, we obtain

$$(\mu_1 - \mu_0)\sum x_k \geqq \ln k + \frac{n}{2}(\mu_1{}^2 - \mu_0{}^2).$$

Using $\sum x_k = n\bar{x}$ and dividing by n, we see that

(9)
$$(\mu_1 - \mu_0)\bar{x} \geqq \frac{\ln k}{n} + \tfrac{1}{2}(\mu_1{}^2 - \mu_0{}^2).$$

From now on it will matter whether $\mu_1 > \mu_0$ or $\mu_1 < \mu_0$. If $\mu_1 > \mu_0$, then (9) gives

(10)
$$\bar{x} \geqq c$$

where

$$c = \frac{\ln k}{n(\mu_1 - \mu_0)} + \tfrac{1}{2}(\mu_1 + \mu_0).$$

If $\mu_1 < \mu_0$, then $\mu_1 - \mu_0 < 0$ and (9) gives

$$(11) \qquad\qquad\qquad \bar{x} \leqq c.$$

The constant k contained in c may be chosen so that the size α of the Type I error equals a desired value. Regions of this type were chosen on an intuitive basis in Example 1, Sec. 13.3. From the Pearson-Neyman lemma it now follows that they are best critical regions.

Furthermore, we see that the test given by (10) is best for each $\mu_1 > \mu_0$; it is therefore called a **uniformly best test** for our problem. When $\mu_1 < \mu_0$, the situation is similar. However, since (10) and (11) define different tests, we also see that there is no uniformly best test for testing

$$H_0: \mu = \mu_0 \qquad \text{against} \qquad H_1: \mu \neq \mu_0.$$

13.8   Likelihood Ratio Method

The Neyman-Pearson lemma in the last section is important in connection with a very simple kind of hypothesis-testing problem. In more general situations involving composite hypotheses, best tests may not exist, as we know from the preceding section. However, we shall now consider the *likelihood ratio method* by Neyman and Pearson (1928, 1933), which produces useful tests for composite hypotheses, and in most of the standard types of problem these tests are as good as those obtained by other methods, for example, by searching for best tests in restricted classes of tests having certain reasonable properties.

Let $x_1, \cdots, x_n$ be a sample from a population with probability density

$$f(x; \theta) \qquad\qquad [\theta = (\theta_1, \cdots, \theta_r)]$$

depending on r parameters $\theta_1, \cdots, \theta_r$. Let Ω denote the corresponding **parameter space**, that is, the set of all r-tuples of values that $\theta = (\theta_1, \cdots, \theta_r)$ can assume. Let H_0 be a hypothesis to be tested. Clearly, H_0 imposes certain restrictions on the values of θ and thus determines a certain subset of Ω, which we denote by Ω_0. We may thus write the hypothesis in the form

$$H_0: \qquad \theta \in \Omega_0$$

and, consequently, the alternative in the form

$$H_1: \qquad \theta \in \Omega_1 \qquad \text{where} \qquad \Omega_1 = \Omega - \Omega_0.$$

For example, if that population is normal, we have the two parameters $\theta_1 = \mu$ and $\theta_2 = \sigma^2$. Hence in this case Ω is the upper half ($\sigma^2 > 0$) of the $\mu\sigma^2$-plane. If the hypothesis is $\mu = \mu_0$ (as in Ex. 2, Sec. 13.3), then Ω_0 is the vertical ray beginning at the point μ_0 on the μ-axis and extending upward. If the hypothesis H_0 is simple, say, $\mu = \mu_0$, $\sigma^2 = \sigma_0^2$, then Ω_0 is the single point (μ_0, σ_0^2). Similarly, if the variance is known, then Ω is the μ-axis, and a hypothesis $H_0: \mu = \mu_0$ specifies a single point, which is Ω_0 in this case.

To the given sample $x_1, \cdots, x_n$ there corresponds the likelihood function

$$l(\theta) = f(x_1; \theta) f(x_2; \theta) \cdots f(x_n; \theta).$$

If we keep the x_k's fixed and let θ vary over Ω, then $l(\theta)$ will ordinarily have a maximum. We denote this maximum value by l_Ω. Similarly we let l_{Ω_0} denote the maximum of l as θ varies over Ω_0. The quotient

$$\lambda = \frac{l_\Omega}{l_{\Omega_0}}$$

is called the **likelihood ratio**. Since l_{Ω_0} can never exceed l_Ω, we always have

$$\lambda \geqq 1.$$

If for a given sample, λ is small (close to 1), then l_{Ω_0} is almost as large as l_Ω. This means that we cannot obtain an appreciably larger value of $l(\theta)$ by searching for a value of θ through the entire parameter space Ω than we can by searching through Ω_0. In this case our intuition will assess the evidence as strongly favoring the proposition that the "most plausible" value of θ belongs to Ω_0, that is, that the hypothesis H_0 is true. This suggests the following decision. Choose a value λ_0 and

> if $\lambda \leqq \lambda_0$, do not reject the hypothesis H_0;
>
> if $\lambda > \lambda_0$, reject the hypothesis H_0.

To determine λ_0 corresponding to a desired significance level α (size of Type I error), we must know the distribution of the random variable Λ for which λ is an observed value.

It can be shown that if the hypothesis is true, then under rather general conditions the distribution function of the random variable

$$V = 2 \ln \Lambda$$

approaches the distribution function of the χ^2-distribution with 1 degree of freedom, as $n \to \infty$. See Wilks (1962), p. 408.

This information may be used for determining good approximations of λ_0 when the sample size n is large.

Example 1. Using a sample $x_1, \cdots, x_n$ from a normally distributed population with known variance $\sigma_0{}^2$ and unknown mean μ, we consider the hypothesis-testing problem:

> Hypothesis: $\mu = \mu_0$,
>
> Alternative: $\mu \neq \mu_0$.

From the preceding section we know that there is no corresponding uniformly best test. In this problem, Ω is the entire μ-axis and Ω_0 is the point $\mu = \mu_0$. Let us apply the likelihood ratio method. From the preceding section we have

$$l(\mu) = (2\pi\sigma_0{}^2)^{-n/2} \exp\left[-\frac{1}{2\sigma_0{}^2} \sum (x_k - \mu)^2\right],$$

where we sum over k from 1 to n. Using the maximum likelihood estimate $\hat{\mu} = \bar{x}$ (cf. Sec. 11.6), we obtain

$$l_\Omega = l(\bar{x}) = (2\pi\sigma_0{}^2)^{-n/2} \exp\left[-\frac{1}{2\sigma_0{}^2} \sum (x_k - \bar{x})^2\right].$$

Since Ω_0 is a point (the hypothesis is simple), we cannot vary μ, and the largest value of l in Ω_0 is simply its only value:

$$l_{\Omega_0} = l(\mu_0) = (2\pi\sigma_0{}^2)^{-n/2} \exp\left[-\frac{1}{2\sigma_0{}^2} \sum (x_k - \mu_0)^2\right].$$

Taking the ratio, we obtain

$$\lambda = \exp\left[\frac{1}{2\sigma_0{}^2} \sum (x_k - \mu_0)^2 - \frac{1}{2\sigma_0{}^2} \sum (x_k - \bar{x})^2\right].$$

Taking logarithms and using $\sum x_k = n\bar{x}$, we find that

(1)
$$2 \ln \lambda = \frac{1}{\sigma_0{}^2} \sum (x_k - \mu_0)^2 - \frac{1}{\sigma_0{}^2} \sum (x_k - \bar{x})^2$$

$$= \frac{n(\bar{x} - \mu_0)^2}{\sigma_0{}^2}.$$

From Theorem 3 in Sec. 12.2 we see that if the hypothesis $\mu = \mu_0$ is true, then the random variable $\sqrt{n}\,(\bar{X} - \mu_0)/\sigma_0$ is normal with mean 0 and variance 1. Hence its square

$$V = 2 \ln \Lambda = n(\bar{X} - \mu_0)^2/\sigma_0{}^2$$

has a chi-square distribution with 1 degree of freedom (cf. Sec. 10.1). We may thus choose α and then determine a number v_0 from

$$P(V > v_0) = \alpha, \qquad \text{thus} \qquad P(V \leq v_0) = 1 - \alpha$$

and Table 6 in Appendix 4. Using (1) and the notation $v = 2 \ln \lambda$, we have

(2)
$$v = \frac{n(\bar{x} - \mu_0)^2}{\sigma_0{}^2}.$$

Hence if

$$v \leq v_0,$$

we do not reject the hypothesis and if

$$v > v_0,$$

we reject it.

For example, if $\alpha = 5\%$, then $v_0 = 3.84$. If $\mu_0 = 24$, $\sigma_0{}^2 = 9$, and $n = 10$, then (2) becomes

$$v = \tfrac{10}{9}(\bar{x} - 24)^2,$$

and we do not reject the hypothesis if

$$\tfrac{10}{9}(\bar{x} - 24)^2 \leq 3.84.$$

This is equivalent to

$$-1.86 \leq \bar{x} - 24 \leq 1.86$$

and agrees with the result given in Case (c) of Example 1, Sec. 13.3.

It is interesting to note that in our present example the distribution of $V = 2 \ln \Lambda$ is identical with the asymptotic distribution of V mentioned before.

Example 2. In the preceding example the likelihood ratio method led to the test given in Sec. 13.3. Let us now consider the same problem, but assume that the variance σ^2 is unknown, the other assumptions being as before. Then

$$l(\mu, \sigma) = (2\pi\sigma^2)^{-n/2} \exp\left[-\frac{1}{2\sigma^2} \sum (x_k - \mu)^2\right]$$

(summation over k from 1 to n). Using the maximum likelihood estimates given in Example 3, Sec. 11.6, we obtain

$$l_\Omega = \left[\frac{2\pi}{n} \sum (x_k - \bar{x})^2\right]^{-n/2} e^{-n/2}.$$

Since the hypothesis is $\mu = \mu_0$, the corresponding maximum likelihood estimate of σ^2 is

$$\frac{1}{n} \sum (x_k - \mu_0)^2.$$

Hence

$$l_{\Omega_0} = \left[\frac{2\pi}{n} \sum (x_k - \mu_0)^2\right]^{-n/2} e^{-n/2}.$$

The likelihood ratio is

$$\lambda = \left[\frac{\sum (x_k - \mu_0)^2}{\sum (x_k - \bar{x})^2}\right]^{n/2}.$$

Large values of λ correspond to large values of

$$\lambda^{2/n} = \frac{\sum (x_k - \mu_0)^2}{\sum (x_k - \bar{x})^2} = \frac{\sum (x_k - \bar{x})^2 + n(\bar{x} - \mu_0)^2}{\sum (x_k - \bar{x})^2}$$

$$= 1 + \frac{n(\bar{x} - \mu_0)^2}{\sum (x_k - \bar{x})^2} = 1 + \frac{t^2}{n-1}$$

where

$$t = \frac{\sqrt{n}\,(\bar{x} - \mu_0)}{s}$$

and s is the standard deviation of the sample. From (4) in Sec. 12.4 we see that t is an observed value of the random variable

$$T = \frac{\sqrt{n}\,(\bar{X} - \mu_0)}{S}.$$

From Theorem 2, Sec. 12.4, we conclude that if the hypothesis is true, then T has a t-distribution with $n-1$ degrees of freedom. Hence we may determine a critical value c from

$$P(-c \leqq T \leqq c)_{\mu_0} = 1 - \alpha$$

and Table 8 in Appendix 4 with $n-1$ degrees of freedom. If

$$-c \leqq t \leqq c,$$

we do not reject the hypothesis. Otherwise we reject it. Cf. also Example 2 in Sec. 13.3 (where the alternative is different from the present one).

CHAPTER 14

Quality Control and Acceptance Sampling

Quality control and acceptance sampling are two important applications of the basic idea of the preceding chapter to practical problems arising in connection with mass-produced articles. Inspection of every piece in a lot is generally uneconomical or even impossible if the inspection involves destructive testing; also, it could not be perfect because mechanical inspection devices have some margin of error and human inspectors are subject to fatigue and other sources of mistakes. These are some of the main reasons for applying methods of sampling and statistical inference in the field.

14.1 Quality Control

No production process is so perfect that all the products are completely alike. There is always a small variation that is caused by a great number of small, uncontrollable factors and must therefore be regarded as a chance variation. It is important to make sure that the products have required values (for example, length, strength, or whatever property may be of importance in a particular case). For this purpose one makes a test of the hypothesis that the products have the required property, say, $\mu = \mu_0$ where μ_0 is a required value. If this is done after an entire lot has been produced (for example a lot of 100,000 screws), the test will tell us how good or how bad the products are, but it is obviously too late to alter undesirable results. It is much better to test during the production run. This is done at regular intervals of time (for example, every 30 minutes or every hour) and is called **quality control.** Each time a sample of the same size is taken, in practice, 3 to 10 items. If the hypothesis is rejected, we stop the process of production and look for the trouble that causes the deviation.

If we stop the production process even though it is progressing properly, we make a Type I error. If we do not stop the process even though something is not in order, we make a Type II error (cf. Sec. 13.2).

The result of each test is marked in graphical form on what is called a **control chart.** This was proposed by W. A. Shewhart in 1924 and makes quality control particularly effective.

Control chart for the mean.   An illustration and example of a control chart is given in the upper part of Fig. 14.1.1. This control chart for the mean shows the **lower control limit** LCL and the **upper control limit** UCL. These two **control limits** correspond to the critical values c_1 and c_2 in Case (*c*) of

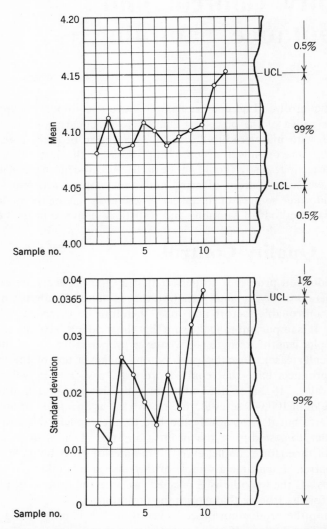

Fig. 14.1.1. Control charts for the mean (upper part of figure) and the standard deviation in the case of the sample in Table 14.1.1

Ex. 1 in Sec. 13.3. As soon as a sample mean falls outside the range between the control limits, we reject the hypothesis and assert that the process of production is "out of control," that is, we assert that there has been a shift in process level. Action is called for whenever a point exceeds the limits.

If we choose control limits that are too loose, we shall not detect process shifts. On the other hand, if we choose control limits that are too tight, we shall be unable to run the process because of a frequent search for non-existent trouble. The usual significance level is $\alpha = 1\%$. From Theorem 2 in Sec. 12.2 and Table 3*b* in Appendix 4 we see that in the case of the normal distribution the corresponding control limits for the mean are

$$(1) \qquad \text{LCL} = \mu_0 - 2.58\,\frac{\sigma}{\sqrt{n}} \quad \text{and} \quad \text{UCL} = \mu_0 + 2.58\,\frac{\sigma}{\sqrt{n}}.$$

Here σ is assumed to be known. If σ is unknown, we may calculate the standard deviations of the first 20 or 30 samples and take their arithmetic mean as an approximation of σ. The broken line connecting the means in Fig. 14.1.1 is merely to display the results effectively.

Choosing $\alpha = 1\%$ means that the Type I error is 1%, so in the long run we risk incorrectly calling a good process "out of control" in about 1% of the cases. If we keep $\alpha = 1\%$ and increase n, we see from (1) that the distance between the UCL and the LCL becomes smaller. This will give a better process of quality control but, of course, the corresponding cost will increase.

What usually happens in practice when quality control charts are introduced is this: After establishing control limits on the basis of 20 or more samples, and after searching for and eliminating causes of process trouble every time a point falls outside the control limits, it is soon found that the variability from

Table 14.1.1. Twelve Samples of 5 Values Each (Diameter of Small Cylinders, Measured in Millimeters)

Sample Number	Sample Values					$\bar{x}$	s	R
1	4.06	4.08	4.08	4.08	4.10	4.080	0.014	0.04
2	4.10	4.10	4.12	4.12	4.12	4.112	0.011	0.02
3	4.06	4.06	4.08	4.10	4.12	4.084	0.026	0.06
4	4.06	4.08	4.08	4.10	4.12	4.088	0.023	0.06
5	4.08	4.10	4.12	4.12	4.12	4.108	0.018	0.04
6	4.08	4.10	4.10	4.10	4.12	4.100	0.014	0.04
7	4.06	4.08	4.08	4.10	4.12	4.088	0.023	0.06
8	4.08	4.08	4.10	4.10	4.12	4.096	0.017	0.04
9	4.06	4.08	4.10	4.12	4.14	4.100	0.032	0.08
10	4.06	4.08	4.10	4.12	4.16	4.104	0.038	0.10
11	4.12	4.14	4.14	4.14	4.16	4.140	0.014	0.04
12	4.14	4.14	4.16.	4.16	4.16	4.152	0.011	0.02

mean to mean becomes smaller than it was for the initial set of samples. A new set of samples can then be taken and new upper and lower control limits established. These control limits, in practice, will usually be closer together than the original ones. After a few stages of this kind we arrive at a stage of statistical control involving control limits which are about as close together as can be hoped for without revolutionary changes in the manufacturing process.

In addition to the mean, one often controls the variance, the standard deviation, or the range.

Control chart for the variance.   To set up a control chart for the variance in the case of a normal distribution, we may employ the method in Ex. 3 of Sec. 13.3 for determining control limits. It is customary to use only one control limit, namely, an upper control limit. From Ex. 3 of Sec. 13.3 we see that this limit is

$$(2) \qquad \text{UCL} = \frac{\sigma^2 c}{n - 1}$$

where c is obtained from the equation

$$P(Y > c) = \alpha, \qquad \text{that is,} \qquad P(Y \leq c) = 1 - \alpha$$

and the table of the chi-square distribution (Table 6 in Appendix 4) with $n - 1$ degrees of freedom; here α (5% or 1%, say) is the probability that an observed value s^2 of S^2 in a sample is greater than the upper control limit.

If we wanted a control chart for the variance with both an upper control limit UCL and a lower control limit LCL, these limits would be

$$(3) \qquad \text{LCL} = \frac{\sigma^2 c_1}{n - 1} \qquad \text{and} \qquad \text{UCL} = \frac{\sigma^2 c_2}{n - 1}$$

where c_1 and c_2 are obtained from the equations

$$(4) \qquad P(Y \leq c_1) = \frac{\alpha}{2} \qquad \text{and} \qquad P(Y \leq c_2) = 1 - \frac{\alpha}{2}$$

and Table 6 in Appendix 4 with $n - 1$ degrees of freedom.

Control chart for the standard deviation.   Similarly, to set up a control chart for the standard deviation, we need an upper control limit, which, of course, may be obtained from (2); thus

$$(5) \qquad \text{UCL} = \frac{\sigma \sqrt{c}}{\sqrt{n - 1}}.$$

For example, in Table 14.1.1 we have $n = 5$. Assuming that the corresponding population is normal with standard deviation $\sigma = 0.02$ and choosing $\alpha = 1\%$, we obtain from the equation

$$P(Y \leq c) = 1 - \alpha = 99\%$$

$f(x) = .99$

and Table 6 in Appendix 4 with 4 degrees of freedom the critical value $c = 13.28$ and from (5) the corresponding value

$$\text{UCL} = \frac{0.02\sqrt{13.28}}{\sqrt{4}} = 0.0365.$$

The corresponding control chart is shown in the lower part of Fig. 14.1.1.

If we want a control chart for the standard deviation with both an upper and a lower control limit, these limits may be obtained from (3); thus

(6) $$\text{LCL} = \frac{\sigma\sqrt{c_1}}{\sqrt{n-1}} \quad \text{and} \quad \text{UCL} = \frac{\sigma\sqrt{c_2}}{\sqrt{n-1}}$$

with c_1 and c_2 as before.

Control chart for the range. If we control σ^2 or σ, we must compute s^2 or s, respectively. Since this may be difficult for mathematically untrained persons, one likes to replace the control of the variance or standard deviation by that of the range R (= largest sample value minus smallest sample value). It can be shown that in the case of the normal distribution, the standard deviation σ is proportional to the expectation of the random variable R^* for which R is an observed value, say, $\sigma = \lambda_n E(R^*)$, where the factor of proportionality λ_n depends on the sample size n and has the values

n	2	3	4	5	6	7	8	9	10
$\lambda_n = \sigma/E(R^*)$	0.89	0.59	0.49	0.43	0.40	0.37	0.35	0.34	0.32

n	12	14	16	18	20	30	40	50
$\lambda_n = \sigma/E(R^*)$	0.31	0.29	0.28	0.28	0.27	0.25	0.23	0.22

Since R depends on two sample values only, it gives less information about a sample than s does. Clearly, the larger the sample size n is, the more information we shall lose in using R instead of s. A practical rule is to use s when n is larger than ten.

Note that the estimate of the standard deviation based on the range is an easy approximate check on the computation of s. It may be useful in cases when somebody else (a computing center, for example) did the numerical work for the statistical investigator. Then misunderstandings and mistakes are quite common, and quick checks are therefore of increasing importance.

Finally we should mention that it is worthwhile to examine control charts for every indication of unusual patterns. One should not be satisfied merely with the observation that "all points are in control." For example, a control chart may indicate a trend (an increase or decrease of the means) or a periodic fluctuation of the values, etc., and if this is repeated, one may examine the production process and try to eliminate the cause of that behavior.

Problems

1. Suppose a machine for filling cans with lubricating oil is set so that it will generate fillings which form a normal population with mean 1 gal and standard deviation 0.02 gal. Set up a control chart of the type shown in Fig. 14.1.1 for controlling the mean (that is, find LCL and UCL), assuming that the sample size is 4.

2. What LCL and UCL do we obtain in Problem 1 if we require the significance level $\alpha = 0.3\%$? *Hint.* Cf. (6) in Sec. 8.2.

3. How does the meaning of the control limits (1) change if we apply a control chart with these limits in the case of a population which is not normal?

4. What LCL and UCL should we use instead of (1) if we use the sum $x_1 + \cdots + x_n$ of the sample values instead of $\bar{x}$?

5. Determine the LCL and UCL mentioned in Problem 4 in the case of Fig. 14.1.1.

6. Since the presence of a point outside control limits for the mean indicates trouble, how often would we be making the mistake of looking for nonexistent trouble if we used (*a*) 1-sigma limits, (*b*) 2-sigma limits? (Assume normality.)

7. How would progressive tool wear in an automatic lathe operation be indicated by a control chart for the mean? Answer the same question for a sudden change in the position of the tool in that operation.

8. Ten samples of size 2 were taken from a production lot of bolts. The values (length in millimeters) are

Sample number	1	2	3	4	5	6	7	8	9	10
Length	27.4	27.4	27.5	27.3	27.9	27.6	27.6	27.8	27.5	27.3
	27.6	27.4	27.7	27.4	27.5	27.5	27.4	27.3	27.4	27.7

Assuming that the population is normal with mean 27.5 and variance 0.024 and using (1), set up a control chart for the mean and graph the sample means on the chart.

9. Graph the means of the following 10 samples (thickness of washers, coded values) on a control chart for means, assuming that the population is normal with mean 5 and standard deviation 1.55.

Time	8:00	8:30	9:00	9:30	10:00	10:30	11:00	11:30	12:00	12:30
Sample values	3	3	5	7	7	4	5	6	5	5
	4	6	2	5	3	4	6	4	5	2
	8	6	5	4	6	3	4	6	6	5
	4	8	6	4	5	6	6	4	4	3

10. Graph the ranges of the samples in Problem 9 on a control chart for ranges.

11. Mark each of 100 equal chips by a number x as follows.

x	11	12	13	14	15	16	17	18	19
Number of chips marked x	1	4	12	20	26	20	12	4	1

Show that this population has mean $\mu = 15$ and standard deviation $\sigma = \sqrt{2.4} = 1.55$. Draw 50 chips with replacement, record the results, and compute the sample mean $\bar{x}$ and the sample variance s^2. Compare the results with the population parameters μ and σ^2. Using $\bar{x}$ and s as approximations for μ_0 and σ in (1), find UCL and LCL in the case of samples of size 2. Make up a control chart for the mean. Drawing with replacement, obtain 20 samples of size 2 and graph their means (in the order obtained) on the control chart.

12. In Problem 11, obtain another 20 samples of size 2, graph their means on another control chart, and compare the results.

13. Do the work in Problem 11, using samples of size 4. Compare the results.

14. Using the values obtained in Problem 11, make up control charts for the standard deviation and for the range. Using the 20 samples in Problem 11, graph their standard deviations and their ranges on the control charts.

15. Do the work in Problem 14, using the 20 samples obtained in Problem 12, and compare the result with that in Problem 14.

16. Graph λ_n in $\sigma = \lambda_n E(R)^*$ as a function of n.

17. λ_n is a monotone decreasing function of n. What is the reason?

18. Assuming normality and using the formula $\sigma = \lambda_n E(R^*)$, determine point estimates of the standard deviations of the populations from which the two samples in Problem 3, Sec. 13.6, were taken. Compare the estimates with the sample standard deviations.

19. Using the range of the sample in Problem 5, Sec. 2.1, and assuming normality, estimate the standard deviation of the population from which the sample was taken.

20. **(Attribute control charts).** Twenty samples of size 100 were taken from a production of containers. The number of defective containers (leaking containers) was as follows.

Sample number	1	2	3	4	5	6	7	8	9	10	11	12	13	14	15	16	17	18	19	20
Number of defectives	3	7	6	1	4	5	4	9	7	0	5	6	13	4	9	0	2	1	12	8

From previous experience it was known that the average fraction defective is $p = 5\%$ provided that the process of production is running properly. Using the binomial distribution, set up a *fraction defective chart* (also called a **p-chart**), that is, choose the LCL $= 0$ and determine the UCL for the fraction defective (in percent) by the use of 3-sigma limits, where σ^2 is the variance of the random variable $\bar{X} = $ *fraction defective in a sample of size* 100. Is the process in control?

14.2 Acceptance Sampling

Acceptance sampling is applied in mass production when a *producer* is supplying to a *consumer* lots of N items. In such a situation the decision to accept or reject an individual lot must be made. This decision is often based on the result of inspecting a sample of size n from the lot and determining the number of **defective items,** that is, items which do not meet the specifications (size, color, strength, or whatever may be important). If the number of defective items x in the sample is not greater than a specified number c ($< n$), the lot is accepted. If $x > c$, the lot is rejected. c is called the *allowable number of defectives* or the **acceptance number.**

It is clear that the producer and the consumer must agree on a certain **sampling plan,** that is, on a certain sample size n and an allowable number c. Such a plan is called a **single sampling plan** because it is based on a single sample. *Double sampling plans*, in which two samples are used, will be mentioned later.

Let A be the event that a lot is accepted. It is clear that the corresponding probability $P(A)$ depends not only on n and c but also on the number of defective items in the lot. Let M denote this number, let the random variable X be the number of defective items in a sample of size n, and suppose that we sample without replacement. Then (cf. Sec. 7.7)

$$(1) \qquad P(A) = P(X \leqq c) = \sum_{x=0}^{c} \binom{M}{x}\binom{N-M}{n-x} \Big/ \binom{N}{n}.$$

If $M = 0$ (no defective items in the lot), then X must assume the value 0, and

$$P(A) = \binom{0}{0}\binom{N}{n} \Big/ \binom{N}{n} = 1.$$

For fixed n and c and increasing M the probability $P(A)$ decreases. If $M = N$ (all items of the lot defective), then X must assume the value n, and we have $P(A) = P(X \leqq c) = 0$ because $c < n$.

The ratio $\theta = M/N$ is called the **fraction defective** in the lot. Note that $M = N\theta$, and (1) may be written

$$(2) \qquad P(A; \theta) = \sum_{x=0}^{c} \binom{N\theta}{x}\binom{N-N\theta}{n-x} \Big/ \binom{N}{n}.$$

Since θ can have one of the $N + 1$ values $0, 1/N, 2/N, \cdots, N/N$, the probability $P(A)$ is defined for these values only. For fixed n and c we may plot $P(A)$ as a function of θ. These are $N + 1$ points. Through these points we may then draw a smooth curve, which is called the **operating characteristic curve** (OC curve) of the sampling plan considered.

Example 1. Suppose that certain tool bits are packaged 20 to a box, and the following single sampling plan is used: A sample of 2 tool bits is drawn, and the corresponding box is accepted if and only if both bits in the sample are good. In this case, $N = 20$, $n = 2$, $c = 0$, and (2) takes the form

$$P(A; \theta) = \binom{20\theta}{0}\binom{20 - 20\theta}{2} \Big/ \binom{20}{2} = \frac{(20 - 20\theta)(19 - 20\theta)}{380}.$$

The numerical values are

θ	0.00	0.05	0.10	0.15	0.20	$\cdots$
$P(A; \theta)$	1.00	0.90	0.81	0.72	0.63	$\cdots$

The OC curve is shown in Fig. 14.2.1.

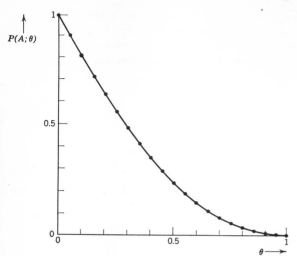

Fig. 14.2.1. OC curve of the single sampling plan with
$n = 2$ and $c = 0$ for lots of size $N = 20$

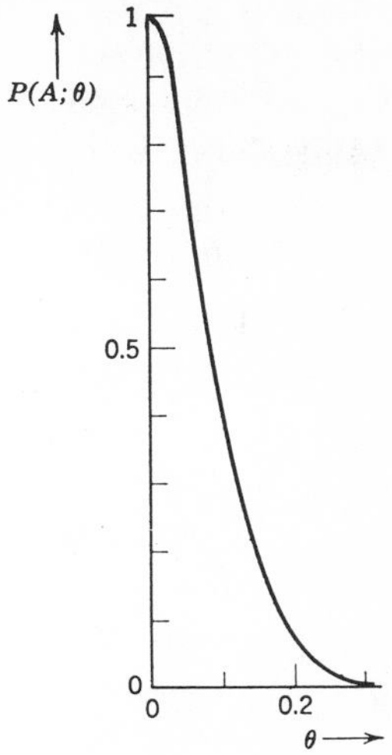

Fig. 14.2.2. OC curve in
Ex. 2

In most practical cases θ will be small (less than 10%). In many cases the lot size N will be very large (1000, 10,000, etc.), so that we may approximate the hypergeometric distribution in (1) and (2) by the binomial distribution with $p = \theta$. Then if n is such that $n\theta$ is moderate (say, less than 20), we may approximate that distribution by the Poisson distribution with mean $\mu = n\theta$. From (2) we then have

$$(3) \qquad P(A;\theta) \sim e^{-\mu} \sum_{x=0}^{c} \frac{\mu^{x}}{x!} \qquad\qquad (\mu = n\theta).$$

Example 2. Suppose that for large lots the following single sampling plan is used. A sample of size $n = 20$ is taken. If it contains not more than 1 defective item, the lot is accepted. If the sample contains 2 or more defective items, the lot is rejected. In this plan, we obtain from (3)

$$P(A;\theta) \sim e^{-20\theta}(1 + 20\theta).$$

The corresponding OC curve is shown in Fig. 14.2.2.

In some cases where attribute inspection is used, a unit may contain one or more defects but still be considered a good product because the defects are small and their number per unit (or per unit area) does not exceed a certain critical value. This situation may arise if the material submitted for inspection is rolls of cloth, film, paper, printed material, or a similar product, or if it consists of large units such as radios, TV sets, and the like. Then a **defect-per-unit sampling plan** instead of a fraction defective plan should be used. The two notions are closely related. Like the fraction defective plans, a single-sample defect-per-unit plan specifies a sample size n and an acceptance number c. If the total number of defects in a sample does not exceed c, the corresponding lot is accepted. If that number is greater than c, the lot is rejected. We may graph an OC curve, as before. The abscissa scale then shows the number of defects per unit (sometimes per 100 units).

Problems

1. Find the binomial approximation of the hypergeometric distribution in Example 1 and compare the approximate and the accurate values.

2. Using the Poisson approximation of the hypergeometric distribution, graph the OC curve corresponding to the following single sampling plan for large lots. A sample of $n = 30$ items is drawn from the lot and the 30 items are inspected. The lot is accepted if the sample contains not more than $c = 1$ defective item. Otherwise the lot is rejected.

3. Do the work required in Problem 2 when $n = 50$ and $c = 0$.

4. Using the binomial distribution, find the probability that a sample of 5 from a lot of 100, containing 10 defective items, will contain (a) 0, (b) 1, (c) 2, (d) 3 defective items.

5. Samples of 5 are drawn from a lot with fraction defective θ. The lot is accepted if the sample contains (a) no defective items, (b) at most 1 defective item. Using the binomial distribution, find, graph, and compare the OC curves.

6. In Problem 4, find the probability of obtaining at most 2 defective items.

7. Samples of 3 items are drawn from lots and a lot is accepted if in the corresponding sample we find no more than 1 defective item. Criticize this sampling plan. In particular, find the probability of accepting a lot which is 50% defective. (Use the binomial distribution.)

8. Graph and compare sampling plans with $c = 0$ and increasing values of n, say, $n = 2, 3, 4$. (Use the binomial distribution.)

9. Do the work required in Problem 8, when $c = 1$.

10. What is the effect of (a) keeping c constant and increasing the sample size n, (b) keeping n constant and increasing the acceptance number c?

11. Why is it impossible for an OC curve to have a vertical portion separating good from poor quality?

12. What values must be changed if the OC curve is to be: (a) made steeper, (b) moved to the left, (c) made steeper and moved to the right?

13. Using Table 1d in Appendix 4, draw the OC curve for a sampling plan of $n = 8$, $c = 2$.

14. Using Table 1d in Appendix 4, draw the OC curve for a sampling plan of $n = 6$, $c = 1$.

15. How large a sample should we take to be 95% sure that a sample to be drawn will have a fraction defective within $k = 10\%$ of the true but unknown lot quality? (Use the normal approximation to the binomial distribution.)

16. Same question as in Problem 15, when $k = 5\%$.

17. The sample sizes in Problems 15 and 16 are large. How much must we permit k to increase if we want to arrive at smaller samples, say, $n = 20$?

14.3   Risks in Acceptance Sampling

We shall now discuss the two types of possible errors in acceptance sampling and the related problem of choosing n and c. In acceptance sampling the producer and the consumer have different interests. The producer may require the probability of rejecting a "good" or "acceptable" lot to be a small number, call it α. The consumer (buyer) may demand the probability of accepting a "bad" or "unacceptable" lot to be a small number β. More precisely, suppose that the two parties agree that a lot for which θ does not exceed a certain number θ_0 is an *acceptable lot* while a lot for which θ is greater than or equal to a certain number θ_1 is an *unacceptable lot*. Then α is the probability of rejecting a lot with $\theta \leq \theta_0$ and is called **producer's risk.** This corresponds to a Type I error in testing a hypothesis (Sec. 13.2). β is the probability of accepting a lot with $\theta \geq \theta_1$ and is called **consumer's risk.** This corresponds to a Type II error in Sec. 13.2. Figure 14.3.1 shows an illustrative example. θ_0 is called the **acceptable quality level** (AQL), and θ_1 is called the **lot tolerance per cent defective** (LTPD) or the **rejectable quality level** (RQL). A lot with $\theta_0 < \theta < \theta_1$ may be called an *indifferent lot.*

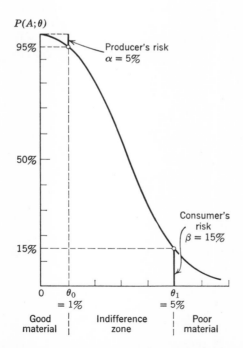

Fig. 14.3.1. OC curve, producer's and consumer's risk

The concepts of producer's risk and consumer's risk were introduced by Dodge and Romig around 1925; see Dodge and Romig (1929) (cf. Appendix 3).

From Fig. 14.3.1 we see that the points $(\theta_0, 1 - \alpha)$ and (θ_1, β) lie on the OC curve. It can be shown that for large lots we can choose θ_0, θ_1 $(>\theta_0)$, α, β and then determine n and c such that the OC curve runs very close to those prescribed points. Sampling plans for specified α, β, θ_0, and θ_1 have been published by Dodge and Romig (1959); cf. Appendix 3.

There is a close relationship between sampling inspection and testing a hypothesis, as follows:

Sampling Inspection	Hypothesis Testing
Acceptable quality level (AQL) $\theta = \theta_0$	Hypothesis $\theta = \theta_0$
Lot tolerance per cent defectives (LTPD) $\theta = \theta_1$	Alternative $\theta = \theta_1$
Allowable number of defectives c	Critical value c
Producer's risk α of rejecting a lot with $\theta \leqq \theta_0$	Probability α of making a Type I error (significance level)
Consumer's risk β of accepting a lot with $\theta \geqq \theta_1$	Probability β of making a Type II error

Figure 14.3.2 illustrates how various sampling plans approach an ideal sampling plan. In this figure the ideal plan is one under which lots with at most 10% defective items are accepted and lots with more than 10% defective items are rejected. Observe that for the other OC curves in the figure, the ratio of c to n is kept constant (1:10).

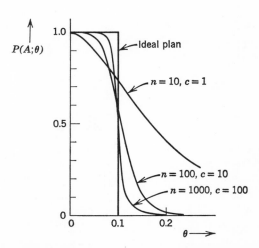

Fig. 14.3.2. OC curves with $c/n = 0.1$ and $n = 10$, 100, 1000 (approach to an ideal OC curve)

Problems

1. Find the risks in the single sampling plan with $n = 5$ and $c = 0$, assuming that the AQL is $\theta_0 = 1\%$ and the RQL is $\theta_1 = 15\%$.

2. Find the risks in the single sampling plan with $n = 5$ and $c = 1$, assuming that the AQL is 10% and the RQL is 30%.

3. How do α and β change if n and θ_0 are kept fixed and c is increased?

4. Show that for small values of θ_0 we have $(1 - \theta_0)^n \approx 1 - n\theta_0$. Using this formula, determine the AQL θ_0 such that in a single sampling plan with $n = 8$ and $c = 0$ the corresponding α is 5%.

5. In Problem 4 determine the RQL θ_1 so that $\beta = 10\%$. Why can the approximation formula in Problem 4 not be used in the present case?

6. What type of sampling plan will be necessary if the AQL and RQL values are relatively close together?

14.4   Average Outgoing Quality

The sampling procedure by itself does not protect the consumer sufficiently well. In fact, if the producer is permitted to resubmit a rejected lot without stating that the lot has already been rejected, then even bad lots will eventually be accepted. To protect the consumer against this and other possibilities, the producer may agree with the consumer that a rejected lot is **rectified,** that is, is 100% inspected, item by item, and all defective items in the lot are removed and replaced by nondefective items.[1] Suppose that a plant produces $100\theta\%$ defective items and rejected lots are rectified. Then K lots of size N contain KN items, $KN\theta$ of which are defective. $KP(A; \theta)$ of the lots are accepted; these contain a total of $KPN\theta$ defective items. The rejected and rectified lots contain no defective items. Hence after the rectification the fraction defective in the K lots equals $KPN\theta/KN = \theta P(A; \theta)$. This function of θ is called the **average outgoing quality** (AOQ) and is denoted by AOQ(θ). Thus

(1) $$\text{AOQ}(\theta) = \theta P(A; \theta).$$

A sampling plan being given, this function and its graph, the *average outgoing quality curve* (AOQ curve), can readily be obtained from $P(A; \theta)$ and the OC curve. An example is shown in Fig. 14.4.1.

Clearly AOQ$(0) = 0$. Also, AOQ$(1) = 0$ because $P(A; 1) = 0$. Since AOQ ≥ 0, we conclude that this function must have a maximum at some $\theta = \theta^*$. The corresponding value AOQ(θ^*) is called the **average outgoing quality limit** (AOQL). This is the worst average quality which may be expected to be accepted under the rectifying procedure.

---

[1] Of course, rectification is impossible if the inspection is destructive, or is not worthwhile if it is too expensive, compared with the value of the lot. The rejected lot may then be sold at a cut-rate price or scrapped.

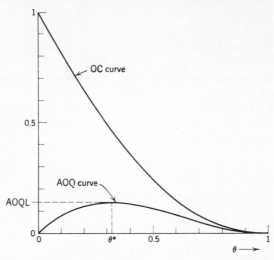

Fig. 14.4.1. OC curve and AOQ curve for the sampling plan in Fig. 14.2.1

It turns out that several single sampling plans may correspond to the same AOQL; see Dodge and Romig (1959) (cf. Appendix 3). Hence if the AOQL is all the consumer cares about, the producer has some freedom in choosing a sampling plan and may select a plan which minimizes the amount of sampling, that is, the number of inspected items per lot. This number is

$$nP(A; \theta) + N(1 - P(A; \theta))$$

where the first term corresponds to the accepted lots and the last term to the rejected and rectified lots; in fact, rectification requires the inspection of all N items of the lot, and $1 - P(A; \theta)$ is the probability of rejecting a lot.

Problems

1. Graph the AOQ curve in Problem 2, Sec. 14.2. Determine the AOQL, assuming that rectification is possible.

2. Graph the OC curve and the AOQ curve for the single sampling plan for large lots with $n = 5$ and $c = 0$.

3. Do the same work as in Problem 2 when $n = 4$ and $c = 1$.

4. Estimate θ_0 and θ_1 in Problem 2 if the producer's risk is 5% and the consumer's risk is 10%.

5. Find the AOQL in Problem 2.

14.5   Further Remarks

We mention that inspection work may be saved by using a **double sampling plan,** in which the sample of size n is broken up into two samples of sizes

n_1 and n_2 (where $n_1 + n_2 = n$). If the lot is very good or very bad, it may then be possible to decide about acceptance or rejection, using one sample only, so that the other sample will only be necessary in the case of a lot of intermediate quality. This method may be especially cost saving, since a decision to reject or accept may be made on the basis of a very small sample. The book by Dodge and Romig (1959) listed in Appendix 3 contains double sampling plans using rectifying inspection of the following type (where x_1 and x_2 are the numbers of defective items in those two samples).

(1) If $x_1 \leq c_1$, accept the lot. If $x_1 > c_2$, reject the lot.

(2) If $c_1 < x_1 \leq c_2$, use the second sample, too. If $x_1 + x_2 \leq c_2$, accept the lot. If $x_1 + x_2 > c_2$, reject the lot.

In the sampling plans considered the decision of accepting or rejecting a lot is based on the number of defective items in a sample. Such a plan is therefore called a **sampling plan based on attributes.** In such a plan the only information about an inspected item is whether the item is defective or not. For example, in acceptance sampling of lots of air mail envelopes we may consider the weight X of an envelope and regard an envelope as defective if its weight exceeds a certain limit. In this procedure we base the decision on the number of defective envelopes in a sample. However we may arrive at a more sensitive sampling plan based on the mean $\bar{x}$ of a sample of size n. The lot is then accepted if $\bar{x}$ does not exceed some number c^*. It is rejected if $\bar{x} > c^*$.

In this sampling we may choose n and c^* such that the producer's and consumer's risks have prescribed values α and β, respectively. For this purpose we must know the distribution of the above variable X. Suppose that X is normal with mean μ and variance σ^2. Then $\bar{x}$ is an observed value of a random variable $\bar{X}$ which is normal with mean μ and variance σ^2/n; cf. Theorem 2, Sec. 12.2. We may now determine n and c^* from

$$P(\bar{X} \leq c^*)_{\mu_0} = \Phi\left(\sqrt{n}\,\frac{c^* - \mu_0}{\sigma}\right) = 1 - \alpha$$

$$P(\bar{X} \leq c^*)_{\mu_1} = \Phi\left(\sqrt{n}\,\frac{c^* - \mu_1}{\sigma}\right) = \beta.$$

For example, suppose that $\sigma = 0.05$, and we require $\alpha = 5\%$, $\beta = 10\%$, $\mu_0 = 1.98$, $\mu_1 = 2.00$. Then $1 - \alpha = 0.95$, and Table 3b in Appendix 4 gives

$$\sqrt{n}\,\frac{c^* - 1.98}{0.05} = 1.645, \qquad \sqrt{n}\,\frac{c^* - 2.00}{0.05} = -1.282.$$

By forming the quotient of the two equations we find

$$\frac{c^* - 1.98}{c^* - 2.00} = -\frac{1.645}{1.282}\,; \qquad \text{thus} \qquad c^* = 1.991\ 24.$$

Inserting this into one of the equations, we obtain $n = 53.5 \approx 54$.

There are many attribute sampling plans available for special situations, and more are appearing in the literature all the time. Even a brief description of the more common sampling plans now being used in industry would require many additional pages.

For example, in the CSP-1 plans developed by Dodge, we start with a 100% inspection of the units of production and continue until j nondefective units. Then we inspect only a fraction f of units by selecting them one at a time from the flow of production. When a defective unit is found, we return to 100% inspection and continue until j nondefective units are found. Values of j and f required for any desired AOQL are given by Dodge (*Industrial Quality Control*, **4,** 1947, 5–9).

CSP-2 is a modification of CSP-1. In this plan, once sampling inspection is started, 100% inspection is not required when a defective unit appears, but is required when a second defective unit occurs in the next k or fewer sample units.

Other plans, in which one starts with sampling·inspection in place of 100% inspection, were developed by Wald (*Annals of Math. Statistics*, **16,** 1945, 30–49) and others.

14.6   Sequential Analysis

Sequential analysis is related to hypothesis testing and is designed to avoid unnecessarily many observations for making a decision. In the present section we shall explain the basic idea of the method and illustrate its application in acceptance sampling.

If, in testing a hypothesis H_0 against a particular alternative H_1, we decide in advance what Type I and Type II errors we are willing to admit, then our sample size n is determined. In this method we do not draw conclusions from the data until a sample of fixed size n has been taken. We may expect that in many cases we would be in a better position to make decisions if we could take samples of size 1, one at a time, and accumulate the information obtained from them. In fact, methods that operate on such an accumulation-of-information basis have been developed to reduce the average amount of sampling. They are called *sequential methods* or *methods of sequential analysis*.

In sequential analysis the number of observations to be made is not determined in advance, but we make one observation at a time, and after every observation we decide to take one of the following three actions.

1. Accept the hypothesis.
2. Reject the hypothesis.
3. Make an additional observation.

To decide which action to take, we must determine the critical region for each sample size. For this purpose we compute the probability, p_{0m}, that the m observations collected thus far would occur if our hypothesis H_0 were true, and the probability, p_{1m}, that these observations would occur if the alternative H_1 were true.

If p_{0m} is large compared with p_{1m}, we accept H_0. If p_{1m} is large compared with p_{0m}, we accept H_1. If there is not much difference between p_{0m} and p_{1m}, we make another observation. It can be shown that the following procedure corresponds to the risks α and β approximately (with sufficient accuracy from the practical point of view when α and β are small). We calculate the ratio

$$v_m = \frac{p_{1m}}{p_{0m}}$$

and decide as follows.

(1)

    1. If $v_m \leqq \dfrac{\beta}{1-\alpha}$,   we accept H_0.

    2. If $v_m \geqq \dfrac{1-\beta}{\alpha}$,   we accept H_1.

    3. If $\dfrac{\beta}{1-\alpha} < v_m < \dfrac{1-\beta}{\alpha}$, we make another observation.

Example 1. We shall apply the sequential test to the acceptance inspection of large lots of items, each of which is either good or defective. Let θ be the fraction of defective items. Suppose that we want to test the hypothesis $H_0: \theta = \theta_0 = 0.05$ against the alternative $H_1: \theta = \theta_1 = 0.15$. We choose $\alpha = 5\%$ and $\beta = 10\%$. Hence we are willing to risk rejection of a lot with $\theta_0 = 0.05$ about 5% of the time and acceptance of a lot with $\theta_1 = 0.15$ about 10% of the time. This implies that lots with $\theta < \theta_0$ will be rejected less frequently than 5% of the time and lots with $\theta > \theta_1$ will be accepted less frequently than 10% of the time.

Using the binomial distribution, we see that the probability that a sample of m items contains precisely x defective items is

$$p_{0m} = \binom{m}{x}\theta_0^x(1-\theta_0)^{m-x} = \binom{m}{x}0.05^x 0.95^{m-x} \quad \text{(if } H_0 \text{ is true),}$$

$$p_{1m} = \binom{m}{x}\theta_1^x(1-\theta_1)^{m-x} = \binom{m}{x}0.15^x 0.85^{m-x} \quad \text{(if } H_1 \text{ is true).}$$

Thus

$$v_m = \frac{p_{1m}}{p_{0m}} = \left(\frac{\theta_1}{\theta_0}\right)^x \left(\frac{1-\theta_1}{1-\theta_0}\right)^{m-x} = 3^x\, 0.895^{m-x}.$$

The critical values are obtained from

$$v_m = 3^x 0.895^{m-x} = \frac{\beta}{1-\alpha} = \frac{0.10}{0.95} = 0.105$$

and

$$v_m = 3^x 0.895^{m-x} = \frac{1-\beta}{\alpha} = \frac{0.90}{0.05} = 18.$$

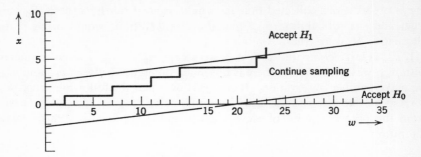

Fig. 14.6.1. Sequential test in Ex. 1

These are straight lines in the xw-plane where $w = m - x$ is the number of nondefective items. In fact, taking logarithms, we have

$$x \ln 3 + w \ln 0.895 = \ln 0.105$$

$$x \ln 3 + w \ln 0.895 = \ln 18$$

or

$$x = 0.1012w - 2.0492$$

$$x = 0.1012w + 2.6309.$$

We may now construct the chart in Fig. 14.6.1 in advance and then record the data as they are observed by drawing a segment one unit to the right if the item is good (nondefective) and a segment one unit up if the item is defective. The figure shows the sample (g = good, d = defective)

g g d g g g g g d g g g g d g g g d g g g g g g g g d g d

which leads to the rejection of H_0 and acceptance of H_1.

In the case of a test for a continuous random variable X, the situation is quite similar. Let $f_0(x)$ be the density of X if the hypothesis H_0 is true, and let $f_1(x)$ be the density of X if the alternative H_1 is true. Then we have to consider the ratio

$$v_m = \frac{p_{1m}}{p_{0m}} = \frac{f_1(x_1)f_1(x_2) \cdots f_1(x_m)}{f_0(x_1)f_0(x_2) \cdots f_0(x_m)}$$

and proceed as before.

Example 2. In a process for producing metal tags, let the thickness X (in millimeters) of the tags be a normal random variable with mean μ and variance $\sigma^2 = 0.04$, the latter value being known from long experience. Prepare a chart for sequentially testing the hypothesis

$$H_0: \qquad \mu_0 = 1.0$$

against the alternative

$$H_1: \qquad \mu_1 = 1.1$$

so that the Type I risk is 3 % and the Type II risk is 5 %.

We have

$$f_0(x) = \frac{1}{\sigma\sqrt{2\pi}} \exp\left[-\frac{1}{2}\left(\frac{x-\mu_0}{\sigma}\right)^2\right],$$

$$f_1(x) = \frac{1}{\sigma\sqrt{2\pi}} \exp\left[-\frac{1}{2}\left(\frac{x-\mu_1}{\sigma}\right)^2\right].$$

Hence, when $m = 1$, we obtain the ratio

$$v_1 = \frac{f_1(x_1)}{f_0(x_1)} = \exp\frac{1}{2}\left[\left(\frac{x_1-\mu_0}{\sigma}\right)^2 - \left(\frac{x_1-\mu_1}{\sigma}\right)^2\right].$$

Simplification gives

$$v_1 = \exp\left[\left(\frac{\mu_1-\mu_0}{\sigma^2}\right)x_1 + \frac{\mu_0{}^2-\mu_1{}^2}{2\sigma^2}\right].$$

From this we see that

$$v_m = \exp\left[\frac{\mu_1-\mu_0}{\sigma^2}\sum_{j=1}^{m}x_j + m\frac{\mu_0{}^2-\mu_1{}^2}{2\sigma^2}\right].$$

This and (1) show that sampling continues as long as

$$\frac{\beta}{1-\alpha} < \exp\left[\frac{\mu_1-\mu_0}{\sigma^2}\sum_{j=1}^{m}x_j + m\frac{\mu_0{}^2-\mu_1{}^2}{2\sigma^2}\right] < \frac{1-\beta}{\alpha}.$$

Taking logarithms, we get

$$\ln\frac{\beta}{1-\alpha} < \frac{\mu_1-\mu_0}{\sigma^2}\sum_{j=1}^{m}x_j + m\frac{\mu_0{}^2-\mu_1{}^2}{2\sigma^2} < \ln\frac{1-\beta}{\alpha}.$$

We graph the region corresponding to this double inequality in the *my*-plane where

$$y = \sum_{j=1}^{m}x_j = x_1 + \cdots + x_m.$$

The region is an infinite strip bounded by the two parallel lines

$$\frac{\mu_1-\mu_0}{\sigma^2}y + m\frac{\mu_0{}^2-\mu_1{}^2}{2\sigma^2} = \begin{cases}\ln\left[\beta/(1-\alpha)\right]\\ \ln\left[(1-\beta)/\alpha\right].\end{cases}$$

Simplification gives

$$y = \frac{\mu_0+\mu_1}{2}m + \frac{\sigma^2}{\mu_1-\mu_0}\ln\frac{\beta}{1-\alpha},$$

$$y = \frac{\mu_0+\mu_1}{2}m + \frac{\sigma^2}{\mu_1-\mu_0}\ln\frac{1-\beta}{\alpha}.$$

By using the above numerical values we find

$$\frac{\mu_0+\mu_1}{2} = \frac{2.1}{2} = 1.05, \qquad \frac{\sigma^2}{\mu_1-\mu_0} = \frac{0.04}{0.1} = 0.4,$$

$$\frac{\beta}{1-\alpha} = \frac{0.05}{0.97} = 0.0515, \qquad \frac{1-\beta}{\alpha} = \frac{0.95}{0.03} = 31.67.$$

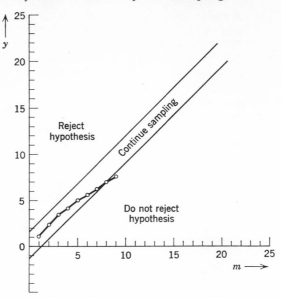

Fig. 14.6.2. Sequential test in Ex. 2

This yields the representations (cf. Fig. 14.6.2)

$$y = 1.05m - 1.19,$$

$$y = 1.05m + 1.38.$$

Hence the test now proceeds as follows.

1. If $\sum_{j=1}^{m} x_j \leqq 1.05m - 1.19$, accept the hypothesis $\mu_0 = 1.0$.

2. If $\sum_{j=1}^{m} x_j \geqq 1.05m + 1.38$, accept the alternative $\mu_1 = 1.1$.

3. If neither inequality is satisfied, make another observation.

The figure shows a typical sampling path leading to the final decision that the hypothesis H_0 is accepted.

The basic idea of a sequential test was first given by Dodge and Romig (1929) (cf. Appendix 3). For further details, see Wilks (1962), Chap. 15, which also includes some references to recent papers on sequential analysis. Cf. also Wald (1947).

Problems

1. With how many observations would the sampling in Example 1 terminate if (*a*) all items were defective, (*b*) all items were nondefective?

2. How will the straight lines in Fig. 14.6.1 be changed if we (*a*) decrease β, (*b*) decrease α?

3. Construct a chart similar to that in Fig. 14.6.1 for sequentially testing the hypothesis $H_0: \theta = \theta_0 = 0.2$ against the alternative $H_1: \theta = \theta_1 = 0.4$, choosing Type I risk 10% and Type II risk 15%.

4. In Fig. 14.6.1 the critical lines are parallel. Is this incidental or typical?

5. Same task as in Problem 3 when H_0 is $\theta_0 = 5\%$, the alternative is $\theta_1 = 10\%$, the Type I risk should be 2% and the Type II risk 5%.

6. In Example 1, with any θ_0, θ_1, α, and β, what is the minimum sample size m for (a) accepting the hypothesis, (b) rejecting the hypothesis?

7. Show that the critical lines in Example 1 have the representations

$$x = w \ln \frac{1-\theta_0}{1-\theta_1} \bigg/ \ln \frac{\theta_1}{\theta_0} + \ln \frac{\beta}{1-\alpha} \bigg/ \ln \frac{\theta_1}{\theta_0}$$

$$x = w \ln \frac{1-\theta_0}{1-\theta_1} \bigg/ \ln \frac{\theta_1}{\theta_0} + \ln \frac{1-\beta}{\alpha} \bigg/ \ln \frac{\theta_1}{\theta_0}.$$

8. Can we conclude without calculation that the slope of the lines in Fig. 14.6.2 must be greater than μ_0 but smaller than μ_1?

CHAPTER **15**

Tests for Distribution Functions (Goodness of Fit)

In this chapter we shall discuss two tests of the hypothesis that a certain function $F(x)$ is the distribution function of a population. Such a hypothesis may arise from previous experience, from a theoretical consideration, or from graphical representations of sufficiently large samples.

For the test we need a sample from that population. Clearly, the corresponding sample distribution function $\tilde{F}(x)$ is an approximation of $F(x)$, and we may expect that the goodness of agreement depends on the sample size. If $\tilde{F}(x)$ approximates $F(x)$ "sufficiently well," we shall not reject the hypothesis that $F(x)$ is the distribution function of that population. If $\tilde{F}(x)$ deviates "too much" from $F(x)$, we shall reject the hypothesis.

To decide in this fashion, we have to know how much $\tilde{F}(x)$ can differ from $F(x)$ if the hypothesis is true. Hence we first have to introduce a measure for the deviation of $\tilde{F}(x)$ from $F(x)$, and we have to know the probability distribution of this measure under the assumption that the hypothesis is true. Then we proceed as follows. We determine a number c such that if the hypothesis is true, a deviation greater than c has a small preassigned probability. If, nevertheless, a deviation larger than c occurs, we have reason to doubt that the hypothesis is true and we reject it. On the other hand, if the deviation does not exceed c, so that $\tilde{F}(x)$ approximates $F(x)$ sufficiently well, we do not reject the hypothesis.

Of course, if we do not reject the hypothesis, this means that we have insufficient evidence to reject it, and does not exclude the possibility that there are other functions which would not be rejected in the test. In this respect the situation is quite similar to that in Chap. 13.

The two tests to be considered are the chi-square test by K. Pearson (1900) and the test by Kolmogorov and Smirnov. The first test is suitable for continuous as well as discrete distributions, while the latter is for continuous distributions only.

248

15.1   Chi-Square Test

The basic idea of the chi-square test is very simple. We first subdivide the x-axis into intervals. Then we compute the probabilities corresponding to these intervals under the hypothesis that a certain function $F(x)$ is the distribution function of the population under consideration. We finally compare these probabilities with the relative class frequencies of a given sample (cf. Sec. 2.3). If the discrepancy is too large, we reject that hypothesis. The technical details of the test are shown in Table 15.1.1. Some of the steps need some further explanations, as follows.

The intervals I_1 and I_K in the first step are infinite. In the case of a discrete distribution the boundary points of the intervals must not coincide with the points where $F(x)$ has jumps.

The numbers e_j in the second step should be equal to or greater than 5. If for some interval this condition is violated, then one should take a larger interval (most simply by uniting that interval with one of its neighbors).

Table 15.1.1. Chi-square Test of the Hypothesis that $F(x)$ is the Distribution Function of a Population from which the Sample $x_1, \cdots, x_n$ is Taken

---

1st step.   Subdivide the x-axis into K intervals $I_1, I_2, \cdots, I_K$ such that each interval contains at least 5 values of the given sample $x_1, \cdots, x_n$. Determine the number b_j of sample values in the interval I_j ($j = 1, \cdots, K$). If a sample value lies at a common boundary point of two intervals, add 0.5 to each of the two corresponding b_j.

2nd step.   Using $F(x)$, compute the probability p_j that the random variable X under consideration assumes any value in the interval I_j ($j = 1, \cdots, K$). Compute

$$e_j = np_j.$$

(This is the number of sample values theoretically expected in I_j if the hypothesis is true.)

3rd step.   Compute the deviation

(1)
$$\chi_0{}^2 = \sum_{j=1}^{K} \frac{(b_j - e_j)^2}{e_j}.$$

4th step.   Choose a significance level α (5%, 1%, or the like).

5th step.   Determine the solution c of the equation

$$P(\chi^2 \leq c) = 1 - \alpha$$

from the table of the chi-square distribution with $K - 1$ degrees of freedom (Table 6 in Appendix 4; cf. also Fig. 15.1.1). If $\chi_0{}^2 \leq c$, do not reject the hypothesis. If $\chi_0{}^2 > c$, reject the hypothesis.

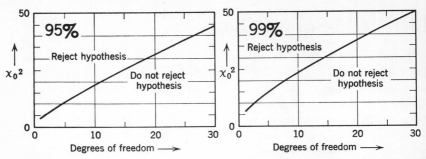

Fig. 15.1.1. Graphical representation of Table 6 in Appendix 4 $(1 - \alpha = 95\%$ and $99\%)$

If the sample is so small that this is impossible, one should continue with the test but use the result with great care. The reason for that condition and for the appearance of the chi-square distribution in the test is a consequence of the following theorem by K. Pearson (1900).

Theorem 1. *Suppose that the hypothesis in Table* 15.1.1 *is true. Then the random variable for which* χ_0^2 *in Table* 15.1.1 *is an observed value has a distribution function which approaches the distribution function of the chi-square distribution with* $K - 1$ *degrees of freedom as n approaches infinity.*

A proof of this theorem can be found in the book by Cramér (1961), pp. 416–420; cf. Appendix 3.

If $F(x)$ *involves* r *unknown parameters, we may use the corresponding maximum likelihood estimates and then the chi-square distribution with* $K - r - 1$ *degrees of freedom (instead of* $K - 1$).

This rule results from a theorem by R. A. Fisher. A proof is included in the book by Cramér (1961), pp. 427–434.

15.2   Examples Illustrating the Chi-Square Test

Example 1 (Mendel's laws). The result of one of Mendel's famous experiments of crossing plants was 355 yellow and 123 green peas. Test whether this is in agreement with Mendel's theory, according to which the result should be 3 : 1.

1st step. We denote the two possible events by

$$X = 0 \text{ (yellow pea)} \quad \text{and} \quad X = 1 \text{ (green pea)}.$$

We choose $K = 2$ intervals each of which contains one of these events. Then $b_1 = 355$ and $b_2 = 123$.

2nd step. Since $n = 355 + 123 = 478$, we obtain

$$e_1 = 478 \cdot \tfrac{3}{4} = 358.5 \quad \text{and} \quad e_2 = 478 \cdot \tfrac{1}{4} = 119.5.$$

3rd step. We compute

$$\chi_0{}^2 = \frac{(355 - 358.5)^2}{358.5} + \frac{(123 - 119.5)^2}{119.5} = 0.137.$$

4th step. We choose the significance level $\alpha = 5\%$.
5th step. For $K - 1 = 1$ degree of freedom the solution of the equation

$$P(\chi^2 \leq c) = 1 - \alpha = 0.95$$

is $c = 3.84$. Hence $\chi_0{}^2 < c$, and we do not reject the hypothesis.

Example 2. Test whether the population from which the sample in Table 15.2.1 was taken is normal.
1st step. We subdivide the x-axis into $K = 10$ intervals as shown in Table 15.2.2 and determine the corresponding b_j shown in the fifth column of that table.
2nd step. $F(x)$ involves the two inknown parameters μ and σ^2. The corresponding maximum likelihood estimates (cf. Sec. 11.6) are $\hat{\mu} = \bar{x} = 364.7$ and $\hat{\sigma}^2 = 712.9$. Hence we have to test whether that population has the distribution function

$$F(x) = \Phi\left(\frac{x - 364.7}{26.7}\right).$$

3rd step. From the auxiliary values in Table 15.2.2 we obtain

$$\chi_0{}^2 = 2.942.$$

4th step. We choose the significance level $\alpha = 5\%$.
5th step. We remember that we estimated $r = 2$ parameters. From the table of the chi-square distribution with $K - r - 1 = 7$ degrees of freedom we see that the equation

$$P(\chi^2 \leq c) = 1 - \alpha = 95\%$$

has the solution $c = 14.07$. Since $\chi_0{}^2 < c$, we do not reject the hypothesis that that population is normal.

Table 15.2.1. Sample of 100 Values of the Splitting Tensile Strength (Pounds/ Inch²) of Concrete Cylinders

320	380	340	410	380	340	360	350	320	370
350	340	350	360	370	350	380	370	300	420
370	390	390	440	330	390	330	360	400	370
320	350	360	340	340	350	350	390	380	340
400	360	350	390	400	350	360	340	370	420
420	400	350	370	330	320	390	380	400	370
390	330	360	380	350	330	360	300	360	360
360	390	350	370	370	350	390	370	370	340
370	400	360	350	380	380	360	340	330	370
340	360	390	400	370	410	360	400	340	360

D. L. Ivey, Splitting tensile tests on structural lightweight aggregate concrete. Texas Transportation Institute, College Station, Texas, 1965.

Table 15.2.2. Calculations in Example 2

x_j	$\dfrac{x_j - 364.7}{26.7}$	$\Phi\left(\dfrac{x_j - 364.7}{26.7}\right)$	$e_j = 100p_j$	b_j	Terms in (1), Sec. 15.1
$-\infty \cdots 325$	$-\infty \ \ \cdots -1.49$	$0.0000 \cdots 0.0681$	6.81	6	0.096
$325 \cdots 335$	$-1.49 \cdots -1.11$	$0.0681 \cdots 0.1335$	6.54	6	0.045
$335 \cdots 345$	$-1.11 \cdots -0.74$	$0.1335 \cdots 0.2296$	9.61	11	0.201
$345 \cdots 355$	$-0.74 \cdots -0.36$	$0.2296 \cdots 0.3594$	12.98	14	0.080
$355 \cdots 365$	$-0.36 \cdots \ \ \ 0.01$	$0.3594 \cdots 0.4960$	13.66	16	0.401
$365 \cdots 375$	$0.01 \cdots \ \ \ 0.39$	$0.4960 \cdots 0.6517$	15.57	15	0.021
$375 \cdots 385$	$0.39 \cdots \ \ \ 0.76$	$0.6517 \cdots 0.7764$	12.47	8	1.602
$385 \cdots 395$	$0.76 \cdots \ \ \ 1.13$	$0.7764 \cdots 0.8708$	9.44	10	0.033
$395 \cdots 405$	$1.13 \cdots \ \ \ 1.51$	$0.8708 \cdots 0.9345$	6.37	8	0.417
$405 \cdots \infty$	$1.51 \cdots \ \ \ \infty$	$0.9345 \cdots 1.0000$	6.55	6	0.046

$$\chi_0^2 = 2.942$$

Problems

1. In another experiment, Gregor Mendel obtained 315 round yellow peas, 108 round green peas, 101 angular yellow peas, and 32 angular green peas. Does this result support or contradict the theory according to which the probabilities of the 4 groups are in the ratios $9:3:3:1$?

2. In another experiment Gregor Mendel obtained 428 green peas and 152 yellow peas. Test the hypothesis that, by Mendel's theory, the probabilities for green peas and for yellow peas are, respectively, $3/4$ and $1/4$.

3. If in Graz, Austria, you dial to get the exact time, the recorded answer will include not only hours and minutes but also seconds in the form 0, 10, 20, 30, 40, 50 seconds. Test whether these 6 outcomes are equally likely, using a sample which was obtained over a longer period of time.

Seconds	0	10	20	30	40	50
Frequency	16	19	18	17	17	13

4. Test the hypothesis that in tossing a coin, heads and tails are equally likely, using a sample of 50 consisting of 27 heads and 23 tails.

5. What is the minimum number (> 25) of *heads* in order that a sample of the kind used in Problem 4 lead to the rejection of the hypothesis if $\alpha = 5\%$ is chosen?

6. Can we assert that the die used by R. Wolf (*Vierteljahresschrift Naturforsch. Ges. Zürich*, **27**, 1882, 242) was fair?

Number x the die turned up	1	2	3	4	5	6
Frequency	3407	3631	3176	2916	3448	3422

7. Test the hypothesis that the daily number of births in a certain population is constant throughout the year, using the following sample taken from that population. (The numbers given are multiples of 1000; J = January, F = February, etc.)

Month	J	F	M	A	M	J	J	A	S	O	N	D
Number of births	80	78	86	82	83	78	79	76	78	76	72	76

8. Test the hypothesis that the population corresponding to the sample in Table 7.5.2 has a Poisson distribution.

9. Test the hypothesis that the population from which the sample in Table 7.5.1 was taken has a Poisson distribution.

10. Test the hypothesis that the population from which the sample in Table 7.5.3 was taken has a Poisson distribution.

11. Using the following data (from Saxony, published in 1889), test the hypothesis that the random variable $X = $ *number of boys in a family having 8 children* has a binomial distribution.

Number of boys	Frequency
0	215
1	1485
2	5331
3	10649
4	14959
5	11929
6	6678
7	2092
8	342

12. Test the hypothesis that the population from which the sample in Table 11.4.1 was taken is normal.

13. Test for normality of the population from which the following sample ($x = $ tensile strength in kilograms/millimeter^2 of steel sheets of 0.3 mm thickness) was taken.

x	Frequency
$-\infty \cdots 42.0$	15
$42.0 \cdots 42.5$	11
$42.5 \cdots 43.0$	15
$43.0 \cdots 43.5$	14
$43.5 \cdots 44.0$	22.5
$44.0 \cdots 44.5$	19.5
$44.5 \cdots 45.0$	12
$45.0 \cdots \infty$	19

14. We throw a die 120 times and obtain:

Face	1	2	3	4	5	6
Frequency	20	14	23	12	26	25

Using this sample, test the hypothesis that the die is fair.

15. In Problem 14 imagine that the sample is replaced by another sample of size n in which the 6 faces have the same relative frequencies as in the original sample. (*a*) Perform the test when $n = 600$. (*b*) What is the smallest n such that the hypothesis is rejected when $\alpha = 5\%$? (*c*) Same question as in (*b*) when $\alpha = 1\%$.

16. Can it happen that in an application of the chi-square test, $\chi_0^2 = 0$ although the sample distribution function differs from the distribution function $F(x)$ to be tested?

17. An examination showed that 3 randomly selected boxes of different brands of canned beans containing 100 cans each contained 10, 2, and 15 cans, respectively,

that did not meet certain high-quality specifications. Test the hypothesis that the 3 brands are of comparable quality.

18. The number of books borrowed from a public library during a particular week was 500 on Monday, 450 on Tuesday, 480 on Wednesday, 460 on Thursday, and 510 on Friday. Test the hypothesis that the number of books borrowed does not depend on the day of the week.

19. Three sets of 200 screws each, randomly selected from the production of each of 3 machines, included 3, 8, and 4 defective screws, respectively. Is this difference significant?

20. Seventy-seven students were asked to select 3 of the 20 numbers $11, 12, 13, \cdots, 30$ in a completely arbitrary fashion. The amazing result was as follows.

Number	11	12	13	14	15	16	17	18	19	20
Frequency	11	10	20	8	13	9	21	9	16	8

Number	21	22	23	24	25	26	27	28	29	30
Frequency	12	8	15	10	10	9	12	8	13	9

If the selected numbers were completely random, each of the following hypotheses should be true.
(*a*) The 20 numbers are equally likely.
(*b*) The 10 even numbers together are as likely as the 10 odd numbers together.
(*c*) The 6 prime numbers together have probability 0.3 and the other numbers together have probability 0.7.
Test these hypotheses.

21. Suppose that a certain disease is regarded as being equally common among men and women. Choosing the significance level $\alpha = 5\%$, show that a sample of 100 patients consisting of 45 men and 55 women who have that disease supports the hypothesis.

22. In Problem 21, find the smallest number (> 50) of women which leads to the rejection of the hypothesis on the level (*a*) $\alpha = 5\%$, (*b*) $\alpha = 1\%$, (*c*) $\alpha = 0.1\%$.

15.3   Kolmogorov-Smirnov Test

The Kolmogorov-Smirnov test is suitable for continuous distributions only. The hypothesis to be tested is that a certain function $F(x)$ is the distribution function of a population from which a sample $x_1, \cdots, x_n$ was taken. The steps of the test are shown in Table 15.3.1 and need some further explanation, as follows.

In the second step of the test, it is not difficult to determine a. In fact, since $\tilde{F}(x)$ is a step function (piecewise constant function), a must correspond to a point of discontinuity. At each such point we may therefore compute the two nonnegative numbers a_1 and a_2 shown in Fig. 15.3.1. The largest of all these numbers is a.

Table 7 in Appendix 4 contains values of the distribution function of the random variable A for which a in Table 15.3.1 is an observed value. Kolmogorov and Smirnov proved that the distribution of A is independent of the special form of $F(x)$ but is the same for all continuous distributions.

Figure 15.3.2 shows a graphical representation of Table 7 in Appendix 4.

Table 15.3.1. Kolmogorov-Smirnov Test of the Hypothesis that $F(x)$ is the Distribution Function of the Population from which the Sample $x_1, \cdots, x_n$ was Taken

> *1st step.* Compute the values of the distribution function $\tilde{F}(x)$ of the sample $x_1, \cdots, x_n$.
>
> *2nd step.* Determine the maximum deviation[1]
>
> $$a = \max |\tilde{F}(x) - F(x)|$$
>
> between $\tilde{F}(x)$ and $F(x)$.
>
> *3rd step.* Choose a significance level α (5%, 1%, or the like).
>
> *4th step.* Determine the solution c of the equation
>
> (1) $$P(A \leqq c) = 1 - \alpha$$
>
> from Table 7 in Appendix 4. If $a \leqq c$, do not reject the hypothesis. If $a > c$, reject the hypothesis.

[1] More precisely, we should write

$$a = \sup_{x} |\tilde{F}(x) - F(x)|.$$

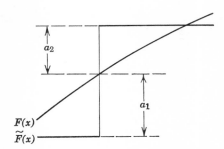

Fig. 15.3.1. Determination of a in Table 15.3.1

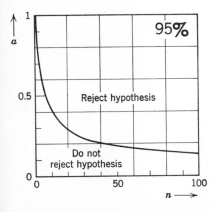
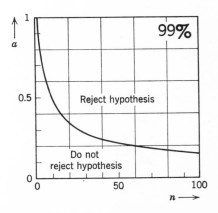

Fig. 15.3.2. Graphical representation of Table 7 in Appendix 4 for the Kolmogorov-Smirnov test

15.4   Example Illustrating the Kolmogorov-Smirnov Test

Example 1 (Normal distribution). Was the sample in Table 3.3.3 taken from a normally distributed population with mean $\mu = 165.05$ cm and variance $\sigma^2 = 34.3106$ cm^2? (The sample mean is $\bar{x} = 165.05$, cf. Problem 6, Sec. 3.3, and the sample standard deviation is $s = \sqrt{34.3106} = 5.858$.)

1st step. The values of the sample distribution function $\tilde{F}(x)$ are sums of the values in the last column of Table 3.3.3.

2nd step. We have to test whether the population has the distribution function

$$F(x) = \Phi\left(\frac{x - 165.05}{5.858}\right).$$

Table 15.4.1. Computation in Example 1

x	$\tilde{F}(x)$	$x - 165.05$	$\dfrac{x - 165.05}{5.858}$	$\Phi\left(\dfrac{x - 165.05}{5.858}\right)$	a_1	a_2
153	0.01	−12.05	−2.06	0.02	0.02	0.01
154	0.02	−11.05	−1.89	0.03	0.02	0.01
155	0.04	−10.05	−1.72	0.04	0.02	0.00
156	0.07	−9.05	−1.55	0.06	0.02	0.01
157	0.10	−8.05	−1.37	0.09	0.02	0.01
158	0.15	−7.05	−1.20	0.12	0.02	0.03
159	0.21	−6.05	−1.03	0.15	0.00	0.06
160	0.25	−5.05	−0.86	0.19	0.02	0.06
161	0.30	−4.05	−0.69	0.25	0.00	0.05
162	0.37	−3.05	−0.52	0.30	0.00	**0.07**
163	0.42	−2.05	−0.35	0.36	0.01	0.06
164	0.47	−1.05	−0.18	0.43	0.01	0.04
165	0.53	−0.05	−0.01	0.50	0.03	0.03
166	0.60	0.95	0.16	0.56	0.03	0.04
167	0.65	1.95	0.33	0.63	0.03	0.02
168	0.69	2.95	0.50	0.69	0.04	0.00
169	0.74	3.95	0.67	0.75	0.06	0.01
170	0.79	4.95	0.85	0.80	0.06	0.01
171	0.85	5.95	1.02	0.85	0.06	0.00
172	0.89	6.95	1.19	0.88	0.03	0.01
173	0.92	7.95	1.36	0.91	0.02	0.01
174	0.94	8.95	1.53	0.94	0.02	0.00
175	0.97	9.95	1.70	0.96	0.02	0.01
176	0.98	10.95	1.87	0.97	0.00	0.01
177	0.99	11.95	2.04	0.98	0.00	0.01
178	1.00	12.95	2.21	0.99	0.00	0.01

The values of $F(x)$ are obtained from Table 3a in Appendix 4. Then we compute a_1 and a_2 in Table 15.4.1. In the first line,

$$a_1 = F(153) - 0 = 0.02 - 0 = 0.02,$$
$$a_2 = F(153) - \tilde{F}(153) = 0.02 - 0.01 = 0.01.$$

In the second line,

$$a_1 = F(154) - \tilde{F}(153) = 0.03 - 0.01 = 0.02,$$
$$a_2 = F(154) - \tilde{F}(154) = 0.03 - 0.02 = 0.01,$$

etc. The greatest of all these numbers is $a = 0.07$.

3rd step. We choose the significance level $\alpha = 5\%$.

4th step. The sample size is $n = 100$. From Table 7 in Appendix 4 we see that the equation

$$P(A \leqq c) = 1 - \alpha = 0.95$$

has the solution $c = 0.134$. Since $a < c$, we do not reject the hypothesis.

Problems

1.–5. Using the Kolmogorov-Smirnov test, test the hypothesis that the population from which the samples are taken are normally distributed.

1. The sample in Table 11.4.1.
2. The sample in Table 11.4.2.
3. The sample in Problem 3, Sec. 12.7.
4. The sample in Table 12.3.2.
5. Density (in grams/square meter) of cotton material.

Class mark	96	98	100	102	104	106	108	110	112
Frequency	1	0	1	2	8	19	28	30	41
Class mark	114	116	118	120	122	124	126	128	130
Frequency	66	50	27	8	5	3	0	1	1

15.5   Chi-Square Test of Independence. Contingency Tables

Contingency tables are used in connection with multiple classifications. The simplest type of a contingency table is obtained if we classify a sample by *two* criteria. For example, in an experiment conducted in Canada in 1956, male pensioners of a certain age (60–64 years of age in 1956) were classified according to smoking habits and mortality. Two classes were considered with respect to smoking habits, namely, nonsmokers and pipe smokers. With respect to mortality, two classes were also considered, namely, persons still living and persons who died within six years of the beginning of the experiment. Table 15.5.1 shows the corresponding 2 × 2 *contingency table*.

A 2 × 2 contingency table is obtained because the individuals are classified by 2 criteria, and for each criterion we distinguished between 2 categories. The distinct classifications are called **cells**.

Table 15.5.1. 2 × 2 Contingency Table

Mortality	Smoking Habit	
	Nonsmokers	Pipe Smokers
Dead	117	54
Alive	950	348

(margin handwriting: 171, 1298)

(handwriting below columns: 1069, 402)

A 2 × 3 *contingency table* would have been obtained if we had used 3 categories of smoking habits, for instance, nonsmokers, pipe smokers, and cigarette smokers. The 2 × 2 and 2 × 3 contingency tables are examples of *two-way* tables. A *three-way contingency table* would have been obtained had the persons been classified according to a third criterion, for example, sex (if male and female persons had been observed in the experiment).

The problem considered in connection with contingency tables is whether the characteristics which led to the classification are independent, that is, the distribution of one characteristic should be the same regardless of the other. Hence, in Table 15.5.1 we may test the hypothesis that smoking habits and mortality are independent. This can be done as follows.

First we record the number of observations in each cell. This yields Table 15.5.1. Then we look at each characteristic separately and record the total numbers as shown in Table 15.5.2.

If the hypothesis is true, the proportion of dead is the same for the two smoking classes. Since 171 of $1067 + 402 = 1469$ persons died, and 1067 are nonsmokers, the expected frequency in the left upper cell, under the hypothesis of independence, is

$$1067 \cdot \frac{171}{1469} = 124.2.$$

(margin handwriting: $CS \cdot \dfrac{RS}{Tot}$)

Similarly, in the left lower cell we expect

$$1067 \cdot \frac{1298}{1469} = 942.8$$

and, in the other two cells,

$$402 \cdot \frac{171}{1469} = 46.8 \quad \text{and} \quad 402 \cdot \frac{1298}{1469} = 355.2.$$

Table 15.5.2. Calculations in Connection with Table 15.5.1

	Observed		Total	Expected		Total	Difference	
	117	54	171	124.2	46.8	171.0	−7.2	7.2
	950	348	1298	942.8	355.2	1298.0	7.2	−7.2
Total	1067	402		1067.0	402.0			

We calculate the differences and then

$$\chi_0^2 = \frac{(-7.2)^2}{124.2} + \frac{7.2^2}{46.8} + \frac{7.2^2}{942.8} + \frac{(-7.2)^2}{355.2}$$

$$= 7.2^2 \left(\frac{1}{124.2} + \frac{1}{46.8} + \frac{1}{942.8} + \frac{1}{355.2} \right) = 1.73.$$

This is an observed value of a random variable X, and it can be shown that the latter has approximately a chi-square distribution with $(v - 1)(w - 1)$ degrees of freedom where v is the number of rows and w is the number of columns of the two-way contingency table. This number of degrees of freedom is plausible: The table has $K = vw$ classes (the cells), we estimate $r = v - 1 + w - 1$ parameters, and thus in the present case the number $K - r - 1$ appearing in Sec. 15.1 equals $vw - (v - 1) - (w - 1) - 1 = (v - 1)(w - 1)$.

In our case, $v = 2$, $w = 2$, hence $(v - 1)(w - 1) = 1$. We choose $\alpha = 5\%$. From Table 6 in Appendix 4 with 1 degree of freedom we see that the equation

$$P(X \leq c) = 1 - \alpha = 95\%$$

has the solution $c = 3.84$. Since $\chi_0^2 < c$, we cannot reject the hypothesis and assert that for the age group being studied smoking habit and mortality are independent.

In the case of a $v \times w$ contingency table, where v and w are any positive integers, the test is quite similar.

For example, Table 15.5.3 is a 2 × 3 contingency table, and we want to test the hypothesis that circumference and height are independent. Table 15.5.4 shows the expected values

$$40 \cdot \frac{78}{99} = 31.5 \qquad 50 \cdot \frac{78}{99} = 39.4 \qquad 9 \cdot \frac{78}{99} = 7.1$$

$$40 \cdot \frac{21}{99} = 8.5 \qquad 50 \cdot \frac{21}{99} = 10.6 \qquad 9 \cdot \frac{21}{99} = 1.9$$

Table 15.5.3. 2 × 3 Contingency Table Showing Frequencies of Observations of Circumference of Head and Height of Babies at Birth (Both Measured in Centimeters)

Circumference of Head (in Centimeters)	Height at Birth (in Centimeters)		
	47–49	50–52	53–55
32–35	40	36	2
36–39	0	14	7
Total	40	50	9

Table 15.5.4. Calculations in Connection with Table 15.5.3

	Observed			Total		Expected			Total		Difference	
	40	36	2	78		31.5	39.4	7.1	78.0	8.5	−3.4	−5.1
	0	14	7	21		8.5	10.6	1.9	21.0	−8.5	3.4	5.1
Total	40	50	9			40.0	50.0	9.0				

and the differences (observed minus expected) $40.0 - 31.5 = 8.5$, etc. From this we obtain

$$\chi_0^2 = \frac{8.5^2}{31.5} + \frac{(-3.4)^2}{39.4} + \frac{(-5.1)^2}{7.1} + \frac{(-8.5)^2}{8.5} + \frac{3.4^2}{10.6} + \frac{5.1^2}{1.9} = 29.5.$$

We choose $\alpha = 5\%$. From Table 6 in Appendix 4 with $(v - 1)(w - 1) = (2 - 1)(3 - 1) = 2$ degrees of freedom, we see that the equation

$$P(X \leqq c) = 1 - \alpha = 95\%$$

has the solution $c = 5.99$. Since $\chi_0^2 > c$, we reject the hypothesis of independence of circumference of head and height of a baby.

If the totals for rows (or columns) in a contingency table are specified in advance, the test is called a **test of homogeneity.** This is a test that the columns (or rows) have the same proportions in the various categories, and the procedure is exactly the same as in the test of independence.

For a detailed investigation of contingency tables, see Goodman and Kruskal (1954). Cf. also Goodman (1954).

Problems

1. Are eye color of father and eye color of son independent?

Son	Father	
	Light	Dark
Light	471	148
Dark	151	230

2. Is color blindness independent of sex in a population from which the following sample was taken?

	Male	Female
Normal	442	514
Color-blind	38	6

3. Does the following sample indicate that in the population sampled, preference for automobiles of certain makes is independent of sex?

| | Make of automobile | | |
	A_1	A_2	A_3
Men	60	80	110
Women	80	70	100

4. Randomly selected students of a certain college were asked to rate the general instruction as poor, fair, good, and excellent, and responded as shown in the table. Test the hypothesis that the rating does not depend on the student classification.

| | Rating of Instruction | | | |
	Poor	Fair	Good	Excellent
Juniors	20	110	170	30
Seniors	10	50	90	20

5. Thirty-four of 77 patients having a certain disease are given a serum; otherwise they are treated in the same fashion as the other 43 patients not given the serum. Using the data shown in the table, test the hypothesis that the serum does not help to cure the disease.

	Recovered	Not Recovered
Serum	26	8
No serum	30	13

6. Are the disciplinary attitude of the father and the behavior of the boy related? (Data from the New York City Youth Board.)

| Attitude of Father | Behavior of Boy | |
	Delinquent	Nondelinquent
Firm but kindly	26	255
Lax	122	82
Overstrict	120	40
Erratic	191	82

7. Using the following data, test the hypothesis that an individual's educational level and his adjustment to marriage are independent.

| Education | Marriage-Adjustment | | |
	Poor	Fair	Very Good
College	72	112	245
High school	65	90	120
Grade school	95	103	98

CHAPTER **16**

Analysis of Variance

The monthly gain in weight of a number of animals, for example, pigs, is different for each animal, even if the living and feeding conditions are the same for all the animals. This is well known and must be regarded as a random variation, since we do not know the precise reasons and cannot control or predict the corresponding effects.

If we use several different kinds of food, we may perhaps cause an additional variation. If we want to know whether the kind of food affects the gain in weight, we must try to design an experiment in which this effect will be separated from random variation as much as possible. This is a typical problem of *analysis of variance*.

As an example from another field, consider the problem of determining the effect of four types of oil on the wear of piston rings. Again, we must try to separate the suspected effect from random variation.

Similarly, we may want to investigate the effect of the carbon content on the hardness of steel, the effect of driver age on the annual number of accidents, the effect of temperature on the output of factory workers, etc.

Analysis of variance is based on an arithmetical decomposition or partition of the **"sum of squares"** (= sum of squares of the deviations between the sample values and the sample mean). In a **one-way experimental layout** or *one-factor experiment* we are interested in the effect of one *factor* (kind of food, type of oil, etc.) and therefore we decompose that sum into two parts, one corresponding to the factor whose effect we want to investigate and the other corresponding to the random variation. All the above examples are of that type. In the first example the factor is the kind of food. The different kinds of food are called the **levels** of the factor. In the second example the factor is the type of oil, and it has four levels (the four types of oil). If there were only two types of oil, we would be able to apply the methods given in Sec. 13.4, so we may expect that in analysis of variance those methods will be generalized. This will in fact be the case.

If we are interested in two factors, we have to design a **two-way experimental layout** or *two-factor experiment*. In this experiment, that sum of squares is decomposed into three parts, corresponding to the two factors to be investigated and the random variation.

For example, in a swine-feeding experiment we may want to find out whether the monthly gain in weight is affected by the kind of food (factor A) and the amount of food (factor B). Then the *levels* of A are the different kinds of food and the *levels* of B are the different rations that are fed in the experiment.

Or we may be interested in the effect of different types of oil on the wear of different kinds of piston rings. Then in this two-factor experiment one factor is the type of oil and the other is the kind of piston ring.

Analysis of variance was developed by R. A. Fisher for biological studies, but from our examples and problems we shall see that it has applications in various other fields, too. It will help to design experiments carefully and to obtain inferences about effects of factors by relatively simple computations.

In this connection we should again note that, clearly, an experiment whose results are to be evaluated by statistical methods must be designed in advance, before the experiment is begun. Otherwise the data to be obtained will in general be of little use for making inferences.

Analysis of variance has become a vast subject that includes various methods and models developed during the past decades. We shall introduce the student to the basic ideas by considering some of the simpler experimental designs and their statistical analyses. Readers interested in further methods are referred to Anderson and Bancroft (1952), Cochran (1963), and Scheffé (1963) (cf. Appendix 3).

16.1 One-Way Experimental Layout. Comparison of the Means of Several Normal Distributions

Suppose that we want to study the effect of the kind of food on the gain in weight of animals, for example, pigs, and we have available r different kinds of food. Then we may design and perform a statistical experiment. We take n animals and determine the weight of each of them. Then we divide them *randomly* into r groups and feed each group with one of the r kinds of food. Random selection is important in forming the groups, and so is *replication*, that is, each group should consist of sufficiently many *experimental units* (*replica;* pigs in our case), so that the danger of biased results will be small. After some time (a month, for instance) we determine the gain in weight of each animal. We then have a sample of size n (the n gains) which is subdivided into r **groups,** say,

$$x_{11}, x_{12}, \cdots, x_{1n_1} \qquad \text{(First group)}$$
$$x_{21}, x_{22}, \cdots, x_{2n_2} \qquad \text{(Second group)}$$

etc., corresponding to the r kinds of food (these are the r *levels* of the *factor* food). The first subscript indicates the group and the last subscript the number of the animal in the group. The first group consists of n_1 animals, the second group of n_2 animals, etc. Of course,

$$n_1 + n_2 + \cdots + n_r = n.$$

We want to find out whether the difference between the mean gains of the r groups is significant (that is, is caused by the different kinds of food) or is merely an effect of random variation. In the latter case, from the viewpoint of gain it would not make any difference what food we use.

We assume that the r groups of numbers arise from r *normally distributed populations with the same variance σ^2 and with means μ_1, μ_2, $\cdots$, μ_r.* We want to test the hypothesis that these means are equal.

This hypothesis implies that the kind of food does not affect the gain in weight. σ^2 need not be known.

Note that for $r = 2$, equality of means was considered in Sec. 13.4; hence our present test will generalize that in Sec. 13.4.

Of course, it is immaterial that we formulated our problem in terms of an animal feeding experiment. There are entirely different applications in which we can obtain samples that are subdivided into groups in a natural fashion, for instance, the examples mentioned before, or if we test materials of different chemical composition, or if we compare the time needed for performing a certain job using different working methods, etc.

We shall solve our problem by the method of analysis of variance. The basic idea is simple, as we shall now show. We decompose the "sum of squares"

(1)
$$q = \sum_{i=1}^{r} \sum_{k=1}^{n_i} (x_{ik} - \bar{x})^2$$

into two parts q_1 and q_2, that is,

$$q = q_1 + q_2,$$

where q_1 results from the variation between the groups while q_2 results from the variation within the groups. These two parts are then compared with each other. The details are shown in Table 16.1.1. It has become customary to arrange the most important numbers in a table as shown in Table 16.1.2. Substantial computational simplifications will be discussed in the next section and the theoretical derivation of the test in Sec. 16.3.

Example 1 (Tensile strength of metal). Table 16.1.3 shows a sample of values of the tensile strength of sheet metal (titanium alloy) obtained by measuring four sheets, each sheet at three different points (corner, middle, edge). The problem was to find out whether the tensile strength is the same at all points of the sheet.

1st step. The groups have the means

$$\bar{x}_1 = 136, \qquad \bar{x}_2 = 133.25, \qquad \bar{x}_3 = 139.$$

Table 16.1.1. Test of the Hypothesis that the *r* Normally Distributed Populations (with Equal Variance) from Which the *r* Groups Are Taken Have the Same Mean (Simplified Calculation see Next Section)

1st step. Compute the *r* means $\bar{x}_1, \cdots, \bar{x}_r$ of the groups. Here

(2)
$$\bar{x}_i = \frac{1}{n_i}(x_{i1} + x_{i2} + \cdots + x_{in_i}).$$

Compute the mean of the entire sample (*grand mean*), that is,

(3)
$$\bar{x} = \frac{1}{n}\sum_{i=1}^{r}\sum_{k=1}^{n_i} x_{ik} = \frac{1}{n}\sum_{i=1}^{r} n_i \bar{x}_i.$$

2nd step. Compute the *sum of squares between the means of the groups*, given by

(4)
$$q_1 = \sum_{i=1}^{r} n_i(\bar{x}_i - \bar{x})^2$$

and the *sum of squares within the groups*, given by

(5)
$$q_2 = \sum_{i=1}^{r}\sum_{k=1}^{n_i}(x_{ik} - \bar{x}_i)^2.$$

Then compute the quotient

(6)
$$v_0 = \frac{q_1/(r-1)}{q_2/(n-r)}.$$

3rd step. Choose a significance level α (5% or 1%).
4th step. Determine the solution c of the equation

(7)
$$P(V \leq c) = 1 - \alpha$$

from Table 9a or 9b of the *F*-distribution with $(r-1, n-r)$ degrees of freedom (cf. Appendix 4). If $v_0 \leq c$, do not reject the hypothesis $\mu_1 = \mu_2 = \cdots = \mu_r$. If $v_0 > c$, reject the hypothesis and assert that not all the mean values are equal.

Table 16.1.2. Analysis of Variance

Source of Variation	Degrees of Freedom	Sum of Squares	Mean Square
Between groups	$r-1$	q_1	$q_1/(r-1)$
Within groups	$n-r$	q_2	$q_2/(n-r)$
Total	$n-1$	q	

Table 16.1.3. Sample in Example 1

Place of Measurement	Sample Values			
1st group (corner)	137	142	128	137
2nd group (middle)	140	139	117	137
3rd group (edge)	142	140	133	141

The mean of the entire sample is

$$\bar{x} = \tfrac{1}{12}(4\bar{x}_1 + 4\bar{x}_2 + 4\bar{x}_3) = \tfrac{1}{3}(\bar{x}_1 + \bar{x}_2 + \bar{x}_3) = 136.083.$$

2nd step. The sum of the squares between the groups is

$$q_1 = 4[(\bar{x}_1 - \bar{x})^2 + (\bar{x}_2 - \bar{x})^2 + (\bar{x}_3 - \bar{x})^2]$$

$$= 4[0.083^2 + 2.833^2 + 2.917^2] = 66.167.$$

The sum of the squares within the groups is

$$q_2 = \sum_{i=1}^{3} \sum_{k=1}^{4} (x_{ik} - \bar{x}_i)^2$$

$$= (137 - 136)^2 + (142 - 136)^2 + \cdots + (141 - 139)^2 = 508.75.$$

From this we obtain

$$v_0 = \frac{q_1/2}{q_2/9} = \frac{33.083}{56.528} = 0.585.$$

3rd step. We choose the significance level $\alpha = 0.05$.

4th step. We have $r = 3$, $n = 12$, thus $r - 1 = 2$, $n - r = 9$. From Table 9a in Appendix 4 we see that the equation

$$P(V \leqq c) = 0.95$$

has the solution $c = 4.26$. Since $v_0 < c$, we do not reject the hypothesis

$$\mu_1 = \mu_2 = \mu_3,$$

that is, we assert that there is no significant difference in the tensile strength at various points of the metal sheets.

Table 16.1.4. Computation in Example 1

Source of Variation	Degrees of Freedom	Sum of Squares	Mean Square
Between groups	2	66.167	33.083
Within groups	9	508.750	56.528
Total	11	574.917	

Table 16.2.1. Analysis of Variance, Simplified Calculation

$$g_i = \sum_{k=1}^{n_i} x_{ik} = \text{Sum of the values of the } i\text{th group}$$

$$\tilde{g} = g_1 + g_2 + \cdots + g_r = \text{Sum of all values}$$

$$g = \tilde{g}^2/n \quad (\text{Auxiliary quantity})$$

$$u = \sum_{i=1}^{r} \sum_{k=1}^{n_i} x_{ik}^2 = \text{Sum of the squares of all the values}$$

$$q = u - g$$

$$q_1 = \frac{g_1^2}{n_1} + \frac{g_2^2}{n_2} + \cdots + \frac{g_r^2}{n_r} - g$$

$$q_2 = q - q_1$$

16.2   Simplified Calculation

The calculations in the last section may be simplified. To obtain q_1 and q_2, we may proceed as is shown in Table 16.2.1. These formulas are obtained from the original formulas for q and q_1 in a fashion similar to that in the case of the formula (1) in Sec. 3.2 for the variance.

Using Table 16.2.1, we see that the calculation in Ex. 1 of Sec. 16.1 takes the form shown in Table 16.2.2.

Of course, we may obtain further simplifications by setting

(1) $$x_{ik} = x_{ik}^* + c$$

Table 16.2.2. Simplified Calculation (cf. Table 16.2.1) in the Case of Example 1 of Sec. 16.1

i	Sample				g_i	g_i^2
1	137	142	128	137	544	295,936
2	140	139	117	137	533	284,089
3	142	140	133	141	556	309,136

$$\text{Sum} \qquad \tilde{g} = 1633 \qquad 889,161$$

$$g = \frac{1633^2}{12} = 222,224.083 \qquad u = 222,799$$

$$q = 222,799.000 - 222,224.083 = 574.917$$

$$q_1 = \frac{889,161.000}{4} - 222,224.083 = 66.167$$

$$q_2 = 574.917 - 66.167 = 508.750$$

Table 16.2.3. Analysis of Variance. Coded Calculations by Means of (1)

$$g_i{}^* = \sum_{k=1}^{n_i} x_{ik}{}^*$$

$$\tilde{g}^* = g_1{}^* + \cdots + g_r{}^*$$

$$g^* = \tilde{g}^{*2}/n$$

$$u^* = \sum_{i=1}^{r} \sum_{k=1}^{n_i} x_{ik}{}^{*2}$$

$$q = u^* - g^*$$

$$q_1 = \sum_{i=1}^{r} \frac{1}{n_i} g_i{}^{*2} - g^*$$

$$q_2 = q - q_1$$

and choosing c so that the $x_{ik}{}^*$ become small in absolute value. The reader may prove that the formulas in Table 16.2.3 are obtained by inserting (1) into the formulas in Table 16.2.1.

If we choose $c = 130$, then the computation in Ex. 1 of Sec. 16.1 takes the form shown in Table 16.2.4.

Table 16.2.4. Computations in Example 1, Sec. 16.1, by Means of (1) with $c = 130$, Arranged as Shown in Table 16.2.3

i	Sample Values Minus 130				$g_i{}^*$	$g_i{}^{*2}$
1	7	12	−2	7	24	576
2	10	9	−13	7	13	169
3	12	10	3	11	36	1296

Sum $\tilde{g}^* = 73$ 2041

$$g^* = \frac{73^2}{12} = 444.083 \qquad u^* = 1019$$

$$q = 1019.000 - 444.083 = 574.917$$

$$q_1 = \frac{2041.000}{4} - 444.083 = 66.167$$

$$q_2 = 574.917 - 66.167 = 508.750$$

Problems

General assumption. In each of the following problems assume that the corresponding populations are normally distributed and have the same variance.

1. Suppose that in a certain experiment a sample of size 20 consisted of 5 groups of equal size and gave the sums of squares $q_1 = 66$ and $q_2 = 30$. Test the hypothesis that the means of the 5 populations corresponding to the 5 groups are equal.

2. Using the sample

1st group	2	4
2nd group	10	12
3rd group	2	6

test the hypothesis that the populations corresponding to the 3 groups have the same mean.

3. Is there a significant difference in the copper content (in percent) among the following three castings of bronze?

Casting Number	Copper Content	
1	85.54	85.25
2	85.72	84.94
3	85.48	84.98

4. Obtain Table 16.2.3 from Table 16.2.1.

5. In the hand-picking process (cf. Problem 5, Sec. 13.4), is the position of the worker relative to the conveyor system (on the right side, left side, at the end) of significant importance? (The sample values have the same meaning as in that problem.)

Worker Number	1	2	3	4	5	6	7	8	9
Right	281	279	260	230	267	253	205	265	299
Left	254	275	278	232	241	245	220	255	302
End	238	280	217	237	246	239	228	252	280

6. The cuckoo (Cuculus canorus), a species of bird found in Europe, has the distinctive habit of laying its eggs in the nests of birds of other species. Measurements of cuckoo eggs found in the nests of 3 different species are given below (lengths in millimeters). Is the difference significant?

Hedge sparrow	22.0	23.9	20.9	23.8	25.0	24.0	21.7	23.8
	22.8	23.1	23.1	23.5	23.0	23.0		
Robin	21.8	23.0	23.3	22.4	22.4	23.0	23.0	23.0
	23.9	22.3	22.0	22.6	22.0	22.1	21.1	23.0
Wren	19.8	22.1	21.5	20.9	22.0	21.0	22.3	21.0
	20.3	20.9	22.0	20.0	20.8	21.2	21.0	

7. Does the planting date of cotton affect the yield of cotton seed? The following 12 values from Kawanda, Uganda, were obtained by dividing 4 fields in 3 plots each and associating the 3 plots with the 3 planting dates at random.

Planting Date	Yield (in Kilograms per Plot)			
May 1	3.35	1.49	2.44	2.44
May 15	3.86	2.71	2.18	1.95
May 29	1.99	2.89	1.68	2.13

8. Does the hay yield of 3 kinds of red fescue-grass (in kilograms per 100 square meters) differ significantly?

Kind I	92.4	87.7	86.6	92.2	98.2	87.2
Kind II	72.4	84.3	89.0	85.5	95.3	84.5
Kind III	96.1	91.5	91.0	100.8	95.2	107.4

9. Does the diameter (in microns) of a certain kind of cotton (American upland cotton; Gossypium hirsutum L.; grown in Raleigh, N.C.) depend significantly on the location on the seed?

Location I	17.8	16.0	16.0	17.3	18.3	17.5	15.7	16.2	18.3	17.0
Location II	16.8	14.1	14.9	16.5	17.0	15.7	16.5	16.0	14.7	17.5
Location III	17.5	14.4	14.7	17.3	17.3	15.5	15.2	13.4	15.7	15.7

10. Does the yield (in hundredweight/acre) of a certain kind of winter wheat (Hybrid 46) depend significantly on the row width?

Row Width (Inches)	Yield of Grain (Hundredweight/Acre)				
4	44.0	43.8	47.7	39.8	43.8
8	41.6	42.4	44.9	40.1	42.2
12	39.5	40.7	42.3	38.9	40.4

11. Does the age of chickens significantly affect the fat content of their meat?

Age (in Days)	Fat (in Percent)			
75	6.3	7.3	5.9	7.8
90	4.1	5.5	9.0	4.4
120	9.6	7.1	7.7	4.8

12. The three following groups of values of velocity of waste gas (measured in feet per seconds) were taken to find out whether the velocity was reasonably constant during an experiment to determine the dust content in the gas. The time between two values within a group was 5 sec and the difference between groups about 1 min. Test the hypothesis that the populations corresponding to the three groups have the same mean.

Group	Velocity (Feet/Second)								
A	20	21	20	20	23	21	26		
B	24	25	27	23	22	22	24	27	26	25
C	25	28	22	24	26	26			

13. Does the amount of fat absorbed by doughnuts during cooking depend significantly on the type of fat?

Type of Fat	Amount of Fat (Grams) Absorbed per Batch (24 Doughnuts)					
A	164	172	168	177	156	195
B	178	191	197	182	185	177
C	175	193	178	171	163	176
D	155	166	149	164	170	168

14. Does the liquid level depend significantly on the type of float cutoffs used in a bottle-filling machine?

Float Cutoff	Liquid Level		
A	14.8	14.0	14.4
B	13.3	13.9	13.6
C	15.3	15.8	16.0

16.3   Theoretical Basis of the Test in Table 16.1.1

In (1), Sec. 16.1, we may write

$$x_{ik} - \bar{x} = [x_{ik} - \bar{x}_i] + [\bar{x}_i - \bar{x}]$$

with $\bar{x}_i$ defined by (2) in Table 16.1.1. Squaring on both sides and performing the multiplication on the right, we obtain

$$(x_{ik} - \bar{x})^2 = [x_{ik} - \bar{x}_i]^2 + 2[x_{ik} - \bar{x}_i][\bar{x}_i - \bar{x}] + [\bar{x}_i - \bar{x}]^2.$$

We now sum over k from 1 to n_i. In this process the second term on the right does not contribute because $\bar{x}_i$ is the mean value of the ith group and, therefore,

$$\sum_{k=1}^{n_i} [x_{ik} - \bar{x}_i] = 0.$$

The last term on the right is independent of k and contributes $n_i[\bar{x}_i - \bar{x}]^2$. Consequently,

$$\sum_{k=1}^{n_i} (x_{ik} - \bar{x})^2 = n_i[\bar{x}_i - \bar{x}]^2 + \sum_{k=1}^{n_i} [x_{ik} - \bar{x}_i]^2.$$

If we now sum over i from 1 to r, we obtain

(1) $$q = q_1 + q_2$$

where q, q_1, and q_2 are given by (1), (4), and (5), all in Sec. 16.1. This is the decomposition or partition mentioned in connection with (1) in Sec. 16.1.

Each sample value x_{ik} may be regarded as a single observation of a normal random variable X_{ik}. These n random variables are independent. Then q is a single observation of the random variable

(2) $$Q = \sum_{i=1}^{r} \sum_{k=1}^{n_i} (X_{ik} - \bar{X})^2$$

where $\bar{X}$ denotes the sum of all the X_{ik}'s, divided by n [cf. (3) in Sec. 16.1], that is,

(3) $$\bar{X} = \frac{1}{n} \sum_{i=1}^{r} \sum_{k=1}^{n_i} X_{ik}.$$

Suppose that the hypothesis

$$\mu_1 = \mu_2 = \cdots = \mu_r$$

is true. Then all the n random variables have exactly the same normal distribution, and $q/(n-1)$ is the variance of the entire sample. From this and Theorem 1 in Sec. 12.4, it follows that Q/σ^2 has a χ^2-distribution with $n-1$ degrees of freedom. The numbers q_1 and q_2 given by (4), Sec. 16.1, and (5), Sec. 16.1, are observed values of the random variables

$$(4) \qquad\qquad Q_1 = \sum_{i=1}^{r} n_i(\bar{X}_i - \bar{X})^2$$

and

$$(5) \qquad\qquad Q_2 = \sum_{i=1}^{r}\sum_{k=1}^{n_i}(X_{ik} - \bar{X}_i)^2,$$

respectively, where [cf. (2) in Sec. 16.1]

$$\bar{X}_i = \frac{1}{n_i}\sum_{k=1}^{n_i} X_{ik}.$$

As in Sec. 12.4 we conclude that Q_1/σ^2 and Q_2/σ^2 have a χ^2-distribution with $r-1$ and $n-r$ degrees of freedom, respectively. Furthermore, Q_1 and Q_2 are independent. From (1) in Sec. 10.2 we see that the mean value of a χ^2-distribution is equal to the number of degrees of freedom. Hence Q_1/σ^2 has the mean value $r-1$, and Q_2/σ^2 has the mean value $n-r$. From this and (2) in Sec. 6.7, it follows that the mean value of the random variables

$$(6) \qquad\qquad S_1^2 = \frac{1}{r-1}Q_1 \qquad \text{and} \qquad S_2^2 = \frac{1}{n-r}Q_2$$

is equal to σ^2. Furthermore, from Theorem 1 in Sec. 13.6 we see that the quotient

$$(7) \qquad\qquad V = \frac{S_1^2}{S_2^2}$$

has an F-distribution with $(r-1, n-r)$ degrees of freedom. The number v_0 given by (6) in Sec. 16.1 is an observed value of V. If the hypothesis is true, then the probability that V assumes a value $v_0 > c$ [cf. (7), Sec. 16.1] is equal to α, that is, this probability is small. Hence if a sample yields a v_0 greater than c, we have a good reason for assuming that our hypothesis is false, and we reject it. If, however, $v_0 \leqq c$, we do not reject the hypothesis.

In this connection we use the fact that if the hypothesis is false, then any difference of the mean values produces the tendency to increase v_0, since then the distribution of Q_2 remains the same as before, whereas that of Q_1 changes in the indicated sense.

The model underlying the present design of experiment and corresponding analysis may also be described as follows. We have said that under our assumptions each sample value can be regarded as a single observation of a normal random variable X_{ik} with mean μ_i and variance σ^2. Hence if we set

$$(8) \qquad X_{ik} = \mu_i + Y_{ik},$$

then $Y_{ik} = X_{ik} - \mu_i$ is normal with mean 0 and variance σ^2, and the Y_{ik} are independent.

Furthermore, $\bar{X}$ in (3) is normal with mean

$$(9) \qquad \mu = E(\bar{X}) = \frac{1}{n}\sum_{i=1}^{r}\sum_{k=1}^{n_i} E(X_{ik}) = \frac{1}{n}\sum_{i=1}^{r} n_i\mu_i,$$

which is the weighted average of the μ_i. We may now find it convenient to reparametrize (8) in terms of μ. Setting

$$\mu_i = \mu + \delta_i,$$

we have

$$(10) \qquad X_{ik} = \mu + \delta_i + Y_{ik}$$

and, using $n_1 + \cdots + n_r = n$, we see that

$$\sum_{i=1}^{r} n_i\delta_i = \sum_{i=1}^{r} n_i(\mu_i - \mu) = \sum_{i=1}^{r} n_i\mu_i - n\mu,$$

which, by (9), implies

$$(11) \qquad n_1\delta_1 + n_2\delta_2 + \cdots + n_r\delta_r = 0.$$

In this setting our *hypothesis* is $\delta_i = 0$ $(i = 1, \cdots, r)$, and the alternative is that the δ_i are not all zero.

μ given by (9) is sometimes called the *overall population mean* or *grand population mean*, and the δ_i are called *differential effects*.

If in our test we reject the hypothesis, a problem may arise from the fact that the test does not tell us which μ_i are significantly different from which. We may apply the test in Sec. 13.4 to a single *prechosen* pair of groups; however, it can be shown that if we make comparisons suggested by the data, and several of them, the significance level becomes incorrect. Methods for the problem have been proposed by H. Scheffé (1953) (see Appendix 3) and others.

Finally, we mention that the model given by (10) is sometimes called *Model I*, in contrast to *Model II*, given by

$$X_{ik} = \mu + W_i + Y_{ik}$$

where instead of the parameter δ_i we have a normal random variable W_i with mean 0 and variance ω^2. Since Model II is similar to Model I, so is the corresponding analysis; readers interested in details are referred to one of the books mentioned in the introduction to this chapter.

16.4 Analysis of Variance Two-Way Experimental Layout

The sample at the beginning of Sec. 16.1 consisted of *r groups* corresponding to *r* different *levels* $A_1, \cdots, A_r$ of some *factor A* (the food) whose effect on some random variable (the gain) we wanted to study. Such a random experiment designed to study the effect of a single factor is called a *one-way experimental layout* or *one-factor experiment;* we have a *one-way classification*, due to the effect of the levels of a *single* factor *A* on a basic random variable.

We shall now consider *two-way experimental layouts* or *two-factor experiments*, in which we shall have a *two-way classification*, resulting from the effect of the levels of *two* factors on a basic random variable. Examples are the effect of humidity and temperature on the rate of growth of certain plants, the effect of machines and skill of workers on the output in a factory, etc.

In a two-way experimental layout we thus have two factors *A* and *B*, where *A* has *r* levels $A_1, \cdots, A_r$, as before, and *B* has *p* levels $B_1, \cdots, B_p$. To study the effect of *A* and *B* on a random variable *X*, we take a sample of $n = rp$ values x_{ik} $(i = 1, \cdots, r; \ k = 1, \cdots, p)$. We may arrange this sample in the form of a rectangular array, consisting of *r* horizontal *rows* and *p* vertical *columns*, that is,

$$
r \text{ rows} \begin{cases} & \overbrace{\qquad\qquad\qquad}^{p \text{ columns}} \\ & \begin{pmatrix} x_{11} & x_{12} & \cdots & x_{1p} \\ x_{21} & x_{22} & \cdots & x_{2p} \\ \cdot & \cdot & \cdots & \cdot \\ x_{r1} & x_{r2} & \cdots & x_{rp} \end{pmatrix} \end{cases}
$$

In this two-way classification the value x_{ik} is an observation on *X* when level A_i of the factor *A* and level B_k of the factor *B* are present. We may thus regard x_{ik} as an observed value of a random variable X_{ik}, and we make the following assumption.

Assumption. *The $n = rp$ observations x_{ik} correspond to n random variables X_{ik} which are independent and normal and have the same variance σ^2, whereas the mean values $\mu_{11}, \cdots, \mu_{rp}$ may be different. σ need not be known.*

We want to test the hypothesis that all those mean values are equal, that is, those random variables X_{ik} have exactly the same normal distribution. Of course, this would mean that the factors *A* and *B* have no effect on *X*, and the sample values differ only because of random variation.

The mean value of the ith row is customarily denoted by $\bar{x}_{i\cdot}$; thus

(1)
$$\bar{x}_{i\cdot} = \frac{1}{p}\sum_{k=1}^{p} x_{ik} = \frac{\text{Sum of the values in the } i\text{th row}}{\text{Number of values per row}}.$$

Similarly, the mean value of the kth column is denoted by $\bar{x}_{\cdot k}$; thus

(2)
$$\bar{x}_{\cdot k} = \frac{1}{r}\sum_{i=1}^{r} x_{ik} = \frac{\text{Sum of the values in the } k\text{th column}}{\text{Number of values per column}}.$$

Note that the two types of means can be distinguished by the position of the dot, which corresponds to that subscript with respect to which we average.

Of course, the mean value of the entire sample is

(3)
$$\bar{x} = \frac{1}{n}\sum_{i=1}^{r}\sum_{k=1}^{p} x_{ik}.$$

From Sec. 16.1 we remember that in the case of a one-way experimental layout (one-way classification) we decompose the sum of squares

(4)
$$q = \sum_{i=1}^{r}\sum_{k=1}^{p}(x_{ik} - \bar{x})^2$$

in two parts. In the present case of a two-way experimental layout (two-way classification) we shall decompose q into three parts q_1, q_2, q_3. This purely algebraic operation is similar to that in Sec. 16.3 and is accomplished as follows. By adding and subtracting terms, we may write

$$x_{ik} - \bar{x} = (\bar{x}_{i\cdot} - \bar{x}) + (\bar{x}_{\cdot k} - \bar{x}) + (x_{ik} - \bar{x}_{i\cdot} - \bar{x}_{\cdot k} + \bar{x}).$$

We now square on both sides. On the right we multiply out so that we obtain three squares $(\bar{x}_{i\cdot} - \bar{x})^2$ etc., and three other products each multiplied by 2. We sum with respect to i and k. Then each of those three squares yields a double sum whereas those three other products do not contribute. This is quite similar to the situation in Sec. 16.3, and the intermediate result is

$$q = \sum_{i}\sum_{k}(\bar{x}_{i\cdot} - \bar{x})^2 + \sum_{i}\sum_{k}(\bar{x}_{\cdot k} - \bar{x})^2 + \sum_{i}\sum_{k}(x_{ik} - \bar{x}_{i\cdot} - \bar{x}_{\cdot k} + \bar{x})^2.$$

Since the first two double sums contain only one subscript, they may be reduced to single sums. We then obtain the desired decomposition

(5)
$$q = q_1 + q_2 + q_3$$

where

(6)
$$q_1 = p\sum_{i=1}^{r}(\bar{x}_{i\cdot} - \bar{x})^2,$$

(7)
$$q_2 = r\sum_{k=1}^{p}(\bar{x}_{\cdot k} - \bar{x})^2,$$

(8)
$$q_3 = \sum_{i=1}^{r}\sum_{k=1}^{p}(x_{ik} - \bar{x}_{i\cdot} - \bar{x}_{\cdot k} + \bar{x})^2.$$

q_1 is called the *A-factor sum of squares*. It represents variation in the x_{ik} due to *A*-factor effects. (Remember that the *r* rows correspond to the *r* levels of the factor *A*.) q_2 is called the *B-factor sum of squares*. It represents variation in the x_{ik} due to *B*-factor effects. q_3 is called the *error sum of squares*. It represents variation in the x_{ik} which is left after removing *A*-factor and *B*-factor effects.

As in the case of one-factor experiments we regard the *n* sample values x_{ik} as single observations of *n* random variables X_{ik}. By assumption, the latter are independent and normal and have the same variance σ^2 and the means μ_{ik}. If we replace x_{ik} in (1)–(8) by X_{ik}, we obtain random variables, which we denote by the corresponding capital letters $\bar{X}_{i\cdot}$, $\bar{X}_{\cdot k}$, $\bar{X}$, Q, Q_1, Q_2, Q_3, respectively.

The hypothesis is that all the μ_{ik} are equal (see above). If the hypothesis is true, then Q/σ^2, Q_1/σ^2, Q_2/σ^2, and Q_3/σ^2 have χ^2-distributions with $n - 1$, $r - 1$, $p - 1$, and $(r - 1)(p - 1)$ degrees of freedom, respectively, and the last three of these variables are independent. Furthermore, the mean values of the variables

$$S_1{}^2 = \frac{1}{r-1} Q_1, \qquad S_2{}^2 = \frac{1}{p-1} Q_2, \qquad S_3{}^2 = \frac{1}{(r-1)(p-1)} Q_3$$

are equal to σ^2. This follows in a fashion similar to that in the previous section. From this and Theorem 1 in Sec. 13.6 we see that the quotients

$$V_1 = \frac{S_1{}^2}{S_3{}^2} \qquad \text{and} \qquad V_2 = \frac{S_2{}^2}{S_3{}^2}$$

have *F*-distributions with

$$[r - 1, (r - 1)(p - 1)] \qquad \text{and} \qquad [p - 1, (r - 1)(p - 1)]$$

degrees of freedom, respectively.

Before entering into the practical details of the test, we mention that the intersection of a row and a column in the representation of our sample is called a **cell**. Since the sample contains precisely one observed value of each random variable X_{ik}, our experiment is called a two-way experimental layout (two-way classification) with *one observation per cell*. If our sample contained *m* (>1) observed values of each X_{ik}, the experiment would be called a two-way experimental layout with *m observations per cell*. Readers interested in corresponding details are referred to the books mentioned in the introduction to the present chapter.

16.5   The Testing Procedure in the Case of a Two-Way Experimental Layout

Table 16.5.1 shows the steps of the test in the case of a two-way experimental layout with one observation per cell. The hypothesis is that all the

Table 16.5.1. Two-Way Experimental Layout with One Observation per Cell. Test of the Hypothesis That All the n Means μ_{ik} Are Equal, in the Case That the Population Satisfies the Assumption Formulated in the Last Section

---

1st step. Compute $q, q_1, q_2, q_3 = q - q_1 - q_2$, and

$$s_1^2 = q_1/(r - 1),$$
$$s_2^2 = q_2/(p - 1),$$
$$s_3^2 = q_3/(r - 1)(p - 1).$$

Arrange the results as shown in Table 16.5.2.

2nd step. Compute the quotients

$$v_1 = \frac{s_1^2}{s_3^2} \quad \text{and} \quad v_2 = \frac{s_2^2}{s_3^2}.$$

3rd step. Choose a significance level α (5% or 1%).

4th step. Determine the solution c_1 of the equation

$$P(V \leq c_1) = 1 - \alpha$$

from the table of the F-distribution with $[r - 1, (r - 1)(p - 1)]$ degrees of freedom (Table 9a or 9b in Appendix 4). If $v_1 \leq c_1$, assert that there is no significant difference between the *rows*. If $v_1 > c_1$, assert that there is such a difference.

5th step. Determine the solution c_2 of the equation

$$P(V \leq c_2) = 1 - \alpha$$

from the Table 9a or 9b of the F-distribution with $[p - 1, (r - 1)(p - 1)]$ degrees of freedom. If $v_2 \leq c_2$, assert that there is no significant difference between the *columns*. If $v_2 > c_2$, assert that there is such a difference.

6th step. If $v_1 \leq c_1$ and $v_2 \leq c_2$, do not reject the hypothesis that all the n mean values μ_{ik} are equal. In any other case, reject the hypothesis.

---

means are equal. Table 16.5.2 shows a suitable arrangement of the values obtained in the first step of the test. Simplified calculations will be discussed in the next section.

If $v_1 > c_1$, we reject the hypothesis. Then the statement about the columns in Step 5 (Table 16.5.1) will nevertheless remain meaningful, provided the nature of the experiment permits us to assume that the effects of the factors A and B act in an *additive* fashion, so that each x_{ik} may be regarded as an observed value of a normal random variable X_{ik} with mean

(1) $\mu_{ik} = \mu + \alpha_i + \beta_k$

Table 16.5.2. Arrangement of the Results in the First Step of Table 16.5.1

Source of Variation	Degrees of Freedom	Sum of Squares	Mean Square
Between rows (A effect)	$r - 1$	q_1	$s_1^2 = q_1/(r - 1)$
Between columns (B effect)	$p - 1$	q_2	$s_2^2 = q_2/(p - 1)$
Deviations	$(r - 1)(p - 1)$	q_3	$s_3^2 = q_3/(r - 1)(p - 1)$
Total	$n - 1$	q	

and variance σ^2, where

$$\alpha_1, \cdots, \alpha_r \text{ are } \textit{effects} \text{ due to level } A_1, \cdots, A_r \text{ of factor } A,$$

$$\beta_1, \cdots, \beta_p \text{ are } \textit{effects} \text{ due to level } B_1, \cdots, B_p \text{ of factor } B,$$

which satisfy the condition

$$(2) \qquad \alpha_1 + \cdots + \alpha_r = 0 \qquad \text{and} \qquad \beta_1 + \cdots + \beta_p = 0.$$

Note that in this **additive model** we may now set

$$(3) \qquad\qquad X_{ik} = \mu + \alpha_i + \beta_k + Y_{ik}$$

where $Y_{ik} = X_{ik} - \mu_{ik}$ is normal with mean 0 and variance σ^2, and these n random variables Y_{ik} are independent.

Furthermore, μ in (3) is the mean of

$$\bar{X} = \frac{1}{n} \sum_{i=1}^{r} \sum_{k=1}^{p} X_{ik},$$

because from (1) and (2) we obtain

$$E(\bar{X}) = \frac{1}{rp} \sum_{i=1}^{r} \sum_{k=1}^{p} \mu_{ik} = \frac{1}{rp}\left(rp\mu + p \sum_{i=1}^{r} \alpha_i + r \sum_{k=1}^{p} \beta_k \right) = \mu.$$

Moreover, the random variables

$$\bar{X}_{i\cdot} = \frac{1}{p} \sum_{k=1}^{p} X_{ik} \qquad \text{and} \qquad \bar{X}_{\cdot k} = \frac{1}{r} \sum_{i=1}^{r} X_{ik}$$

have means

$$(4) \qquad\qquad \mu_{i\cdot} = \mu + \alpha_i \qquad \text{and} \qquad \mu_{\cdot k} = \mu + \beta_k,$$

respectively (cf. Problem 11 in the next section).

We mention that the model given by (3) is sometimes called *Model I*, in contrast to *Model II*, in which the constants α_i and β_k are replaced by normal random variables with mean 0. For details, see the references given in the introduction to this chapter.

16.6   Two-Way Experimental Layout Simplified Calculation

The following example will illustrate how to simplify the calculations in the case of a two-way classification.

Example 1 (Swine-feeding experiment).   Twelve hogs were grouped into $r = 4$ groups of $p = 3$ hogs, according to their weight at the beginning of the experiment, so the factor A in the sense of the theory is the initial weight of a hog and has four levels. In each group the three hogs were given three different diets B_1, B_2, B_3. After a certain interval of time the gain in weight was as is shown in Table 16.6.1. Using this sample, we want to test

Table 16.6.1. Sample in Example 1

	Diet		
	B_1	B_2	B_3
Group A_1	7.0	14.0	8.5
Group A_2	16.0	15.5	16.5
Group A_3	10.5	15.0	9.5
Group A_4	13.5	21.0	13.5

G. Dunlop, *J. Agr. Sci.*, **25**, 1935, 445.

the hypothesis that neither the initial weight nor the type of diet affects the gain. We suppose that in this experiment the assumption in Sec. 16.4 is satisfied, so that we may use the test in Table 16.5.1.

1st step. We compute the values shown in Table 16.6.2. For details of the computation, see below.

2nd step. We have

$$v_1 = \frac{29.24}{4.702} = 6.219 \quad \text{and} \quad v_2 = \frac{27.06}{4.702} = 5.755.$$

3rd step. We choose the significance level $\alpha = 0.05$.

4th step. For the F-distribution with $(3, 6)$ degrees of freedom, the equation

$$P(V \le c_1) = 1 - \alpha = 0.95$$

has the solution

$$c_1 = 4.76.$$

We see that $v_1 = 6.219 > c_1 = 4.76$. Therefore we assert that there is a significant difference between the groups, that is, we assert that the initial weight affects the gain. Consequently, we reject the hypothesis.

5th step. We may assume that in the present case the additivity characterized at the end of the last section holds.

For the F-distribution with $(2, 6)$ degrees of freedom, the equation

$$P(V \le c_2) = 1 - \alpha = 0.95$$

Table 16.6.2. First Step in Example 1

Source of Variation	Degrees of Freedom	Sum of Squares	Mean Square
Between rows	$r - 1 = 3$	$q_1 = 87.73$	$s_1^2 = q_1/3 = 29.24$
Between columns	$p - 1 = 2$	$q_2 = 54.12$	$s_2^2 = q_2/2 = 27.06$
Deviations	$(r-1)(p-1) = 6$	$q_3 = 28.21$	$s_3^2 = q_3/6 = 4.702$
Total	$n - 1 = 11$	$q = 170.06$	

has the solution

$$c_2 = 5.14.$$

We have $v_2 = 5.755 > c_2 = 5.14$. Therefore we assert that there is a significant difference between the columns, that is, we assert that the type of diet affects the gain.

The computations in the first step may be simplified. To obtain q_1, q_2, and q_3, compute the quantities shown in Table 16.6.3. These formulas are obtained from (1)-(8) in Sec. 16.4. They are similar to those in Sec. 16.2. As before, we may set

$$x_{ik} = x_{ik}* + c,$$

Table 16.6.3. Analysis of Variance, Simplified Calculations in the Case of Two-Factor Experiments

$$g_i = \sum_{k=1}^{p} x_{ik} = \text{Sum of the values of the } i\text{th row}$$

$$h_k = \sum_{i=1}^{r} x_{ik} = \text{Sum of the values of the } k\text{th column}$$

$$\tilde{g} = g_1 + g_2 + \cdots + g_r = \text{Total sum}$$

$$g = \tilde{g}^2/n$$

$$u = \sum_{i=1}^{r} \sum_{k=1}^{p} x_{ik}^2 = \text{Sum of the squares of all values}$$

$$q = u - g$$

$$q_1 = \frac{1}{p}(g_1^2 + g_2^2 + \cdots + g_r^2) - g$$

$$q_2 = \frac{1}{r}(h_1^2 + h_2^2 + \cdots + h_p^2) - g$$

$$q_3 = q - q_1 - q_2$$

Table 16.6.4. Computations in the First Step in Example 1

	Sample Values Minus 15.0			$g_i{}^*$	$g_i{}^{*2}$
	−8.0	−1.0	−6.5	−15.5	240.25
	1.0	0.5	1.5	3.0	9.00
	−4.5	0	−5.5	−10.0	100.00
	−1.5	6.0	−1.5	3.0	9.00
$h_k{}^*$	−13.0	5.5	−12.0	$\tilde{g}^* = -19.5$	358.25
$h_k{}^{*2}$	169.00	30.25	144.00	343.25	

$$\tilde{g}^* = -19.5 \qquad g^* = \frac{19.5^2}{12} = 31.69 \qquad u^* = 201.75$$

$$q = 201.75 - 31.69 = 170.06$$

$$q_1 = \frac{358.25}{3} - 31.69 = 87.73$$

$$q_2 = \frac{343.25}{4} - 31.69 = 54.12$$

$$q_3 = 170.06 - 87.73 - 54.12 = 28.21$$

choosing c so that the $x_{ik}{}^*$ are small in absolute value. Then, to the formulas in Table 16.6.3, there correspond similar formulas which are obtained by replacing x_{ik} by $x_{ik}{}^*$, and the new quantities are characterized by an asterisk.

For instance, in Ex. 1 we may choose $c = 15$. Table 16.6.4 shows the corresponding computations in the first step of the test.

Problems

General assumption. In the following problems, suppose that the assumption stated in Sec. 16.4 holds.

1. Reconsider Problem 5 in Sec. 16.2, and test the hypothesis that neither the effect of the 3 positions nor the effect of the skill of the 9 workers is significant.

2. The following data are taken from an experiment about safe handling of tools in a missile silo, where personnel and missile damage could result from a dropped tool. The numbers given are times (in seconds) necessary for removing 6 screws that hold a particular component on the missile, inserting the screws back into place, turning each screw with a force of 10–12 in. lb, and inserting 5 bolts. The hand tools used were a screwdriver, a torque wrench with an extension with a Phillips bit, and a socket wrench ($4\frac{1}{4}$ in. in length). The lanyard configurations were: (*A*) a strand between a swivel on the tool and a belt around the technician's waist; (*B*) a strand between a swivel on the tool and a wrist band; (*C*) a loop around the wrist leading

from a swivel in the tool. Test the hypothesis that there is no significant difference, either among the types of haltering or among the participants.

Haltering	Technician Number											
	1	2	3	4	5	6	7	8	9	10	11	12
A	93	98	91	65	74	80	84	81	55	94	49	64
B	97	62	100	70	76	68	73	73	61	85	61	61
C	133	64	71	76	66	76	74	94	64	82	49	67
Without	108	62	62	62	68	78	74	67	53	71	47	63

3. In a study of manual work, rapid motions of the right arm were tested. The numbers in the table are ratios of maximum and average velocities. M_1 is a horizontal motion from the right to the left, M_2 is a horizontal motion toward the body, and M_3 is a vertical motion. In each experiment 90 motions per minute were performed. Test the hypothesis that neither the directions nor the weights have a significant effect.

Weight	Type of Motion		
	M_1	M_2	M_3
0	1.59	1.55	1.85
400 g	1.53	1.53	1.60
800 g	1.50	1.47	1.80

4. Bacteria in soil can be counted by dissolving a certain amount of soil in salt water, adding more water, putting a small portion of this dilution onto a glass slide with culture-medium, and counting the colonies of bacteria that develop on the slide. The table shows corresponding values in a case where the original soil was divided into 4 portions A, B, C, D. Each portion was dissolved independently, and 5 slides were prepared from each. For the usefulness and accuracy of the method, it is important that in this case there should be no significant difference among the 4 portions or the 5 slides. Test this hypothesis.

Slide Number	Portion			
	A	B	C	D
1	26	28	31	37
2	30	33	26	32
3	30	32	28	32
4	29	26	32	30
5	32	27	31	26

5. Is there a significant difference in yield with respect to the kind of barley or with respect to the location (three places in Minnesota)?

Place	Yield (Bushels per Acre)				
	Manchuria	Svansota	Velvet	Trebi	Peatland
1	27	31	33	33	30
2	41	43	44	57	42
3	31	30	32	45	37

6. The table shows values of current (in milliamperes) necessary to produce a given amount of brightness in a television tube. Is the effect of the kind of glass (I, II) or the kind of phosphorus (A, B, C) significant?

Kind of Glass	Kind of Phosphorus		
	A	B	C
I	285	302	282
II	235	245	225

7. The table shows values of rounds per minute fired from a Navy gun. Test the hypothesis that neither the weight of the loading crew (I slight men, II normal men, III heavy men) nor the method of loading has a significant effect.

Crew	Method	
	Old	New
I	15.9	24.4
II	15.3	23.4
III	14.0	23.0

8. Voltage regulators for cars which are required to operate within the range of 15.8 volts to 16.4 volts are set at a setting station and then later controlled at a testing station. Is there a significant difference between the 3 setting stations A, B, C or between the 4 testing stations 1–4? (The table shows values of regulated voltage of a regulator first set at Station A, then tested at Stations 1–4, then again set at Station B, etc.)

Setting Station	Testing Stations			
	1	2	3	4
A	16.5	16.5	16.6	16.6
B	16.0	16.1	16.0	16.1
C	16.0	16.0	15.9	16.3

9. pH measurements of soil were made for soil at two different distances A_1, A_2 from the surface and at three different locations B_1, B_2, B_3. The coded values are as given in the table. Does the pH depend significantly on the depth or on those locations?

	A_1	A_2
B_1	2	4
B_2	10	12
B_3	2	6

10. Three kinds of gasoline were used in four makes of automobile. Do the values (miles per gallon) indicate a significant difference among the kinds of gasoline or among the makes of automobile?

Gasoline	Automobile			
	B_1	B_2	B_3	B_4
A_1	14.8	15.2	15.1	14.6
A_2	15.3	14.8	17.0	16.1
A_3	17.2	16.9	17.5	16.6

11. Prove (4) in Sec. 16.5.

16.7   Randomized Block Design

It is interesting to note that the analysis explained in Sec. 16.5 also arises in connection with the design of a different type of experiment, which is called a *randomized block design* and is used to reduce the experimental error. We shall describe this experiment in terms of an agricultural application, but from the nature of the experiment it will be obvious that the same design may also be used in various other situations, for example, in industry, medical research, etc.

Suppose we want to study the effect of a single factor A on a basic random variable, for instance, the effect of fertilizing treatments on the crop yield of wheat, assuming that A has r levels. We may then design the experiment in such a fashion that the observations to be obtained will be arranged in p blocks of r observations each; this will be done in order to try to eliminate the effect of soil heterogeneity. For this purpose we lay out p *blocks* of equal size on a piece of land. We then divide each block into r equal *plots*. In performing the experiment we randomly allocate the r levels of A to the r plots of the first block, repeat the randomization for the second block, etc. Thus each block contains one plot for each level of A (each of the r different fertilizing treatments), and for each particular treatment we have p different plots.

Let x_{ik} be the weight of the crop from the plot receiving the ith treatment (level A_i of A) and belonging to the kth block. Then we may regard x_{ik} as an observed value of a random variable X_{ik}, and we assume that X_{ik} is normal with mean μ_{ik} and variance σ^2 and the X_{ik} are independent.

q_1 (cf. Sec. 16.5) may now be called the sum of squares due to variation *between treatments*, and q_2 may be called the sum of squares *between blocks*.

The means μ_{ik} may differ because of soil heterogeneity and differences in treatment. Since in each block the treatments are randomly allocated, we may assume the effects of soil heterogeneity *within each block* to be included in the random part of X_{ik}, so that if we assume *additivity*, we may write $\mu_{ik} = \mu + \alpha_i + \beta_k$ and

$$X_{ik} = \mu + \alpha_i + \beta_k + Y_{ik}$$

where $Y_{ik} = X_{ik} - \mu_{ik}$ is normal with mean 0 and variance σ^2 and the Y_{ik} are independent.

To test the hypothesis that there are no differences between the fertilizing treatments, we compute v_1 and c_1 as defined in Table 16.5.1. If $v_1 \leqq c_1$, we do not reject the hypothesis. If $v_1 > c_1$, we reject it.

CHAPTER **17**

Pairs of Measurements. Regression Analysis

In Chaps. 11–16 we were concerned with random experiments involving a single random variable. We shall now consider random experiments involving two variables, at least one of which is a random variable. Typical examples will be mentioned below, and they will illustrate the practical importance of those experiments.

In practice we may distinguish between two types of situations and corresponding experiments, as follows.

1. Regression analysis. In regression[1] analysis one of the two variables, call it x, can be regarded as an ordinary variable, that is, can be measured without appreciable error. The other variable, Y, is a random variable. x is called the *independent* (sometimes the *controlled*) *variable*, and one is interested in the dependence of Y on x. Typical examples are the dependence of the blood pressure Y on the age x of a person or, as we shall now say, the regression of Y on x, the regression of the gain of weight Y of certain animals on the daily ration of food x, the regression of the heat conductivity Y of cork on the specific weight x of the cork, etc.

In the experiment the experimenter first selects n values $x_1, \cdots, x_n$ of x and then observes Y at those values of x, so that he obtains a sample of the form $(x_1, y_1), (x_2, y_2), \cdots, (x_n, y_n)$. In regression analysis the mean μ of Y is assumed to depend on x, that is, is a function $\mu = \mu(x)$ in the ordinary sense. The curve of $\mu(x)$ is called the *regression curve of Y on x*. In the simplest case, it may be a straight line, represented by

$$\mu(x) = \alpha + \beta x.$$

This is called the *regression line of Y on x*, and the slope β is called the *regression coefficient*. This linear case is particularly important because any

---

[1] This term was suggested by Galton's observation that on the average the sons of tall fathers are not as tall as their fathers and the sons of short fathers are not as short as their fathers, so that there is tendency to *regress* toward the mean. The term *correlation* (*co-relation*) was also proposed by Galton (*Proc. Roy. Soc. London*, **45**, 1888).

function $\mu(x)$ can be approximated sufficiently accurately by a linear function if x varies in a *short* interval. That sample may then be used to estimate the parameters α and β. Point estimates of α and β can be obtained by the *method of least squares* (Sec. 17.1, example in Sec. 17.2, proofs in Sec. 17.3). If we make the assumptions that

> (*A1*) for each fixed x the variable Y is normal with mean $\alpha + \beta x$ and variance σ^2 (not depending on x) and
>
> (*A2*) the n performances of the experiment that give the sample are independent,

then the estimates of α and β obtained by the method of least squares are identical with the maximum likelihood estimates (cf. Sec. 17.4).

Under those assumptions it will be possible to obtain confidence intervals for the regression coefficient β (Sec. 17.5) and for the mean $\mu(x)$ (Sec. 17.6), to test hypotheses about β (Sec. 17.7, theory in Sec. 17.8), to apply methods from analysis of variance (Sec. 17.9), and to test the assumption that the regression curve is a straight line (Sec. 17.10). The method of least squares can also be applied in cases in which the regression curve is not a straight line (Sec. 17.11), and corresponding tests can be developed (Sec. 17.12).

2. Correlation analysis (*to be considered in Chap. 18*). In correlation analysis, both variables, call them X and Y, are random variables, and one is interested in relations between them. Hence, whereas problems of regression analysis still involve but one *random* variable (because in regression analysis, x is an ordinary variable), correlation analysis is concerned with problems involving *two* random variables. Typical examples are the relation between age X of husband and age Y of wife in marriages or, as we shall now say, the correlation between that age X and that age Y, the correlation between "beauty" and "brains," the correlation between the humidity of soil at two different points of observation, the correlation between wear X and wear Y of the two front tires of cars, etc.

17.1 Regression Line.
Method of Least Squares

Suppose that in a certain random experiment we are concerned simultaneously with two quantities, an ordinary variable x and a random variable Y, whose mean depends on x, and we perform the experiment so that we first select n values $x_1, \cdots, x_n$ of x and then for each selected x_j we obtain an observed value y_j of Y. We then have a sample of n pairs of values

$$(x_1, y_1), (x_2, y_2), \cdots, (x_n, y_n).$$

To get a first impression, we may graph the n pairs as n points in the xy-plane in the usual fashion. In some cases we may see that the n points lie nearly on a straight line, and we may then fit such a line by eye. This line is

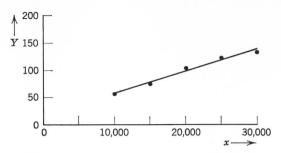

Fig. 17.1.1. Regression of the luminosity Y (measured in arbitrary units) of positive rays of hydrogen on the voltage x (volts) of the discharge (R. Gebauer and E. Kreyszig, *Zeitschr. f. Physik*, **135**, 1953, 358)

called the *regression line of the y-values of the sample on the x-values of the sample*. It may be used to predict values of Y for a given x that interests us, so that we get some idea of the values of Y to be expected for that x.

An illustrative example is shown in Fig. 17.1.1. In fact, the voltage x can be regarded as an ordinary variable because it can be measured without appreciable error, whereas the luminosity Y is measured by a complicated photographic process and must be regarded as a random variable because it is affected by various small random factors (such as slight changes of pressure in the tube and relatively large random errors in that photographic process).

If the points are scattered (as in Fig. 17.1.2 or worse), then fitting a straight line by eye becomes difficult and unreliable in the sense that different persons may fit by eye quite different straight lines through those points. Therefore we should have a mathematical method for fitting lines that yields a unique result depending only on the points. A widely used procedure of this type is the **method of least squares** developed by Gauss. In our present situation it may be formulated as follows.

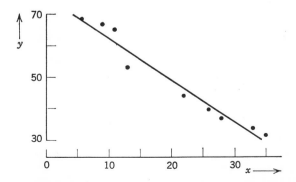

Fig. 17.1.2. Regression of the Brinell hardness Y (kg/mm^2) of steel on the amount of deformation x (mm) at normal temperature (80°F)

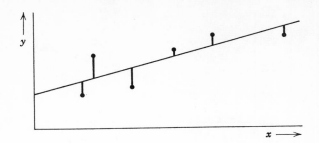

Fig. 17.1.3. Vertical distance of given points from a straight line

The straight line should be fitted through the given points so that the sum of the squares of the distances of those points from the straight line is minimum, where the distance is measured in vertical direction (in y-direction), as is illustrated in Fig. 17.1.3.

It is clear that the distances must enter into the method. To use squares of distances rather than absolute values turns out to be practical from the standpoint of computation as well as from that of the theory. This makes the method preferable, compared with other methods that might be used in this connection. The use of the *vertical* distance (instead of the shortest distance) is justified and is suggested by the fact that x is an independent variable whose values are selected at the beginning of the experiment and we want to estimate values of Y corresponding to given values of x.

Moreover, another motivation for the present method will become obvious in Sec. 17.4. In fact, we shall see that if the random variable Y is normal with mean $\alpha + \beta x$ and variance σ^2 (independent of x) and the n performances of the experiment that gave the sample are independent, then the values a and b obtained below are the maximum likelihood estimates of α and β.

Let us now explain the method in terms of formulas. First of all, we have to make the following assumption.

General assumption (G).   *The x-values $x_1, \cdots, x_n$ of our sample $(x_1, y_1), \cdots,$ (x_n, y_n) are not all equal.*

The vertical distance of a point (x_j, y_j) from a straight line

$$(1) \qquad\qquad\qquad y = a + bx$$

is $|y_j - a - bx_j|$, cf. Fig. 17.1.4. Hence the squares of the vertical distances of the n points of our sample from the line (1) have the sum

$$(2) \qquad\qquad\qquad q = \sum_{j=1}^{n} (y_j - a - bx_j)^2.$$

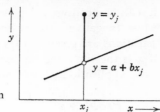

Fig. 17.1.4. Vertical distance of a point (x_j, y_j) from a line $y = a + bx$

q is a function of a and b. In order that it have a minimum, it is necessary that

$$\frac{\partial q}{\partial a} = 0 \quad \text{and} \quad \frac{\partial q}{\partial b} = 0.$$

In Sec. 17.3 we shall prove that from these two conditions we obtain the straight line

(3) $$y - \bar{y} = b(x - \bar{x})$$

where $\bar{x}$ and $\bar{y}$ are the means of the x and the y values in the sample, that is,

(4) $$\bar{x} = \frac{1}{n}(x_1 + \cdots + x_n), \qquad \bar{y} = \frac{1}{n}(y_1 + \cdots + y_n),$$

and the slope of the line is given by the formula

(5) $$b = \frac{s_{xy}}{s_x^2}$$

with the denominator

(6) $$s_x^2 = \frac{1}{n-1} \sum_{j=1}^{n} (x_j - \bar{x})^2 = \frac{1}{n-1}\left[\sum_{j=1}^{n} x_j^2 - \frac{1}{n}\left(\sum_{j=1}^{n} x_j \right)^2 \right]$$

and the numerator

(7) $$s_{xy} = \frac{1}{n-1} \sum_{j=1}^{n} (x_j - \bar{x})(y_j - \bar{y}).$$

The straight line (3) is called the **regression line** *of the y-values of the sample on the x-values of the sample.* b is called the corresponding **regression coefficient.** s_x^2 may be called the *variance of the x-values* in the sample (but remember that x is not a random variable). s_{xy} is called the **covariance** of the sample. The reader may show that

(8)
$$s_{xy} = \frac{1}{n-1}\left(\sum_{j=1}^{n} x_j y_j - n\bar{x}\bar{y} \right)$$

$$= \frac{1}{n-1}\left[\sum_{j=1}^{n} x_j y_j - \frac{1}{n}\left(\sum_{i=1}^{n} x_i \right)\left(\sum_{j=1}^{n} y_j \right) \right].$$

We see that the regression line (3) passes through the point $(\bar{x}, \bar{y})$.

s_{xy} can be positive, zero, or negative. Hence the same holds for b. If b is positive (negative), the regression is called *positive (negative) regression*. Illustrations are given in Figs. 17.1.1 and 17.1.2, respectively.

If x is the time, the regression is also called **trend.** This term is used in various applications, for instance, in statistical problems of economics.

Problems

1. Derive (8) from (7).
2. Construct a simple sample for which $b = 0$.
3. Fit a straight line by eye. Estimate the weight of a student whose height is 68 in.

$x =$ Height (inches)	72	66	67	69	74	61	66	62	70	63
$y =$ Weight (pounds)	178	141	158	165	180	133	159	140	160	136

4. Fit a straight line by eye. Estimate the stopping distance of the car traveling at 35 miles per hour.

$x =$ Speed (miles/hour)	20	30	40	50
$y =$ Stopping distance (feet)	50	95	150	210

5. Graph the following sample, fit a straight line by eye, and convince yourself that the fit is poor. Show that for values corresponding to a shorter subinterval on the x-axis (for example, from 2 to 5), a much better fitting straight line can be found.

x	0	1	2	3	4	5	6	7	8
y	5.0	2.0	1.5	1.0	1.0	0.9	1.0	1.5	3.0

17.2   Examples

Example 1 (Density and iron content of ore). Scraps of a certain type of iron ore were selected on the basis of their density x and then their iron content Y was measured. The results are shown in Table 17.2.1, and we want to determine the corresponding regression line; cf. (3) in the preceding section.

For this purpose we calculate the auxiliary values x_j^2 and $x_j y_j$ and the sums

$$\sum x_j = 28.1 \qquad \sum y_j = 267$$
$$\sum x_j^2 = 88.03 \qquad \sum x_j y_j = 837.2.$$

Since $n = 9$, the mean values are

$$\bar{x} = \frac{28.1}{9} = 3.12 \quad \text{and} \quad \bar{y} = \frac{267}{9} = 29.67.$$

Using (6) and (8) in the last section, we obtain

$$s_x^2 = \frac{1}{8}\left(88.03 - \frac{28.1^2}{9}\right) = 0.03694$$

$$s_{xy} = \frac{1}{8}\left(837.2 - \frac{28.1 \cdot 267}{9}\right) = 0.4458$$

Table 17.2.1. Regression of the Iron Content Y (Percent) of Iron Ore on the Density x (Grams/centimeter^3) (H. Bottke, *Bergbauwiss.*, 10, 1963, 377)

	Sample Values		Auxiliary Values	
	x_j	y_j	x_j^2	$x_j y_j$
	2.8	27	7.84	75.6
	2.9	23	8.41	66.7
	3.0	30	9.00	90.0
	3.1	28	9.61	86.8
	3.2	30	10.24	96.0
	3.2	32	10.24	102.4
	3.2	34	10.24	108.8
	3.3	33	10.89	108.9
	3.4	30	11.56	102.0
Sum	28.1	267	88.03	837.2

and from this the regression coefficient

$$b = \frac{0.4458}{0.03694} = 12.07.$$

Hence the regression line has the representation (cf. Fig. 17.2.1)

$$y - 29.67 = 12.07(x - 3.12).$$

This may also be written

$$y = 12.07x - 7.99.$$

In many cases the determination of the regression line can be simplified by **coding,** that is, by the use of a linear transformation

(1)
$$x_j = c_1 x_j^* + l_1$$
$$y_j = c_2 y_j^* + l_2$$

In this transformation we choose the constants c_1, c_2, l_1, and l_2 so that the transformed values x_j^* and y_j^* become as simple as possible. We first compute the mean values $\bar{x}^*$ and $\bar{y}^*$, the variance s_x^{*2}, and the covariance s_{xy}^* corresponding to the transformed values. Then, using (6) and (7) in Sec. 3.2, we obtain

(2)
$$\bar{x} = c_1 \bar{x}^* + l_1, \qquad \bar{y} = c_2 \bar{y}^* + l_2$$
$$s_x^2 = c_1^2 s_x^{*2}, \qquad s_{xy} = c_1 c_2 s_{xy}^*.$$

The reader may prove the formula for s_{xy} (cf. Problem 1).

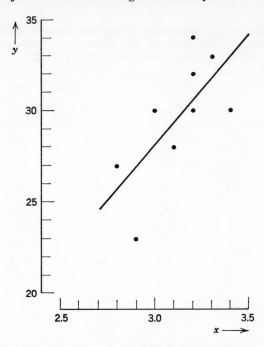

Fig. 17.2.1. Sample values and regression line in Ex. 1

Example 2.   In the last example, let

$$x_j = 0.1x_j{}^* + 3.0, \qquad y_j = y_j{}^* + 30.$$

Then (cf. Table 17.2.2)

$$x_j{}^* = 10x_j - 30, \qquad y_j{}^* = y_j - 30.$$

**Table 17.2.2. Coded Values in
Example 2**

$x_j{}^*$	$y_j{}^*$
−2	−3
−1	−7
0	0
1	−2
2	0
2	2
2	4
3	3
4	0
11	−3

Consequently,

$$\bar{x}^* = \frac{11}{9} = 1.2, \qquad \bar{y}^* = \frac{-3}{9} = -0.33,$$

$$\sum x_j^{*2} = 43, \qquad \sum x_j^* y_j^* = 32.$$

From this we obtain

$$s_x^{*2} = \frac{1}{8}\left(43 - \frac{11^2}{9}\right) = 3.694, \qquad s_{xy}^* = \frac{1}{8}\left(32 - \frac{11\cdot(-3)}{9}\right) = 4.458.$$

We now apply (2). Since $c_1 = 0.1$ and $c_2 = 1$, it follows that

$$\bar{x} = 0.1\cdot 1.2 + 3.0 = 3.12, \qquad \bar{y} = -0.33 + 30 = 29.67,$$

$$b = \frac{s_{xy}}{s_x^2} = \frac{c_2 s_{xy}^*}{c_1 s_x^{*2}} = \frac{4.458}{0.3694} = 12.07,$$

in agreement with our previous results.

Problems

1. Prove the formula for s_{xy} in (2).

2.-10. In each case determine and graph the regression line of the y-values on the x-values of the sample.

2.

x	5	10	15	20
y	10.0	8.9	8.2	7.0

3.

x	1	2	3
y	1.0	1.7	3.0

4. Number of revolutions x (per minute) and power y (hp) of a Diesel engine

x	400	500	600	700	750
y	580	1030	1420	1880	2100

5. x = height of a baby at birth (in centimeters), y = period of pregnancy (in days). [To avoid a false impression, we should note that the given values are mean values of many observations, equally many in each case; here these given values should be treated as if they were single observations.]

x	48	49	50	51	52
y	277.1	279.3	281.4	283.2	284.8

6. Oxygen content y (milligrams/liter) of the Wörther Lake, Austria, at distance x (meters) from the surface:

x	15	20	30	40	50	60	70
y	6.5	5.6	5.4	6.0	4.6	1.4	0.1

7. x = disulphide content of S-methyl wool (in percent of the content in the unreduced fibres), y = saturation water content (in percent):

x	10	15	30	40	50	55	80	100
y	50	46	43	43	36	39	37	33

8. x = height of female workers (in centimeters), y = distance between the eyes of a seated worker and the seat of the chair (in centimeters). These data were obtained in connection with redesigning screw presses.

x	y			x	y					
146	62									
150	60			162	58	61	61			
152	61			163	63					
154	60			164	59	63	63	64	68	
155	61	64		165	60	60	65	65	65	66	67
158	61			166	62	66				
159	64	65	65	168	62	65	65	66	69	
160	63	63	65	170	68					
161	63			172	62	63	66	69		

9. Number of errors y (per hour and per radiotelegraphist) made by 11 radiotelegraphists who had to receive 9 telegrams of 250 coded 5-letter words each, at a speed of 22 words per minute and at various temperatures x (in centigrades). These data were obtained in a study of the effect of air conditioning in offices and other rooms.

x	26	28	31	33
y	12.0	11.5	15.3	17.3

10. Speed x (miles/hour) and draft y (pounds) of plows drawn by tractors

x	0.9	1.3	2.0	2.7	3.4	3.4	4.1	5.2	5.5	6.0
y	425	420	480	495	540	530	590	610	690	680

17.3   Derivation of the Formulas in Sec. 17.1

Differentiating (2) in Sec. 17.1, we obtain

$$\frac{\partial q}{\partial a} = -2 \sum (y_j - a - bx_j)$$

$$\frac{\partial q}{\partial b} = -2 \sum x_j(y_j - a - bx_j)$$

where we sum over j from 1 to n. Equating these expressions to zero, we find

$$\sum y_j - na - b \sum x_j = 0$$
$$\sum x_j y_j - a \sum x_j - b \sum x_j{}^2 = 0.$$

Using (4) in Sec. 17.1, we thus have

$$a + b\bar{x} = \bar{y}$$
$$n\bar{x}a + b \sum x_j{}^2 = \sum x_j y_j.$$

Since we assumed that not all x-values are equal, this system of linear equations in the unknowns a and b has the solution

(1) $$a = \bar{y} - b\bar{x}, \qquad b = \frac{\sum x_j y_j - n\bar{x}\bar{y}}{\sum x_j{}^2 - n\bar{x}^2}.$$

From (6) and (8) in Sec. 17.1 we see that the numerator of b is equal to $(n - 1)s_{xy}$ and the denominator is equal to $(n - 1)s_x{}^2$. Hence we obtain (5), Sec. 17.1. If we substitute the expression for a in (1), Sec. 17.1, it follows that

$$y = bx + \bar{y} - b\bar{x},$$

and this is equivalent to (3), Sec. 17.1. This completes our derivation of the sample regression line from the principle of least squares.

If we substitute the expression (1) for a in (2), Sec. 17.1, we obtain

(2) $$q = \sum_{j=1}^{n} [(y_j - \bar{y}) - b(x_j - \bar{x})]^2.$$

Since all the terms are squares, they are nonnegative. It follows that q is zero if and only if each term is zero, that is, if and only if the relations

$$y_j - \bar{y} = b(x_j - \bar{x}) \qquad\qquad (j = 1, 2, \cdots, n)$$

hold. Because of (3), Sec. 17.1, we thus obtain the following result.

The sum of squares (2), Sec. 17.1, is zero if and only if all the points of the sample lie on the regression line (3), Sec. 17.1.

In (2),

$$[(y_j - \bar{y}) - b(x_j - \bar{x})]^2 = (y_j - \bar{y})^2 - 2b(y_j - \bar{y})(x_j - \bar{x}) + b^2(x_j - \bar{x})^2.$$

Thus

$$q = \sum(y_j - \bar{y})^2 - 2b\sum(y_j - \bar{y})(x_j - \bar{x}) + b^2\sum(x_j - \bar{x})^2.$$

Introducing the *variance of the y-values*

(3) $$s_y{}^2 = \frac{1}{n-1} \sum_{j=1}^{n}(y_j - \bar{y})^2 = \frac{1}{n-1}\left[\sum_{j=1}^{n} y_j{}^2 - \frac{1}{n}\left(\sum_{j=1}^{n} y_j \right)^2 \right]$$

and using the formulas (6) and (7) in Sec. 17.1, we readily see that

$$q = (n - 1)[s_y{}^2 - 2bs_{xy} + b^2 s_x{}^2].$$

Because of (5), Sec. 17.1, we may take the last two terms together and find that

(4) $$q = (n - 1)(s_y{}^2 - b^2 s_x{}^2).$$

From (5), Sec. 17.1, and the result above we now obtain the following final result.

All the points of a sample lie on the corresponding regression line (3), *Sec. 17.1, if and only if*

(5) $$s_{xy}{}^2 = s_x{}^2 s_y{}^2.$$

17.4   A Regression Model.
Maximum Likelihood Estimates

In Secs. 17.1–17.3 it was not necessary to make specific assumptions about the distribution of the random variable Y. From now on we have to do so because we want to determine confidence intervals and test hypotheses. We make the following assumptions.

Assumptions.

(A1) *For each fixed x the random variable Y is normal with mean*

(1) $$\mu(x) = \alpha + \beta x$$

and variance σ^2 where the latter is independent of x (cf. Fig. 17.4.1).

(A2) *The n performances of the experiment by which we obtain a sample* $(x_1, y_1), \cdots , (x_n, y_n)$ *are independent (cf. p. 147).*

Assumption (A2) is satisfied, for instance, in Ex. 1 of Sec. 17.2. It is not satisfied, for example, in an experiment where x is the time and Y is the height of a growing plant.

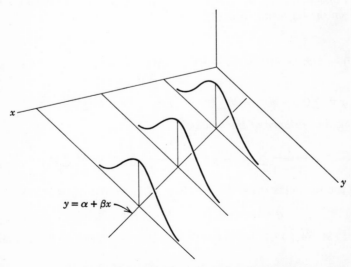

Fig. 17.4.1. Illustration of Assumption (A1)

β in (1) is called the **regression coefficient** of the population. To justify this name, we shall prove the following theorem.

Theorem 1. *Under Assumptions (A1) and (A2) the regression coefficient b in sample regression line*

$$y = a + bx \qquad\qquad (cf.\ Sec.\ 17.1)$$

is the maximum likelihood estimate (Sec. 11.5) of β, and a is the maximum likelihood estimate of α.

Proof. y_j in the sample value (x_j, y_j) may be regarded as an observed value of a random variable Y_j which, by Assumption (A1), is normal with mean $\alpha + \beta x_j$ and variance σ^2. Hence Y_j has the probability density function (cf. Sec. 8.1)

$$\frac{1}{\sqrt{2\pi}\,\sigma} \exp\left(-\frac{1}{2\sigma^2}(y_j - \alpha - \beta x_j)^2\right)$$

where exp u means e^u. From Assumption (A2) it follows that the random variables $Y_1, \cdots, Y_n$ are independent. Thus the likelihood function is

$$l = \frac{1}{(2\pi)^{n/2}\sigma^n} \exp\left(-\frac{1}{2\sigma^2}\sum(y_j - \alpha - \beta x_j)^2\right)$$

where $\sum$ indicates summation over j from 1 to n. Taking logarithms, we have

$$\ln l = -\frac{n}{2}\ln 2\pi - n\ln\sigma - \frac{1}{2\sigma^2}\sum(y_j - \alpha - \beta x_j)^2.$$

We now obtain the maximum likelihood estimates of α, β, and σ by differentiating and setting the partial derivatives equal to zero; thus

$$(a)\qquad \frac{\partial \ln l}{\partial \alpha} = \frac{1}{\sigma^2}\sum(y_j - \alpha - \beta x_j) = 0$$

(2) $\qquad (b)\qquad \dfrac{\partial \ln l}{\partial \beta} = \dfrac{1}{\sigma^2}\sum(y_j - \alpha - \beta x_j)x_j = 0$

$$(c)\qquad \frac{\partial \ln l}{\partial \sigma} = -\frac{n}{\sigma} + \frac{1}{\sigma^3}\sum(y_j - \alpha - \beta x_j)^2 = 0.$$

Denoting the maximum likelihood estimates by $\hat{\alpha}$, $\hat{\beta}$, and $\hat{\sigma}$, we see that (2a) and (2b) may be written

$$\sum y_j - n\hat{\alpha} - \hat{\beta}\sum x_j = 0$$
$$\sum x_j y_j - \hat{\alpha}\sum x_j - \hat{\beta}\sum x_j^2 = 0.$$

If we set $\hat{\alpha} = a$ and $\hat{\beta} = b$, this becomes identical with the second pair of formulas in the preceding section, and Theorem 1 is proved.

Furthermore, from (2c) we obtain the maximum likelihood estimate

$$\hat{\sigma}^2 = \frac{1}{n} \sum (y_j - \alpha - \hat{\beta}x_j)^2.$$

17.5   Confidence Intervals for the Regression Coefficient

Table 17.5.1 shows how to determine a confidence interval for the regression coefficient β when Assumptions (A1) and (A2), Sec. 17.4, hold. In this connection we remember that β is the slope of the mean

(1) $\mu(x) = \alpha + \beta x$

that has been introduced in connection with those assumptions. The theory corresponding to the method in Table 17.5.1 will be discussed in Sec. 17.8, together with the theory of two other methods to be presented in the next two sections.

Table 17.5.1. Determination of a Confidence Interval for the Regression Coefficient β under Assumptions (A1) and (A2) in Sec. 17.4

> *1st step.*   Choose a confidence level γ (95%, 99% or the like).
> *2nd step.*   Determine the solution of the equation
>
> (2) $F(c) = \frac{1}{2}(1 + \gamma)$
>
> from the table of the t-distribution with $n - 2$ degrees of freedom (Table 8 in Appendix 4; $n =$ sample size).
> *3rd step.*   Using a sample $(x_1, y_1), \cdots , (x_n, y_n)$, compute
>
> $(n - 1)s_x^2$ from (6) in Sec. 17.1,
> $(n - 1)s_{xy}$ from (8) in Sec. 17.1,
> b from (5) in Sec. 17.1,
> $(n - 1)s_y^2$ from (3) in Sec. 17.3,
> q from (4) in Sec. 17.3.
>
> *4th step.*   Compute
>
> (3) $k = c\sqrt{\dfrac{q}{(n - 2)(n - 1)s_x^2}}.$
>
> The confidence interval is
>
> (4)   CONF $\{b - k \leqq \beta \leqq b + k\}.$

Example 1 (Regression of the hardness of steel on the amount of deformation at normal temperatures). In the production of tools the method of deforming steel at normal temperature (80°F, for example) is of increasing importance. We may expect that this process affects the hardness of the steel. To investigate this relationship, the sample in

Table 17.5.2. Deformation x (in Millimeters) and Brinell Hardness y (in kilograms/millimeter²) of a Certain Type of Steel (Type 556-5) (K. Schimz, *Industr. Organisation*, **26**, 1957, 107)

Deformation x_j (in millimeters)	Brinell Hardness y_j (in kilograms/millimeter²)
6	68
9	67
11	65
13	53
22	44
26	40
28	37
33	34
35	32

Table 17.5.2 was taken. The corresponding graphical representation (Fig. 17.5.1) shows that we may regard the regression curve corresponding to the regression of the Brinell hardness Y on the deformation x as a straight line. (A corresponding test for linearity will be discussed later.) We suppose that in the present experiment Assumptions (A1) and (A2), Sec. 17.4, are satisfied, so that we may use the procedure in Table 17.5.1 for determining a confidence interval for the regression coefficient β.

From the given data we obtain

$$\sum x_j = 183 \qquad \text{and} \qquad \sum y_j = 440.$$

Since $n = 9$, it follows that

$$\bar{x} = \frac{183}{9} = 20.33 \qquad \text{and} \qquad \bar{y} = \frac{440}{9} = 48.89.$$

Furthermore,

$$\sum x_j{}^2 = 4665, \qquad \sum x_j y_j = 7701, \qquad \sum y_j{}^2 = 23{,}232.$$

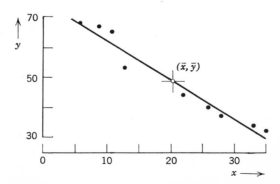

Fig. 17.5.1. Sample values and regression line in Ex. 1

Inserting these values, we obtain from (6), Sec. 17.1,

$$8s_x^2 = 4665 - \frac{183^2}{9} = 944$$

and from (8), Sec. 17.1,

$$8s_{xy} = 7701 - \frac{183 \cdot 440}{9} = -1246.$$

This yields the regression coefficient

$$b = \frac{-1246}{944} = -1.32,$$

which is negative. Hence the regression line has the representation (cf. Fig. 17.5.1)

(5) $$y - 48.89 = -1.32(x - 20.33).$$

This can also be written

(6) $$y = 75.73 - 1.32x.$$

We shall now determine a confidence interval for the regression coefficient (cf. Table 17.5.1).

1st step. We choose the confidence level $\gamma = 0.95$.

2nd step. The right-hand side of (2) equals $(1 + \gamma)/2 = 0.975$, and Table 8 with $n - 2 = 7$ degrees of freedom gives the solution $c = 2.37$.

3rd step. Using the above values and (3), Sec. 17.3, we compute

$$8s_y^2 = 23{,}232 - \frac{440^2}{9} = 1721.$$

From (4) in Sec. 17.3 we obtain

$$q = 1721 - 1.32^2 \cdot 944 = 76$$

(more exactly, $q = 77.15$, as can be seen by using more digits and rounding at the end of the computation). Formula (3) thus gives

$$k = 2.37 \sqrt{\frac{76}{7 \cdot 944}} = 0.254.$$

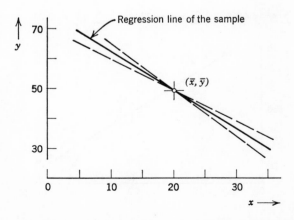

Fig. 17.5.2. Illustration of the confidence interval (7)

Since $b = -1.32$ (see above), the confidence interval is

(7)   CONF $\{-1.58 \leq \beta \leq -1.06\}$.

Figure 17.5.2 shows two straight lines through $(\bar{x}, \bar{y})$ with slopes -1.58 and -1.06.

Problems

1.–6. In each case find a 95%-confidence interval for the regression coefficient β, using the given sample and supposing that Assumptions (A1) and (A2), Sec. 17.4, are satisfied.

   1. The sample in Problem 4, Sec. 17.2.
   2. The sample in Example 1, Sec. 17.2.
   3. The sample in Problem 3, Sec. 17.2.

   4.

x	1	2	3
y	1	$2 + p$	3

(p a constant)

   5. $x =$ date of first appearance of shoots of wheat where $1 =$ June 1, $2 =$ June 2, etc.; $y =$ percentage of plants attacked by gout-flies:

x	2	3	3	5	6	7	8	8	9	10
y	4	10	12	12	8	38	32	52	32	28

x	10	11	11	12	13	13	13	14	16	16
y	55	40	60	72	51	63	65	69	76	78

   6. $x =$ humidity of air (in percent), $y =$ expansion of gelatine (in percent):

x	10	20	30	40
y	0.8	1.6	2.3	2.8

17.6 Confidence Intervals for the Mean Value

We shall now see how to determine a confidence interval for the mean value [cf. (1), Sec. 17.5]

(1) $\mu = \alpha + \beta x$

when the regression curve is a straight line and Assumptions (A1) and (A2) (cf. Sec. 17.4) hold. Table 17.6.1 shows how to proceed. The corresponding theory will be presented in Sec. 17.8.

The confidence interval (4) has length $2k(x)$. For a chosen γ and a given sample, this length depends on x because h depends on x. It is minimum for $x = \bar{x}$. This can be seen from (3) and is illustrated in Fig. 17.6.1. The length increases with increasing distance of x from $\bar{x}$. This becomes understandable if we remember the confidence interval for β.

Table 17.6.1. Determination of a Confidence Interval for the Mean Value (1) under Assumptions (A1) and (A2) in Sec. 17.4

> *1st step.*   Choose a confidence level γ (95%, 99%, or the like).
> *2nd step.*   Determine the solution c of the equation
>
> (2) $$F(c) = \tfrac{1}{2}(1 + \gamma)$$
>
> from the table of the t-distribution with $n - 2$ degrees of freedom (Table 8 in Appendix 4; n = size of the sample).
> *3rd step.*   Using a sample $(x_1, y_1), \cdots , (x_n, y_n)$, compute
>
> $$\begin{aligned} (n - 1)s_x{}^2 &\quad \text{from (6) in Sec. 17.1,} \\ (n - 1)s_{xy} &\quad \text{from (8) in Sec. 17.1,} \\ b &\quad \text{from (5) in Sec. 17.1,} \\ (n - 1)s_y{}^2 &\quad \text{from (3) in Sec. 17.3,} \\ q &\quad \text{from (4) in Sec. 17.3.} \end{aligned}$$
>
> *4th step.*   Compute y from (3), Sec. 17.1, and then
>
> (3) $$k(x) = c\,\frac{h\sqrt{q}}{\sqrt{n-2}} \qquad \text{where} \qquad h^2 = \frac{1}{n} + \frac{(x - \bar{x})^2}{(n-1)s_x{}^2}.$$
>
> The confidence interval is
>
> (4) $$\text{CONF}\ \{y - k(x) \leqq \mu \leqq y + k(x)\}.$$

Example 1. Using the sample in Example 1, Sec. 17.5, determine a 95%-confidence interval for the mean value.

Some of the quantities computed in that example can be used for the present purpose. According to (6), Sec. 17.5, we have

$$y = 75.73 - 1.32x,$$

and this will be needed in (4). Furthermore, from (3) we obtain

$$k = 2.37\,\frac{h\sqrt{76}}{\sqrt{7}} = 7.8h$$

Table 17.6.2. Confidence Region (4) in Example 1

x	h	$7.8h$	$75.7 - 1.32x$	Confidence Interval (4)
5	0.600	4.7	69.1	$64.4 \cdots 73.8$
10	0.473	3.7	62.5	$58.8 \cdots 66.2$
15	0.376	2.9	55.9	$53.0 \cdots 58.8$
20	0.334	2.6	49.3	$46.7 \cdots 51.9$
20.33	0.333	2.6	48.9	$46.3 \cdots 51.5$
25	0.366	2.9	42.7	$39.8 \cdots 45.6$
30	0.458	3.6	36.1	$32.5 \cdots 39.7$
35	0.582	4.5	29.5	$25.0 \cdots 34.0$

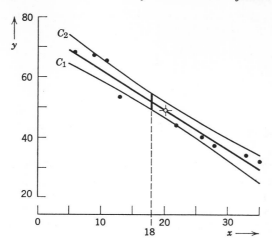

Fig. 17.6.1. Confidence region for the mean value in Ex. 1

where

$$h = \sqrt{\frac{1}{9} + \frac{(x - 20.33)^2}{944}} \, .$$

h becomes minimum when $x = \bar{x} = 20.33$. Then $h = 1/3$, and $k = 7.8/3 = 2.6$. The corresponding confidence interval has the endpoints

$$48.9 - 2.6 = 46.3 \qquad \text{and} \qquad 48.9 + 2.6 = 51.5.$$

The more x deviates from $\bar{x}$, the bigger h becomes and the longer the confidence interval (4) will be; cf. Table 17.6.2. Fig. 17.6.1 shows the curves of the endpoints of this interval for variable x; these curves are denoted by C_1 and C_2. The figure may be used for determining the length of that interval for a given x (with a limited degree of precision). For example, for $x = 18$ we find that

$$\text{CONF } \{49 \leq \mu \leq 55\}.$$

The region between C_1 and C_2 is called a **confidence region** or **confidence belt**.

Problems

1.–4. In each case find a 95%-confidence interval for the mean (1), using the given sample and supposing that Assumptions (A1) and (A2), Sec. 17.4, hold.

1. The sample in Example 1, Sec. 17.2.

2.

x	1	2	4	6	8
y	2	0	2	4	3

3. Height x (in centimeters) and fronto-occipitalic circumference of head y (in centimeters) of 10 babies at birth:

x	47	48	48	50	50	51	52	52	52	54
y	35	34	33	35	34	34	36	36	37	38

4. Deviation y (in multiples of 1/10000 radian) of a certain type of telescopic sight at temperature x (in centigrades):

x	8	9	9	12	13	14	14	16	16	16
y	−55	−55	−53	−50	−50	−35	−37	−35	−27	−24

17.7 Test for the Regression Coefficient

Table 17.7.1 shows how to test a hypothesis $\beta = \beta_0$ against an alternative $\beta > \beta_0$. The testing procedure is similar to those in Chap. 13. In Table 17.7.1 we use the notation α^* because α was used in Sec. 17.4 for a different purpose. The theory of the test will be considered in the next section.

In the case of the two-sided alternative $\beta \neq \beta_0$ we must replace (1) by

$$P(T \leqq c) = 1 - \frac{\alpha^*}{2}.$$

Then if $-c \leqq t_0 \leqq c$, the hypothesis is not rejected; otherwise it is rejected.

Of particular practical importance is the test of the hypothesis $\beta = 0$. If this hypothesis is true, then the regression line of the population is horizontal, that is, Y is independent of x.

Table 17.7.1. Test of the Hypothesis $\beta = \beta_0$ Against the Alternative $\beta > \beta_0$ under Assumptions (A1) and (A2) in Sec. 17.4

1st step. Choose a significance level α^* (5%, 1%, or the like).

2nd step. Determine the number c from

$$(1) \qquad P(T \leqq c) = 1 - \alpha^*$$

and the table of the t-distribution with $n - 2$ degrees of freedom (Table 8 in Appendix 4; n = size of the sample to be used in the test).

3rd step. Using a sample $(x_1, y_1), \cdots , (x_n, y_n)$, compute

$(n - 1)s_x^2$ from (6) in Sec. 17.1,
$(n - 1)s_{xy}$ from (8) in Sec. 17.1,
b from (5) in Sec. 17.1,
$(n - 1)s_y^2$ from (3) in Sec. 17.3,
q from (4) in Sec. 17.3.

4th step. Compute

$$(2) \qquad t_0 = (b - \beta_0)\sqrt{\frac{(n - 2)(n - 1)s_x^2}{q}}.$$

If $t_0 \leqq c$, do not reject the hypothesis. If $t_0 > c$, reject the hypothesis.

Table 17.7.2. "Elbow Distance" y_j and Height x_j of 22 Women (M. Enzmann, *Industr. Organisation*, **27**, 1958, 185)

Height x_j (centimeters)	"Elbow Distance" y_j (centimeters)			
159	24	24		
160	23	25	27	
161	24	24	25	26
162	23	24	24	29
166	23	23	25	
168	24	29	30	31
172	24	25		

Example 1 ("Elbow distance" of seated persons). In connection with the design of certain working tables, it was of interest to consider the distance from the seat to the elbows (in lowest position) of a seated person. For the sake of brevity we shall call this quantity the "elbow distance" and denote it by Y. We ask for the regression of Y on the height x of a person. Both x and Y will be measured in centimeters. Table 17.7.2 shows a sample of values, the sample size being $n = 22$. Observed values of Y corresponding to the same value of x are written in the same row, and the x-value is written only once per row. The corresponding figure (Fig. 17.7.1) shows that the sample values are scattered. We want to test the hypothesis $\beta = 0$ against the alternative $\beta > 0$, suggested by the nature of the problem. It is rather obvious that Assumption (A2), Sec. 17.4, is satisfied, and we shall also assume that (A1) holds.

We set

$$(3) \qquad x_j = x_j{}^* + 159, \qquad y_j = y_j{}^* + 23$$

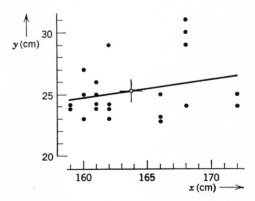

Fig. 17.7.1. Sample values in Table 17.7.2 and the regression line of the y-values on the x-values

Table 17.7.3. Coded Values in Example 1

$x_j^* = x_j - 159$	$y_j^* = y_j - 23$			
0	1	1		
1	0	2	4	
2	1	1	2	3
3	0	1	1	6
7	0	0	2	
9	1	6	7	8
13	1	2		

Then we obtain from Table 17.7.2 the more convenient values shown in Table 17.7.3 and from the latter

$$\sum x_j^* = 0 \cdot 2 + 1 \cdot 3 + 2 \cdot 4 + \cdots + 13 \cdot 2 = 106$$

$$\sum x_j^{*2} = 0^2 \cdot 2 + 1^2 \cdot 3 + \cdots + 13^2 \cdot 2 = 864$$

$$\sum x_j^* y_j^* = 0 \cdot (1 + 1) + 1 \cdot (0 + 2 + 4) + \cdots + 13 \cdot (1 + 2) = 295$$

$$\sum y_j^* = 1 + 1 + 0 + \cdots + 8 + 1 + 2 = 50$$

$$\sum y_j^{*2} = 1^2 + 1^2 + \cdots + 8^2 + 1^2 + 2^2 = 234.$$

Formula (2) in Sec. 17.2 thus gives the mean values

$$\bar{x} = \bar{x}^* + 159 = \frac{106}{22} + 159 = 163.8$$

$$\bar{y} = \bar{y}^* + 23 = \frac{50}{22} + 23 = 25.27.$$

We further need

$$21 s_x^2 = \sum x_j^{*2} - \frac{1}{22} \left(\sum x_j^* \right)^2 = 864 - 510.727 = 353.273$$

$$21 s_y^2 = \sum y_j^{*2} - \frac{1}{22} \left(\sum y_j^* \right)^2 = 234 - 113.636 = 120.364$$

(cf. Sec. 17.1 and 17.3) and

$$21 s_{xy} = \sum x_j^* y_j^* - \frac{1}{22} \sum x_j^* \sum y_j^* = 295 - 240.909 = 54.091.$$

It follows that the regression coefficient (5), Sec. 17.1, has the value

$$b = \frac{54.091}{353.273} = 0.1531.$$

Hence the regression line of the sample has the representation [cf. (3) in Sec. 17.1]

(4) $$y - 25.27 = 0.1531(x - 163.8).$$

To find out whether the obtained value of b differs significantly from zero or is merely due to random effects, we shall now test the

hypothesis $\beta = 0$

(β = regression coefficient of the population from which the sample was taken) against the alternative $\beta > 0$, suggested by the nature of the problem. In this test we suppose that Assumptions (A1) and (A2) in Sec. 17.4 hold.

1st step. We choose the significance level $\alpha^* = 5\%$.

2nd step. From Table 8 in Appendix 4 we see that for $n - 2 = 20$ degrees of freedom the equation

$$P(T \leq c) = 0.95$$

has the solution $c = 1.73$.

3rd and 4th steps. We compute t_0. From (4), Sec. 17.3, we have

$$q = 120.364 - 0.1531^2 \cdot 353.273 = 112.08.$$

Since $\beta_0 = 0$, formula (2) gives the value

$$t_0 = 0.1531 \sqrt{\frac{20 \cdot 353.273}{112.08}} = 1.22.$$

We see that $t_0 < c$, and we do not reject the hypothesis.

In our present test we accepted the hypothesis $\beta = 0$, although b is relatively large (0.15). However, we should note that t_0 contains q, and q is large because our sample values are scattered. This makes t_0 small. Our example illustrates that no conclusion can be drawn from the numerical value of b without using further information.

Of course, the use of another sample might give another result for the test because each test involves a certain risk, as we know from Chap. 13. If the result of the test seems to be doubtful, the proper thing to do is to take another random sample and to repeat the test.

Problems

1.–5. Using the given sample and supposing that Assumptions (A1) and (A2) in Sec. 17.4 are satisfied, test the hypothesis $\beta = 0$ against the alternative $\beta > 0$.

1. The sample in Problem 4, Sec. 17.6.

2. Emulsification of mercury in a solution of sodium zitrate through agitation produced by sound at ultrasonic frequencies. x = time of application in seconds, y = amount of dispersed material in grams per liter.

x	15	30	60	120	300	600
y	4.0	6.3	5.2	6.4	5.5	6.4

3.

x	0	1	2	
y	0	$1+p$	2	(p a constant)

4. Mortality y (percent) of termites depending on the concentration x (percent) of chloronaphthalene

x	0.01	0.02	0.04	0.08	0.15	0.30	0.50	1.00	2.00
y	12	18	3	27	16	13	10	70	90

5. A sample of 8 values (x_j, y_j) with $b = 0.31$, $q = 0.4$, $s_x = 0.3$, where x_j (inches) is the amount of water applied to fields of alfalfa and y_j (tons per acre) is the yield.

6. Compute q in Example 1 directly from (2), Sec. 17.1.

7. Construct a sample for which b is large ($b = 5$ or 10 or 100), but the use of the sample in the test in Table 17.7.1 leads to the acceptance of the hypothesis $\beta = 0$.

17.8 Theoretical Basis of the Methods in Secs. 17.5-17.7

In each of the methods in Secs. 17.5–17.7 we use a sample $(x_1, y_1), \cdots,$ (x_n, y_n), and for the theoretical justification of these methods, Assumptions (A1) and (A2) in Sec. 17.4 will be essential. y_j in the sample value (x_j, y_j) may be regarded as an observed value of a random variable Y_j, which, by Assumption (A1), is normal with mean $\alpha + \beta x_j$ and variance σ^2. Assumption (A2) implies that these variables $Y_1, \cdots, Y_n$ are independent. From (5)–(7) in Sec. 17.1 we see that the sample regression coefficient $b = s_{xy}/s_x^2$ may then be regarded as an observed value of the random variable

$$(1) \qquad B = \frac{1}{(n-1)s_x^2} \sum_{j=1}^{n} (x_j - \bar{x})(Y_j - \bar{Y})$$

where

$$(2) \qquad \bar{Y} = \frac{1}{n}(Y_1 + \cdots + Y_n).$$

Similarly, from (1) in Sec. 17.3 we see that the other coefficient, a, in the least square regression line $y = a + bx$ of the sample can then be regarded as an observed value of the random variable

$$(3) \qquad A = \bar{Y} - B\bar{x}.$$

Finally, the sum of squares (2) in Sec. 17.1 is an observed value of the random variable

$$(4) \qquad Q = \sum_{j=1}^{n} (Y_j - A - Bx_j)^2.$$

Theorem 1. *Under Assumptions (A1) and (A2) in Sec. 17.4 the random variable B is normal with mean*

$$(5) \qquad \mu_B = \beta$$

and variance

$$(6) \qquad \sigma_B^2 = \frac{\sigma^2}{\sum_{j=1}^{n}(x_j - \bar{x})^2} = \frac{\sigma^2}{(n-1)s_x^2}.$$

Proof. Since Y_j is normal with mean and variance as mentioned above, it follows from Theorem 1 in Sec. 8.3 that the random variable

$$(7) \qquad V_j = \lambda_j Y_j \qquad \text{where} \qquad \lambda_j = \frac{x_j - \bar{x}}{(n-1)s_x^2}$$

is normal with mean $\lambda_j(\alpha + \beta x_j)$ and variance $\lambda_j^2 \sigma^2$. In (1) we have

$$\sum (x_j - \bar{x})(Y_j - \bar{Y}) = \sum (x_j - \bar{x})Y_j - \bar{Y} \sum (x_j - \bar{x});$$

here and in the subsequent formulas, $\sum$ denotes summation over j from 1 to n. The last sum on the right is zero. Using (7), we thus obtain

$$(8) \qquad B = \frac{1}{(n-1)s_x^2} \sum (x_j - \bar{x})Y_j = \sum \lambda_j Y_j = \sum V_j.$$

The summands V_j are independent because the Y_j are independent. Hence, from Theorem 1 in Sec. 12.2, it follows that B is normal with mean

$$(9) \qquad \mu_B = \sum \lambda_j (\alpha + \beta x_j) = \alpha \sum \lambda_j + \beta \sum \lambda_j x_j$$

and variance

$$(10) \qquad \sigma_B{}^2 = \sum \lambda_j{}^2 \sigma^2.$$

We now substitute λ_j [cf. (7)] in (9). Since $\sum(x_j - \bar{x}) = 0$, we also have $\sum \lambda_j = 0$, and

$$\mu_B = \frac{\beta}{(n-1)s_x^2} \sum (x_j - \bar{x})x_j.$$

In this formula,

$$\sum (x_j - \bar{x})x_j = \sum x_j{}^2 - n\bar{x}^2 = \sum (x_j - \bar{x})^2 = (n-1)s_x{}^2.$$

This gives (5). Formula (6) follows immediately by inserting λ_j into (10). This completes the proof of Theorem 1.

Theorem 2.   *Under Assumptions (A1) and (A2) in Sec. 17.4 the random variable*

$$(11) \qquad T_1 = s_x \sqrt{(n-1)(n-2)} \frac{B - \beta}{\sqrt{Q}},$$

with B and Q given by (1) and (4), has a t-distribution with $n-2$ degrees of freedom.

Sketch of proof.   Theorem 1 in Sec. 8.3 and Theorem 1 in the present section imply that

$$W = \frac{B - \mu_B}{\sigma_B} = (B - \beta) \frac{s_x \sqrt{n-1}}{\sigma}$$

is normal with mean 0 and variance 1. The variables W and $U = Q/\sigma^2$ are independent, and U has a chi-square distribution with $n-2$ degrees of freedom. This statement, which we do not prove, is similar to Theorem 1 in Sec. 12.4. It is plausible because q, the observed value of Q, is similar in nature to the sample variance in the case of a single random variable. The number of degrees of freedom ($n-2$ instead of $n-1$) becomes plausible if we take into account that $q = 0$ when $n = 2$, since a straight line is determined by two points. Hence $W/\sqrt{U/(n-2)}$ satisfies the assumptions in Sec. 10.3 (with $n-2$ instead of n), that is, this variable has a t-distribution with $n-2$ degrees of freedom. A simple calculation shows that this variable is identical with T_1 in (11). This proves Theorem 2.

Theorem 2 is the basis of the method in Table 17.5.1. From

$$P(-c \leqq T_1 \leqq c) = F(c) - F(-c) = \gamma$$

and the symmetry of the t-distribution we obtain (2), Sec. 17.5. If we insert (11) into $-c \leqq T_1 \leqq c$, convert the result into an inequality for β, and replace B and Q by the observed values b and q, respectively, we obtain the formula (4) in Sec. 17.5 for a confidence interval for the regression coefficient β.

Theorem 2 also forms the basis of the test in Sec. 17.7. In fact, (2) in Sec. 17.7 is an observed value of the random variable (11) with $\beta = \beta_0$. If the hypothesis is true, the probability that this variable assumes a value larger than c is small, since $1 - \alpha^*$ in (1), Sec. 17.7, is large when α^* is small. This gives the reason for the decision in Table 17.7.1.

The procedure in Table 17.6.1 results from the following theorem.

Theorem 3. *Under Assumptions (A1) and (A2) in Sec. 17.4 the random variable*

(12)
$$T_2 = \sqrt{n-2}\, \frac{(x - \bar{x})B + \bar{Y} - \mu}{h\sqrt{Q}}$$

has a t-distribution with $n - 2$ degrees of freedom; here B, Q, and $\bar{Y}$ are given by (1), (4), and (2), respectively, and h is given by (3) in Sec. 17.6.

Sketch of proof. From Theorem 1 in Sec. 12.2 it follows that $Y_1 + \cdots + Y_n$ is normal with mean

$$\sum_{j=1}^{n}(\alpha + \beta x_j) = n\alpha + \beta n\bar{x}$$

and variance $n\sigma^2$. Hence, by Theorem 1 in Sec. 8.3, the random variable $\bar{Y}$ is normal with mean $\alpha + \beta\bar{x}$ and variance σ^2/n. From Theorems 1, Sec. 8.3, and 1, this section, we see that $(x - \bar{x})B$ is normal with mean $(x - \bar{x})\beta$ and variance

$$\sigma^2 \frac{(x - \bar{x})^2}{(n-1)s_x{}^2}.$$

The random variables $(x - \bar{x})B$ and $\bar{Y}$ are independent. This statement will not be proved. It follows that, by Theorem 1 in Sec. 12.2, the random variable

(13)
$$\tilde{Y} = (x - \bar{x})B + \bar{Y}$$

is normal with mean

$$(x - \bar{x})\beta + \alpha + \beta\bar{x} = x\beta + \alpha = \mu$$

and variance

(14)
$$\tilde{\sigma}^2 = \sigma^2 \frac{(x - \bar{x})^2}{(n-1)s_x{}^2} + \frac{\sigma^2}{n} = h^2\sigma^2$$

where h^2 is given by (3), Sec. 17.6. Hence the variable

$$Z = \frac{\tilde{Y} - \mu}{\tilde{\sigma}} = \frac{(x - \bar{x})B + \bar{Y} - \mu}{h\sigma}$$

is normal with mean 0 and variance 1. We already noted that $U = Q/\sigma^2$ has a chi-square distribution with $n - 2$ degrees of freedom. We state without proof that Z and U are independent. It follows that the quotient

$$\frac{Z}{\sqrt{U/(n - 2)}} = \frac{(x - \bar{x})B + \bar{Y} - \mu}{h\sigma\sqrt{Q/\sigma^2(n - 2)}}$$

has a t-distribution with $n - 2$ degrees of freedom (cf. Sec. 10.3). This quotient is identical with T_2 in (12), and our theorem is proved.

The derivation of (2) in Table 17.6.1 is similar to that of (2) in Sec. 17.5, which was explained before. Furthermore, we obtain (4), Sec. 17.6, by inserting (12), this section, into $-c \leqq T_2 \leqq c$, converting the result into an inequality for μ, and then replacing B, Q, and $\bar{Y}$ by the observed values b, q, and $\bar{y}$, respectively (cf. Problem 3).

Problems

1. Obtain (4), Sec. 17.5, from $-c \leqq T_1 \leqq c$.
2. Show that (11) and $W/\sqrt{U/(n - 2)}$ are identical.
3. Obtain (4), Sec. 17.6, from $-c \leqq T_2 \leqq c$.

17.9 Regression Analysis and Analysis of Variance

It is quite interesting to see that methods of analysis of variance can also be applied in connection with regression problems.

For this purpose we write each value y_i in a given sample (x_1, y_1), $\cdots$, (x_n, y_n) in the form (cf. Fig. 17.9.1)

$$(1) \qquad\qquad y_i = \bar{y} + y_i{}^* + d_i.$$

Then d_i is the vertical distance of the sample value (x_i, y_i) from the sample regression line [cf. (3), Sec. 17.1]

$$y - \bar{y} = b(x - \bar{x}).$$

Furthermore,

$$y_i{}^* = b(x_i - \bar{x}).$$

We denote the sum of the squares of the d_i by q_2. This quantity q_2 is identical with the quantity q in (2), Sec. 17.1, corresponding to the regression line.

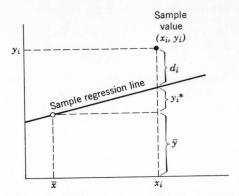

Fig. 17.9.1. Notation in formula (1)

From (4) in Sec. 17.3 we thus obtain

$$q_2 = \sum_{i=1}^{n} d_i^2 = (n-1)s_y^2 - (n-1)b^2 s_x^2.$$

We denote the first summand on the right by $\tilde{q}$ and the last by q_1. Then

(2) $$\tilde{q} = q_1 + q_2$$

and, by (3), Sec. 17.3, and (5), Sec. 17.1,

(3a) $$\tilde{q} = \sum_{i=1}^{n}(y_i - \bar{y})^2 = \sum_{i=1}^{n} y_i^2 - \frac{1}{n}\left(\sum_{i=1}^{n} y_i\right)^2$$

and

(3b) $$q_1 = (n-1)b^2 s_x^2 = (n-1)\frac{s_{xy}^2}{s_x^2}.$$

$\tilde{q}$ is called the *total* sum of squares. q_1 is called the sum of squares *due to regression*. q_2 is called the *residual* or *remainder* sum of squares or the sum of squares *due to deviation from regression*.

q_1 has 1 degree of freedom because it depends on b only. $\tilde{q}$ has $n-1$ degrees of freedom, as we know from Sec. 3.1. Hence $q_2 = \tilde{q} - q_1$ has

Table 17.9.1. Analysis of Variance Corresponding to the Decomposition (2)

Source of Variation	Degrees of Freedom	Sum of Squares	Mean Square
Due to regression	1	q_1	q_1
Residual (deviation from regression)	$n-2$	q_2	$q_2/(n-2)$
Total	$n-1$	$\tilde{q}$	

Table 17.9.2. Test of the Hypothesis $\beta = 0$ against the Alternative $\beta \neq 0$ ($\beta =$ Regression Coefficient of the Population) under Assumptions (A1) and (A2) in Sec. 17.4

1st step.   Using a given sample $(x_1, y_1), \cdots, (x_n, y_n)$, compute $\tilde{q}$ and q_1 according to (3), then $q_2 = \tilde{q} - q_1$ and, from this,

$$v_0 = \frac{q_1}{q_2/(n-2)}.$$

2nd step.   Choose a significance level α (5% or 1%).

3rd step.   Determine c from

$$P(V \leq c) = 1 - \alpha$$

and the table of the F-distribution with $(1, n-2)$ degrees of freedom (Table 9a or 9b in Appendix 4). If $v_0 \leq c$, do not reject the hypothesis $\beta = 0$. If $v_0 > c$, reject the hypothesis.

$n - 1 - 1 = n - 2$ degrees of freedom. The quantities corresponding to the decomposition (2) may be arranged in tabular form as shown in Table 17.9.1.

Table 17.9.2 shows the steps of a test that is based on the decomposition (2). If the hypothesis $\beta = 0$ holds, v_0 is an observed value of a random variable which, under Assumptions (A1) and (A2) in Sec. 17.4, has an F-distribution with $(1, n-2)$ degrees of freedom. The proof is similar to that in Sec. 16.3.

Example 1.   Test the hypothesis $\beta = 0$, using the sample in Table 17.7.2 and supposing that Assumptions (A1) and (A2) in Sec. 17.4 apply to the present case.

1st step.   From Table 17.7.2 we obtain

$$\tilde{q} = \sum y_i^2 - \frac{1}{n}\left(\sum y_i\right)^2 = 120.36.$$

We may also use Table 17.7.3 (why?) and obtain more simply

$$\tilde{q} = \tilde{q}^* = \sum y_i^{*2} - \frac{1}{n}(\sum y_i^*)^2 = 234 - \frac{1}{22} \cdot 50^2 = 120.36.$$

Furthermore (cf. Example 1 in Sec. 17.7),

$$q_1 = \frac{54.091^2}{353.273} = 8.28 \quad \text{and} \quad q_2 = \tilde{q} - q_1 = 112.08.$$

q_2 agrees with q in Example 1, Sec. 17.7. Consequently (cf. Table 17.9.3, below),

$$v_0 = \frac{8.28}{5.60} = 1.48.$$

2nd step.   We choose $\alpha = 5\%$.

3rd step.   From Table 9a we see that for $(1, 20)$ degrees of freedom, the equation

$$P(V \leq c) = 0.95$$

Table 17.9.3. First Step of the Test in Example 1

Source of Variation	Degrees of Freedom	Sum of Squares	Mean Square
Due to regression	1	8.28	8.28
Residual (deviation from regression)	20	112.08	5.60
Total	21	120.36	

has the solution $c = 4.35$. Since $v_0 < c$, we do not reject the hypothesis. Hence our present test gives the same result as that in Example 1, Sec. 17.7. Note that the present test is two-sided (alternative $\beta \neq 0$) whereas the test in Example 1, Sec. 17.7, is one-sided (alternative $\beta > 0$).

Problems

1.–5. Using the given sample, test the hypothesis $\beta = 0$ by the method explained in this section, supposing that Assumptions (A1) and (A2) in Sec. 17.4 hold.

1.

x	-1	0	0	1
y	-1	-1	1	1

2.

x	-1	0	1
y	-1	k	1

3. Angle y (measured in multiples of 0.1 degree) between the axes of the lower and upper part of a press and its dependence on the vertical distance x (millimeters) between the two parts:

x	y			
12	8	9	10	11
13	9			
14	10	13		
18	10	12	15	

4. The sample in Problem 2, Sec. 17.7.

5. The sample in Problem 4, Sec. 17.6.

17.10   Test of Linearity of the Regression Curve

In our previous discussions we have always made the assumption that the regression curve is a straight line. In many cases this will be true. However, in other cases this may be doubtful, and then we may want to test that assumption. We shall now see that such a test can be obtained by the method of analysis of variance.

For the test we need a sample $(x_1, y_1), \cdots, (x_n, y_n)$, as before, but in the present situation it is important that every x-value appear at least twice in the sample, so that corresponding to each occurring x-value we have several y-values. This will be necessary for our purpose and should be planned for in the design of the experiment; the reason is that variance will be estimated by variation within fixed abscissas and we shall compare residual variation with this to check the adequacy of the model.

In our sample we take together those values of y for which x has the same numerical value. For example, in the case of the sample

$$(1, 5) \quad (2, 6) \quad (1, 4) \quad (4, 11) \quad (1, 6) \quad (2, 10) \quad (4, 7)$$

we form three groups and write

$$(1, 4) \quad (1, 5) \quad (1, 6) \qquad\qquad x = 1 \quad y = 4, 5, 6$$
$$(2, 6) \quad (2, 10) \qquad \text{or} \qquad x = 2 \quad y = 6, 10$$
$$(4, 7) \quad (4, 11) \qquad\qquad x = 4 \quad y = 7, 11$$

For each such group we calculate the mean value and reason as follows.

If the regression curve is a straight line, those mean values should lie on a straight line, approximately, and their deviation from the regression line should not be too large, compared with the deviations of the values of each group from the corresponding mean. In other words, the ratio

$$\frac{\text{Deviation of the means from the regression line}}{\text{Deviation of the } y\text{-values from the corresponding mean of the group}}$$

should not be too large. In fact, if this ratio is large, the numerator must be large compared with the denominator, that is, the means of the groups then deviate considerably from the regression line, although the values in each group deviate relatively little from the mean of the group, that is, have only a small random variation. In this case we reject the hypothesis that the regression curve is a straight line.

We shall now derive formulas corresponding to this idea. For this purpose we introduce the following notations:

n sample size
r number of groups (that is, number of numerically different x-values in the sample)
$x_1, x_2, \cdots, x_i, \cdots, x_r$ those x-values
n_i number of y-values in the ith group (that is, number of times x_i appears in the sample)
$y_{i1}, y_{i2}, \cdots, y_{ij}, \cdots, y_{in_i}$
   the y-values in the ith group where the first subscript denotes the group and the second denotes the number of the y-value in the group
$\bar{y}_i$ mean of the y-values in the ith group
$\bar{y}$ mean of all the y-values in the sample.

Of course,

$$n_1 + n_2 + \cdots + n_r = n.$$

Furthermore,

(1)
$$\bar{y}_i = \frac{1}{n_i} \sum_{j=1}^{n_i} y_{ij} = \frac{1}{n_i}(y_{i1} + y_{i2} + \cdots + y_{in_i})$$

and

(2)
$$\bar{y} = \frac{1}{n} \sum_{i=1}^{r} \sum_{j=1}^{n_i} y_{ij} = \frac{1}{n} \sum_{i=1}^{r} n_i \bar{y}_i.$$

The notations are similar to those in Sec. 16.1, but instead of x we now have y.

Example 1. In the case of the above sample, $n = 7$, $r = 3$, $n_1 = 3$, $n_2 = 2$, $n_3 = 2$, and

$$\bar{y}_1 = \frac{1}{3}(4 + 5 + 6) = 5, \qquad \bar{y}_2 = \frac{1}{2}(6 + 10) = 8, \qquad \bar{y}_3 = \frac{1}{2}(7 + 11) = 9$$

$$\bar{y} = \frac{1}{7}(4 + 5 + 6 + 6 + 10 + 7 + 11) = 7.$$

We may arrange the sample as shown in Table 17.10.1, which also contains the mean values.

Table 17.10.1. Values in Example 1

x_i	n_i	y_{ij}			Row Sum	$\bar{y}_i$
1	3	4	5	6	15	5
2	2	6	10		16	8
4	2	7	11		18	9

Now we shall partition the sum of squares

(3)
$$q = \sum_{i=1}^{r} \sum_{j=1}^{n_i} (y_{ij} - \eta_i)^2$$

where (cf. Fig. 17.10.1)

$$\eta_i = \bar{y} + b(x_i - \bar{x}).$$

$b \stackrel{?}{=}$ see p. 289

We decompose q into a sum

(4)
$$q = q_1 + q_2.$$

Here q_1 arises from the deviation of the mean values $\bar{y}_i$ from the regression line and has the form

(5)
$$q_1 = \sum_{i=1}^{r} n_i (\bar{y}_i - \eta_i)^2.$$

q_2 arises from the scattering within the groups of our sample and has the form

(6)
$$q_2 = \sum_{i=1}^{r} \sum_{j=1}^{n_i} (y_{ij} - \bar{y}_i)^2.$$

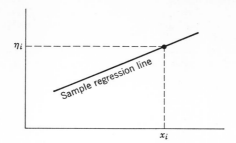

Fig. 17.10.1. The quantity η_i in formula (3)

The proof of this decomposition is similar to that in Sec. 16.3 and is left to the reader (cf. Problem 1). The quantities corresponding to (4)–(6) may be arranged as shown in Table 17.10.2. Our present q in (3) contains the deviations from η_i while q in Sec. 16.1 contains the deviations from $\bar{y}$. In this way we exclude variation due to regression. In doing so we lose one degree of freedom in each case. This explains the degrees of freedom given in Table 17.10.2.

We may use the decomposition (4) for testing whether the regression curve is a straight line. Table 17.10.3 shows the corresponding test. If the hypothesis holds, then (7) is an observed value of a random variable V which, under Assumptions (A1) and (A2) in Sec. 17.4, has an F-distribution with $(r - 2, n - r)$ degrees of freedom. This follows in a fashion similar to that in Sec. 16.3 and explains the decision in Table 17.10.3.

Note that in the first step in Table 17.10.3 we may use (4), Sec. 17.3, because q is identical with q (referred to the regression line) in (2), Sec. 17.1.

Of course, if we accept the hypothesis, this does not mean that a straight line is the only possible curve of regression or the best one compatible with the sample values. If we reject the hypothesis, this means that we cannot regard the regression curve as a straight line (save for the error involved in any test).

Table 17.10.2. Analysis of Variance Corresponding to the Decomposition (4)

Source of Variation	Degrees of Freedom	Sum of Squares	Mean Square
Deviation of means from regression	$r - 2$	q_1	$q_1/(r - 2)$
Within groups (deviation from mean)	$n - r$	q_2	$q_2/(n - r)$
Total	$n - 2$	q	

Table 17.10.3. Test of the Hypothesis That the Regression Curve Is a Straight Line under the Assumption That for Each Fixed x the Random Variable Y Is Normal with Variance Independent of x

> *1st step.* From the given sample, compute q and q_1 by (3) [or (4), Sec. 17.3] and (5), respectively, then $q_2 = q - q_1$ and
>
> (7) $$v_0 = \frac{q_1/(r - 2)}{q_2/(n - r)}.$$
>
> *2nd step.* Choose a significance level α^* (5% or 1%).
> *3rd step.* Determine the solution c of the equation
>
> $$P(V \leqq c) = 1 - \alpha^*$$
>
> from the table of the F-distribution with $(r - 2, n - r)$ degrees of freedom (Table 9a or 9b in Appendix 4). If $v_0 \leqq c$, do not reject the hypothesis. If $v_0 > c$, reject the hypothesis.

Example 2. In Ex. 1, Sec. 17.7, and Ex. 1, Sec. 17.9, we regarded the regression curve as a straight line. We may now apply our present test to justify this assumption.

1st step. From Ex. 1, Sec. 17.7, we obtain $q = 112.1$. Table 17.7.3 yields Table 17.10.4. Here [cf. (3) and (4) in Sec. 17.7]

$$\eta_i^* = y^*(x_i^*) = 0.1531x_i^* + 1.535.$$

The y_i^* are related to the y_i by (3), Sec. 17.7, which is a translation. Consequently, in (5) we simply have

$$\bar{y}_i - \eta_i = \bar{y}_i^* - \eta_i^*.$$

Hence from Table 17.10.4 we obtain the value $q_1 = 47.2$. From this and (4) it follows that

$$q_2 = q - q_1 = 112.1 - 47.2 = 64.9.$$

Furthermore, from Table 17.10.5 we calculate the value

$$v_0 = 9.4/4.3 = 2.2.$$

2nd step. We choose the significance level $\alpha^* = 5\%$.

Table 17.10.4. First Step in Example 2

y_{ij}^*				n_i	$\bar{y}_i^*$	η_i^*	$(\bar{y}_i^* - \eta_i^*)^2$	$n_i(\bar{y}_i^* - \eta_i^*)^2$
1	1			2	1.000	1.535	0.286	0.572
0	2	4		3	2.000	1.688	0.097	0.291
1	1	2	3	4	1.750	1.841	0.008	0.032
0	1	1	6	4	2.000	1.994	0.000	0.000
0	0	2		3	0.667	2.607	3.764	11.292
1	6	7	8	4	5.500	2.913	6.693	26.772
1	2			2	1.500	3.525	4.101	8.202
								Sum 47.161

Table 17.10.5. Analysis of Variance in Example 2

Source of Variation	Degrees of Freedom	Sum of Squares	Mean Square
Deviation of means from regression	5	47.2	9.4
Within groups (deviation from mean)	15	64.9	4.3
Total	20	112.1	

3rd step. For (5, 15) degrees of freedom the equation

$$P(V \leq c) = 1 - 0.05 = 0.95$$

has the solution $c = 2.90$, as follows from Table 9a in Appendix 4. We see that $v_0 < c$, and we do not reject the hypothesis.

Problems

1. Prove the decomposition (4)–(6).
2. Check q_2 in Example 2 by direct calculation.
3.–5. Using the given sample, test for linearity of the regression curve; suppose that the assumption stated in Table 17.10.3 holds.

3.

x	y	
0	−1	1
1	0	2
2	1	5
4	8	12
6	11	13

4.

x	y	
1	0	2
2	5	7
3	9	13
4	10	14

5.

x	y	
2	60	64
5	171	176
10	242	245
15	298	304
20	345	351
25	383	388

6. Prove the decomposition

$$\tilde{q} = \sum_{i=1}^{r} \sum_{j=1}^{n_i} (y_{ij} - \bar{y})^2 = q_0 + q_1 + q_2$$

where

$$q_0 = \sum_{i=1}^{r} n_i(\eta_i - \bar{y})^2$$

and q_1 and q_2 are given by (5) and (6). Make up a corresponding table similar to Table 17.10.2.

17.11 Nonlinear Regression Curve. Method of Least Squares

Let a sample $(x_1, y_1), \cdots, (x_n, y_n)$ be given, as before, where the x_i are chosen values of an ordinary variable x and the y_i are observed values of a random variable Y corresponding to those x_i. From Sec. 17.1 we know how to determine the straight line (the sample regression line)

$$y(x) = a + bx$$

for which the sum of the squares of the vertical distances, that is,

$$(1) \qquad\qquad q = \sum_{i=1}^{n'} [y_i - y(x_i)]^2,$$

is minimum. Instead of a straight line we may equally well use a curve. The type of such a curve will depend largely on the amount of available theoretical information about the dependence of Y on x, and one should try to select a simple type of curve. For instance, we may choose

$$(2) \qquad\qquad y(x) = b_0 + b_1 x + \cdots + b_m x^m,$$

if in a certain practical case this seems more suitable than a straight line, and we may still apply the same method as before. For this purpose we first substitute the n expressions

$$y(x_i) = b_0 + b_1 x_i + \cdots + b_m x_i^m$$

in (1). Then q has a minimum for those values $b_0, b_1, \cdots, b_m$ which satisfy the conditions

$$(3) \qquad\qquad \frac{\partial q}{\partial b_0} = 0, \qquad \frac{\partial q}{\partial b_1} = 0, \cdots, \qquad \frac{\partial q}{\partial b_m} = 0.$$

These $m + 1$ linear equations in the $m + 1$ unknowns $b_0, \cdots, b_m$ are called **normal equations.** Their solution gives the desired values of the coefficients in (2). Theoretically there are no difficulties. Practically, solving these equations may require a considerable amount of work. For this purpose we may use **Gauss's elimination method,**[2] which is of general importance and will be explained in Example 1 (below).

In the case of a parabola

$$(4) \qquad\qquad y(x) = b_0 + b_1 x + b_2 x^2$$

we have

$$y(x_i) = b_0 + b_1 x_i + b_2 x_i^2.$$

Then (1) takes the form

$$q = \sum_{i=1}^{n} (y_i - b_0 - b_1 x_i - b_2 x_i^2)^2.$$

---

[2] Several variations of this method have been proposed, for example, the Doolittle method [see, e.g., Croxton and Cowden (1955)]. Computer programs for this and other methods are available for the standard machines.

Differentiating this, we see that the normal equations are

$$\frac{\partial q}{\partial b_0} = -2 \sum (y_i - b_0 - b_1 x_i - b_2 x_i^2) = 0$$

$$\frac{\partial q}{\partial b_1} = -2 \sum x_i(y_i - b_0 - b_1 x_i - b_2 x_i^2) = 0$$

$$\frac{\partial q}{\partial b_2} = -2 \sum x_i^2(y_i - b_0 - b_1 x_i - b_2 x_i^2) = 0.$$

These are three linear equations in the three unknowns b_0, b_1, and b_2. We may write these normal equations in the form

(5)
$$b_0 n + b_1 \sum x_i + b_2 \sum x_i^2 = \sum y_i$$
$$b_0 \sum x_i + b_1 \sum x_i^2 + b_2 \sum x_i^3 = \sum x_i y_i$$
$$b_0 \sum x_i^2 + b_1 \sum x_i^3 + b_2 \sum x_i^4 = \sum x_i^2 y_i.$$

Example 1 (Mortality of babies). If we represent the sample values in Table 17.11.1 in a graphical form, we obtain Fig. 17.11.1. This makes it plausible to describe the regression of the mortality on the height by a parabola. The coefficients of the parabola (4) are obtained by solving the system of equations (5).
   The calculation becomes simpler if we set

$$x_i = x_i^* + 53.5 \qquad \text{(thus } x_i^* = x_i - 53.5).$$

We know that in grouping, the values of the grouped sample are assumed to coincide with the corresponding class marks. From Table 17.11.2 we thus obtain

$$\sum x_i^* = 124 \cdot (-6) \quad + 1255 \cdot (-3) \ + 1441 \cdot 3 \ + 175 \cdot 6 \quad = \quad 864$$
$$\sum x_i^{*2} = 124 \cdot 36 \qquad + 1255 \cdot 9 \qquad + 1441 \cdot 9 \ + 175 \cdot 36 \quad = \quad 35{,}028$$
$$\sum x_i^{*3} = 124 \cdot (-216) \ + 1255 \cdot (-27) + 1441 \cdot 27 + 175 \cdot 216 \ = \ 16{,}038$$
$$\sum x_i^{*4} = 124 \cdot 1296 \quad + 1255 \cdot 81 \qquad + 1441 \cdot 81 + 175 \cdot 1296 = 605{,}880$$

Table 17.11.1. Regression of the Mortality of Babies (in Percent) on their Height at Birth (H. Hosemann, *Die Naturwiss.*, **37**, 1950, 410)

Height		Number of Babies in the Class	Number of Babies that Died	Mortality y (Percent)
Class Interval	Class Mark x_i			
46–49	47.5	124	14	11.29
49–52	50.5	1255	13	1.04
52–55	53.5	3149	28	0.89
55–58	56.5	1441	31	2.15
58–61	59.5	175	16	9.14

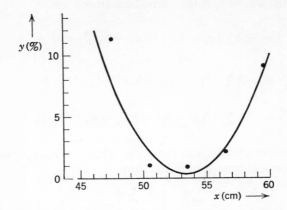

Fig. 17.11.1. The sample in Table 17.11.1 and the parabola (9)

because the sample consists of $n = 6144$ pairs of values and after grouping the value $x_1{}^* = -6$ appears 124 times, the value $x_2{}^* = -3$ appears 1255 times, $\cdots$, the value $x_5{}^* = 6$ appears 175 times. Similarly,

$$\sum y_i = 124 \cdot 11.29 \qquad\quad + 1255 \cdot 1.04 \qquad\quad + \cdots = \;\; 10{,}205.42$$
$$\sum x_i{}^* y_i = 124 \cdot (-6) \cdot 11.29 + 1255 \cdot (-3) \cdot 1.04 + \cdots = \;\;\;\; 6576.09$$
$$\sum x_i{}^{*2} y_i = 124 \cdot 36 \cdot 11.29 \quad + 1255 \cdot 9 \cdot 1.04 \quad\; + \cdots = 147{,}610.71.$$

Hence in the present case the normal equations are

(6)
$$\begin{aligned}
(a) \quad & 6144 b_0 + \qquad 864 b_1 + \;\;\; 35{,}028 b_2 = \;\; 10{,}205.42 \\
(b) \quad & \;\;\; 864 b_0 + 35{,}028 b_1 + \;\;\; 16{,}038 b_2 = \quad\; 6576.09 \\
(c) \quad & 35{,}028 b_0 + 16{,}038 b_1 + 605{,}880 b_2 = 147{,}610.71.
\end{aligned}$$

1st step. Elimination of b_0 from (6b) and (6c). To eliminate b_0 from (6b) we multiply (6a) by 864/6144, finding

$$864 b_0 + 121.500 b_1 + 4925.813 b_2 = 1435.137.$$

This equation we subtract from (6b). The result is

(7a)
$$34{,}906.500 b_1 + 11{,}112.187 b_2 = 5140.953.$$

Table 17.11.2. Computations in Example 1

$x_i{}^* = x_i - 53.5$	$x_i{}^{*2}$	$x_i{}^{*3}$	$x_i{}^{*4}$	Number	y_i	$x_i{}^* y_i$	$x_i{}^{*2} y_i$
-6	36	-216	1296	124	11.29	-67.74	406.44
-3	9	-27	81	1255	1.04	-3.12	9.36
0	0	0	0	3149	0.89	0	0
3	9	27	81	1441	2.15	6.45	19.35
6	36	216	1296	175	9.14	54.84	329.04

We now eliminate b_0 from (6c). For this purpose we multiply (6a) by 35,028/6144, finding

$$35,028b_0 + 4925.813b_1 + 199,700.648b_2 = 58,182.853.$$

This equation we subtract from (6c). The result is

(7b) $$11,112.187b_1 + 406,179.352b_2 = 89,427.857.$$

2nd step. Elimination of b_1 from (7b). To eliminate b_1 from (7b) we multiply (7a) by 11,112.187/34,906.500, finding

$$11,112.187b_1 + 3537.470b_2 = 1636.579.$$

This equation we subtract from (7b). The result is

(8) $$402,641.882b_2 = 87,791.278.$$

Final step. Solution of the system of equations:

(6a) $$6144.000b_0 + 864.000b_1 + \ 35,028.000b_2 = 10,205.420$$
(7a) $$34,906.500b_1 + \ 11,112.187b_2 = \ 5140.953$$
(8) $$402,641.882b_2 = 87,791.278.$$

Each solution of this system of equations is a solution of the system (6) and conversely. This follows from the derivation. We shall now see that our new system has a unique solution. From (8) we obtain

$$b_2 = \frac{87,791.278}{402,641.882} = 0.218\ 038.$$

If we insert this into (7a), we have

$$b_1 = \frac{1}{34,906.5} (5140.953 - 11,112.187b_2) = 0.077\ 867.$$

By inserting this and b_2 in (6a) we find that

$$b_0 = \frac{1}{6144} (10,205.42 - 864b_1 - 35,028b_2) = 0.407\ 016.$$

Hence the desired parabola has the representation

$$y = 0.407 + 0.078x^* + 0.218x^{*2}.$$

Substituting $x^* = x - 53.5$ and simplifying, we obtain (Fig. 17.11.1)

(9) $$y = 620.205 - 23.248x + 0.218x^2.$$

If in a given problem we are not certain what degree polynomial we should use, we may wish to compare different degree polynomials for their adequacy. In this situation we would like to use a fitting technique which permits an easy transition from one degree to the next. Such a technique is available if we use *orthogonal polynomials*. In adding a higher degree term we would have to compute only one coefficient, whereas in the usual method, all coefficients would have to be recomputed in that transition. For details, see Fisher (1958); cf. Appendix 3.

Problems

1.–7. Using the given sample, determine the parabola (4) by the method of least squares. Graph this parabola and the sample values.

1.

x	−1	0	0	1
y	2	0	1	2

2.

x	0	1	2	4	6
y	3	1	0	1	4

3. Power y (kilograms) of a special tractor in the lowest gear where x is the speed (kilometers/hour):

x	1.4	1.8	2.3	3.0	4.0
y	7400	7500	7600	7500	7200

4. Number y of impulses per minute counted by a CZ-scintillator, where x (grams/centimeter^3) is the density of molding sand (this experiment was conducted in connection with the development of methods for measuring the humidity of molding sand):

x	1.09	1.28	1.36	1.44	1.60	1.65
y	1.35	1.58	1.68	1.85	2.23	2.38

5. Dow-Jones Average of industrial stocks in 1962; values somewhat simplified (1 = January, 2 = February, etc.):

Month	1	2	3	4	5	6	7	8	9	10	11	12
D.J.A.	730	720	720	720	680	630	580	590	600	600	580	630

6. Time of reaction y (seconds) of female workers in a monotonous routine work, where x (hours) is the time the workers were on duty. The workers had to press a foot pedal when a lamp gave a signal, and y is the time that elapsed between the signal and the reaction by the worker.

x	1	2	3	4	5	6
y	1.50	1.48	1.75	1.65	1.72	1.55

7. Unproductive time y (percent) on an assembly line, where x (minutes) is the time a product remains at a station before it is moved on to the next station:

x	0.5	1	2	3	4	7
y	5.6	4.1	3.9	3.9	4.2	4.5

8. Determine the normal equations in the case of a polynomial

$$y = b_0 + b_1 x + b_2 x^2 + b_3 x^3.$$

17.12   Test in the Case of a Nonlinear Regression Curve

The test in Sec. 17.10 may also be applied in the case of a nonlinear regression curve in a slightly modified form. Then the number of degrees of freedom changes. Instead of the F-distribution with $(r - 2, n - r)$ degrees of freedom in Table 17.10.3, we now have an F-distribution with $(r - m - 1, n - r)$ degrees of freedom where m is the degree of the polynomial used [cf. (2), Sec. 17.11].

It suffices to illustrate the test with an example.

Example 1 (Amplification of a telescope). In Table 17.12.1 the quantity x_i (meters) is the distance of an object (a scale) which was observed through a small telescope. The observer looked with one eye through the telescope. With the other eye he looked directly at the scale, and y_{ij} is the length of a segment that appeared as big as a segment of length 1 appeared through the telescope. We see that for each of the 5 distances, 2 measurements were made, so that our sample has size 10. Any measurement is subject to an *error* due to small unpredictable and uncontrollable factors that disturb the measurement. This is the reason for the two y_{ij} in each row not being equal. (An introduction to the theory of errors of measurements will be given in Chap. 19.)

If we graph our sample, we get the impression that the regression curve of Y on x is not a straight line (cf. Fig. 17.12.1) and a parabola may be more suitable. In fact, we may support this conjecture by the test in Sec. 17.10, proceeding as follows.

We first determine the regression parabola (4), Sec. 17.11, finding

$$(1) \qquad\qquad y = 32.450 - 1.021x + 0.037x^2.$$

We shall now test the hypothesis that this parabola may be chosen as a regression curve. We make the assumptions that for each fixed x the corresponding random variable Y is normal and its variance does not depend on x and the $n = 10$ performances of the experiment are independent.

1st step. The calculation becomes simpler if we set

$$y_{ij}^* = y_{ij} - 25.$$

Then the parabola (1) has the representation

$$(2) \qquad\qquad y^* = 7.450 - 1.021x + 0.037x^2.$$

Table 17.12.1. Sample in Example 1

x_i	y_{ij}	
3	29.7	30.1
5	28.1	27.8
7	27.4	26.9
10	26.0	26.2
14	25.5	25.2

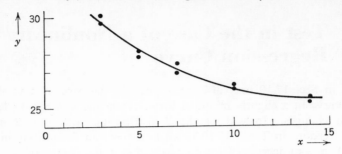

Fig. 17.12.1. Sample values and regression parabola in Ex. 1

We now perform the calculations shown in Table 17.12.2. Since $n_i = 2$, we obtain

$$q_1 = 2 \cdot 0.165 = 0.330.$$

Furthermore, from (6) in Sec. 17.10 it follows that

$$q_2 = \sum_{i=1}^{5} \sum_{j=1}^{2} (y_{ij} - \bar{y}_i)^2 = \sum_{i=1}^{5} \sum_{j=1}^{2} (y_{ij}^* - \bar{y}_i^*)^2 = 0.315.$$

Important intermediate results are shown in Table 17.12.3 in the usual arrangement. From this table and (7) in Sec. 17.10 we obtain

$$v_0 = \frac{0.165}{0.063} = 2.62.$$

2nd step. We choose the significance level $\alpha = 5\%$.

3rd step. We have $r = 5$ and $m = 2$, hence $r - m - 1 = 2$. For $(2, 5)$ degrees of freedom the equation

$$P(V \leqq c) = 1 - 0.05 = 0.95$$

(cf. Table 17.10.3) has the solution $c = 5.79$. This follows from Table 9a in Appendix 4.

4th step. We see that $v_0 = 2.62 < c$, and we do not reject the above hypothesis.

Again, this does not mean that a parabola is the only possible regression curve in the interval $3 \leqq x \leqq 14$, nor that in another interval, for instance, in a larger one, the regression can be described by that or by another parabola.

Table 17.12.2. Computation in Example 1

x_i	$0.037x_i^2$	$1.021x_i$	$\eta_i^* = y^*(x_i)$	$y_{ij}^* = y_{ij} - 25$		$\bar{y}_i^*$	$(\bar{y}_i^* - \eta_i^*)^2$
3	0.333	3.063	4.72	4.7	5.1	4.90	0.032
5	0.925	5.105	3.27	3.1	2.8	2.95	0.102
7	1.813	7.147	2.12	2.4	1.9	2.15	0.001
10	3.700	10.210	0.94	1.0	1.2	1.10	0.026
14	7.252	14.294	0.41	0.5	0.2	0.35	0.004
							Sum 0.165

Table 17.12.3. Analysis of Variance in Example 1

Source of Variation	Degrees of Freedom	Sum of Squares	Mean Square
Mean values about the regression	2	0.330	0.165
Within groups	5	0.315	0.063
Total	7	0.645	

Problems

1. For a given sample [y (°C) = temperature reading of a thermometer, x (seconds) = time], determine the parabola

$$y = b_0 + b_1 x + b_2 x^2$$

by the method of least squares. Test the hypothesis that this quadratic parabola may be chosen as a curve of regression; in this test assume that for each fixed x the random variable Y for which the given y-values are observed values is normal with variance independent of x.

x	10	20	30	60	90	120	180	240	300
y	27.9	25.9	24.3	19.6	15.9	12.9	8.5	5.6	3.6
	28.0	26.1	24.4	19.8	16.0	13.1	8.7	5.7	3.8

2. In problems of growth it is often required to fit an exponential function

$$y = b_0 e^{bx}$$

by the method of least squares. Show that by taking logarithms this task can be reduced to that of determining a straight line.

3. Determine the exponential function explained in Problem 2 for the sample in Problem 1.

4. Determine the regression line for the sample in Problem 1, and show that the test in Sec. 17.10 leads to the rejection of the hypothesis that the regression curve is a straight line.

5. Carry out the details of the derivation of the parabola (1).

CHAPTER **18**

Correlation Analysis

We shall continue our discussion of random experiments involving two variables. However, whereas in the last chapter one of the two variables was an ordinary variable, in the present chapter both variables will be random variables. A comparison of these two types of situations and corresponding examples is given in the introduction to Chap. 17, and the student is advised to reread that introduction now.

In applying statistical methods it is important to define precisely the population from which a sample is taken, and to keep in mind that any inferences are strictly applicable only to that population; in correlation analysis, this may require somewhat more care than in applications involving only one variable.

18.1   Correlation Coefficient of a Sample

We consider a sample

$$(x_1, y_1), \qquad (x_2, y_2), \cdots, \qquad (x_n, y_n)$$

of size n taken from a two-dimensional (X, Y)-population. The mean value of the x-values in the sample is

$$\bar{x} = \frac{1}{n}(x_1 + \cdots + x_n),$$

and the variance of these values is

(1)
$$s_x{}^2 = \frac{1}{n-1}\sum_{j=1}^{n}(x_j - \bar{x})^2.$$

These quantities already appeared in Sec. 17.1. Similarly, the mean value of the y-values in the sample is

$$\bar{y} = \frac{1}{n}(y_1 + \cdots + y_n)$$

and the variance of these values is

(2)
$$s_y{}^2 = \frac{1}{n-1} \sum_{j=1}^{n} (y_j - \bar{y})^2.$$

Furthermore, the covariance of the sample is [cf. (7) in Sec. 17.1]

(3)
$$s_{xy} = \frac{1}{n-1} \sum_{j=1}^{n} (x_j - \bar{x})(y_j - \bar{y}).$$

The quotient

(4)
$$r = \frac{s_{xy}}{s_x s_y} \qquad\qquad (s_x > 0, s_y > 0)$$

is called the **correlation coefficient of the sample.**

Note that if we multiply the sample values by a common factor (for example, the factor 12 in the transition from feet to inches), then s_{xy} will change, but r will retain its value. More generally, coding does not affect the value of r.

Since $s_x s_y > 0$ and s_{xy} may be positive, zero, or negative, r may be positive, zero, or negative (cf. Fig. 18.1.1).

We shall now prove that, more specifically, for any sample,

(5)
$$-1 \leqq r \leqq 1.$$

From (4) we have

$$s_{xy} = r s_x s_y.$$

If we insert this and [cf. (5) in Sec. 17.1]

$$b = \frac{s_{xy}}{s_x{}^2} = \frac{r s_y}{s_x}$$

into (4) in Sec. 17.3, we obtain

$$q = (n-1)(1 - r^2)s_y{}^2.$$

Since q is a sum of squares, it must be nonnegative. Hence the same holds for the expression on the right. Since $s_y{}^2 > 0$ and $n > 1$, we thus obtain

$$1 - r^2 \geqq 0, \qquad \text{that is,} \qquad r^2 \leqq 1,$$

and (5) is proved.

From (4) we see that $r^2 = 1$ if and only if (5) in Sec. 17.3 holds. Hence the statement involving (5), Sec. 17.3, may now be formulated as follows.

The sample values $(x_1, y_1), \cdots, (x_n, y_n)$ *lie on a straight line if and only if the corresponding correlation coefficient has the values* 1 *or* -1.

In practice, this will happen only in very rare cases. However, we may guess that large values of r^2 (that is, values close to 1) will appear if and only

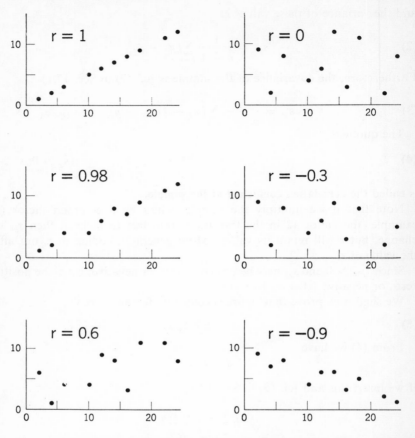

Fig. 18.1.1. Graphical representation of samples with various values of the correlation coefficient *r*

if those sample values lie nearly on a straight line. Figure 18.1.1 illustrates this conjecture. It gives the impression that *r* has something to do with a measure for the *linear* dependence between the random variables *X* and *Y*. We shall discuss this in more detail in the next section.

In this section let us present an example, which will also illustrate tabular and graphical representations of two-dimensional samples.

Example 1 (Height and circumference of the head of babies). Table 18.1.1 shows a sample of *n* = 100 pairs of values. *x* is the height of a baby and *y* the circumference of its head, both measured in centimeters and taken immediately after birth. For each pair of values we make a tally mark in the corresponding square in Table 18.1.2. Then we count the tallies and obtain Table 18.1.3. A corresponding graphical representation is shown in Fig. 18.1.2.

Table 18.1.1. Height *x* (Centimeters) and Circumference of Head *y* (Centimeters) of Babies right after Birth. (Data from Prof. E. Navratil, University Hospital, Graz, 1962)

x	y	x	y	x	y	x	y	x	y
52	36	50	33	51	34	51	36	48	33
48	34	48	34	49	34	53	33	48	33
50	34	51	36	51	36	51	36	50	36
51	34	54	38	51	34	49	34	49	32
47	35	49	34	50	35	51	35	49	35
51	35	49	33	47	35	50	34	48	34
52	36	49	33	49	34	49	35	50	34
52	36	50	34	49	33	50	33	49	34
53	37	48	33	49	35	47	33	49	34
48	34	52	34	52	36	50	35	49	33
50	34	50	34	51	37	49	34	48	34
52	37	50	33	50	35	50	34	50	35
52	36	49	35	56	39	48	34	49	33
50	35	51	35	52	34	47	35	50	32
50	34	53	35	47	34	50	35	54	37
49	34	48	32	53	36	53	36	50	35
48	34	48	33	49	34	52	36	52	34
48	33	50	33	49	35	53	38	51	35
50	35	51	35	49	34	50	34	52	35
50	35	52	36	51	35	53	39	48	33

Table 18.1.2. Tally Chart Corresponding to the Sample in Table 18.1.1

Circumference of Head *y* (Centimeters)	Height *x* (Centimeters)									
	47	48	49	50	51	52	53	54	55	56
39							I			I
38							I	I		
37					I	I	I	I		
36				I	IIII	ͰͰͰ II	II			
35	III		ͰͰͰ	ͰͰͰ IIII	ͰͰͰ I	I	I			
34	I	ͰͰͰ II	ͰͰͰ ͰͰͰ	ͰͰͰ IIII	III	III				
33	I	ͰͰͰ I	ͰͰͰ	IIII			I			
32		I	I	I						

Table 18.1.3. Frequency Distribution of the Sample in Table 18.1.1

Circumference of Head y (Centimeters)	Height x (Centimeters)										Row Sum
	47	48	49	50	51	52	53	54	55	56	
39							1			1	2
38							1	1			2
37					1	1	1	1			4
36				1	4	7	2				14
35	3		5	9	6	1	1				25
34	1	7	10	9	3	3					33
33	1	6	5	4			1				17
32		1	1	1							3
Column Sum	5	14	21	24	14	12	7	2	0	1	

Disadvantages of tallying were characterized in Sec. 2.1, and the more modern methods mentioned in that section can be applied also in two-dimensional cases like that under consideration.

From Table 18.1.2 or 18.1.3 we see that the sample values are concentrated in an "elliptically" shaped domain in the middle; the major axis is inclined upward to the right, and the frequencies pile up along that axis, leaving two corners blank. In Table 18.1.2 the values of y increase from the bottom to the top of the table. This corresponds to Fig. 18.1.2, in which the volume of each column is proportional to the corresponding frequency. Of course, we might equally well arrange that table so that y increases in the opposite direction.

We shall now compute the correlation coefficient of our sample. For this purpose we may use the formula

(6)
$$r = \frac{\sum x_j y_j - \dfrac{1}{n} \sum x_j \sum y_j}{\sqrt{\left[\sum x_j^2 - \dfrac{1}{n}(\sum x_j)^2\right]\left[\sum y_j^2 - \dfrac{1}{n}(\sum y_j)^2\right]}}.$$

This formula follows immediately from (4) if we insert (8), Sec. 17.1, into the numerator and (6), Sec. 17.1, and the corresponding formula for s_y into the denominator. Using the

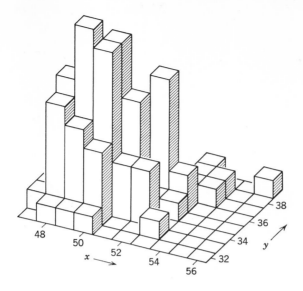

Fig. 18.1.2. Histogram corresponding to Table 18.1.3

numerical values

$$\sum x_j = 5 \cdot 47 + 14 \cdot 48 + \cdots + 1 \cdot 56 = 5009$$
$$\sum x_j^2 = 5 \cdot 47^2 + 14 \cdot 48^2 + \cdots + 1 \cdot 56^2 = 251{,}215$$
$$\sum y_j = 3 \cdot 32 + 17 \cdot 33 + \cdots + 2 \cdot 39 = 3460$$
$$\sum y_j^2 = 3 \cdot 32^2 + 17 \cdot 33^2 + \cdots + 2 \cdot 39^2 = 119{,}908$$
$$\sum x_j y_j = 47(33 + 34 + 3 \cdot 35) + \cdots + 56 \cdot 39 = 173{,}477$$

we obtain

$$r = \frac{173{,}477 - 0.01 \cdot 5009 \cdot 3460}{\sqrt{(251{,}215 - 0.01 \cdot 5009^2)(119{,}908 - 0.01 \cdot 3460^2)}} = 0.674.$$

In the case of very large samples, it may be worthwhile to group the data with respect to both variables, just as was done for one variable in Sec. 2.3.

Problems

1.–8. In each case plot the given pairs of values as points in the xy-plane and compute the correlation coefficient r.

   1. Play x (millimeters) and y (millimeters) in two beds of the main shaft of certain tractor engines before overhaul:

x	0.14	0.17	0.18	0.21	0.23	0.17	0.18
y	0.16	0.18	0.18	0.12	0.20	0.20	0.20

2. Length x (millimeters) and shrinkage y (percent) in casting of certain small parts:

x	y	x	y	x	y
6	0.7	9	1.0	15	0.5
14	−0.2	25	0.0	11	0.2
9	−1.2	14	0.1	35	0.1
23	0.0	47	−0.4	18	−0.2
8	0.3	11	−0.2	10	0.3
39	0.1	25	−0.5	23	0.4
13	0.5	38	−0.2	30	−0.6
30	−0.4	9	0.8	13	0.5
8	0.8	41	0.8	15	1.1
15	−0.1	14	−0.1	12	−0.3

3. Monthly hours of sunshine in the morning (x) and in the afternoon (y) in 1961 in Graz, Austria:

Month	x	y
January	26	36
February	45	59
March	111	102
April	92	90
May	119	97
June	114	116
July	136	114
August	156	143
September	132	131
October	55	59
November	30	41
December	35	37

4. Midterm grades x and final grades y of nine mathematics students:

x	80	75	45	75	70	60	45	80	80
y	80	75	75	95	100	80	45	70	90

5.

x	−1	−1/$\sqrt{2}$	0	1/$\sqrt{2}$	1
y	0	1/$\sqrt{2}$	1	1/$\sqrt{2}$	0

6.

x	1	2	3
y	1	2	1

7.

x	0	1	2
y	0	k	$2k$

(k a constant)

8.

x	0	2	4	6
y	1	2	3	4

9. A factory hired 172 persons for various jobs. The applicants had to undergo a qualification test; from the table we see that $37 + 12 + 1 = 50$ of the persons hired got the highest grade (A, here denoted by $x = 1$), $19 + 48 + 3 + 1 = 71$ of the persons hired got the second highest grade (B, here denoted by $x = 2$), etc. One year later the performance of the 172 persons hired was graded; from the table we see that $37 + 19 + 1 = 57$ persons got the highest grade (A, here denoted by $y = 1$), etc. Compute the correlation coefficient and graph a histogram of the sample.

Qualification	Performance y				
x	1	2	3	4	5
1	37	12			1
2	19	48	3	1	
3	1	28	15		1
4		1	3	2	

10. Compute the correlation coefficient r of the following sample of mathematics and physics grades.

Physics grades y (class marks)	Mathematics grades x (class marks)			
	65	75	85	95
95			2	4
85	1	6	11	1
75	2	10	7	
65	3	3		

11. Show that coding leaves the value of the sample correlation coefficient unchanged.

18.2 Correlation Coefficient of the Population

In the last section we used a sample consisting of n pairs of values $(x_1, y_1), \cdots, (x_n, y_n)$ taken from an XY-population. To the mean values $\bar{x}$ and $\bar{y}$ in that section there correspond the mean value μ_X of X and the mean value μ_Y of Y, respectively, that is

(1) $$\mu_X = E(X), \qquad \mu_Y = E(Y).$$

To the variances s_x^2 and s_y^2 in that section there correspond the variances

$$\sigma_X^2 = E([X - \mu_X]^2) \quad \text{and} \quad \sigma_Y^2 = E([Y - \mu_Y]^2)$$

of those variables. *The degeneracies $\sigma_X = 0$ and $\sigma_Y = 0$ will be excluded from all our further considerations.*
The quantity

(2) $$\sigma_{XY} = E([X - \mu_X][Y - \mu_Y])$$

is called the **covariance** of the random variables X and Y. Performing the indicated multiplication and using (2), Sec. 9.7, we see that the right-hand side is equal to

$$E(XY) - \mu_X E(Y) - \mu_Y E(X) + \mu_X \mu_Y.$$

From this and (1) it follows that

(3) $$\sigma_{XY} = E(XY) - E(X)E(Y).$$

This agrees with (4) in Sec. 9.8.

The quotient

(4) $$\rho = \frac{\sigma_{XY}}{\sigma_X \sigma_Y}$$

is called the **correlation coefficient** of X and Y.

If $\rho = 0$, then X and Y are said to be **uncorrelated.**

If X and Y are independent, then, by (6) in Sec. 9.7, $\sigma_{XY} = 0$ and also $\rho = 0$. This may be formulated as follows.

Theorem 1. *If the random variables X and Y are independent, they are uncorrelated.*

In the next section we shall see that for the two-dimensional normal distribution, the converse of Theorem 1 holds. In general, this is not true, however, as can be seen from the following example.

Example 1. Suppose that a random variable X assumes each of the values -1, 0, and 1 with probability $1/3$. Then X has mean $E(X) = 0$. Let $Y = X^2$. Then in (3),

$$E(XY) = E(X^3) = (-1)^3 \cdot \tfrac{1}{3} + 0^3 \cdot \tfrac{1}{3} + 1^3 \cdot \tfrac{1}{3} = 0.$$

From this and $E(X) = 0$ we obtain $\sigma_{XY} = 0$, thus $\rho = 0$. Hence the variables X and Y are uncorrelated, but they are not independent because they are related, even by a functional relation.

The example shows that the correlation coefficient is not a measure of *general* dependence, but we shall see that it is a measure of *linear* dependence.

Let us first show that

(5) $$-1 \leqq \rho \leqq 1.$$

For this purpose we introduce the random variables

$$X^* = \frac{X - \mu_X}{\sigma_X} \quad \text{and} \quad Y^* = \frac{Y - \mu_Y}{\sigma_Y}.$$

From Theorem 2 in Sec. 6.7 it follows that these variables have mean 0 and variance

(6) $$E(X^{*2}) = 1 \quad \text{and} \quad E(Y^{*2}) = 1,$$

respectively. Consequently, the random variable

(7) $$Z = tX^* + Y^* \qquad (t \text{ real, constant})$$

has mean 0 and variance

$$E(Z^2) = E([tX^* + Y^*]^2)$$
$$= t^2 E(X^{*2}) + 2tE(X^*Y^*) + E(Y^{*2}) \geqq 0.$$

By using the expressions for X^* and Y^* we see that

$$E(X^*Y^*) = \frac{1}{\sigma_X \sigma_Y} E([X - \mu_X][Y - \mu_Y]) = \frac{\sigma_{XY}}{\sigma_X \sigma_Y} = \rho.$$

This implies

(8*) $$E(Z^2) = t^2 + 2t\rho + 1 \geq 0.$$

Hence, for any real t,

(8) $$(t + \rho)^2 + (1 - \rho^2) \geq 0.$$

If $1 - \rho^2 < 0$, then this inequality would not hold when $t = -\rho$. If $1 - \rho^2 \geq 0$, then, since $(t + \rho)^2 \geq 0$, the inequality holds for all t. Hence we must have $\rho^2 \leq 1$. This implies (5).

We shall now prove the following basic theorem.

Theorem 2. *Two random variables X and Y with positive variance are related by a linear relation*

(9)   (a) $Y = \beta X + \gamma$ [*and*   (b) $X = \beta^* Y + \gamma^*$]

if and only if the corresponding correlation coefficient has the values -1 or 1.

Proof. *(a)* Suppose that (9a) holds. Since $\sigma_Y > 0$, we must have $\beta \neq 0$ and from (9a) we may obtain (9b). From (2) and (4) in Sec. 6.7 we see that Y has the mean value

$$\mu_Y = \beta \mu_X + \gamma$$

and the variance

$$\sigma_Y^2 = \beta^2 \sigma_X^2.$$

Hence, if $\beta > 0$, then $\sigma_Y = \beta \sigma_X$; and if $\beta < 0$, then $\sigma_Y = -\beta \sigma_X > 0$. Furthermore, by (9a),

$$Y - \mu_Y = \beta X + \gamma - \mu_Y = \beta(X - \mu_X).$$

Consequently, the covariance takes the form

$$\sigma_{XY} = E([Y - \mu_Y][X - \mu_X]) = \beta E([X - \mu_X]^2) = \beta \sigma_X^2.$$

We thus obtain

$$\rho = \frac{\sigma_{XY}}{\sigma_X \sigma_Y} = \pm \frac{\beta \sigma_X^2}{\sigma_X \beta \sigma_X} = \pm 1.$$

(b) Conversely, suppose that $\rho = 1$ or $\rho = -1$. Then (7) with $t = -1$ and $t = 1$, respectively, has variance 0, as can be seen immediately from (8*). Hence Z assumes only one value (the mean 0), with probability 1. With respect to the original variables X and Y from which Z was formed, this means the existence of a relation of the form (9), and Theorem 2 is proved.

Hence the correlation coefficient appears as a measure of linear dependence between X and Y. However, we want to warn the reader to beware of erroneous statements and conclusions, as follows.

(A) Nonsense correlations. A large value of $|\rho|$ does not necessarily mean that the corresponding formal relation between two random variables X and Y must have a reason; so it does *not* prove that X causes Y or conversely. In some cases there may be a reason, for example, if X and Y are grades of students in mathematics and mechanics, or if X and Y are the numbers of daily traffic accidents in two adjacent communities, and so on. In other cases there may be no reason, even for a strong correlation with correlation coefficient close to 1 or -1. For example, in southern Europe people are short and there are relatively few Protestants. Toward the north the height X and the relative number of Protestants Y both increase, but X does not cause Y. After World War I there was a strong correlation between the decrease of the number of storks and the birth rate in Central Europe. Both examples illustrate what is called a *nonsense correlation*. For further examples, see, for instance, Yule and Kendall (1965).

Table 18.2.1. Yield of Rye x from the First Half and Yield of Wheat y from the Other Half of Each of Eight Fields

Field Number	1	2	3	4	5	6	7	8
x	12	13	8	12	9	9	14	16
y	17	13	14	14	9	11	20	15

(B) Meaningless comparisons. This may be illustrated by Table 18.2.1. The given sample of 8 pairs of values has the correlation coefficient 0.60. If we unite the fields in pairs, taking together 1 and 2, then 3 and 4, etc., we obtain 4 pairs of values, and the corresponding correlation coefficient has the value 0.92. If we unite once more, we are left with 2 pairs of values, and the correlation coefficient is 1. (Why?) This shows that if we want to compare tables like 18.2.1 corresponding to various years, we should choose the same units (single fields or pairs of fields, etc.). Otherwise the comparison will be meaningless.

Problems

1. The **moments** of a two-dimensional random variable (X, Y) with probability function $f(x, y)$ or density $f(x, y)$ are defined by

$$(10) \quad m_{kl} = E(X^k Y^l) = \begin{cases} \displaystyle\sum_i \sum_j x_i^k y_j^l f(x_i, y_j) & \text{(Discrete distribution)} \\[2ex] \displaystyle\int_{-\infty}^{\infty} \int_{-\infty}^{\infty} x^k y^l f(x, y) \, dx \, dy & \text{(Continuous distribution)} \end{cases}$$

and the **central moments** by

(11)
$$m_{kl}{}^* = E([X - \mu_X]^k[Y - \mu_Y]^l);$$

here the (x_i, y_j) have the same meaning as in (1), Sec. 9.2, and k and l are non-negative integers. $k + l$ is called the *order* of the moment. Show that the moments

$$m_{10} = E(X) = \mu_X \qquad \text{and} \qquad m_{01} = E(Y) = \mu_Y$$

are the means, the central moments

$$m_{20}{}^* = E([X - \mu_X]^2) = \sigma_X{}^2 \qquad \text{and} \qquad m_{02}{}^* = E([Y - \mu_Y]^2) = \sigma_Y{}^2$$

are the variances of X and Y, respectively, and the moment

$$m_{11}{}^* = E([X - \mu_X][Y - \mu_Y])$$

is the covariance of (X, Y).

2. Show that $f(x, y) = f(y, x)$ for all (x, y) implies $m_{kl} = m_{lk}$.

3.–5. In each case represent the density $f(x, y)$ graphically as a surface in space and find the moments $m_{10}, m_{01}, m_{20}{}^*, m_{02}{}^*, m_{11}{}^*$, and the correlation coefficient ρ.

3. $f(x, y) = x + y$ when $0 \leq x \leq 1, 0 \leq y \leq 1$, and $f(x, y) = 0$ otherwise.

4. $f(x, y) = 0.5$ in the rectangle $1 \leq x \leq 3, 1 \leq y \leq 2$, and $f = 0$ otherwise.

5. $f(x, y) = 4(1 - x)(1 - y)$ when $0 \leq x \leq 1, 0 \leq y \leq 1$, and $f = 0$ otherwise.

6. In Problem 3 find the probability that (X, Y) assumes any value (x, y) for which (*a*) $x > 0.5$, y arbitrary, (*b*) $x > 1/3$, y arbitrary, (*c*) $x + y < 1$.

7. Find some more examples of nonsense correlations.

8. Show that the values of the covariance σ_{XY} are restricted to the interval $-\sigma_X\sigma_Y \leq \sigma_{XY} \leq \sigma_X\sigma_Y$.

9. Two fuses are drawn without replacement from a box containing 10 fuses, 3 of which are defective. Let $X = $ *number of defective fuses in the first drawing*, $Y = $ *number of defective fuses in the second drawing*. Find ρ.

10. Two items are drawn without replacement from a box containing N items, M of which are defective, $0 < M < N$. Let $X = $ *number of defective items in the first drawing*, $Y = $ *number of defective items in the second drawing*. Show that $\rho = -1/(N - 1)$. (Note the surprising fact that ρ does not depend on M.)

11. Show that if X and Y have means μ_X and μ_Y and variances $\sigma_X{}^2$ and $\sigma_Y{}^2$, then $Z = c_1X + c_2Y$ has the mean $\mu = c_1\mu_X + c_2\mu_Y$ and the variance

$$\sigma^2 = c_1{}^2\sigma_X{}^2 + 2c_1c_2\sigma_{XY} + c_2{}^2\sigma_Y{}^2.$$

18.3 Two-Dimensional Normal Distribution

We know that if X^* is a normal random variable with mean 0 and variance 1 and we introduce a random variable X by setting

$$X^* = \frac{X - \mu}{\sigma} \qquad (\sigma > 0),$$

then X is normal with mean μ and standard deviation σ. This shows that for a *single* normal random variable we may proceed from a special case to the general case by means of a linear transformation. We shall now see that a similar procedure may be applied in the case of the so-called *two-dimensional* normal distribution, which is important in connection with various applications.

Suppose that X^* and Y^* are independent normal random variables with mean 0 and variance 1. Since the variables are independent, their joint distribution has the density

$$(1) \qquad f^*(x^*, y^*) = \frac{1}{2\pi} e^{-(x^{*2}+y^{*2})/2}.$$

This follows immediately from (1) in Sec. 8.1 and (2) in Sec. 9.5.

The function in (1) can be represented graphically as a surface in space, as is shown in Fig. 18.3.1. The level curves $f^* = const$ are called *curves of equal probability*. In the present case these are circles, and we obtain a surface of revolution. The intersection of this surface and any plane through the axis of revolution is a bell-shaped curve.

We shall now introduce new random variables X and Y by setting

$$(2) \qquad \begin{aligned} X^* &= \frac{X - \mu_X}{\sigma_X} \\ Y^* &= \frac{1}{\sqrt{1 - \rho^2}}\left[\frac{Y - \mu_Y}{\sigma_Y} - \rho\frac{X - \mu_X}{\sigma_X}\right]. \end{aligned}$$

Here we assume that $\rho^2 < 1$ and σ_X and σ_Y are positive. Formula (2) represents a linear transformation. It is written in such a complicated fashion because then the inverse transformation has the simple form

$$X = \mu_X + \sigma_X X^*$$
$$Y = \mu_Y + \rho\sigma_Y X^* + \sqrt{1 - \rho^2}\,\sigma_Y Y^*$$

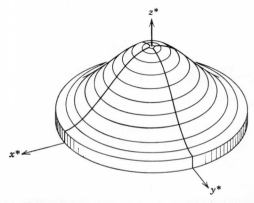

Fig. 18.3.1. Graphical representation of the density (1) as a surface in space. (The figure shows only the central part of the surface.)

and we see that X and Y are normal (cf. Theorems 1, Sec. 12.2, and 1, Sec. 8.3) with mean μ_X and μ_Y and standard deviation σ_X and σ_Y, respectively. Furthermore, the reader may show that the variables have the correlation coefficient ρ, as follows from (4), Sec. 18.2, by a simple calculation.

We shall now determine the density $f(x, y)$ of the two-dimensional variable (X, Y). We know that the distribution function of the original variable (X^*, Y^*) is a double integral with integrand $f^*(x^*, y^*)$. In the transition to the new variables we have to transform this double integral, using the general rule for transforming double integrals. According to this rule, the integrand of the transformed integral equals f^*, expressed as a function of x and y, times the Jacobian D of the transformation (2), that is,

$$D = \begin{vmatrix} \dfrac{1}{\sigma_X} & 0 \\[2ex] -\dfrac{\rho}{\sigma_X\sqrt{1-\rho^2}} & \dfrac{1}{\sigma_Y\sqrt{1-\rho^2}} \end{vmatrix} = \dfrac{1}{\sigma_X\sigma_Y\sqrt{1-\rho^2}}.$$

f^* can be expressed in terms of the new variables by means of (2), written with x^*, y^*, x, y instead of X^*, Y^*, X, Y, respectively. The result of this elementary calculation is

$$f^*(x^*(x, y), y^*(x, y)) = \frac{1}{2\pi} e^{-h(x,y)/2}$$

where we used the abbreviated notation

(3) $$h(x, y) = \frac{1}{1-\rho^2}\left[\left(\frac{x-\mu_X}{\sigma_X}\right)^2 - 2\rho\left(\frac{x-\mu_X}{\sigma_X}\right)\left(\frac{y-\mu_Y}{\sigma_Y}\right) + \left(\frac{y-\mu_Y}{\sigma_Y}\right)^2\right].$$

It follows that the density of (X, Y) has the form

(4) $$f(x, y) = \frac{1}{2\pi\sigma_X\sigma_Y\sqrt{1-\rho^2}} e^{-h(x,y)/2}$$

with h given by (3). This is the general form of the density of the two-dimensional normal distribution. Note that this distribution involves the five parameters μ_X, μ_Y, σ_X, σ_Y, and ρ.

The corresponding marginal distributions have the density

(5) $$f_1(x) = \frac{1}{\sqrt{2\pi}\,\sigma_X} \exp\left[-\frac{1}{2}\left(\frac{x-\mu_X}{\sigma_X}\right)^2\right]$$

and

(6) $$f_2(y) = \frac{1}{\sqrt{2\pi}\,\sigma_Y} \exp\left[-\frac{1}{2}\left(\frac{y-\mu_Y}{\sigma_Y}\right)^2\right],$$

where exp z means e^z. In fact, X and Y are normal with mean μ_X and μ_Y and variance σ_X^2 and σ_Y^2, respectively, as we already know.

The equiprobability curves $f(x, y) = const$ are homothetical ellipses with common center (μ_X, μ_Y).

If $\sigma_X = \sigma_Y$, the square of the eccentricity ϵ of these ellipses is

$$\epsilon^2 = 2 |\rho|/(1 + |\rho|).$$

Hence if $|\rho|$ is small, these ellipses look almost like circles.

From (3) we see that when $\rho = 0$, then

$$f(x, y) = f_1(x)f_2(y),$$

that is, in the case of the normal distribution, $\rho = 0$ implies that the variables are independent. For other distributions, this may not hold as we know from Ex. 1 in the last section. We may formulate our result as follows.

Theorem 1. *Two normal random variables are independent if and only if the corresponding correlation coefficient is zero.*

Problems

1. Show that the random variables X and Y in the text have the correlation coefficient ρ.

2. Verify (3).

3. Verify the formula for the eccentricity of the ellipses of equal probability in the text. Find the angle between the principal axes and the x-axis in the case $\sigma_X = \sigma_Y$.

4. Graph some of the ellipses of equal probability for the two-dimensional normal distribution with $\mu_X = \mu_Y = 0$, $\sigma_X = \sigma_Y = 1$ and (*a*) $\rho = 0.1$, (*b*) $\rho = 0.5$, (*c*) $\rho = 0.9$.

5. What are the curves of equal probability of the two-dimensional normal distribution with $\rho = 0$ and arbitrary σ_X and σ_Y?

6. Find a formula for the eccentricity of the ellipses in Problem 5.

7. Let a continuous two-dimensional (X, Y)-distribution be given. Consider the event $y < Y < y + \Delta y$ under the hypothesis $x < X < x + \Delta x$ and show that for small Δx and Δy,

$$P(y < Y < y + \Delta y \mid x < X < x + \Delta x) \approx \frac{f(x, y)}{f_1(x)} \Delta y,$$

where $f(x, y)$ is the density of the (X, Y)-distribution and

$$f_1(x) = \int_{-\infty}^{\infty} f(x, y) \, dy$$

is the density of one of the two marginal distributions. It is customary to set

$$f(y \mid x) = \frac{f(x, y)}{f_1(x)} \qquad [f_1(x) \neq 0].$$

This function is called the **conditional density** of Y under the hypothesis $X = x$. The distribution with density $f(y \mid x)$ is called the **conditional distribution** of Y under that hypothesis.

8. Show that in the case of the two-dimensional normal distribution,

$$f(y \mid x) = \frac{1}{\sqrt{2\pi} \, \sigma_Y \sqrt{1 - \rho^2}} \exp \left(-\frac{h(x, y)}{2} + \frac{(x - \mu_X)^2}{2\sigma_X^2} \right)$$

and this is the density of a normal distribution with mean

$$E(Y \mid X = x) = \int_{-\infty}^{\infty} yf(y \mid x)\, dy = \mu_Y + \frac{\rho \sigma_Y}{\sigma_X}(x - \mu_X)$$

and variance $(1 - \rho^2)\sigma_Y{}^2$. The mean $E(Y \mid X = x)$ is called the **conditional mean** of Y under the hypothesis $X = x$. The function $y(x) = E(Y \mid X = x)$ is called the **regression function** of Y with respect to X, and its curve is called the **regression curve** of the mean of Y with respect to X.

9. Consider the distribution in Problem 8 and the restriction of the analogous mass distribution in the strip $x < X < x + \Delta x$. Show that the ordinate of the center of gravity of the latter distribution is approximately equal to $y(x) = E(Y \mid X = x)$.

10. Show that among all curves $y = g(x)$ the regression curve in Problem 8 has the property that the mean square vertical distance $E([Y - g(X)]^2)$ is minimum, that is, that curve is a regression curve in the sense of the method of least squares.

11. Let X and Y be independent normal random variables with means zero and variances 1. Find the probability that $X^2 + Y^2 < 1$.

12. In Problem 11, find k^2 so that the probability $P(X^2 + Y^2 < k^2)$ equals 99%.

13. Using (1), obtain (3) in Sec. 10.1 with 2 degrees of freedom.

18.4 Tests and Confidence Intervals for the Correlation Coefficient

In the case of the two-dimensional normal distribution, the correlation coefficient r of a sample is an estimate for the correlation coefficient ρ of the corresponding population [cf. (4), Sec. 18.1, and (4), Sec. 18.2]. In this case we may test the hypothesis $\rho = 0$ against an alternative, for instance, $\rho > 0$. The steps of the test are shown in Table 18.4.1. They follow from the fact that if the hypothesis is true, then t_0 corresponds to a random variable

Table 18.4.1. Test of the Hypothesis ρ = 0 Against the Alternative ρ > 0 in the Case of the Two-Dimensional Normal Distribution

---

1st step. Choose a significance level α (5%, 1%, or the like).
2nd step. Determine the solution c of the equation

$$(1) \qquad P(T \leq c) = 1 - \alpha$$

from the table of the t-distribution with $n - 2$ degrees of freedom (Table 8 in Appendix 4; $n =$ size of sample).
3rd step. Compute the correlation coefficient r of the given sample $(x_1, y_1), \cdots, (x_n, y_n)$.
4th step. Compute

$$(2) \qquad t_0 = r\sqrt{\frac{n-2}{1-r^2}}.$$

If $t_0 \leq c$, do not reject the hypothesis. If $t_0 > c$, reject the hypothesis.

---

which has a t-distribution with $n - 2$ degrees of freedom. This was shown by R. A. Fisher (1915) (cf. Appendix 3). In this case t_0 should be small. Hence if t_0 is too large, we reject the hypothesis.

If the hypothesis is $\rho = 0$, as before, but the alternative is $\rho \neq 0$, we must use

$$P(T \leqq c) = 1 - \frac{\alpha}{2}$$

instead of (1); then we do not reject the hypothesis if $-c \leqq t_0 \leqq c$, and reject it if $t_0 < -c$ or $t_0 > c$.

Example 1. Consider the sample in Table 18.1.1. Suppose that the corresponding population has a two-dimensional normal distribution. Test the hypothesis $\rho = 0$ against the alternative $\rho > 0$, suggested by the nature of the problem.

1st step. We choose the significance level $\alpha = 5\%$.

2nd step. We have $n = 100$, hence $n - 2 = 98$. Table 8 in Appendix 4 does not contain a corresponding column. For 100 degrees of freedom the equation (1) with $1 - \alpha = 0.95$ has the solution $c = 1.66$. Comparing this with the neighboring values to the left and to the right, we see that we may use this value c in our test.

3rd step. From Example 1 in Sec. 18.1 we have $r = 0.674$.

4th step. We compute

$$t_0 = 0.674 \sqrt{\frac{98}{1 - 0.674^2}} = 9.03.$$

We see that $t_0 > c$, and we reject the hypothesis.

From (2) and Table 8 in Appendix 4 we obtain Fig. 18.4.1. We may use this figure for performing the test in a graphical fashion. If the point with coordinates n and r lies above the curve, we reject the hypothesis. Otherwise we do not reject it.

It is interesting that in Fig. 18.4.1, for small values of n, the acceptance region includes points with large values of r. For instance, if $r = 0.674$, as

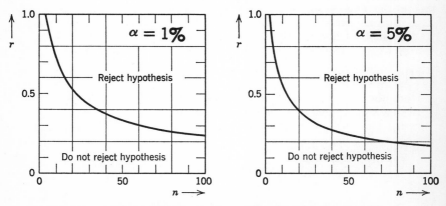

Fig. 18.4.1. Test of the hypothesis $\rho = 0$ against the alternative $\rho > 0$

in the last example, and n is small, say, $n = 5$, then we would not reject the hypothesis $\beta = 0$.

Confidence intervals for the correlation coefficient ρ. We shall now see how to obtain confidence intervals for the correlation coefficient ρ in the case of the two-dimensional normal distribution.

From the correlation coefficient r of the sample we compute the auxiliary value

$$(3) \qquad\qquad z_0 = \frac{1}{2} \ln \frac{1 + r}{1 - r} .$$

R. A. Fisher (*Metron*, **1**, 1921, 3) has shown that this is an estimate for the mean

$$\mu^* = \frac{1}{2} \ln \frac{1 + \rho}{1 - \rho}$$

of a random variable Z which is asymptotically normal and has variance

$$\sigma^{*2} = \frac{1}{n - 3} .$$

Here n is the size of the sample. This means that we may obtain a confidence interval for μ^* by using the method in Sec. 12.1. Then z_0 plays the role of $\bar{x}$ in (2), Sec. 12.1, and instead of $\sigma/\sqrt{n}$ we now have $\sigma^* = 1/\sqrt{n - 3}$. In this way we first obtain the confidence interval

$$\text{CONF } \{z_0 - k \leqq \mu^* \leqq z_0 + k\} \qquad \text{where} \qquad k = \frac{c}{\sqrt{n - 3}}$$

and c must be obtained from Table 12.1.1. This interval we convert into an interval for ρ of the form

$$(4) \qquad\qquad \text{CONF } \{r_1 \leqq \rho \leqq r_2\}.$$

For this purpose we have to apply the inverse transformation of (3). We find that

$$(5) \qquad r_1 = \tanh (z_0 - k) \qquad \text{and} \qquad r_2 = \tanh (z_0 + k),$$

where the hyperbolic tangent is defined in terms of the exponential function by the formula

$$\tanh u = \frac{e^u - e^{-u}}{e^u + e^{-u}}$$

and corresponding numerical values can be found in Table 4*b* of Appendix 4.

The following example illustrates that the interval (4) can also be obtained from Fig. 18.4.2 in a graphical fashion.

Example 2. Suppose that the population from which the sample in Table 18.1.1 was taken has a two-dimensional normal distribution. Determine a 95%-confidence interval

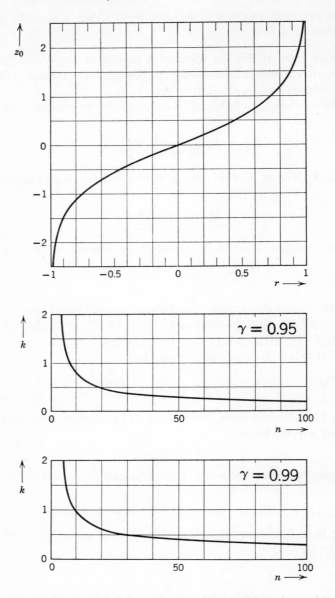

Fig. 18.4.2. Graphical determination of the confidence interval (4)

for the corresponding correlation coefficient ρ. We have $r = 0.674$ (cf. Example 1 in Sec. 18.1). From the first curve in Fig. 18.4.2 we obtain the corresponding value $z_0 = 0.8$. From the second curve in that figure we see that to $n = 100$ there corresponds the value $k = 0.2$. Consequently,

$$z_0 - k = 0.6 \qquad \text{and} \qquad z_0 + k = 1.0.$$

Now we again use the first curve in Fig. 18.4.2 and find

$$r_1 = \tanh 0.6 = 0.54, \qquad r_2 = \tanh 1.0 = 0.76.$$

We thus obtain the confidence interval

$$\text{CONF } \{0.54 \leq \rho \leq 0.76\}.$$

Graphical methods are fast, and their disadvantage, the limited accuracy, does not matter in the present case. In fact, the corresponding computation would yield the confidence interval

$$\text{CONF } \{0.550 \leq \rho \leq 0.769\},$$

and this differs very little from our graphical result.

Problems

1.–5. Assuming that in each case the population from which the sample was taken has a two-dimensional normal distribution, determine a 99%-confidence interval for the correlation coefficient ρ.

1.

x	1	3	4	6	8
y	2	4	1	2	5

2. The sample in Problem 1, Sec. 18.1.

3. Greatest and smallest diameters of hen eggs (in millimeters):

x	58	56	57	52	62	55	60	55	61	58
y	41	43	42	44	44	40	42	45	45	44

4. Humus content x (kilograms/square meter) and nitrogen content y (kilograms/square meter) of forest soil:

x	3.0	4.3	7.5	5.5	5.5	6.0	6.6	7.3	8.0	8.0
y	0.07	0.15	0.15	0.14	0.13	0.17	0.29	0.31	0.25	0.21

5. Classification of 420 men into 3 social classes by means of certain criteria (education, profession, income, etc.) and by the use of 2 methods: (i) a scoring method (objective method) and (ii) personal interview (subjective method).

By Interviewer Placed in Class	By Method (i) Placed in Class		
	$x = 1$	$x = 2$	$x = 3$
$y = 1$	116	20	8
$y = 2$	33	48	60
$y = 3$	14	13	108

6. In a sample of 100 members of a certain race the correlation coefficient between facial index X and cephalic index Y was $r = 0.15$. Assuming that the (X, Y)-distribution is normal, test the hypothesis $\rho = 0$.

7. Determine the rejection region (critical region) of the test in Table 18.4.1 with $\alpha = 5\%$ in the case of a sample of size 12 when the alternative is

$$(a) \; \rho > 0 \qquad (b) \; \rho < 0 \qquad (c) \; \rho \neq 0.$$

8. Graph figures similar to Fig. 18.4.1 corresponding to the alternative (*a*) $\rho < 0$, (*b*) $\rho \neq 0$.

9. In the test in Table 18.4.1, how large a correlation coefficient is needed for a sample of size 50 before one may claim that (*a*) $\rho > 0$, (*b*) $\rho \neq 0$? (Use both $\alpha = 5\%$ and $\alpha = 1\%$.)

10. Test the hypothesis $\rho = 0$ against the alternative $\rho > 0$, using a sample of size 20 with $r = 0.5$ taken from a population that has a two-dimensional normal distribution and choosing the significance level (*a*) $\alpha = 5\%$, (*b*) $\alpha = 1\%$.

CHAPTER **19**

Errors of Measurements

Statistical considerations also play a role in connection with physical measurements, since any such measurement involves an error, that is, an inaccuracy caused by small random disturbances, which cannot be completely eliminated. For this reason it is important to develop a theory of errors of measurements consisting of methods for obtaining "good" approximations of unknown physical quantities (lengths, masses, pressures, etc.) from measured values and information about the accuracy of such approximations. We shall now introduce the reader to some of the basic ideas in this area.

19.1 Types of Errors of Measurements

It is known that the sum of the angles of a plane triangle equals 180°. However, if we *measure* these angles, we shall in general obtain three values the sum of which differs slightly from 180°, and repeated measurements may produce still other slightly different values. In the case of other physical quantities, for example, length, pressure, voltage, and temperature, the situation is similar. We say that each measurement involves an **error of measurement** or *error of observation*. This error is caused by the nature of physical measurements, because the person who performs the measurement, the instruments used in the measurement, and the system to be measured are affected by small unpredictable disturbances. The error of measurement can be decreased in size by the use of better methods and instruments but cannot be eliminated completely.

There are several types of errors of measurements, as we shall now see.

If we use an instrument, for example, a voltmeter, that is poorly calibrated, then each measurement is affected in the same fashion. The corresponding error is called a *constant error* or **systematic error.** These errors are of no interest to us because they have nothing to do with probabilistic considerations.

We shall be concerned with **statistical errors** of measurements. By this we mean errors that are caused by a large number of small disturbances affecting the measurement and whose effect cannot be predicted. Hence these errors cannot be avoided or eliminated. However, their effect can be understood, through a theory of statistical errors first developed by Gauss and Laplace. The theory is supposed to give methods for obtaining "good" approximations of the unknown physical value from results of measurements and for obtaining information about the accuracy of these approximations.

The latter information cannot be obtained from a single measurement. For this reason one has to measure a physical quantity several times, say, n times. The result is a sample of n values $x_1, \cdots, x_n$. In most cases—but *not* always—the sample would seem to come from a normal population. This is quite surprising because physical measurements may be of an entirely different nature.

We might inquire why in most cases statistical errors correspond to normal or approximately normal random variables. It may be convincing to imagine that a statistical error results from the superposition of a large number of very small disturbances (*elementary errors*). If we regard the random variables corresponding to the elementary errors as being independent, then their sum, which corresponds to the statistical error, is approximately normal. This effect is a consequence of the central limit theorem (Sec. 12.7), as first noticed by Gauss. And it was in this connection that Gauss introduced the normal distribution.

In many physical experiments it may be impossible even to enumerate all the elementary errors that affect a certain type of measurement. Examples of such errors may be small changes of temperature, pressure, humidity, voltage, small motions of air, particles of dust, small effects of light, mechanical vibrations, electric or magnetic fields, and other factors that vary from one measurement to the next.

Let us now introduce numbers that characterize the accuracy of measurements.

Suppose that we made n measurements of a certain physical quantity, for example, the length of a rod. This gives n measured values

$$x_1, \cdots, x_n.$$

We may then compute the sample mean

$$\bar{x} = \frac{1}{n}(x_1 + \cdots + x_n)$$

and regard it as an approximate value of the unknown quantity μ which we measure. The sample standard deviation is

(1)
$$s = \sqrt{\frac{1}{n-1}\sum_{j=1}^{n}(x_j - \bar{x})^2}.$$

This quantity may be regarded as an estimate of the standard deviation σ of the population from which the sample is taken and, therefore, as a measure for the accuracy of the measurements. In the theory of errors of measurement, s is called the *mean square error* or, simply, the **mean error.**

If the statistical error is normal, or approximately normal, we may expect that about $\frac{2}{3}$ of the values of a sufficiently large sample of measurements will lie between $\bar{x} - s$ and $\bar{x} + s$ (cf. Sec. 8.2).

Similarly, about 50% of the values of a sufficiently large sample will then lie between

$$\bar{x} - 0.67s \quad \text{and} \quad \bar{x} + 0.67s.$$

This follows from Table 3*b* in Appendix 4. The number $0.67s$ is sometimes called the *probable error.* It has lost importance because it is more convenient to work with standard deviations than with probable errors, and the use of the probable error is being abandoned.

Instead of (1) the maximum likelihood estimate (cf. Sec. 11.6)

$$(2) \qquad \tilde{s} = \sqrt{\frac{1}{n} \sum_{j=1}^{n} (x_j - \bar{x})^2}$$

may be used and is also called the **mean error** (even in the case of a population which is not normal).

Furthermore, if the distribution of the statistical error is known, we may also determine confidence intervals for μ and σ.

Example 1. Table 19.1.1 shows a sample of $n = 5$ values obtained by a planimeter. The mean value is

$$\bar{x} = \frac{2011}{5} = 402.2 \ (\text{mm}^2).$$

The mean square error is

$$s = \sqrt{\frac{44.8}{4}} = 3.3 \ (\text{mm}^2).$$

This result is sometimes written in the form

$$x = 402.2 \pm 3.3 \ (\text{mm}^2).$$

Table 19.1.1. Area (in Centimeter^2) of a Region Measured by a Planimeter

x_j	$|x_j - \bar{x}|$	$(x_j - \bar{x})^2$
402	0.2	0.04
398	4.2	17.64
405	2.8	7.84
406	3.8	14.44
400	2.2	4.84
Sum 2011	13.2	44.80

We further obtain

$$0.67\,s = 2.2\ (\text{mm}^2) \qquad \text{and} \qquad \tilde{s} = \sqrt{\frac{44.8}{5}} = 3.0\ (\text{mm}^2).$$

By applying formula (1) in Sec. 3.2 we have

$$s^2 = \frac{1}{4}\left(808{,}869 - \frac{2011^2}{5}\right) = \frac{44.8}{4},$$

as before.

Problems

1.–3. In each case determine the mean value and the mean square error.

  1. Calorimeter constant (BTU/pound/°F)

  2435.6   2433.6   2428.8   2428.6   2435.9   2441.7   2433.7   2437.8

  2. Tensile strength (kilograms/millimeter^2) of sheet iron

  44.0   42.8   40.8   41.4   44.4   43.9   42.8   44.0   42.2   44.8

  3. Period (seconds/50 oscillations) of a pendulum

  80.1   80.1   79.8   80.0   80.0   80.1   80.1   80.0   79.8   80.2

  4. Calculate and graph $\tilde{s}/s$ [cf. (1) and (2)] when $n = 2, 3, \cdots, 10$.
  5. Assuming that the population corresponding to the sample in Problem 2 is normally distributed, find a 95%-confidence interval for the variance.
  6. A sample of 10 measurements of the length of a rod gave a mean $\bar{x} = 5.02$ in. and a standard deviation $s = 0.03$ in. Find a 95%-confidence interval for the mean, assuming normality of the corresponding population.
  7. A sample of 6 values of pH (degree of acidity) of a chemical solution had mean 2.10 and mean square error 0.20. Assuming normality of the corresponding population, find a 99%-confidence interval for the mean.
  8. A chemist made 5 determinations of the melting point of aluminum and obtained 665, 671, 664, 669, 661 degrees centigrade. Are these in agreement with the published value 660°C? Assume normality of the corresponding population and use $\alpha = 5\%$ for the test.
  9. If we round results of measurements to the nearest integer and if we assume that the rounding error is uniformly distributed on the interval $-0.5 \leqq x \leqq 0.5$, what is the probability that the error due to rounding in the sum of 100 independent rounded values will not exceed 5? *Hint.* Use the central limit theorem (Sec. 12.7).

19.2   Weighted Mean

It often happens that in a sample $x_1, \cdots, x_n$, certain values are more reliable than others. To understand this, let us discuss a simple example.

Suppose that we want to determine the period (time of a single oscillation) of a pendulum. For this purpose we may measure the times $t_1, \cdots, t_4$ of subsequent passages in the same direction of the pendulum through the position of static equilibrium and then compute the approximate values

$$x_1 = \tfrac{1}{3}(t_4 - t_1) \qquad \text{and} \qquad x_2 = t_3 - t_2$$

for the period. Clearly, these two values are independent. Suppose that from the nature of the experiment we may conclude that to the two differences of time there correspond two random variables with the same (unknown) variance σ^2. Then from (4) in Sec. 6.7 it follows that x_1 and x_2 are observed values of two independent random variables X_1 and X_2 with variance $\sigma_1^2 = \sigma^2/9$ and $\sigma_2^2 = \sigma^2$. Hence the accuracy of the two measurements is different. Therefore, x_1 should have a larger weight than x_2 when we form the mean. That is, instead of the usual mean

$$\bar{x} = \tfrac{1}{2}(x_1 + x_2) = \tfrac{1}{2}x_1 + \tfrac{1}{2}x_2,$$

we should use an expression of the form

$$\bar{x}^* = g_1 x_1 + g_2 x_2 \qquad (g_1 + g_2 = 1)$$

where g_1 and g_2 are positive numbers to be determined, so that the corresponding random variable

$$\bar{X}^* = g_1 X_1 + g_2 X_2$$

has the smallest possible standard deviation. This means that $\bar{x}^*$ should have a mean square error which is as small as possible. From (4) in Sec. 6.7 and Theorem 1 in Sec. 9.8 we find that $\bar{X}^*$ has the variance

$$\sigma^{*2} = g_1^2 \sigma_1^2 + g_2^2 \sigma_2^2.$$

Since $g_2 = 1 - g_1$, we obtain

$$\sigma^{*2} = g_1^2 \sigma_1^2 + (1 - g_1)^2 \sigma_2^2.$$

By equating to zero the derivative with respect to g_1 and using $g_2 = 1 - g_1$ we have

$$(1) \qquad\qquad\qquad g_1 \sigma_1^2 = g_2 \sigma_2^2.$$

It follows that the standard deviation σ^* is minimum if and only if we choose the numbers g_1, g_2 proportional to the reciprocal of the variances of the variables X_1 and X_2, respectively. Since $\sigma_1^2 = \sigma^2/9$ and $\sigma_2^2 = \sigma^2$ and $g_1 + g_2 = 1$, we thus obtain from (1) the values $g_1 = 9g_2$, $g_1 = 0.9$, $g_2 = 0.1$; consequently, the result is

$$\bar{x}^* = 0.9 x_1 + 0.1 x_2.$$

This expression is called a *weighted mean* of x_1 and x_2. The positive numbers 0.9 and 0.1 are called *weights* or *weight factors*.

Our problem is typical of situations that arise quite frequently (for example, in geodesy) and may be characterized in general terms, as follows.

Let a sample $x_1, \cdots, x_n$ be given. The corresponding independent variables $X_1, \cdots, X_n$ have variances $\sigma_1^2, \cdots, \sigma_n^2$, respectively. Then, assuming that these variances are not all equal, we have measurements of varying degrees of accuracy. *Under these assumptions the mean square error of the expression*

(2) $$\bar{x}^* = g_1 x_1 + \cdots + g_n x_n \qquad (g_1 + \cdots + g_n = 1)$$

is minimum if and only if we choose the numbers $g_1, \cdots, g_n$ *proportional to* $1/\sigma_1^2, \cdots, 1/\sigma_n^2$, *respectively. These numbers are called* **weights,** *and* (2) *is called the corresponding* **weighted mean** *of the n sample values* $x_1, \cdots, x_n$. The random variable $\bar{X}^*$ for which $\bar{x}^*$ is an observed value is then called a **best linear unbiased estimator** (or *minimum variance linear estimator*).

If those variances are equal, then (2) becomes identical with the usual sample mean.

Note that for determining the weights we need not know the variances $\sigma_1^2, \cdots, \sigma_n^2$, but only the ratios between any two of them. If we set

(3) $$\sigma_j^2 = \frac{\sigma^2}{c_j},$$

then σ^2 may be an unknown constant whereas $c_1, \cdots, c_n$ must be known.

From the computational point of view, it is advantageous to drop the condition $g_1 + \cdots + g_n = 1$ in (2). Then

(4) $$\bar{x}^* = \frac{g_1 x_1 + \cdots + g_n x_n}{g_1 + \cdots + g_n}.$$

Problems

1. Assuming that $X_1, \cdots, X_n$ are independent normal random variables with mean μ and variance (3), obtain (4) by the maximum likelihood method.

2. The statement involving (2) has been proved when $n = 2$. Prove it for any n.

3. If we unite two samples $x_1, \cdots, x_n$ and $x_1', \cdots, x_m'$ taken from the same population and having means $\bar{x}$ and $\bar{x}'$, respectively, then the resulting sample has the mean

$$\bar{x}^* = g_1 \bar{x} + g_2 \bar{x}' \qquad \text{where} \qquad g_1 = \frac{n}{n+m} \qquad \text{and} \qquad g_2 = \frac{m}{n+m}.$$

   (*a*) Prove this formula by the use of the definition of the usual mean. (*b*) Show that the choice of the weights g_1 and g_2 agrees with the minimum requirement in the text.

4. Unite the samples

$$2.3 \quad 2.1 \quad 1.9 \qquad \text{and} \qquad 2.0 \quad 2.2 \quad 2.1 \quad 2.0 \quad 1.8$$

   and compute the mean of the resulting single sample (*a*) from the means of the given samples, (*b*) directly.

5. While surveying, the crew measured an angle a number of times by each of two theodolites. Find the weighted mean of the two resulting values $73°2'7'' \pm 10''$ and $73°2'12'' \pm 20''$.

6. Two samples (sizes 10 and 4, respectively) of the breaking force of hard-soldered sheet-titanium and sheet-aluminum had the mean values 448 kg and 418 kg. Find the mean of the sample consisting of all 14 values.

19.3   Indirect Observations

To determine the area of a rectangle, we may measure its sides and then compute the area. The result of the computation is then called an **indirect observation** (of that area) because we did not measure the area directly but got it through a computation from some other quantities which we measured (the lengths of the sides). In contrast, if we measure some physical quantity directly, the result is called a **direct observation** of that quantity. A simple example is the determination of the weight of a body by using scales.

In connection with indirect observations, it is important to know how the error of measurement affects the final computational result. This is the problem that we shall now discuss.

Suppose that two independent quantities X and Y are measured and then the quantity

$$Z = h(X, Y)$$

is computed; here h is any function of X and Y. We assume that X is measured n times and Y is measured m times. We then have the values

$$x_1, \cdots, x_n \qquad \text{and} \qquad y_1, \cdots, y_m,$$

respectively. The mean values are

$$\bar{x} = \frac{1}{n}(x_1 + \cdots + x_n) \qquad \text{and} \qquad \bar{y} = \frac{1}{m}(y_1 + \cdots + y_m).$$

To X there corresponds the mean square error (1), Sec. 19.1, which we shall now denote by s_x instead of s. Let us use the notation

$$x_i = \bar{x} + u_i, \qquad \text{thus} \qquad x_i - \bar{x} = u_i.$$

Then (1), Sec. 19.1, yields

$$(1) \qquad\qquad s_x = \sqrt{\frac{1}{n-1}\sum_{i=1}^{n} u_i^2}.$$

Similarly, we set

$$y_j = \bar{y} + v_j, \qquad \text{thus} \qquad y_j - \bar{y} = v_j.$$

Then the mean square error s_y corresponding to Y is

$$(2) \qquad\qquad s_y = \sqrt{\frac{1}{m-1}\sum_{j=1}^{m} v_j^2}.$$

If we take any measured value x_i and any measured value y_j, we may compute the corresponding value

$$z_{ij} = h(x_i, y_j).$$

From the Taylor formula we obtain

(3)
$$z_{ij} = h(\bar{x} + u_i, \bar{y} + v_j)$$

$$= h(\bar{x}, \bar{y}) + u_i \frac{\partial h}{\partial x} + v_j \frac{\partial h}{\partial y} + \cdots .$$

Here the dots designate terms containing higher powers of u_i and v_j. We may assume that $|u_i|$ and $|v_j|$ are small and disregard those terms. If we sum over i from 1 to n and over j from 1 to m, then on the right we obtain the expressions

(4)
$$\Sigma u_i = 0 \quad \text{and} \quad \Sigma v_j = 0,$$

and the remaining term is $nmh(\bar{x}, \bar{y})$. On the left we have a double sum over all the z_{ij}. Dividing by nm, we obtain $\bar{z}$, the mean value of the z_{ij}, on the left, and on the right we have $h(\bar{x}, \bar{y})$. Consequently, we simply have

(5)
$$\bar{z} = \frac{1}{mn} \sum_{i=1}^{n} \sum_{j=1}^{m} z_{ij} = h(\bar{x}, \bar{y}).$$

We shall now represent the corresponding mean square error

(6)
$$s = \sqrt{\frac{1}{nm - 1} \sum_{i=1}^{n} \sum_{j=1}^{m} (z_{ij} - \bar{z})^2}$$

in terms of the mean square errors s_x and s_y. From (3) and (5) it follows that

$$z_{ij} - \bar{z} \approx u_i \frac{\partial h}{\partial x} + v_j \frac{\partial h}{\partial y} .$$

We square both sides, perform the multiplication on the right, and finally sum with respect to i and j. Then on the left we obtain the sum in (6). On the right we obtain, taking (4) into account,

$$\sum_{i=1}^{n} \sum_{j=1}^{m} u_i^2 \left(\frac{\partial h}{\partial x}\right)^2 + \sum_{i=1}^{n} \sum_{j=1}^{m} v_j^2 \left(\frac{\partial h}{\partial y}\right)^2.$$

This is equal to

$$\left(\frac{\partial h}{\partial x}\right)^2 m \sum_{i=1}^{n} u_i^2 + \left(\frac{\partial h}{\partial y}\right)^2 n \sum_{j=1}^{m} v_j^2.$$

From (1) and (2) it follows that

$$\sum_{i=1}^{n} u_i^2 = (n - 1)s_x^2 \quad \text{and} \quad \sum_{j=1}^{m} v_j^2 = (m - 1)s_y^2.$$

By inserting all these expressions into (6) we obtain

(7)
$$s = \sqrt{\frac{1}{nm - 1} \left\{(n - 1)m \left(\frac{\partial h}{\partial x}\right)^2 s_x^2 + (m - 1)n \left(\frac{\partial h}{\partial y}\right)^2 s_y^2\right\}}.$$

We see that for large n and m,

(8)
$$s \approx \sqrt{\left(\frac{\partial h}{\partial x}\right)^2 s_x{}^2 + \left(\frac{\partial h}{\partial y}\right)^2 s_y{}^2}.$$

In these formulas the partial derivatives have to be evaluated at $(\bar{x}, \bar{y})$.

Example 1. Suppose that the resistance of two resistors is measured several times, the result being $R_1 = 100$ ohms with mean square error 0.8 ohm and $R_2 = 200$ ohms with mean square error 1.0 ohm; this is often written

$$R_1 = 100 \pm 0.8 \text{ (ohms)} \qquad \text{and} \qquad R_2 = 200 \pm 1.0 \text{ (ohms)}.$$

Find the resistance when the two resistors are (a) in series, (b) parallel, and determine the corresponding mean square error.

(a) The resistance is

$$R = R_1 + R_2 = 100 + 200 = 300.$$

In (8) we need

$$\frac{\partial R}{\partial R_1} = 1 \qquad \text{and} \qquad \frac{\partial R}{\partial R_2} = 1.$$

Since the mean square errors of R_1 and R_2 are $s_1 = 0.8$ and $s_2 = 1.0$, respectively, it follows from (8) that R has the mean square error

(9)
$$s = \sqrt{\left(\frac{\partial R}{\partial R_1}\right)^2 s_1{}^2 + \left(\frac{\partial R}{\partial R_2}\right)^2 s_2{}^2} = \sqrt{0.8^2 + 1.0^2} = 1.3.$$

Our result may be written

$$R = 300.0 \pm 1.3 \text{ (ohms)}.$$

(b) If the two resistors are parallel, the resistance R is obtained from

$$\frac{1}{R} = \frac{1}{R_1} + \frac{1}{R_2}.$$

By solving for R and inserting the above numerical values, we obtain

$$R = \frac{R_1 R_2}{R_1 + R_2} = \frac{100 \cdot 200}{100 + 200} = 66.67 \text{ (ohms)}.$$

For the computation of the corresponding error, we need the partial derivatives

$$\frac{\partial R}{\partial R_1} = \frac{R_2{}^2}{(R_1 + R_2)^2} = \frac{200^2}{(100 + 200)^2} = 0.44$$

and

$$\frac{\partial R}{\partial R_2} = \frac{R_1{}^2}{(R_1 + R_2)^2} = \frac{100^2}{(100 + 200)^2} = 0.11.$$

If we insert these numerical values into (8) and use the given values $s_1 = 0.8$ and $s_2 = 1.0$, we see that R has the mean square error

$$s = \sqrt{0.44^2 \cdot 0.8^2 + 0.11^2 \cdot 1.0^2} = 0.37.$$

Our result may be written

$$R = 66.67 \pm 0.37 \text{ (ohms)}.$$

Problems

1.–3. Using the given results of measurements, determine the desired quantity and its mean square error.

    1. Area A of a rectangle with sides $a = 150 \pm 0.1$ in. and $b = 80 \pm 0.1$ in.

    2. Angle γ of a plane triangle whose other angles are $\alpha = 40° \pm 30''$ and $\beta = 45° \pm 30''$.

    3. Specific weight γ of an iron ball of weight $W = 1000 \pm 0.1$ g and diameter $D = 6.2 \pm 0.01$ cm.

    4. Show that if $h(x, y) = xy$ in (8) and we use the *relative mean errors*

$$m = \frac{s}{h(\bar{x}, \bar{y})}, \qquad m_x = \frac{s_x}{\bar{x}}, \qquad m_y = \frac{s_y}{\bar{y}},$$

then we may write (8) in the form

$$m \approx \sqrt{m_x{}^2 + m_y{}^2}.$$

    5. What form does (8) take if $h = kx^a y^b$ (a, b, k constant) and we use the relative mean errors in Problem 4?

    6. Solve Problem 3 by the use of the formula for the error given in Problem 5.

19.4 ^omit Measurements and Regression Analysis

It is clear that the method of least squares used in regression analysis may be employed for curve fitting in connection with physical measurements. Since our discussion in Chap. 17 was very detailed, we shall now restrict ourselves to the presentation of a few typical problems.

Problems

1.–3. In each case determine the regression line by the method of least squares.

    1. Voltage y (millivolts) of a thermocouple where x (°C) is the difference of temperatures:

x	20	30	40	50	60	70	80	90
y	0.50	0.77	1.06	1.35	2.02	2.40	2.80	3.15

    2. Resistance R (ohms) of a resistor depending on temperature T (°C):

T	15	25	35	50	70	90
R	5.43	5.60	5.81	6.10	6.52	6.95

    3. Relative decrease y of volume of leather under very high pressure x (in multiples of 1000 atm):

x	2	4	6	8	10
y	0.000	0.023	0.041	0.057	0.069

4.–6. In each case determine the regression parabola (4), Sec. 17.11.

   4. Resistance R (ohms) of a carbon filament lamp depending on the current I (milli-amperes):

I	20	30	40	50	60	70	80	90	100
R	1.45	1.33	1.30	1.24	1.20	1.17	1.15	1.12	1.10

5.

x	-1	0	1	2
y	1	0	1	2

6. Frequency y (cycles/second) of a small plate spring depending on the angle of displacement x from the position of static equilibrium:

x	1.5	2.0	2.5	3.0	4.0	5.0	6.5	9.0	12.0
y	98.98	98.97	98.97	98.96	98.96	98.98	99.00	99.07	99.19

CHAPTER 20

Nonparametric Methods

Nonparametric methods are methods which can be applied to various distributions, in contrast to other methods which are restricted to a certain type of distributions, for example, to normal distributions. It follows that nonparametric methods are suitable if the distribution of the population is not known, for example, in exploratory research. Furthermore, an advantage is that the corresponding computations are in general simpler.

Of course, we cannot expect that in the case of a certain distribution the amount of information given by a nonparametric method is the same as that given by a method which is applicable to that particular distribution only. However, in many cases the loss of information caused by the use of a nonparametric method is not very large. For example, in the case of large samples from normal populations the tests in Secs. 13.3 and 20.5 give the same amount of information if in the latter case we use samples which contain 5% more sample values. Consequently, in each case the decision as to which of the two tests is preferable will depend on the increase of cost and time necessitated by the larger sample size compared with the decrease of cost and time resulting from the simpler computation for nonparametric methods.

The term **nonparametric methods** is suggested by the fact that most of these methods are not concerned with testing or estimating the parameters of a distribution function of a given type. A synonymous term is **distribution-free methods;** it indicates that these methods do not require a knowledge of how the population is distributed.

General assumption. Throughout this chapter we shall assume that the distributions of the populations are **continuous.**

There has been a rapid growth in the use and development of nonparametric methods during the last two decades, and these methods are of increasing importance in many branches of statistics. Readers interested in further literature on nonparametric methods are referred to the presentations by Fraser (1966) and Noether (1967); cf. also Kendall (1953), Kendall and

Sundrum (1953), Moran, Whitfield, and Daniels (1950), Savage (1962), Scheffé (1943), Wilks (1959), and Wolfowitz (1949).

20.1   Sign Test for the Median

We know that the mean μ is an important measure of the "location" or "central tendency" of a distribution, in particular if the distribution is symmetric or almost symmetric, and we have discussed this fact from various points of view in connection with the normal and other distributions. If we do not specify the distribution, the mean will in many cases lose some of its attractiveness, and the median $\tilde{\mu}$ may then be preferred as a measure for central tendency.

A **median** is a solution $x = \tilde{\mu}$ of the equation

$$(1) \qquad\qquad\qquad F(x) = \tfrac{1}{2}$$

where F is the distribution function of the distribution under consideration, and we regard any vertical step (occurring in the discrete case) as part of the curve, so that we have a single, connected, never-decreasing curve and, consequently, at least one solution of (1).

We shall now describe a very simple test of the hypothesis that the median $\tilde{\mu}$ has a certain given value $\tilde{\mu}_0$, starting with the case $\tilde{\mu}_0 = 0$. The test is applicable to any continuous distribution.

For a practical situation, let us suppose that someone wanted to find out whether a certain special sowing machine M_s is better than an ordinary sowing machine M_o. For this purpose he divided each of ten equiareal fields into two equal parts and used M_s on one part (chosen randomly) and M_o on the other. For each of the ten fields, he subtracted the yield of the half corresponding to M_o from that corresponding to M_s. The results were

$$2.4 \quad 1.0 \quad 0.7 \quad 0.0 \quad 1.1 \quad -0.4 \quad 0.1 \quad 0.7 \quad 1.6 \quad 1.1$$

(measured in bushels) (J. Wishart, *Suppl. J. Royal Statist. Soc.*, **1**, 1934, 26–51). Using this sample, we want to test the hypothesis that both machines give the same yield against the alternative that M_s gives a higher yield. That is, we want to test the hypothesis that the population corresponding to the sample has median $\tilde{\mu} = 0$ against the alternative $\tilde{\mu} > 0$. We choose the significance level $\alpha = 5\%$.

If the hypothesis is true, the probability p of a positive value (higher yield) is the same as that of a negative value (lower yield), hence $p = 0.5$. Then the random variable

$$X = number\ of\ positive\ values\ among\ n\ values$$

has a binomial distribution with $p = 0.5$. Our sample has 10 values. We omit the value 0.0 because it does not contribute to the decision.[1] Of the

---

[1] Ties in nonparametric tests are discussed by Putter (1955) (cf. Appendix 3).

remaining 9 values, 8 are positive. If the hypothesis is true, the probability of obtaining at least 8 positive values among 9 values is

$$P(X \geq 8) = 1 - P(X \leq 7) = 1 - 0.9805 = 1.95\%$$

(cf. Table 1*d* in Appendix 4). Since this is less than 5%, we reject the hypothesis and assert that the special sowing machine M_s gives better yields.

This was a one-sided test because the alternative was $\tilde{\mu} > 0$. If the alternative is $\tilde{\mu} \neq 0$, we reject the hypothesis $\tilde{\mu} = 0$ if the observed value of X is too large or too small. For example, when $n = 9$, we have from Table 1*d*

$$P(X \leq 1) = 1.95\%, \qquad P(X \geq 8) = 1.95\%,$$

and we may take $x \leq 1$ and $x \geq 8$ as a rejection region (critical region) in this two-sided case.

Very little changes if instead of $\tilde{\mu} = 0$ we consider an arbitrary hypothesis $\tilde{\mu} = \tilde{\mu}_0$. Then instead of the sample values $x_1, \cdots, x_n$ we have to take the values $x_1 - \tilde{\mu}_0, x_2 - \tilde{\mu}_0, \cdots, x_n - \tilde{\mu}_0$. If the hypothesis is true, the random variable

$$X^* = \textit{number of positive values among n values}$$

(corresponding to the transformed values $x_1 - \tilde{\mu}_0, \cdots$) has a binomial distribution, as before.

For example, if we want to test the hypothesis $\tilde{\mu} = 210$ against the alternative $\tilde{\mu} \neq 210$, using a sample of 15 values

194 200 230 202 176 195 184 226 185 208 190 205 215 199 203

we have to take the values

-16 -10 20 -8 -34 -15 -26 16 -25 -2 -20 -5 5 -11 -7.

From Table 1*d* we see that when $n = 15$ and the hypothesis is true,

$$P(X^* \leq 3) = P(X^* \geq 12) = 1.76\%, \quad P(X^* \leq 4) = P(X^* \geq 11) = 5.92\%.$$

This suggests that we choose the rejection region $x < 4$, $x > 11$. In our sample, $x = 3$, we reject the hypothesis $\tilde{\mu} = 210$ and assert that $\tilde{\mu} \neq 210$.

For further tests concerning medians, see Walsh (1949) (cf. Appendix 3).

Problems

1. Assume that the population from which the first sample in the text was taken is normally distributed and apply the test presented in Example 2, Sec. 13.3.

2. Each of 10 patients was given two different sedatives *A* and *B*. The table shows the increase of sleeping time in hours. Is the difference between *A* and *B* significant? (D = difference between corresponding values.)

A	1.9	0.8	1.1	0.1	−0.1	4.4	5.5	1.6	4.6	3.4
B	0.7	−1.6	−0.2	−1.2	−0.1	3.4	3.7	0.8	0.0	2.0
D	1.2	2.4	1.3	1.3	0.0	1.0	1.8	0.8	4.6	1.4

3. Apply the method of Example 2, Sec. 13.3, to the data in Problem 2, assuming normality of the corresponding population.

4. Apply the sign test to the sample in Problem 7, Sec. 13.3.

5. Patties of ground beef had been stored for 8 months at low temperatures in home freezers. Eight patties were stored at the constant temperature of $0°F$ the whole time while another eight patties were stored at temperatures fluctuating between $0°F$ and $15°F$. Afterwards, each of 8 persons was asked to judge the flavor of one patty from each sample. Seven persons preferred the patty kept at $0°F$, whereas one person preferred the other. Is the difference in flavor significant?

6. Thirty new employees were grouped into 15 pairs on the basis of intelligence and previous experience and were then instructed in data processing. Two methods of instruction were applied, an old method (A) to one (randomly selected) person of each pair and a new, presumably better, method (B) to the other. Test the hypothesis that the methods are equally effective against the alternative that (B) is better, using the following scores obtained at the end of the training period.

A	60	70	80	85	75	40	70	45	95	80	90	60	80	75	65
B	65	85	85	80	95	65	100	60	90	85	100	75	90	60	80

7. Assuming that the differences of corresponding values in Problem 6 come from a normally distributed population, apply the test in Example 2, Sec. 13.3, and compare the results.

20.2   Test for Trend

If a random variable Y depends on an ordinary variable x (as in Chap. 17), where x may be the time or some other quantity, it may be of interest to know whether, as x increases, Y has a tendency of assuming larger and larger values (*positive trend*) or smaller and smaller values (*negative trend*). So we may want to test the hypothesis that there is no trend against an alternative, for instance, that there is trend (or positive trend, or negative trend). If the assumptions in Chap. 17 are satisfied, we should apply methods developed there. In other cases we can use the following rather simple test.

To consider a practical problem, suppose that grains of barley were exposed to certain rays to find out how the amount of rays x affects the yield y. The result was:

Amount of rays x	0	$2r$	$4r$	$40r$	$400r$
Yield y	29.2	30.2	28.2	29.7	30.4

where y is measured in grams per jar (A. Süss, *Atompraxis*, **9**, 1963, 91). We want to test the hypothesis that, within the range considered, the rays do not affect the yield against the alternative that y increases as x increases, that is, that there is positive trend, as suggested by a corresponding theory.

The x-values in our sample are ordered in an ascending fashion. In the case of a positive trend the y-values should increase from the left to the right. If there is no trend, the y-values should behave in a completely irregular fashion and have no monotonicity. We count how often a sample value precedes a smaller one:

29.2 precedes 28.2	(1 transposition)
30.2 precedes 28.2 and 29.7	(2 transpositions).

The other values of the sample follow in order. Hence, in our sample we have 3 transpositions. We shall now obtain the distribution of the variable

$$T = \textit{number of transpositions}$$

under the hypothesis that there is no trend. If there is no trend, then all the $5! = 120$ permutations of 5 elements 1 2 3 4 5 are equally likely (cf. Sec. 4.9), and we arrange them according to their number of transpositions. This gives

$T = 0$	$T = 1$	$T = 2$	$T = 3$	
1 2 3 4 5	1 2 3 5 4	1 2 4 5 3	1 2 5 4 3	
	1 2 4 3 5	1 2 5 3 4	1 3 4 5 2	
	1 3 2 4 5	1 3 2 5 4	1 3 5 2 4	
	2 1 3 4 5	1 3 4 2 5	1 4 2 5 3	
		1 4 2 3 5	1 4 3 2 5	
		2 1 3 5 4	1 5 2 3 4	
		2 1 4 3 5	2 1 4 5 3	
		2 3 1 4 5	2 1 5 3 4	etc.
		3 1 2 4 5	2 3 1 5 4	
			2 3 4 1 5	
			2 4 1 3 5	
			3 1 2 5 4	
			3 1 4 2 5	
			3 2 1 4 5	
			4 1 2 3 5	

We see that

$$P(T \leqq 3) = \tfrac{1}{120} + \tfrac{4}{120} + \tfrac{9}{120} + \tfrac{15}{120} = \tfrac{29}{120} = 24\%.$$

Hence we do not reject the hypothesis.

For this test we may use Table 10*a* in Appendix 4. Our method and that table are valid in the case of a continuous distribution. Theoretically we may then expect that all the sample values are numerically different. Practically, because of rounding, several sample values may be equal. Suppose that m values are equal. Then we should count transpositions as before and add to their number the number $m(m - 1)/4$ (= mean value of the transpositions in the case of permutations of m objects), that is, 1/2 for 2 equal values, 3/2 for each triple of equal values, etc. If the distribution of the population is discrete, we must take into account that theoretically the same value may appear several times in a sample, and we must modify the above method in a suitable fashion.

Problems

1. Complete the table in the text.
2. Make a table similar to that in the text when $n = 4$.

3.–5. In each case apply the test explained in the text to the given sample.

3. The sample in Problem 6, Sec. 17.2.
4. The sample in Problem 7, Sec. 17.2.
5. Diastolic blood pressure x (in mm Hg) and weight of heart y (in grams) of 10 male patients who died of cerebral hemorrhage:

x	121	120	95	123	140	112	92	100	102	91
y	521	465	352	455	490	388	301	395	375	418

20.3   Test of Randomness in Samples. Runs

Suppose that we toss a coin ten times and record the results. With H and T denoting head and tail:

$$\underbrace{H\ H}\ \underbrace{T\ T\ T}\ \underbrace{H\ H}\ \underbrace{T}\ \underbrace{H}.$$

The brackets underneath indicate adjacent alike letters, and in this fashion our sample of ten values is subdivided into five parts, which are called **runs.** If in a sample there are too few runs, for example,

$$\underbrace{H\ H\ H\ H\ H\ H}\ \underbrace{T\ T\ T\ T} \qquad (2\ runs),$$

or too many runs, for example,

$$\underbrace{H}\ \underbrace{T}\ \underbrace{H}\ \underbrace{T}\ \underbrace{H}\ \underbrace{T}\ \underbrace{H}\ \underbrace{T}\ \underbrace{H}\ \underbrace{T} \qquad (10\ runs),$$

this may indicate that the sample values are not arranged at random.

If we have reason to believe that observations taken over some time interval may not behave like a random set, we should test the randomness of the sequence of observations before we apply a statistical method based on randomness.

We shall immediately see how to define runs below and above the median in the case of *numerical* observations. Then, for example, in testing products taken from a production line every hour, too few runs may indicate a tendency of the machine to produce larger and larger (or smaller and smaller) items, and too many runs may indicate an undesirable oscillatory behavior of the machine.

We first want to show how to define and to determine runs in the case of a sample consisting of numerical values. We graph the sample values in their

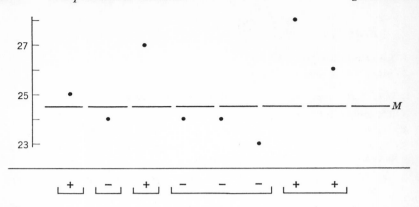

Fig. 20.3.1. Illustration of the definition of runs in the case of the sample 25, 24, 27, 24, 24 23, 28, 26

order. An example is shown in Fig. 20.3.1. Then we draw a horizontal straight line M (*median*) so that 50% of the sample values lie above M and the other 50% lie below M. At the bottom of the figure, each value above M is labeled by a plus sign and each value below M by a minus sign. Then we are in a position to count runs as before.

It may happen that for a sample no such line M exists and that, on the horizontal line M^* which divides the sample into two parts of almost equal size, there lie two or three or more sample values. Then we should add some of the values on M^* to the part of the smaller size, so that afterwards both parts have the same size. This process of addition should be performed in such a fashion that the number of runs becomes as large as possible. For example, in Fig. 20.3.2 we may add the value characterized by the arrow to the lower part which then consists of eight values.

We mention without proof that if the hypothesis of complete randomness of the values in the sample (from a *continuous* distribution) holds, then the

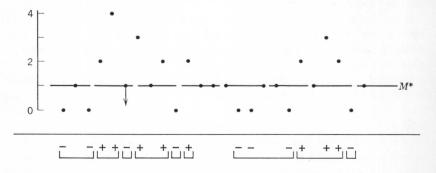

Fig. 20.3.2. Nine runs in a sample of size 25

random variable

$$U = \text{number of runs}$$

has the probability function

$$f(u) = P(U = u) = 2\binom{m-1}{\frac{1}{2}u - 1}^2 \bigg/ \binom{2m}{m} \qquad (u \text{ even})$$

$$f(u) = P(U = u) = 2\binom{m-1}{\frac{1}{2}u - \frac{1}{2}}\binom{m-1}{\frac{1}{2}u - \frac{3}{2}} \bigg/ \binom{2m}{m} \qquad (u \text{ odd})$$

where $2 \leqq u \leqq 2m$ and m is the number of plus signs that we obtain in the process just described. By assumption, this number is equal to the number of minus signs. m plus signs and m minus signs may be arranged in $\binom{2m}{m}$ differ-ent ways, and we obtain those expressions for the probability function $f(u)$ by regarding these different arrangements as equally likely and then counting the number of runs in each case.

If the number of runs is too small or too large, we reject that hypothesis. Critical values are contained in Table 10b of Appendix 4.

In Fig. 20.3.2 we have $m = 8$, and the number of runs is $u = 9$. We choose the significance level 5%. From Table 10b (with $\alpha^* = 2.5\%$ and $m = 8$) we obtain the corresponding critical values 4 and 13. Since $u = 9$ lies between these values, we do not reject the hypothesis that the values of our sample are arranged at random.

It can be shown that for large m the distribution of U is approximately normal with mean

$$\mu_U = m + 1$$

and variance

$$\sigma_U{}^2 = \frac{m(m-1)}{2m-1}.$$

This fact may be used for determining critical values when m exceeds the values given in Table 10b.

We mention that distributions of runs above and below the median of specified lengths, of runs up and down by number and by length have also been studied and are available in the literature; see Mosteller (1941), Olmstead (1946), Wolfowitz (1944), Moore and Wallis (1943), and Mood (1940) (cf. Appendix 3).

Problems

1.–3. Apply the test explained in the text, using the following samples.

    1. The sample in Problem 1, Sec. 2.1.

    2. The sample in Problem 4, Sec. 2.1.

    3. 97 3 16 12 55 16 84 63 33 57 18 26 23 52 37 70 56 99 16 31

4. What is the probability that the larger of 2 observations taken from a continuous distribution will exceed the true median? Answer the same question for the smaller of the two values.

5. Apply the test for randomness to the set of the 50 digits in the first row of Table 5 in Appendix 4.

6. A machine is used for cutting wire, and the lengths of the pieces of wire are measured. In the first 50 pieces measured, there is a total of 14 runs above and below the median. Test the hypothesis that the machine is turning out pieces of wire whose lengths vary randomly.

7. Write down a sequence of 0's and 1's totaling 40 digits that you feel is random. Test for randomness.

8. Would you expect our present test to show up a lack of randomness in the sequence 0, 0, 1, 1, 0, 0, 1, 1, $\cdots$, 0, 0, 1, 1 totaling 40 numbers?

9. Show that the present test for randomness is unaffected by multiplying each sample value by the same constant?

10. Using the normal approximation for the distribution of U explained in the text, compute c so that $P(U \leq c) = 5\%$ when $m = 20$ and compare the value with that given in Table 10b.

20.4   Test of Equality of Distribution Functions

Runs may also be used to test the hypothesis H_0 that the distribution functions of two continuous distributions are identical. Such a test was designed by Wald and Wolfowitz (1940) [see also Stevens (1939)] and uses two samples

$$(S1) \quad x_1, \cdots, x_{n_1} \qquad \text{and} \qquad (S2) \quad y_1, \cdots, y_{n_2}.$$

We shall explain this test of the hypothesis

$$H_0: \qquad F_1(x) = F_2(x)$$

where $F_1(x)$ is the distribution function of the population from which (S1) was taken and $F_2(x)$ is the distribution function of the population from which (S2) was taken. As an alternative we choose

$$H_1: \qquad F_1(x) \neq F_2(x).$$

In the first step of the test, we combine the two samples into one pooled sample and arrange the values in the pooled sample in increasing order of magnitude, underscoring the n_1 values from (S1). This may look like this:

$$1.6 \quad \underline{2.3} \quad \underline{2.5} \quad 2.9 \quad 3.2 \quad 3.8 \quad \underline{4.6} \quad 5.2 \quad \underline{8.9} \quad 9.1$$

(here $n_1 = 5$ and $n_2 = 5$). Then we count the total number of runs in the pooled sample, where a *run* is a cluster of one or more underscored values or a cluster of one or more nonunderscored values. In our example the number of runs is 6. If the hypothesis is true, we may expect that in the pooled and ordered sample the values from (S1) and (S2) appear randomly mixed so that the number of runs is neither very small nor very large. Hence, if in our pooled sample there are very few or very many runs, we have reason to believe that the hypothesis does not hold, and we reject it.

It can be shown that if the hypothesis is true, the random variable

$$U = number\ of\ runs$$

has the probability function

$$f(u) = P(U = u) = 2 \binom{n_1 - 1}{\frac{1}{2}u - 1}\binom{n_2 - 1}{\frac{1}{2}u - 1} \bigg/ \binom{n_1 + n_2}{n_1} \qquad (u\ \text{even})$$

$$f(u) = \left[\binom{n_1 - 1}{\frac{1}{2}u - \frac{1}{2}}\binom{n_2 - 1}{\frac{1}{2}u - \frac{3}{2}} + \binom{n_1 - 1}{\frac{1}{2}u - \frac{3}{2}}\binom{n_2 - 1}{\frac{1}{2}u - \frac{1}{2}} \right] \bigg/ \binom{n_1 + n_2}{n_1} \qquad (u\ \text{odd}).$$

Note that when $n_1 = n_2 = m$, this is identical with the corresponding formula in the last section.

The critical values needed for the test are obtained from Table 10c in Appendix 4 when n_1 and n_2 are small; for large n_1 and n_2 we may use the fact that U is approximately normal with mean

$$\mu_U = 1 + \frac{2n_1 n_2}{n_1 + n_2}$$

and variance

$$\sigma_U{}^2 = \frac{2n_1 n_2 (2n_1 n_2 - n_1 - n_2)}{(n_1 + n_2)^2 (n_1 + n_2 - 1)} .$$

The approximation is usually sufficiently accurate for practical purposes when both n_1 and n_2 are greater than 10.

If a tie x_i, y_j of values from the two original samples occurs, it should be "broken." This can be done by tossing a coin. If a head appears, leave the underscoring $\underline{x_i}$, y_j; if a tail appears, change to x_i, $\underline{y_j}$.

Example 1. Weight of dust (in milligrams) in waste gas was measured in two different systems of tubes. The values obtained were as follows.

$$A \quad 20 \quad 37 \quad 55 \quad 50 \quad 64 \quad 41$$

$$B \quad 75 \quad 21 \quad 72 \quad 71 \quad 85 \quad 43 \quad 34 \quad 65 \quad 90 \quad 35$$

Test the hypothesis that the corresponding populations are equal against the alternative that they are different, choosing the significance level $\alpha = 5\%$.

The ordered pooled sample is

$$\underline{20} \quad 21 \quad 34 \quad 35 \quad \underline{37} \quad \underline{41} \quad 43 \quad \underline{50} \quad \underline{55} \quad \underline{64} \quad 65 \quad 71 \quad 72 \quad 75 \quad 85 \quad 90.$$

We see that there are $u = 6$ runs. The test is two-sided. From Table 10c in Appendix 4 with $n_1 = 6$ and $n_2 = 10$, we find that to

$$P(U \leqq c_1) \leqq 2.5\%, \qquad P(U \geqq c_2) \leqq 2.5\%$$

there correspond the values $c_1 = 4$ and $c_2 = 12$. Since $u = 6$ lies between c_1 and c_2, we do not reject the hypothesis.

Problems

1. Suppose that two samples of size 8 and 9, respectively, are such that the pooled ordered sample has 4 runs. Test the hypothesis that the corresponding populations are equal against the alternative that they are different, choosing the significance level $\alpha = 5\%$.

2. Using the normal approximation, compute the critical values c_1 and c_2 when $n_1 = 9$ and $n_2 = 10$ for a two-sided test with significance level $\alpha = 5\%$ and compare the result with the exact values in Table 10c.

3. The relative output of workers under two different working conditions (A: not air conditioned, B: air conditioned) was as follows.

A: 89 103 93 99 81 103 116 92 105 85
B: 95 109 98 114 108 94 106 98 96 113

Test the hypothesis that the corresponding populations are equal against the alternative that they are different, choosing the significance level $\alpha = 5\%$.

4. Splitting tensile strength (pounds/inch^2) of concrete cylinders made of two different types of concrete was as follows.

I	358	333	373	325	382	349	316	371	356	379
	376	313	341	312	350	375	336	360	309	349

II	321	330	361	305	368	330	306	367	322	308
	348	328	322	330	367					

Is the splitting tensile strength significantly different?

5. The lifetime of 40-watt bulbs under two conditions C_1 and C_2 was measured (C_1: bulbs in a glass sphere with a small hole at the bottom; C_2: bulb in the open air). The values (measured in multiples of 100 hours) were as follows.

C_1	18.3	13.5	12.6	14.7	13.2	14.8	13.6	12.8	23.1	14.8
	14.9	12.2	14.5	25.1	12.9	15.0	11.4	13.2	18.5	10.2

C_2	15.8	19.4	13.8	17.0	9.4	18.8	16.3	19.9	13.9	19.2
	14.2	13.0	16.5	21.2	15.3	22.8	17.6	13.1	26.0	16.9

Test the hypothesis that the corresponding populations are equal against the alternative that they are different.

6. Pressure in a cylinder of (compressed) gas was measured by two different methods A and B. Test the hypothesis that both methods give similar results, using the following two samples (values measured in atmospheres).

A 1.56 1.72 1.60 1.69 1.63
B 1.67 1.68 1.58 1.61 1.65

20.5 A Rank Test

In the test in Sec. 20.1, only the sign of each sample value is taken into account, whereas the size of the sample values is completely disregarded.

There are other types of tests in which we also lose some information but the loss is not so great because the size of each sample value is taken into account, at least to some extent. We shall now discuss a test of this sort. It is a rank test by Wilcoxon (1947) (cf. Appendix 3), which is called the **Wilcoxon one-sample** or **signed rank test** and may be explained as follows.

Suppose that we are concerned with different methods A and B of measurement, for example, for measuring the content of starch of potatoes. To compare two such methods, we set up an experiment in which each of 16 potatoes is cut into two portions; to each of the two portions one of the two methods is applied, so that from each potato we obtain two values, one from method A and the other from method B. Then we form the difference of corresponding values; suppose that the results (in multiples of .1%) are

$$2 \quad 0 \quad 0 \quad 1 \quad 2 \quad 2 \quad 3 \quad -3 \quad 1 \quad 2 \quad 3 \quad 0 \quad -1 \quad 1 \quad -2 \quad 1.$$

Using this sample, we want to test the hypothesis that the two methods give the same result. We proceed as follows.

We omit the three values 0. Then we order the remaining $m = n - 3 = 13$ values in ascending order of their absolute values. Underneath we write the sign (plus or minus). Then in the third row we write the **rank** (current number) from 1 to 13. In the last row we write the **signed rank,** which is defined to be the rank taken with the sign of the sample value, or the arithmetic mean of sample values of like absolute value taken with that sign. This looks as follows.

Absolute value	1	1	1	1	1		2	2	2	2	2		3		3		3
Sign	$-$	$+$	$+$	$+$	$+$		$-$	$+$	$+$	$+$	$+$		$-$		$+$		$+$
Rank	1	2	3	4	5		6	7	8	9	10		11		12		13
Signed rank	-3	3	3	3	3		-8	8	8	8	8		-12		12		12

In fact, the first 5 sample values have the same absolute value, and the arithmetic mean of their ranks is $(1 + 2 + 3 + 4 + 5)/5 = 3$, etc. The sum of the negative signed ranks is $-3 - 8 - 12 = -23$. Its absolute value $u_0 = 23$ is the quantity to be used in the test. If either the positive or the negative signed ranks dominate too much, then u_0 is too small or too large, respectively, and we reject the hypothesis. This is a two-sided test. The lower critical values can be obtained from Table 10d in Appendix 4. We have $m = n - 3 = 13$. Hence to the significance level $\alpha = 5\%$ there corresponds the critical value 17 and to $\alpha = 1\%$ there corresponds the critical value 10. If we see that in a sample the number u_0 is not larger than the sum of the positive signed ranks, we do not need the upper critical value. If u_0 were larger than that sum, we would take the latter as the quantity to be used in the test. In our case, $u_0 = 23$, and we do not reject the hypothesis if we choose $\alpha = 1\%$ or $\alpha = 5\%$.

Table 10d is obtained by combinatorial considerations. For example, when $m = 8$, it follows from Theorem 3 in Sec. 4.9 that there are precisely

$2^8 = 256$ samples having different combinations of signs. We may write these samples in the order of ascending values u_0, that is:

				Rank				u_0
1	2	3	4	5	6	7	8	
+	+	+	+	+	+	+	+	0
−	+	+	+	+	+	+	+	1
+	−	+	+	+	+	+	+	2
+	+	−	+	+	+	+	+	3
−	−	+	+	+	+	+	+	3
+	+	+	−	+	+	+	+	4
−	+	−	+	+	+	+	+	4

and so on. The sample values are differences of corresponding sample values from two samples. We assume that the corresponding two populations are continuous. When the hypothesis is true, the two distributions are identical. It can be shown that then the above 256 types of samples are equally likely. Hence the first 6 ($\approx 2.5\%$ of 256) and the last 6 of them constitute the rejection region of the two-sided test with the significance level $\alpha = 5\%$. The corresponding critical values are $u_0 = 4$, in agreement with Table 10d, and $u_0 = 36 - 4 = 32$.

Problems

1. Apply the test explained in the text to the sample in Problem 5, Sec. 13.3.
2. Apply the test explained in the text to the first sample in Sec. 20.1.
3. Compute approximations of the critical values for $m = 10, 15, 20$ as explained at the end of Table 10d in Appendix 4, and compare these values with the exact values given in that table.
4. Using the approximation formula in Table 10d, Appendix 4, compute the critical values when $m = 25, 30, 40$.
5. Is the result in Problem 2 better than that in Sec. 20.1, where $P(X \geq 8) = 1.95\%$?
6. One member of each of 10 pairs of corn seedlings was treated by a small electric current whereas the other member was left untreated. After a period of growth the differences in elongation (treated minus untreated) were

   6.0   1.3   10.2   23.9   3.1   6.8   −1.5   −14.7   −3.3   11.1.

   Test the hypothesis that the electric current treatment does not affect the elongation.

20.6   Two-Sample Rank Test

The following two-sample rank test by Wilcoxon (1945) and Mann and Whitney (1947) can be used to test the hypothesis that two populations have the same (continuous) distribution[2] against the alternative that they differ by a translation.

In this test we first arrange the two samples together in order of size and assign rank score 1 to the smallest value in this pooled sample, rank score 2 to the second smallest, etc. In the case of ties we replace the observation by the mean of the ranks for which it is tied. Then we compute the sum of the ranks of the values in the smaller of the two samples; let w denote this sum. (If the samples are of the same size, we may choose either sample.)

w is an observed value of a random variable W. If the hypothesis is true, we may expect that W will assume neither very small nor very large values. Hence, if a very small or very large value is obtained from the samples, we may suspect that the hypothesis does not hold, and we reject it. For small sample sizes n_1, n_2 some critical values c_1 and c_2 are given in Table 10e in Appendix 4.

For large n_1 and n_2 we may obtain critical values using the fact that if the hypothesis is true, then the random variable W is approximately normal with mean

$$\mu_W = \frac{n_1(n_1 + n_2 + 1)}{2}$$

and variance

$$\sigma_W{}^2 = \frac{n_1 n_2(n_1 + n_2 + 1)}{12}.$$

Example 1. Let us reconsider Example 1 in Sec. 20.4 and apply the present test to the two samples (weights of dust in milligrams)

$$A \quad 20 \quad 37 \quad 55 \quad 50 \quad 64 \quad 41$$

and

$$B \quad 75 \quad 21 \quad 72 \quad 71 \quad 85 \quad 43 \quad 34 \quad 65 \quad 90 \quad 35.$$

That is, we shall test the hypothesis that the corresponding populations are equal against the alternative that they differ by a translation. We choose the significance level $\alpha = 5\%$.
The pooled sample and the rank scores of the smaller sample (A) are as follows.

20	21	34	35	37	41	43	50	55	64	65	71	72	75	85	90
Rank 1				5	6		8	9	10						

We see that $w = 39$. From Table 10e in Appendix 4 with $n_1 = 6$, $n_2 = 10$ we find that to

$$P(W \leqq c_1) \leqq 2.5\%, \qquad P(W \geqq c_2) \leqq 2.5\%$$

there correspond the values $c_1 = 32$ and $c_2 = 70$. Since $w = 39$ lies between c_1 and c_2, we do not reject the hypothesis.

Example 2. Using samples of sizes $n_1 = 50$ and $n_2 = 100$ for which $w = 3050$, test the hypothesis that the corresponding populations have the same distribution against the alternative that these distributions differ by a translation; choose the significance level $\alpha = 5\%$.

---

[2] For other nonparametric tests of this hypothesis, see Sec. 20.4, Dixon (1940), Mathisen (1943), Smirnov (1939), and Wilks (1961) (cf. Appendix 3).

We use the normal approximation and obtain

$$\mu_W = \frac{50 \cdot 151}{2} = 3775$$

and

$$\sigma_W{}^2 = \frac{50 \cdot 100 \cdot 151}{12} = 62{,}917, \qquad \sigma_W = 251.$$

Hence the critical values c_1 and c_2 are obtained from

$$P(W \leq c_1) = \Phi\left(\frac{c_1 - 3775}{251}\right) = 2.5\%,$$

$$P(W \geq c_2) = 1 - \Phi\left(\frac{c_2 - 3775}{251}\right) = 2.5\%.$$

This gives

$$\frac{c_1 - 3775}{251} = -1.96, \qquad \frac{c_2 - 3775}{251} = 1.96.$$

Solving for c_1 and c_2, we have $c_1 = 3283$ and $c_2 = 4267$. Since $w = 3050 < c_1$, we reject the hypothesis.

Problems

1. What are the smallest and the largest possible values of w?

2. Using the normal approximation, find c_1 and c_2 so that $P(W \leq c_1) = 5\%$, $P(W \geq c_2) = 5\%$ when $n_1 = n_2 = 10$, and compare the result with the values given in Table 10e, Appendix 4.

3. Samples of two types of paint exposed to certain weather conditions for 3 months were scored as follows.

A:	92	95	94	85	82	
B:	78	74	81	69	88	75

   Test the hypothesis that the corresponding populations have the same distribution against the alternative that these distributions differ by a translation. Use the 5% level of significance.

4. Apply the present test to the samples in Problem 5, Sec. 20.4, using the 5% level of significance.

5. Using the two samples in Problem 4 of Sec. 20.4, test the hypothesis that the distributions of the corresponding populations are equal against the alternative that they differ by a translation.

CHAPTER **21**

Decision Functions

In this last chapter we shall be concerned with the decision theoretical approach to statistical problems, which was initiated by Wald (1949, 1950) and uses unifying ideas from the theory of games.

We shall confine ourselves to some basic notions and principles of decision theory. Readers interested in more details are referred to the books by Wald (1950), Blackwell and Girshick (1966), and Raiffa and Schlaifer (1961). See also the more elementary treatments by Chernoff and Moses (1967) and Luce and Raiffa (1966) (cf. Appendix 3).

21.1 Introduction

From Chap. 13 we know that in the theory of testing statistical hypotheses the risks involved in falsely accepting or falsely rejecting a hypothesis are recognized and emphasized. Wald (1949, 1950) has extended the theory of such risks to a wider class of statistical problems. This generalized theory is called *statistical decision theory*. It has certain relations to the theory of games, as developed by J. v. Neumann (1928); cf. also v. Neumann and Morgenstern (1953).

We shall consider some basic concepts and ideas of decision theory. We shall see that decision theory can be regarded as a unifying approach to statistics that includes point estimation, interval estimation, and the testing of hypotheses as special types of problems. However, we shall also see that decision theory has certain practical limitations.

In statistical decision theory we use the result of an experiment as an aid for a decision to take one or another of several possible actions.

A simple example is a test of a hypothesis where the two possible actions are the acceptance or rejection of the hypothesis. In other statistical problems there may be more than just two possible actions.

Let us now explain why and how the theory of statistical decision problems is related to the theory of games.

The theory of **two-person games** is concerned with games in which two players participate. These players are trying simultaneously to maximize their winnings (or minimize their losses).

A statistical decision problem may be regarded as a two-person game. One player is "nature" and the other is the statistician.

For example, a statistician may be interested in a normal random variable X with known variance and unknown mean μ. If the statistician knew μ (and could foresee all consequences of the possible actions available to him), he would know what action to take. Since he does not know μ, he may imagine himself to be involved in a game with nature, in which nature chooses a value μ and the statistician does a little spying, his random experiment, and then chooses an action, makes a decision.

The manner in which this spying is done will form a basic part of the statistician's strategy, as we shall see.

This view of statistics as a game against nature has led to important advances in statistics.

21.2   Decision Problem. Loss. Risk

We may now give the following characterization of a decision problem as a game the statistician plays against nature, and thereby introduce some basic notions and notations.

1. Nature chooses a state θ from a set Ω consisting of possible states of nature. Ω is called the **parameter space.**

(Note that in our previous example, $\theta = \mu$ is a parameter but in more general situations, this need not be the case.)

2. The statistician chooses an action a from a set A consisting of possible actions for the statistician. A is called the **space of actions** available to the statistician.

3. In the game the statistician will have a gain or loss, depending on his choices. Hence this gain or loss depends on θ and a. We may thus introduce a real-valued function $L(\theta, a)$, called the **loss function,** whose value for a pair (θ, a) is called the *loss* corresponding to that pair (θ, a), and we may also permit $L(\theta, a)$ to take negative values, where such a negative loss may be interpreted as a gain to the statistician.

Thus $L(\theta, a)$ is the loss to the statistician if he takes action a when θ is the true state of nature.

The loss is measured in utiles rather than in some monetary way.

A game with parameter space Ω, set of actions A, and loss function L may now be denoted by (Ω, A, L).

If the statistician knew the true state of nature, the values of the loss function $L(\theta, a)$ would tell him what action (or actions) would be the best for him, and no statistical experiment (random experiment) would be necessary.

Since the true state of nature is unknown to him, he first collects information about that state by observing a random variable X [or (X, Y), etc.] whose distribution depends on the true state of nature, θ; the sample space of X will be denoted by S. Using the information thus obtained, he decides what action a in A to choose.

The game (Ω, A, L), together with a random experiment involving a random variable X with distribution function $F(x, \theta)$ depending on the state θ chosen by nature is called a **statistical decision problem** or **statistical game**.

We recall that the choice of the action a in A depends on the value x of X observed in that experiment, that is, is a real-valued function of x. This function is denoted by d, thus

$$a = d(x),$$

and is called a (nonrandomized) **decision function** or *decision rule* (a **pure strategy** in game theoretical language).

Any real-valued function d with sample space S of X as domain of definition and with values in A may serve as a decision function, but we shall assume, by definition, that the risk function R (defined below) is finite.

If we use a sample $x_1, \cdots, x_n$ of n observed values of n random variables $X_1, \cdots, X_n$, then

$$a = d(x_1, \cdots, x_n).$$

If we insert $a = d(x)$, the loss function becomes a function of x,

$$L(\theta, d(x)).$$

Clearly, $d(X)$ is a random variable, and so is now the loss

$$L(\theta, d(X)).$$

The mean value of this random variable depends on the state of nature θ as well as on the decision function d. Denoting this mean by R, we may write

$$R(\theta, d) = E(L(\theta, d(X))).$$

This function is called the **risk function** (or *payoff*). It represents the average loss to the statistician when he uses that particular function d and the true state of nature is θ.

In the definition of a decision function we now assume that the corresponding R is finite for all θ in Ω. The class of decision functions corresponding to a game (Ω, A, L) will be denoted by D.

Problems

1. Each of two players I and II chooses an integer. If the two numbers are odd, I pays \$1 to II. If they are even, I pays \$3 to II   In each of the two remaining cases II pays \$2 to I. What are Ω and A in this game? Give a table of the loss function. What action should I take if he is permitted to choose his number first? Same question for II.

2. Let θ be the probability of heads in tossing a coin, and suppose that either $\theta = \theta_1 = 0.4$ or $\theta = \theta_2 = 0.6$. Let A be the real line and consider the decision function $d(x)$ defined by $d(0) = a_0, d(1) = a_1$ where a_0 and a_1 are real numbers and x is an observed value of the random variable $X = $ *number of heads in a single trial.* Let the loss function be $L(\theta, a) = (\theta - a)^2$, so that $L(\theta_1, d(0)) = (0.4 - a_0)^2$, etc. Show that the risk function $R(\theta, d)$ has the values

$$R(\theta_1, d) = 0.6(0.4 - a_0)^2 + 0.4(0.4 - a_1)^2,$$

$$R(\theta_2, d) = 0.4(0.6 - a_0)^2 + 0.6(0.6 - a_1)^2.$$

3. An urn contains two balls. Let θ be the number of white balls; thus $\Omega = \{0, 1, 2\}$. Let $A = \{a_0, a_1, a_2\}$ where $a_0 = 0$, $a_1 = 1$, and $a_2 = 2$. The statistician draws one ball at random and observes $X = $ *number of white balls drawn.* How many nonrandomized decision functions are available to him? Some of them are nonsensical. List the others.

4. In Problem 3 let the loss function be

$$L(\theta, a) = |\theta - a|.$$

Find the values of the risk functions corresponding to the following decision functions.

	$x = 0$	$x = 1$
$d_1(x)$	a_0	a_1
$d_2(x)$	a_0	a_2
$d_3(x)$	a_1	a_1
$d_4(x)$	a_1	a_2

5. Same task as in Problem 4, when the loss function is

$$L(\theta, a) = (\theta - a)^2.$$

6. In Problem 3, suppose that the statistician draws two balls with replacement and observes $X = $ *number of white balls drawn.* List the nonrandomized decision functions, omitting nonsensical ones.

7. In Problem 3 suppose that the statistician draws two balls with replacement and observes $X = $ *number of white balls drawn.* Let the loss function be $L(\theta, a) = |\theta - a|$. Determine the risk $R(\theta, d_j)$ for the following decision functions.

x	$d_1(x)$	$d_2(x)$	$d_3(x)$	$d_4(x)$
0	0	0	1	1
1	1	1	1	1
2	1	2	1	2

21.3   Examples

Let us illustrate that testing of hypotheses and point estimation of parameters are special decision problems.

Example 1.   In testing a hypothesis there are two possible actions,

a_1: accept (do not reject) the hypothesis

a_2: reject the hypothesis.

Thus in this case, $A = \{a_1, a_2\}$. Suppose, for simplicity, that nature can take two states $\theta = \theta_0$ and $\theta = \theta_1$, and we want to test the hypothesis $H_0: \theta = \theta_0$ against the alternative $H_1: \theta = \theta_1$. Then we may take a loss function $L(\theta, a)$ with values as follows.

	$\theta = \theta_0$	$\theta = \theta_1$
$a = a_1$	0	L_{II}
$a = a_2$	L_I	0

Here, L_I and L_{II} are positive constants. If the true state of nature is θ_0 and we take action a_1 (accept the hypothesis), the loss is 0, and the same holds if the true state of nature is θ_1 and we take action a_2 (reject the hypothesis). This is what we should do. Otherwise we make a Type I error (corresponding loss L_I) or a Type II error (corresponding loss L_{II}); cf. Sec. 13.2. The corresponding probabilities

$$\alpha = P(d(X_1, \cdots, X_n) = a_2; \ \theta = \theta_0 \text{ is true})$$

and

$$\beta = P(d(X_1, \cdots, X_n) = a_1; \ \theta = \theta_1 \text{ is true})$$

depend on the choice of the decision function d. It follows that the risk function

$$R(\theta, d) = E(L(\theta, d(X_1, \cdots, X_n)))$$

has the values

$$R(\theta_0, d) = (1 - \alpha) \cdot 0 + \alpha L_I = \alpha L_I$$

and

$$R(\theta_1, d) = \beta L_{II} + (1 - \beta) \cdot 0 = \beta L_{II}.$$

We should mention that the theory of testing statistical hypotheses is perhaps not yet in its final form, since at present many tests are to some extent based on practical conventions.

A choice between different tests for the same hypothesis may in some cases be made by introducing a loss function that specifies the relative importance of (or the loss caused by) the error committed by not rejecting the hypothesis when it is false. The test may then be found as the test which minimizes the expected loss. However, this program involves difficulties; corresponding critical remarks will be made later.

Example 2. Point estimation of a parameter may be regarded as a decision problem. For instance, suppose that we are interested in a random variable whose variance is known and whose mean μ we want to estimate. Then μ is the parameter θ. Now let us assume that μ can be any real number. Then the parameter space Ω is the real line. Suppose that there is a distinct action for every μ. Then the space of actions A is also the real line, and every estimate $\hat{\mu}$ of μ represents an action.

As a decision function d that yields such estimates $\hat{\mu}$, we may take the function

$$a = d(x_1, \cdots, x_n) = \bar{x} = \frac{1}{n}(x_1 + \cdots + x_n).$$

Other decision functions could be used, so that we are confronted with the problem of choosing a function which gives "good" estimates.

As a loss function, let us take

$$L(\theta, a) = (\theta - a)^2.$$

This is sometimes called a *square error loss function*. We may now try to choose $d(x_1, \cdots, x_n)$ such that the risk function

$$R(\theta, d) = E((\theta - \hat{\Theta})^2)$$

is minimized. In this formula,

$$\hat{\Theta} = d(X_1, \cdots, X_n)$$

is an estimator, and if we assume that it is unbiased, we see from (7), Sec. 11.2, that minimizing $R(\theta, d)$ means choosing d to be efficient.

If we take $d(x_1, \cdots, x_n) = \bar{x}$, the risk is

$$R(\theta, d) = E((\bar{X} - \theta)^2) = \frac{\sigma^2}{n}$$

where σ^2 is the variance of X; cf. Theorem 2 in Sec. 9.8.

Other appropriate loss functions would be

$$L(\theta, a) = |\theta - a|, \qquad L(\theta, a) = (\theta - a)^4,$$

etc.

Example 3.   Let X be a random variable with known mean μ and unknown variance σ^2, and suppose that we want to obtain point estimates for σ^2. Assume that σ^2 can take any positive value. Then Ω is the positive ray of the real axis, and if every estimate of σ^2 represents an action, then A also is the positive ray of the real axis. This is similar to the situation in the previous example.

As a decision function we could use

$$d(x_1, \cdots, x_n) = s^2 = \frac{1}{n-1} \sum_{i=1}^{n} (x_i - \bar{x})^2$$

[cf. (2) in Sec. 11.1] and as a loss function

(1) $$L(\sigma^2, d) = (d - \sigma^2)^2$$

with d as given before.

More generally we could take

(2) $$L(\sigma^2, d) = k(\sigma)(d - \sigma^2)^2$$

and try to find $k(\sigma)$ such that the loss is realistic. A major argument in favor of a loss function of the form (2) is that many reasonably smooth functions of $\hat{\sigma}$ which assume a minimum at $\hat{\sigma} = \sigma$ can be approximated by quadratic functions for $\hat{\sigma}$ close to σ. If $k(\sigma) = 1$, then (2) reduces to the square error loss function (1).

Problems

1. Let x_1, x_2 be a sample from a population with unknown mean μ and variance 1, where μ can vary between $-\infty$ and ∞. Consider the decision function

$$d(x_1, x_2) = \bar{x} = \tfrac{1}{2}(x_1 + x_2)$$

and the quadratic loss function

$$L(\mu, d) = (\mu - d)^2 = (\mu - \bar{x})^2.$$

Find the risk function.

2. In Problem 1, replace d by

$$d_1(x_1, x_2) = \tfrac{1}{4}x_1 + \tfrac{3}{4}x_2,$$

find the risk function, and compare the result with that of Problem 1.

3. In Problem 1, replace d by

$$d_2(x_1, x_2) = kx_1 + (1 - k)x_2$$

and determine the risk function $R(\mu, d_2)$. For what k is this function minimum?

4. Let x_1, x_2, x_3 be a sample from a population with unknown mean μ and known variance σ^2, where μ can vary between $-\infty$ and ∞. Find the risk function $R(\mu, d)$ corresponding to the decision function

$$d(x_1, x_2, x_3) = k_1 x_1 + k_2 x_2 + (1 - k_1 - k_2) x_3$$

and the loss function

$$L(\mu, d) = (\mu - d)^2$$

and determine the values of k_1 and k_2 for which $R(\mu, d)$ is minimum.

5. Extend the task in Problem 4 to samples of size n, using

$$d(x_1, \cdots, x_n) = k_1 x_1 + \cdots + k_n x_n \qquad (k_1 + \cdots + k_n = 1)$$

and L as before.

6. Let θ be the probability of a coin coming up heads, where $0 \leq \theta \leq 1$ and θ is unknown. Show that in estimating θ on the basis of one toss of the coin, A is the closed interval $0 \leq a \leq 1$ and the set D of nonrandomized decision functions consists of all functions $d(x)$ with $d(0) = a_0$, $d(1) = a_1$, $0 \leq a_0 \leq 1$, $0 \leq a_1 \leq 1$, where x is an observed value of $X = $ *number of heads in one toss*. Find the risk function if the loss function is $L(\theta, a) = (\theta - a)^2$.

7. Show that $d(X_1, \cdots, X_n)$ with $d(x_1, \cdots, x_n)$ given in Problem 5 is an unbiased estimator for the mean μ.

21.4   General Remarks about the Decision-Theoretical Approach

Let us add some general remarks about the decision-theoretical approach to statistical problems and the corresponding concepts introduced in the previous sections.

We shall first characterize differences between game theory and decision theory. These differences result from the fact that in decision theory nature chooses a state (for instance, a value μ in Ex. 2, Sec. 21.3) without the view of maximizing winnings in mind, that is, without being antagonistically motivated, but acting in a presumably neutral fashion. This affects the interpretation of what may be considered a good decision for the statistician and broadens the class of rules for a "reasonable" decision.

For example, let the loss function $L(\theta, a)$ in a game have the values given in the following table.

	θ_1	θ_2
a_1	3	1
a_2	5	-2

Then in game theory Player I (choosing a θ) is assumed to be intelligent. Since L is his gain, his only good choice is θ_1, because then he will gain more than if he chooses θ_2, no matter what Player II chooses. Hence Player II should choose a_1 (loss 3), but not a_2 (loss 5).

However, if Player I is nature and chooses a state without a clear objective in mind, the situation changes, and action a_1 will no longer be the only rational choice for Player II (the statistician). In fact, if nature chooses θ_2, then a_2 becomes preferable to the statistician because it then entails a gain (2).

Let us now try to give some indication of the difference between the approach to statistical problems in the previous chapters and the decision-theoretical method.

In those chapters the action problem is broken up into two stages: for instance, first an interval estimate and then its conversion into an action.

The decision-theoretical model includes a formal attempt to incorporate the actual terminal acts and the specific economic and psychological losses due to wrong terminal decisions. In those chapters this is done only indirectly, via such concepts as significance levels, confidence levels, and lengths of confidence intervals. This need not be a disadvantage but may often be more efficient than dealing with the action problem directly. For example, a confidence interval may help to eliminate certain feasible terminal actions, thereby reducing some of the delicate and time-consuming appraisals of losses.

In fact, one of the main difficulties in applying decision-theoretical methods to practical situations is that of specifying a realistic loss function.

For instance, how can a scientist realistically appraise the losses from falsely rejecting or accepting a research hypothesis? How can he put cash values on the lives that might be lost if he erroneously decides not to release a new drug that is really effective? How can he evaluate the losses in estimating a parameter when this estimate may be used for a variety of purposes—some of which may be unknown or irrelevant to him? How can an engineer foresee all conceivable consequences in connection with the decision that a shipment of steel be used in the construction of a bridge? Even in gambling, where the loss could reflect actual numerical loss, it is questionable whether the mathematical expectation of loss is an appropriate measure of the random losses when the statistical problem is faced only once.

However, the situation is definitely not hopeless. In fact, in many practical problems it will be possible to find a realistic loss function. Furthermore, small inaccuracies in assigning losses are immaterial because experience shows that "good" procedures are not sensitive to small changes. Finally, there are some methods of game theory that offer help in assigning losses in a more systematic fashion; we shall return to this point later.

The use of the risk function can now be motivated as follows. Once the loss function has been introduced, the statistician can examine the effect of a decision function $d(x)$ in various states θ. Unfortunately, the loss he will suffer depends not only on θ and the particular function d he uses but also on the value of the random variable X (or $X_1, \cdots, X_n$) to be observed. This suggests that he introduce and examine the expected or average loss $R(\theta, d)$, called the risk (cf. Sec. 21.2), which depends on θ and d only.

21.5   Loss and Utility

How to assign losses? How to choose a "good" decision function? We shall discuss corresponding principles, starting with the first of these two problems and investigating the loss function $L(\theta, a)$. It will be convenient to introduce the **utility function** u, a notion taken from game theory. For our purposes it suffices to define

$$u(\theta, a) = -L(\theta, a).$$

It is clear that different persons have different tastes and will therefore have different utility functions.

By a *probability distribution on a set S* we mean the distribution of a random variable which can take values in S. For the sake of simplicity we shall denote a probability distribution by its probability function or density. Then p_1 and p_2 are distributions with probability functions (or densities) p_1 and p_2, and $\kappa p_1 + \lambda p_2$ ($\kappa \geqq 0, \lambda \geqq 0, \kappa + \lambda = 1$) denotes the distribution with the probability function (or density) $\kappa p_1 + \lambda p_2$.

Let K be the set of outcomes of a decision problem, where a specific *outcome* is the result of a specific action by the statistician. Then a probability distribution on K is called a **prospect.**

Why do we consider such distributions on K?

The simplest conceivable case would be that a decision function will lead to an outcome r_0 in K with certainty. However, probability distributions enter into decision problems because $d(X)$ is a random variable.

Moreover, instead of choosing a fixed decision function d, the statistician may consider a probability distribution on the set of decision functions D and perform an auxiliary random experiment for selecting a d in D, where the random variable in this experiment has the aforementioned distribution. For example, he may toss a coin and choose one of two possible decision functions, depending on the outcome of this auxiliary experiment.

Such a "random mixture of decision functions" is called a **randomized decision function** (or **mixed strategy** in game-theoretical language), in contrast to a *nonrandomized decision function* (*pure strategy*), which is a fixed chosen function $d(x)$, as introduced in Sec. 21.2.

This auxiliary randomization process induces probability distributions on K and explains why these are of interest in connection with utility.

We remember that the utility function has been defined by

$$u(\theta, a) = -L(\theta, a)$$

where L is the loss function of the decision problem, so that $u(\theta, a)$ may be interpreted as the gain to the statistician. Keeping in mind that a prospect of the statistician depends on the state of nature θ and the action $a = \delta(x)$ where δ denotes a (nonrandomized or randomized) decision function, we may regard utility as a function of prospects, $u = u(p)$. It will exist if we make some rather natural assumptions about prospects [(P1)–(P4), below].

Suppose that the statistician has formulated his objectives with sufficient clarity to declare which of two outcomes he prefers (or that he is indifferent between them) and, more generally, for any two prospects to declare which he prefers. Formally we have:

(P1) The statistician faced with two prospects p_1 and p_2 is able to decide whether he prefers p_1 to p_2, whether he likes each equally well, or whether he prefers p_2 to p_1, in symbols,

$$p_1 \succ p_2 \qquad (p_1 \text{ preferred to } p_2)$$
$$p_1 \sim p_2 \qquad (\text{indifference})$$
$$p_2 \succ p_1 \qquad (p_2 \text{ preferred to } p_1).$$

(P2) If the statistician regards p_1 at least as well as p_2, and p_2 at least as well as p_3, then he regards p_1 at least as well as p_3, in symbols ($p_1 \succeq p_2$ meaning p_1 is preferred or indifferent to p_2):

$$p_1 \succeq p_2 \text{ and } p_2 \succeq p_3 \qquad \text{implies} \qquad p_1 \succeq p_3.$$

(P1) and (P2) define a linear ordering on the prospects, which is called a **preference pattern.**

A prospect p which consists of some chance process to select one of several prospects may be called a *mixture of these prospects.*

(P3) If the statistician prefers p_1 to p_2 and p_2 to p_3, then there is a mixture of p_1 and p_3 which is preferred to p_2 and another mixture of p_1 and p_3 over which p_2 is preferred, in symbols:

If $p_1 \succ p_2 \succ p_3$, there are numbers k and l, $0 < k < 1$, $0 < l < 1$, such that

$$kp_1 + (1 - k)p_3 \succ p_2 \qquad \text{and} \qquad p_2 \succ lp_1 + (1 - l)p_3.$$

(P4) If the statistician prefers p_1 to p_2, and p_3 is another prospect, then he prefers a mixture of p_1 and p_3 to the same mixture of p_2 and p_3, in symbols:

If $p_1 \succ p_2$, then for any prospect p_3 and number k, $0 < k < 1$,

$$kp_1 + (1 - k)p_3 \succ kp_2 + (1 - k)p_3.$$

It can be shown that these properties of prospects are sufficient for the existence of a utility function $u(p)$ which associates with each prospect p on K a number $u(p)$, called the **utility** of the prospect p (to the statistician), and has the following properties.

Utility function properties

(U1) $u(p_1) > u(p_2)$ if and only if the statistician prefers prospect p_1 to prospect p_2.

(U2) Let p be the prospect where, with probability k, the statistician faces p_1 and, with probability $1 - k$, he faces p_2. Then

$$u(p) = ku(p_1) + (1 - k)u(p_2).$$

Assumptions (P1)–(P4) guarantee not only the existence but also the uniqueness (up to a linear transformation) of u for a given preference pattern.

Note that utility was derived from preferences among prospects and offers computational convenience, so that difficult and time-consuming introspection in connection with preferences may be replaced by simple computations. In particular, property (U2) enables the computation of various further utilities if a few are known.

21.6   Minimax Principle for Choosing Decision Functions

The utility function (cf. in the previous section) may be regarded as an auxiliary function introduced to give some structure to the process of comparing and evaluating prospects and assigning losses. We shall now discuss the problem of choosing decision functions, starting with the *minimax principle*.

For this purpose we return to the loss function and the corresponding risk function $R(\theta, d)$, as introduced in Sec. 21.2. We may order the decision functions according to the worst that could happen to the statistician. We then prefer d_1 to d_2 if

$$\sup_\theta R(\theta, d_1) < \sup_\theta R(\theta, d_2).$$

The **minimax principle** is to choose d in the set D of decision functions so as to minimize the maximum possible risk, that is, to minimize

$$\sup_\theta R(\theta, d).$$

If D and Ω contain only a finite number of elements, there is at least one minimax decision function, with corresponding risk

$$\min_{d \in D}\left[\max_{\theta \in \Omega} R(\theta, d) \right].$$

This gives the reason for the name of the principle.

If D contains infinitely many elements, the situation is more complicated. Then there may not be a minimax decision function, and the statistician may have to be satisfied with a function whose maximum risk is within ϵ of the minimax value. For further details, see Blackwell and Girshick (1966).

Application of the minimax procedure usually requires a considerable amount of computation. Furthermore, a serious objection is that it is generally too pessimistic, as we shall see after the following example.

Example 1. Let $\Omega = \{\theta_1, \theta_2\}$ where $\theta_1 = 0.25$ and $\theta_2 = 0.5$, let $A = \{a_1, a_2\}$, and let the loss function $L(\theta, a)$ have the following values.

	θ_1	θ_2
a_1	0	2
a_2	3	1

Let X be a discrete random variable with sample space $S = \{0, 1\}$ and probability function

$$f(0) = 0.75, \qquad f(1) = 0.25 \qquad \text{when} \quad \theta = \theta_1 = 0.25;$$

$$f(0) = 0.5, \qquad f(1) = 0.5 \qquad \text{when} \quad \theta = \theta_2 = 0.5.$$

Find the minimax decision function in the set D of the possible nonrandomized decision functions.

The set D consists of four functions $d(x)$ having the following values.

Decision Function	Value at $x = 0$	$x = 1$
d_1	a_1	a_1
d_2	a_1	a_2
d_3	a_2	a_1
d_4	a_2	a_2

Note that d_1 and d_4 disregard the outcome of the random experiment involving X. We compute the values of the risk functions, first for d_1,

$$R(\theta_1, d_1) = 0.75 \cdot 0 + 0.25 \cdot 0 = 0$$
$$R(\theta_2, d_1) = 0.50 \cdot 2 + 0.50 \cdot 2 = 2$$

then for d_2,

$$R(\theta_1, d_2) = 0.75 \cdot 0 + 0.25 \cdot 3 = 0.75$$
$$R(\theta_2, d_2) = 0.50 \cdot 2 + 0.50 \cdot 1 = 1.50$$

then for d_3,

$$R(\theta_1, d_3) = 0.75 \cdot 3 + 0.25 \cdot 0 = 2.25$$
$$R(\theta_2, d_3) = 0.50 \cdot 1 + 0.50 \cdot 2 = 1.50$$

and finally for d_4,

$$R(\theta_1, d_4) = 0.75 \cdot 3 + 0.25 \cdot 3 = 3$$
$$R(\theta_2, d_4) = 0.50 \cdot 1 + 0.50 \cdot 1 = 1.$$

This shows that the maximum risks are as follows.

Decision function	d_1	d_2	d_3	d_4
max $R(\theta, d_j)$	2	1.5	2.25	3

The minimum is 1.5; thus d_2 is the minimax solution in the present case.

There are serious objections against the minimax principle, for the following reasons.

If in a game against an antagonistic opponent who has it in his power to choose θ we chose d, he would choose θ so as to maximize our loss; hence in choosing the strategy that minimizes that maximum we would salvage as much as possible from the situation. This is the minimax principle.

When the "opponent" is nature, such an attitude seems too pessimistic. In fact, the minimax principle says to proceed as if nature will select a probability distribution on the possible states of nature which is "least favorable" to the statistician. This is very conservative because there is no reason to expect nature to use this distribution. Thus the application of the principle may even lead to unreasonable decisions. This may be illustrated with the following example.

Example 2.   Suppose that in a process of producing gaskets the probability θ of producing a defective item is constant but unknown. Consider a lot of 1000 items and the two actions

a_1: *Do not sell the lot but junk it,*

a_2: *Sell the gaskets at 20 cents each, giving a double-your-money-back guarantee for each defective item.*

If we choose a_1, the loss is 0. Thus $L(\theta, a_1) = 0$. If we choose a_2, since the expected number of defective items is 1000θ, we have an expected loss of $1000\theta \cdot 0.4 = 400\theta$, but also a negative loss (gain) of $1000 \cdot 0.2 = 200$. Thus $L(\theta, a_2) = 400\theta - 200$. Hence if we choose a_1 with probability k and a_2 with probability $1 - k$, the expected loss corresponding to this randomized decision function d_k is

$$R(\theta, d_k) = k \cdot 0 + (1 - k)(400\theta - 200).$$

For fixed k this is maximum when $\theta = 1$,

$$\max R(\theta, d_k) = (1 - k) \cdot 200.$$

This depends on k and is minimum when $k = 1$. Hence by the minimax principle we should junk the lot if we regard $\theta > 0.5$ as remotely possible.

This pessimistic result follows from the fact that if a hostile opponent could choose θ, he would choose θ as large as possible, that is, $\theta = 1$.

Even if we use sampling, we do not change the minimax conclusion. In fact, suppose we draw n (<1000) items with replacement and decide to take action a_1 if the sample contains at least one defective item and a_2 if it contains no defective items. Then we propose to take action a_2 with probability $(1 - \theta)^n$, hence action a_1 with probability $1 - (1 - \theta)^n$. The expected loss is

$$[1 - (1 - \theta)^n] \cdot 0 + (1 - \theta)^n(400\theta - 200)$$

and is positive when $\theta > 0.5$, so that we should junk the lot even if we find no defective items but regard $\theta > 0.5$ as remotely possible.

Problems

1. Find the minimax decision function in the set $D = \{d_1, \cdots, d_4\}$ of Ex. 1 if the loss function $L(\theta, a)$ has the values

	θ_1	θ_2
a_1	0	1
a_2	1	0

and the other assumptions are as in Ex. 1.

2. Let $\Omega = \{\theta_1, \theta_2, \theta_3\}$ where $\theta_1 = 0.2$, $\theta_2 = 0.5$, $\theta_3 = 0.8$, let $A = \{a_1, a_2\}$, and let the loss function $L(\theta, a)$ have the following values.

	θ_1	θ_2	θ_3
a_1	0	1	2
a_2	1	0	1

Let X be a discrete random variable with sample space $S = \{0, 1\}$ and probability function $f(x \mid \theta)$ having the following values.

	$x = 0$	$x = 1$
θ_1	0.1	0.9
θ_2	0.5	0.5
θ_3	0.9	0.1

Find the minimax decision function in the set $D = \{d_1, \cdots, d_4\}$ given in Ex. 1.

3. A decision function d^* is said to be **better** than a decision function d if

$$R(\theta, d^*) \leq R(\theta, d) \quad \text{for all } \theta \text{ in } \Omega$$

and

$$R(\theta, d^*) < R(\theta, d) \quad \text{for at least one } \theta \text{ in } \Omega.$$

Apply this notion to the decision functions in Ex. 1.

4. A decision function d in D is said to be **admissible** if there is no decision function in D that is better. It is said to be *inadmissible* if there exists a better decision function in D. Find the admissible decision functions in the set D of Ex. 1.

5. A class C of decision functions in D is said to be **complete** if for each decision function in D but not in C there is a decision function in C that is better. Show that an admissible decision function d is contained in any complete class.

6. Why is the notion of a complete class important?

7. A **minimal complete class** is a complete class that contains no proper subclass that is complete. Show that if a minimal complete class exists, it is equal to the class of admissible decision functions.

8. In Problem 2, find all the decision functions in D which are better than d_2. Is the minimax decision function better than one of the other three functions in D?

9. Consider the game (Ω, A, L) with $\Omega = \{1, 2\}$, $A = \{1, 2\}$, and $L(\theta, a)$ having the values:

	$\theta_1 = 1$	$\theta_2 = 2$
$a_1 = 1$	-1	2
$a_2 = 2$	2	-3

Let the set D of decision functions consist of the functions

d_k: *Choose a_1 with probability k and a_2 with probability $1 - k$*

where k is a real number, $0 \leq k \leq 1$. Find the minimax decision function in D and compute the corresponding risk. Graph the maximum risk $R(\theta, d_k)$ as a function of k.

10. Modify Problem 9 by taking another loss function, with values

	$\theta_1 = 1$	$\theta_2 = 2$
$a_1 = 1$	$-c$	1
$a_2 = 2$	1	$-2 + c$

where c is a constant, $-1 \leq c \leq 3$. Find the minimax decision function in D (D as before).

11. Which of the decision functions in Problem 7, Sec. 21.2, is minimax?

12. Which of the decision functions in Problem 4, Sec. 21.2, is minimax?

13. Plot the risks corresponding to $d_1, \cdots, d_4$ in Example 1 as points in the plane with coordinates

$$z_{1j} = R(\theta_1, d_j), \qquad z_{2j} = R(\theta_2, d_j), \qquad j = 1, \cdots, 4.$$

Let δ denote the randomized decision function given by a distribution $p(d)$ on $D = \{d_1, \cdots, d_4\}$. Show that the risk corresponding to δ lies inside or on the quadrilateral with vertices (z_{1j}, z_{2j}), $j = 1, \cdots, 4$ (cf. Fig. 21.6.1).

14. Using Fig. 21.6.1, find the minimax decision function in the set of decision functions obtained by randomizing $d_1, \cdots, d_4$.

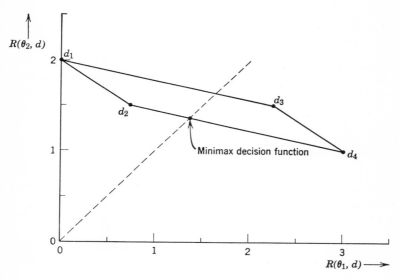

Fig. 21.6.1. Probs. 13 and 14

21.7   Bayes's Principle for Choosing Decision Functions

Suppose that the statistician is able to describe his information about θ by a probability distribution over $\Omega = (\theta_1, \cdots, \theta_m)$ with the probability function

(1) $$q(\theta) \qquad\qquad (\theta = \theta_1, \cdots, \theta_m).$$

Then if d is a decision function in the available class D, we may consider the corresponding risk function $R(\theta, d)$ and average over θ with respect to the distribution $q(\theta)$. This gives the **average risk function**

$$\bar{R}(q, d) = \sum_{j=1}^{m} q(\theta_j) R(\theta_j, d).$$

A decision function that minimizes this function $\bar{R}(q, d)$ is called a **Bayes solution** or **Bayes decision function** with respect to the particular prior distribution[1] $q(\theta)$.

Example 1.   In Example 1 of the preceding section we studied four decision functions d_1, d_2, d_3, d_4. The corresponding risks had the values

$$0, 2 \qquad 0.75, 1.5 \qquad 2.25, 1.5 \qquad 3, 1,$$

respectively. The possible states of nature were

$$\theta = \theta_1 = 0.25 \qquad \text{and} \qquad \theta = \theta_2 = 0.5.$$

Suppose that the prior distribution is

$$(2) \qquad\qquad q(\theta_1) = 0.6, \qquad q(\theta_2) = 0.4.$$

Then we obtain the average risk functions

$$\bar{R}(q, d_1) = 0.6 \cdot 0 + 0.4 \cdot 2 = 0.8$$
$$\bar{R}(q, d_2) = 0.6 \cdot 0.75 + 0.4 \cdot 1.5 = 1.05$$
$$\bar{R}(q, d_3) = 0.6 \cdot 2.25 + 0.4 \cdot 1.5 = 1.95$$
$$\bar{R}(q, d_4) = 0.6 \cdot 3 + 0.4 \cdot 1 = 2.2.$$

Hence d_1 is the Bayes solution in the set $D = \{d_1, d_2, d_3, d_4\}$ and with respect to the given prior distribution.

Let $\Omega = \{\theta_1, \cdots, \theta_m\}$, as before. Then a prior distribution $q(\theta)$ is determined by an m-tuple of nonnegative numbers

$$q_1 = q(\theta_1), \cdots, q_m = q(\theta_m) \qquad (q_1 + \cdots + q_m = 1)$$

where $q_j = q(\theta_j)$ is the probability that nature chooses θ_j. The risk function $R(\theta, d)$ corresponding to a decision function d may be represented by a point with coordinates $z_1 = R(\theta_1, d), \cdots, z_m = R(\theta_m, d)$ in an m-dimensional space. Let Q be the set of all points obtained as d varies in D, the set of available (nonrandomized and randomized) decision functions. The average risk corresponding to q and d is

$$\bar{R}(q, d) = \sum_{j=1}^{m} q_j R(\theta_j, d) = \sum_{j=1}^{m} q_j z_j.$$

Hence all decision functions for which

$$(3) \qquad\qquad \bar{R}(q, d) = \sum_{j=1}^{m} q_j z_j = k = const$$

yield the same average risk with respect to that prior distribution. (3) represents a hyperplane H in that space, and $(q_1, \cdots, q_m)$ is the normal vector of H, that is, H is perpendicular to that vector. A Bayes decision function then corresponds to the infimum of those values k for which (3) intersects the set Q. (It may not exist if Q does not contain its boundary.)

[1] Cf. Example 3 in Sec. 4.7.

Figure 21.7.1 shows $d_1, \cdots, d_4$ in Ex. 1, the normal vector $\mathbf{q}$ of (3) in the case of the prior distribution (2), and the hyperplane (straight line) H_{tain} for which k in (3) is minimum in the sense explained before. d_1 lies on $H_{\min}$, which means that d_1 is the Bayes decision function in $D = \{d_1, \cdots, d_4\}$. We also see that no other point in the quadrilateral with vertices $d_1, \cdots, d_4$ lies on $H_{\min}$. These points in the quadrilateral correspond to decision functions obtained by randomizing $d_1, \cdots, d_4$. The situation is typical. In fact, it can be shown that if a Bayes decision function with respect to a prior

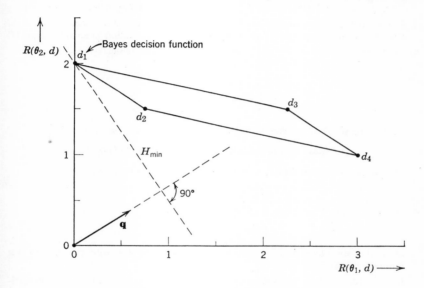

Fig. 21.7.1. Bayes decision function in Ex. 1

distribution q exists, there exists a nonrandomized Bayes decision function with respect to q. This is a definite computational advantage of the Bayes approach over the minimax approach. Figure 21.6.1 illustrates that the latter does not have that advantage.

Furthermore, if $q(\theta)$ is such that (3) is parallel to the segment $d_2 d_4$ in Fig. 21.7.1, we obtain infinitely many corresponding Bayes decision functions, which include the nonrandomized d_2 and d_4. They also include the minimax solution (cf. Fig. 21.6.1); this means that there is a prior distribution which is so unfavorable that the minimax solution becomes a Bayes solution with respect to that distribution.

A disadvantage of the Bayes principle is that in most decision problems the prior distribution is an expression of the personal judgment of the statistician and, if the prior distributions used by two statisticians differ markedly, these statisticians may arrive at different conclusions, although they use the same data collected in the course of the investigation.

Problems

1. Find a Bayes decision function in Example 1 if the prior distribution is:

   (a) $q(\theta_1) = 0.1,$ $q(\theta_2) = 0.9$
   (b) $q(\theta_1) = 0.3,$ $q(\theta_2) = 0.7$
   (c) $q(\theta_1) = 0.5,$ $q(\theta_2) = 0.5$

2. Find the four average risk functions in Example 1 if the prior distribution is $q(\theta_1) = q_1$, $q(\theta_2) = 1 - q_1$ $(0 \leq q_1 \leq 1)$. Graph these four functions as functions of q_1. Find the values of q_1 for which (a) d_1, (b) d_2, (c) d_4 is a Bayes decision function.

3. In Problem 2, the function d_3 is not a Bayes decision function for any q_1, $0 \leq q_1 \leq 1$. Can this be seen immediately from the values of the risk function given in Example 1?

4. Let $\Omega = \{1, 2\}$ and $A = \{1, 2\}$. Let $L(\theta, a)$ have these values:

	$\theta_1 = 1$	$\theta_2 = 2$
$a_1 = 1$	-1	2
$a_2 = 2$	2	-3

   and let the set D of decision functions consist of the functions

   d_k: *Choose a_1 with probability k and a_2 with probability $1 - k$.*

   Find a Bayes decision function in D with respect to the prior distribution

   $$q(\theta_1) = 0.4,   q(\theta_2) = 0.6.$$

5. Same task as in Problem 4, with $q(\theta)$ replaced by

   $$q(\theta_1) = \tfrac{5}{8},   q(\theta_2) = \tfrac{3}{8}.$$

   Show that the Bayes decision function with respect to this prior distribution is a minimax decision function. Explain the reason.

6. In Problem 4, find a Bayes decision function in D with respect to the prior distribution

   $$q(\theta_1) = q_1,   q(\theta_2) = 1 - q_1$$

   and show that $q_1 = \tfrac{5}{8}$ is the only value for which that Bayes decision function is a minimax decision function in D.

7. Show that for $q_1 \neq \tfrac{5}{8}$ in Problem 6 the average risk of the Bayes decision function is smaller than the risk corresponding to the minimax solution.

8. Let $\Omega = \{\theta_1, \theta_2\}$, $A = \{a_1, a_2\}$, and let $L(\theta, a)$ have these values:

	θ_1	θ_2
a_1	$-c$	1
a_2	1	$-2 + c$

   where c is a constant, $-1 \leq c \leq 3$. Consider the set D of decision functions of the form

   d_k: *Choose a_1 with probability k and a_2 with probability $1 - k$*

   and determine a Bayes decision function relative to the prior distribution

   $$q(\theta_1) = q_1,   q(\theta_2) = 1 - q_1   (q_1 \text{ constant}, 0 \leq q_1 \leq 1).$$

9. It can be shown that if a Bayes decision function with respect to a prior distribution q exists, there exists a nonrandomized Bayes decision function with respect to q. Show that the result of Problem 8 illustrates this theorem.

10. In Problem 4, Sec. 21.2, find a Bayes decision function with respect to the prior distribution $q(0) = 0.2$, $q(1) = 0.6$, $q(2) = 0.2$.

11. In Problem 4, Sec. 21.2, find a Bayes decision function with respect to the prior distribution $q(0) = 0.5$, $q(1) = q_1$, $q(2) = 0.5 - q_1$, where $0 \leq q_1 \leq 0.5$.

12. In Problem 7, Sec. 21.2, find a Bayes decision function with respect to the prior distribution $q(0) = 0.1$, $q(1) = 0.3$, $q(2) = 0.6$.

13. In Problem 7, Sec. 21.2, find a Bayes decision function with respect to the prior distribution $q(0) = 0.25$, $q(1) = q_1$, $q(2) = 0.75 - q_1$, where $0 \leq q_1 \leq 0.75$.

14. Find a Bayes decision function in Problem 2, Sec. 21.2, in the set of nonrandomized decision functions,

$$D = \{d(x) \mid d(0) = a_0, d(1) = a_1, a_0 \text{ and } a_1 \text{ arbitrary}\},$$

assuming that the prior distribution is $q(\theta_1) = 0.5$, $q(\theta_2) = 0.5$.

15. Same task as in Problem 14, when $q(\theta_1) = q_1$, $q(\theta_2) = 1 - q_1$.

16. In Ex. 1 find a prior distribution so that *any* random mixture of d_1 and d_2 is a Bayes decision function with respect to that distribution.

Additional Remarks and Proofs

Addition to Sec. 5.1. Notion of Interval

A **finite interval** I is a segment on the real line. I is said to be **closed** if its two end points are regarded as points belonging to I. Hence, if a and b are these end points, then I includes all the real numbers x for which

$$a \leqq x \leqq b,$$

but no other number. Similarly, I is said to be **open** if its end points a and b are not regarded as points belonging to I. Then I consists of all the real numbers x for which

$$a < x < b.$$

If we regard only one of the two end points as a point of I, then I is of the form

$$a \leqq x < b \qquad \text{or} \qquad a < x \leqq b$$

and is neither open nor closed.

An interval is said to be **infinite** if it is the whole real line

$$-\infty < x < \infty$$

or if it extends to infinity to the left or the right. In the latter cases it is of the form

$$-\infty < x \leqq a \qquad (\text{or } -\infty < x < a)$$

and

$$b \leqq x < \infty \qquad (\text{or } b < x < \infty),$$

respectively. Instead of this we may simply write

$$x \leqq a \qquad (\text{or } x < a)$$

and

$$x \geqq b \qquad (\text{or } x > b),$$

respectively.

394

Proof of Theorem 1 in Sec. 8.4

From Stirling's formula

$$k! = \sqrt{2\pi k}\left(\frac{k}{e}\right)^{k} e^{\theta/12k} \qquad (0 < \theta < 1)$$

(for the proof, see, for example, K. Knopp, *Theory and Application of Infinite Series*, 2nd ed., Blackie, Glasgow, 1966) it follows that

$$f(x) = \frac{n!}{x!\,(n-x)!}\, p^{x} q^{n-x} = \frac{1}{\sqrt{2\pi npq}}\left(\frac{np}{x}\right)^{x+\frac{1}{2}}\left(\frac{nq}{n-x}\right)^{n-x+\frac{1}{2}} e^{\tau}$$

$$= \frac{1}{\sqrt{2\pi npq}}\, e^{-h} e^{\tau}$$

where

$$\tau = \frac{1}{12}\left(\frac{\theta_1}{n} - \frac{\theta_2}{x} - \frac{\theta_3}{n-x}\right) \qquad (0 < \theta_i < 1)$$

and

$$h = (x + \tfrac{1}{2})\ln\frac{x}{np} + (n - x + \tfrac{1}{2})\ln\frac{n-x}{nq}$$

$$= \left(np + \tfrac{1}{2} + z\sqrt{npq}\right)\ln\left(1 + z\sqrt{\frac{q}{np}}\right)$$

$$+ \left(nq + \tfrac{1}{2} - z\sqrt{npq}\right)\ln\left(1 - z\sqrt{\frac{p}{nq}}\right),$$

where z is defined in (4). By assumption, $|z|$ is bounded. Hence for sufficiently large n we have

$$\left|z\sqrt{\frac{q}{np}}\right| < 1, \qquad \left|z\sqrt{\frac{p}{nq}}\right| < 1.$$

Using

$$\ln(1 + u) = u - \frac{u^2}{2} + \frac{u^3}{3} - \frac{u^4}{4} + - \cdots \qquad (|u| < 1),$$

we thus obtain the developments

$$\ln\left(1 + z\sqrt{\frac{q}{np}}\right) = z\sqrt{\frac{q}{np}} - \tfrac{1}{2}z^2\frac{q}{np} + \cdots$$

and

$$\ln\left(1 - z\sqrt{\frac{p}{nq}}\right) = -z\sqrt{\frac{p}{nq}} - \tfrac{1}{2}z^2\frac{p}{nq} - \cdots.$$

This we insert into the expression for h, perform the multiplications, and use $p + q = 1$. Then we obtain

$$h = \frac{z^2}{2} + \frac{1}{\sqrt{n}} R.$$

Here R is a function which remains bounded in absolute value as n approaches infinity. Consequently,

$$e^{-h} \to e^{-z^2/2} \qquad \text{as } n \to \infty$$

uniformly in any finite interval $\alpha \leqq z \leqq \beta$. From $\alpha \leqq z \leqq \beta$ and $1 - p = q$ we have

$$x \geqq np\left(1 + \alpha\sqrt{\frac{q}{np}}\right), \qquad n - x \geqq nq\left(1 - \beta\sqrt{\frac{p}{nq}}\right)$$

and therefore

$$|\tau| < \frac{1}{12}\left(\frac{1}{n} + \frac{1}{x} + \frac{1}{n-x}\right)$$

$$\leqq \frac{1}{12n}\left(1 + \frac{1}{p\left(1 + \alpha\sqrt{\dfrac{q}{np}}\right)} + \frac{1}{q\left(1 - \beta\sqrt{\dfrac{p}{nq}}\right)}\right).$$

Hence

$$\tau \to 0 \qquad \text{and} \qquad e^\tau \to 1 \qquad \text{as } n \to \infty$$

uniformly in $\alpha \leqq z \leqq \beta$. Altogether this implies

$$f(x) \to \frac{1}{\sqrt{2\pi npq}}\, e^{-z^2/2},$$

the first statement of the theorem.

We shall now prove the last statement of the theorem. Let

$$Z = \frac{X - np}{\sqrt{npq}}, \qquad \gamma = \frac{a - np}{\sqrt{npq}}, \qquad \delta = \frac{b - np}{\sqrt{npq}}.$$

Suppose that γ and δ remain finite, even as $n \to \infty$. Then it follows from the statement just proved that

$$P(a \leqq X \leqq b) = P(\gamma \leqq Z \leqq \delta)$$

(6)
$$= \sum_{x=a}^{b}\binom{n}{x}p^x q^{n-x} = \frac{1}{\sqrt{2\pi npq}}\sum e^{-z_j^2/2} + \sum\frac{R_j}{n}$$

(summation over all z_j for which x is integral and lies in the interval $a \leqq x \leqq b$). Here $|R_j|$ remains bounded as $n \to \infty$. If we apply the first mean value theorem to the integral

$$I_j = \frac{1}{\sqrt{2\pi}}\int_{z_j-\lambda}^{z_j+\lambda} e^{-u^2/2}\, du \qquad \left(\lambda = \frac{1}{2\sqrt{npq}}\right),$$

we obtain

$$I_j = \frac{1}{\sqrt{2\pi}\sqrt{npq}} e^{-(z_j+\theta)^2/2} \qquad (|\theta| < \lambda)$$

$$= \frac{1}{\sqrt{2\pi npq}} e^{-z_j^2/2} + \frac{R_j^*}{n}$$

where $|R_j^*|$ remains bounded as $n \to \infty$. Hence we may replace the exponential functions in (6) by integrals and find that

$$P(\gamma \leqq Z \leqq \delta) = \frac{1}{\sqrt{2\pi}} \int_{\gamma-\lambda}^{\delta+\lambda} e^{-u^2/2}\, du + \sum \frac{\tilde{R}_j}{n}$$

$$= \Phi(\beta) - \Phi(\alpha) + \sum \frac{\tilde{R}_j}{n}$$

with α and β as in (5). Here $|\tilde{R}_j|$ remains bounded as $n \to \infty$. The last sum has

$$b - a + 1 = (\delta - \gamma)\sqrt{npq} + 1$$

terms. Hence its value approaches 0 as $n \to \infty$.

Derivation of the Density of the Chi-Square Distribution in Sec. 10.1

The terms in (1) are squares. Hence χ^2 cannot assume negative values. It follows that $f(x) = 0$ when $x < 0$. To the interval $0 \leqq X_j^2 \leqq x$ there corresponds the interval $-\sqrt{x} \leqq X_j \leqq \sqrt{x}$. Consequently,

$$P(X_j^2 \leqq x) = P(0 \leqq X_j^2 \leqq x) = P(-\sqrt{x} \leqq X_j \leqq \sqrt{x}).$$

Since X_j is normal with mean 0 and variance 1, we see from the last expression that X_j^2 has the distribution function

$$F_1(x) = P(X_j^2 \leqq x) = \frac{1}{\sqrt{2\pi}} \int_{-\sqrt{x}}^{\sqrt{x}} e^{-u^2/2}\, du.$$

The integrand is symmetric. Thus

$$F_1(x) = \frac{2}{\sqrt{2\pi}} \int_0^{\sqrt{x}} e^{-u^2/2}\, du.$$

We set $u^2 = v$. Then we have to integrate over v from 0 to x. Since $u = \sqrt{v}$, $du = dv/2\sqrt{v}$, we obtain

$$F_1(x) = \frac{1}{\sqrt{2\pi}} \int_0^x \frac{e^{-v/2}}{\sqrt{v}}\, dv.$$

Differentiation with respect to x gives the density

(9) $$f_1(x) = \frac{dF_1}{dx} = \frac{1}{\sqrt{2\pi}} \, x^{-1/2} e^{-x/2} \qquad\qquad (x > 0).$$

This is the density of X_j^2 and therefore the density of χ^2 when $n = 1$, since then $\chi^2 = X_1^2$. In fact, from (8) we see that (9) and (2) with $n = 1$ are identical.

This proves (2) when $n = 1$. For arbitrary n, the proof will now follow by induction. Instead of f we write f_n, and instead of χ^2 we write χ_n^2, for the purpose of the proof. We show that if (2) holds for $n - 1$ degrees of freedom, it also holds for n degrees of freedom.

From the induction hypothesis we have

$$f_{n-1}(x) = \frac{1}{2^{(n-1)/2} \Gamma\left(\dfrac{n-1}{2}\right)} \, x^{(n-3)/2} e^{-x/2} \qquad\qquad (x > 0).$$

Now

$$\chi_n^{\,2} = \chi_{n-1}^2 + X_n^{\,2}$$

where χ_{n-1}^2 has the density $f_{n-1}(x)$ and X_n^2 has the density $f_1(x)$. These two variables are independent because the same is true for the variables $X_1, \cdots, X_n$. Hence we may apply (5a) in Problem 5, Sec. 9.6, and find that the density of χ_n^2 is given by

$$f_n(x) = \int_{-\infty}^{\infty} f_1(x - y) f_{n-1}(y) \, dy.$$

$f_{n-1}(y)$ is zero for negative y, and $f_1(x - y)$ is zero when $x - y < 0$, that is, $y - x > 0$ or $y > x$. Hence we need integrate from 0 to x only. By inserting f_1 and f_{n-1} we first have

$$f_n(x) = \frac{1}{\sqrt{2\pi}} \, \frac{1}{2^{(n-1)/2} \Gamma\left(\dfrac{n-1}{2}\right)} \int_0^x (x - y)^{-1/2} e^{-(x-y)/2} y^{(n-3)/2} e^{-y/2} \, dy.$$

Simplification gives

(10) $$f_n(x) = \frac{1}{2^{n/2} \sqrt{\pi} \, \Gamma\left(\dfrac{n-1}{2}\right)} \, e^{-x/2} \int_0^x y^{(n-3)/2} (x - y)^{-1/2} \, dy.$$

We denote the integral by I. We set $y = xu$. Then u runs from 0 to 1, we have $x - y = x - xu = x(1 - u)$, $dy = x \, du$, and

$$I = x^{(n-2)/2} \int_0^1 u^{(n-3)/2} (1 - u)^{-1/2} \, du.$$

We now use the well-known formula

$$(11) \qquad \int_0^1 u^{a-1}(1-u)^{b-1}\,du = \frac{\Gamma(a)\Gamma(b)}{\Gamma(a+b)} \qquad (a > 0,\, b > 0),$$

for which we shall give a proof at the end of this discussion. Then

$$I = x^{(n-2)/2}\,\frac{\Gamma\!\left(\dfrac{n-1}{2}\right)\Gamma(\tfrac{1}{2})}{\Gamma\!\left(\dfrac{n}{2}\right)}.$$

If we insert this into (10) and use $\Gamma(1/2) = \sqrt{\pi}$, we obtain (2). This completes the proof.

Formula (11) can be derived as follows. From (5) we have

$$\Gamma(a)\Gamma(b) = \int_0^\infty e^{-t}t^{a-1}\,dt \int_0^\infty e^{-v}v^{b-1}\,dv$$

$$= \int_0^\infty \int_0^\infty e^{-(t+v)}t^{a-1}v^{b-1}\,dt\,dv.$$

We now introduce new variables of integration r and u by setting

$$t = ru \qquad \text{and} \qquad v = r(1-u).$$

Then we have to replace $dt\,dv$ by $dr\,du$ times the absolute value of the Jacobian

$$\frac{\partial(t,v)}{\partial(r,u)} = \begin{vmatrix} \dfrac{\partial t}{\partial r} & \dfrac{\partial t}{\partial u} \\[2mm] \dfrac{\partial v}{\partial r} & \dfrac{\partial v}{\partial u} \end{vmatrix} = \begin{vmatrix} u & r \\ 1-u & -r \end{vmatrix} = -r.$$

This gives

$$\Gamma(a)\Gamma(b) = \int_0^1 \int_0^\infty e^{-r}(ru)^{a-1}[r(1-u)]^{b-1}r\,dr\,du$$

$$= \int_0^\infty e^{-r}r^{a+b-1}\,dr \int_0^1 u^{a-1}(1-u)^{b-1}\,du$$

$$= \Gamma(a+b)\int_0^1 u^{a-1}(1-u)^{b-1}\,du.$$

Division by $\Gamma(a+b)$ yields (11).

Derivation of the Density of the t-Distribution in Sec. 10.3

By assumption, X in (1) has the density

$$f_1(x) = \frac{1}{\sqrt{2\pi}}\,e^{-x^2/2},$$

and Y has the density [cf. (2) in Sec. 10.1]

$$f_2(y) = \frac{1}{2^{n/2}\Gamma\left(\dfrac{n}{2}\right)}\, y^{(n-2)/2}e^{-y/2} \qquad\qquad (y > 0)$$

and $f_2(y) = 0$ for $y < 0$. Since X and Y are independent, the corresponding two-dimensional distribution has the density

$$f(x, y) = f_1(x)f_2(y).$$

For the distribution function

$$F(z) = P(T \leq z) = P\left(\frac{X}{\sqrt{Y/n}} \leq z\right) = P\big(X \leq z\sqrt{Y/n}\big)$$

of the t-distribution we thus obtain

$$F(z) = \iint\limits_{x \leq z\sqrt{y/n}} f(x, y)\, dx\, dy.$$

If we insert $f = f_1 f_2$, we have

$$F(z) = C_n \iint\limits_{\substack{x \leq z\sqrt{y/n} \\ y > 0}} e^{-(x^2+y)/2}y^{(n-2)/2}\, dx\, dy$$

where

$$C_n = \frac{1}{\sqrt{2\pi}\, 2^{n/2}\Gamma\left(\dfrac{n}{2}\right)}.$$

In this double integral we may first integrate over x from $-\infty$ to $z\sqrt{y/n}$, keeping y fixed, and then over y from 0 to ∞. This gives

$$F(z) = C_n \int_0^\infty \left[\int_{-\infty}^{z\sqrt{y/n}} e^{-(x^2+y)/2}y^{(n-2)/2}\, dx\right] dy.$$

If we set $x = u\sqrt{y/n}$, then $dx = du\sqrt{y/n}$ and

$$\frac{x^2}{2} + \frac{y}{2} = \frac{Hy}{2} \qquad \text{where} \qquad H = 1 + \frac{u^2}{n}$$

and we must integrate over u from $-\infty$ to z. Since these new limits of integration are independent of y, we may reverse the order of integration and have

$$F(z) = \frac{C_n}{\sqrt{n}} \int_{-\infty}^z \int_0^\infty e^{-Hy/2}y^{(n-1)/2}\, dy\, du.$$

Setting $Hy = 2v$, we may express the inner integral in terms of the gamma function; then $y = 2v/H$, $dy = 2\,dv/H$, and we obtain

$$F(z) = 2^{(n+1)/2} \frac{C_n}{\sqrt{n}} \int_{-\infty}^{z} \frac{du}{H^{(n+1)/2}} \int_{0}^{\infty} e^{-v} v^{(n-1)/2}\,dv.$$

From (5) in Sec. 10.1 we see that the last integral equals $\Gamma\left(\dfrac{n+1}{2}\right)$. By writing H and C_n out we obtain (3), and by differentiating (3) we finally have (2).

Proof of Theorem 1 in Sec. 12.4

If we replace $X_1, \cdots, X_n$ by $X_1 - \mu, \cdots, X_n - \mu$, this does not affect Y, since then we must replace $\bar{X}$ by $\bar{X} - \mu$. Hence we may assume $\mu = 0$, without loss of generality. The n variables $(X_j - \bar{X})^2$ are *not* independent because

$$\sum_{j=1}^{n}(X_j - \bar{X}) = \sum_{j=1}^{n} X_j - n\bar{X} = 0.$$

We want to show that the sum of squares

$$Q_n = \sum_{j=1}^{n}(X_j - \bar{X})^2$$

can be represented in the form

(8) $$Q_n = Y_1^2 + \cdots + Y_{n-1}^2$$

where $Y_1, \cdots, Y_{n-1}$ are independent normal random variables with mean 0 and variance σ^2. We set

$$Y_1 = \frac{1}{\sqrt{1 \cdot 2}}(X_1 - X_2)$$

$$Y_2 = \frac{1}{\sqrt{2 \cdot 3}}(X_1 + X_2 - 2X_3)$$

(9) $$\cdots\cdots\cdots\cdots\cdots\cdots\cdots\cdots\cdots\cdots$$

$$Y_{n-1} = \frac{1}{\sqrt{(n-1)n}}(X_1 + X_2 + \cdots + X_{n-1} - (n-1)X_n)$$

$$Y_n = \frac{1}{\sqrt{n}}(X_1 + X_2 + \cdots + X_{n-1} + X_n).$$

This so-called *Helmert transformation* is a linear transformation of the form

$$
\begin{aligned}
Y_1 &= a_{11}X_1 + a_{12}X_2 + \cdots + a_{1n}X_n \\
Y_2 &= a_{21}X_1 + a_{22}X_2 + \cdots + a_{2n}X_n
\end{aligned}
$$

(10)

$$\cdots\cdots\cdots\cdots\cdots\cdots\cdots\cdots\cdots\cdots\cdots$$

$$
Y_n = a_{n1}X_1 + a_{n2}X_2 + \cdots + a_{nn}X_n
$$

From (9) we see that the coefficients satisfy the "orthogonality conditions"

$$
a_{j1}a_{k1} + a_{j2}a_{k2} + \cdots + a_{jn}a_{kn} = \begin{cases} 0 & (j \neq k), \\ 1 & (j = k). \end{cases}
$$

When $n = 3$ these are the well-known conditions that (10) represents a rotation (possibly combined with a reflection in a plane through the origin) of a rectangular coordinate system about the origin. This transformation leaves the square of the distance of each point from the origin invariant,

$$
X_1{}^2 + X_2{}^2 + X_3{}^2 = Y_1{}^2 + Y_2{}^2 + Y_3{}^2.
$$

The same is true for any n, that is,

$$
X_1{}^2 + X_2{}^2 + \cdots + X_n{}^2 = Y_1{}^2 + Y_2{}^2 + \cdots + Y_n{}^2.
$$

From (9) we immediately see that

$$
Y_n{}^2 = \frac{1}{n}(n\bar{X})^2 = n\bar{X}^2.
$$

Hence

$$
Q_n = \sum_{j=1}^{n}(X_j - \bar{X})^2 = \sum_{j=1}^{n}X_j{}^2 - n\bar{X}^2 = \sum_{j=1}^{n}Y_j{}^2 - Y_n{}^2,
$$

and (8) is proved.

From Theorem 1 in Sec. 8.3 it follows that the random variables $-X_2$, $-2X_3$, $-3X_4$, $\cdots$ in (9) are normal with mean 0 and variance σ^2, $4\sigma^2$, $9\sigma^2$, $\cdots$. Furthermore, in each row of (9) the terms on the right are independent. From this, Theorem 1 in Sec. 12.2 and (2) and (4) in Sec. 6.7 we conclude that the variables Y_1/σ, $\cdots$, Y_n/σ are normal with mean 0 and variance 1. From a consideration of the n-dimensional normal distribution, which we shall not present here, it follows that these variables are independent; cf. H. Cramér (1961). Since

$$
Y = \frac{1}{\sigma^2}Q_n = \frac{Y_1{}^2}{\sigma^2} + \cdots + \frac{Y_{n-1}^2}{\sigma^2},
$$

Y is represented as the sum of the squares of $n - 1$ independent normal variables with mean 0 and variance 1 and therefore has a χ^2-distribution with $n - 1$ degrees of freedom (cf. Sec. 10.1).

Furthermore the random variables Y_1, $\cdots$, Y_{n-1} are independent of $Y_n = \sqrt{n}\,\bar{X}$. Consequently, Y and Z are independent.

APPENDIX 2

Answers to Odd-Numbered Problems

SECTION 2.3

7. For example, class marks 75, 80, 85, $\cdots$; corresponding class intervals 72.5–77.5, 77.5–82.5, 82.5–87.5, $\cdots$

SECTION 3.2

1. $\bar{x} = 0.811$, $s^2 = 0.000\ 054$

3. $\bar{x} = 3$, $s^2 = 3.3$

5. $-1/\sqrt{2}$, $1/\sqrt{2}$

7. $91.6 - 87.9 = 3.7$. It may; in the case of class intervals of equal length l, the maximum possible change is l.

9. $\bar{x} = 0.103$

11. $dh/dt = 0$ yields $t = \bar{x}$.

15. $x_j - \bar{x} = (c + x_j{}^*) - (c + \bar{x}^*) = x_j{}^* - \bar{x}^*$. Thus $(x_j - \bar{x})^2 = (x_j{}^* - \bar{x}^*)^2$, and the result follows.

17. Let b be that proportion. Then $a = nb$ values x_j are such that

$$|x_j - \bar{x}| \geq M, \qquad (x_j - \bar{x})^2 \geq M^2,$$

their sum is greater than or equal to $aM^2 = nbM^2$; since $(n-1)s^2$ consists of this sum and perhaps some further terms which are nonnegative, we have

$$(n-1)s^2 \geq nbM^2; \qquad \text{thus} \qquad b \leq \frac{(n-1)s^2}{nM^2} < \frac{s^2}{M^2}.$$

19. $s^2 \geq 0$ and (2) imply $\sum x_j{}^2 \geq n\bar{x}^2$, which gives the result.

21. The mean and the standard deviation are multiplied by 12, and the variance is multiplied by 144.

23. $s^2 = \dfrac{1}{n-1} \left\{ \sum_{1}^{n_1} [(x_j - \bar{x}_1) + (\bar{x}_1 - \bar{x})]^2 + \sum_{n_1+1}^{n_1+n_2} [(x_j - \bar{x}_2) + (\bar{x}_2 - \bar{x})]^2 \right\}$

$= \dfrac{1}{n-1} \left[(n_1 - 1)s_1{}^2 + (n_2 - 1)s_2{}^2 + \dfrac{n_1 n_2}{n} (\bar{x}_1 - \bar{x}_2)^2 \right]$

27. $\bar{y} = \dfrac{1}{n} \sum \dfrac{x_j - \bar{x}}{s} = \dfrac{1}{s} \left(\dfrac{1}{n} \sum x_j - \dfrac{n\bar{x}}{n} \right) = \dfrac{1}{s} (\bar{x} - \bar{x}) = 0,$

$$s_y{}^2 = \dfrac{1}{n-1} \sum y_j{}^2 = \dfrac{1}{n-1} \sum \dfrac{(x_j - \bar{x})^2}{s^2} = \dfrac{s^2}{s^2} = 1$$

SECTION 3.3

1. $\bar{x} = 83.3,\ s^2 = 13.17$

3. $\bar{x} = 3.47,\ s^2 = 2.98$

5. $\bar{x} = 1502.7,\ s^2 = 41{,}665$

7. $l/2$ is the maximum distance of a sample value from its class mark. Hence $nl/2$ is the maximum possible change of $x_1 + \cdots + x_n$ due to grouping. Division by n yields the result.

SECTION 4.1

7. The space of the ordered triples of nonnegative numbers

9. The diameter is smaller than 2.3 in. or larger than 2.4 in.

SECTION 4.2

1. $A \cup B$: *At most* 1 *defective gasket.* $B \cup C$: 1 *or* 2 *defective gaskets;* $A \cap B = \phi$, since in a single trial we may obtain either 0 or 1 defective gasket. Hence the occurrence of A excludes that of B.

3. $\tilde{f}(A) = 3/50,\ \tilde{f}(B) = 4/50,\ \tilde{f}(A \cap B) = 1/50,\ \tilde{f}(A \cup B) = 6/50$

5. $\tilde{f}(A \mid B) = 1/4,\ \tilde{f}(B \mid A) = 1/3$

7. Numbers of outcomes 8, 5, 3, 5, 2, 10, 10, 20, 18, 17

9. 26

SECTION 4.3

1. $P(H) = 1/2,\ P(T) = 1/2,\ H = $ head, $T = $ tail

3. 5 outcomes, probability 1/5

5. $6^3 = 216$ outcomes, probability $1/216,\ P(A) = 4/216 = 1/54$

7. 36 outcomes, $P(A) = 13/18$

9. 20 outcomes, $P(A) = 1/2$

SECTION 4.6

3. $6^3 = 216$ outcomes. E^c consists of the 6 outcomes $(1, 1, 1), \cdots, (6, 6, 6)$. Ans. $P(E) = 1 - 6/216 = 35/36$.

7. $1 - 0.5^{10} = 1023/1024 = 99.9\%$

9. 5/6

SECTION 4.7

1. $P(A) = (7/10)(6/9)(5/8) = 29\%$

3. 1/12

5. 1/3

7. $P(E_B \mid E_A) = P(E_A \cap E_B)/P(E_A) = 0.02/0.10 = 20\%$

9. 0.43

SECTION 4.8

1. $P(A \cup B) = 1 - P((A \cup B)^c) = 1 - P(A^c \cap B^c) = 1 - P(A^c)P(B^c)$;   cf. (4) in Sec. 4.6 and Problem 12 in Sec. 4.2.

3. 1/16

5. 1/4

7. 1/16

9. 1/8, 3/8, 3/8, 1/8 for 0, 1, 2, 3 boys, respectively

SECTION 4.10

1. If all n elements are different, we have $n!$ permutations. If n_1 elements are alike (but different from the other $n - n_1$ elements), then a permutation p_1 becomes identical with those permutations which are obtained from p_1 by altering the order of those n_1 elements but retaining the order of the other $n - n_1$ elements. Since there are $n_1!$ permutations of n_1 elements, we see that only $n!/n_1!$ permutations are left. If, in addition, n_2 elements of those $n - n_1$ other elements are alike (but different from the other elements), the number of permutations reduces to $n!/n_1!n_2!$, etc.

5. $\binom{100}{10} = 17{,}310{,}309{,}456{,}440$;   cf. (4a) in Sec. 4.9.

7. 1/1260, because there are $9!/2!3!4! = 1260$ different permutations; cf. Theorem 2 in Sec. 4.9.

11. $6!/6^6 = 5/324 = 1.5\%$

13. $\binom{10}{3} = 120$

15. $1/6! = 1/720 = 0.14\%$

17. The probability of winning is 10%.

19. $\binom{52}{13} = 635{,}013{,}559{,}600$

SECTION 5.1

1. $\frac{1}{4}, \frac{1}{2}, \frac{1}{4}, 0, \frac{3}{4}, \frac{3}{4}, \frac{1}{4}, \frac{3}{4}$

SECTION 5.3

3. $f(3) = 1/216, f(4) = 3/216, f(5) = 6/216$, etc.

5. $f(x) = \frac{1}{6}(\frac{5}{6})^{x-1}, x = 1, 2, \cdots$

7. $f(1) = 1/36, f(2) = 2/36, f(3) = 2/36, f(4) = 3/36, f(5) = 2/36$, etc.

9. $f(0) = 2/9, f(1) = 5/9, f(2) = 2/9$

SECTION 5.5

5. $f(0) = 1/3, f(1) = 8/15, f(2) = 2/15$

7. $F(x) = 0 \ (x < 0), F(x) = 1/16 \ (0 \leqq x < 1), F(x) = 5/16 \ (1 \leqq x < 2)$, etc.

9. $F_1(x) = 0 \ (x < 0), 20/56 \ (0 \leqq x < 1), 50/56 \ (1 \leqq x < 2), 1 \ (x \geqq 2)$,
   $F_2(x) = 0 \ (x < 0), 25/64 \ (0 \leqq x < 1), 55/64 \ (1 \leqq x < 2), 1 \ (x \geqq 2)$

SECTION 5.6

1. The first property follows from the fact that probabilities are nonnegative and the last from $P(-\infty < X < \infty) = 1$.

3. $k = 1/2$, $F(x) = 0$ $(x < 0)$, $F(x) = x^2/4$ $(0 \leq x \leq 2)$, $F(x) = 1$ $(x > 2)$

5. $F(x) = 0$ $(x \leq a)$, $F(x) = \dfrac{x-a}{b-a}$ $(a < x \leq b)$, $F(x) = 1$ $(x > b)$

7. 27/32

9. $P(X > 0.5) = \displaystyle\int_{0.5}^{1} 2x\, dx = \frac{3}{4}$. Ans. $\frac{9}{16} = 56\%$.

11. $F(z) = 0$ $(z \leq 0)$, $F(z) = P(Z \leq z) = P(X^2 \leq z) = P(-\sqrt{z} \leq X \leq \sqrt{z}) = P(0 \leq X \leq \sqrt{z}) = \sqrt{z}$ $(0 < z \leq 1)$, $F(z) = 1$ when $z > 1$, $f(z) = 1/2\sqrt{z}$ $(0 < z \leq 1)$, $f(z) = 0$ otherwise

SECTION 6.1

1. 7

3. $\mu = \displaystyle\int_{0}^{\infty} x^2 e^{-x}\, dx = 2$ (integration by parts)

5. $\mu = \displaystyle\sum_{x=1}^{\infty} \frac{x}{2^x}$. Now $\displaystyle\sum_{x=0}^{\infty} y^x = \frac{1}{1-y}$ $(|y| < 1)$. Differentiation with respect to y yields

$$\sum_{x=0}^{\infty} xy^{x-1} = \sum_{x=1}^{\infty} xy^{x-1} = \frac{1}{(1-y)^2}.$$

Setting $y = 1/2$, we have

$$\sum_{x=1}^{\infty} \frac{x}{2^{x-1}} = 2\sum_{x=1}^{\infty} \frac{x}{2^x} = \frac{1}{(1-\frac{1}{2})^2} = 4,$$

thus $\mu = 2$.

7. (a) Distribution with probability function $f(0) = 1/2$, $f(1) = 1/2$, (b) uniform distribution, (c) distribution with density $f(x) = e^{-x}$ $(x > 0)$ and zero otherwise.

9. $\tilde{\mu} = (\ln 2)/\theta$, $\mu = 1/\theta$

13. Let $a \leq x \leq b$ be the interval. Then $af(x) \leq xf(x) \leq bf(x)$ because $f(x) \geq 0$. In the continuous case, integrate from a to b and use (2), Sec. 5.6. In the discrete case sum over all possible values and use (2) in Sec. 5.2.

SECTION 6.2

1. $\mu = 4/3$, $\sigma^2 = 2/9$

3. $k = 750$, $\mu = 1$, $\sigma^2 = 0.002$

5. $\displaystyle\int_{1-a}^{1+a} f(x)\, dx = 0.9$; $a = 0.073$ is the maximum possible deviation.

7. 800 gallons

9. $1/\sqrt{3}$

SECTION 6.3

1. In the discrete case,

$$E(ag(X) + bh(X)) = \sum [ag(x_j) + bh(x_j)]f(x_j)$$

$$= a \sum g(x_j)f(x_j) + b \sum h(x_j)f(x_j) = aE(g(X)) + bE(h(X)).$$

3. $1.50

5. $1/3$

SECTION 6.4

3. $E([X - c]^2) = E([(X - \mu) - (c - \mu)]^2)$

$$= E([X - \mu]^2) - 2(c - \mu)E(X - \mu) + (c - \mu)^2$$

$$= \sigma^2 - 2(c - \mu) \cdot 0 + (c - \mu)^2 \geq \sigma^2,$$

and the last equality sign holds if and only if $c = \mu$.

5. $\sigma^2 = E(X(X - 1) + X - 2\mu X + \mu^2)$, etc.

9. $E(X^k) = 1/(k + 1)$, $\mu = 1/2$, $E([X - \mu]^k) = 1/2^k(k + 1)$ when k is even and 0 when k is odd

11. $E(|X - c|) = \displaystyle\int_{-\infty}^{\infty} |x - c| f(x) \, dx = -\int_{-\infty}^{c} (x - c)f(x) \, dx$

$$+ \int_{c}^{\infty} (x - c)f(x) \, dx,$$

$$\frac{\partial E}{\partial c} = \int_{-\infty}^{c} f(x) \, dx - \int_{c}^{\infty} f(x) \, dx = 0,$$

$$F(c) - [1 - F(c)] = 0, \ F(c) = 1/2$$

SECTION 6.5

1. By assumption, $f(\mu - t) = f(\mu + t)$. Set $x - \mu = t$ and later $t = -\tau$. Then

$$E([X - \mu]^3) = \int_{-\infty}^{\infty} t^3 f(\mu + t) \, dt$$

$$= \int_{-\infty}^{0} t^3 f(\mu + t) \, dt + \int_{0}^{\infty} t^3 f(\mu + t) \, dt$$

$$= \int_{\infty}^{0} (-\tau)^3 f(\mu - \tau)(-d\tau) + \int_{0}^{\infty} t^3 f(\mu + t) \, dt$$

$$= -\int_{0}^{\infty} \tau^3 f(\mu + \tau) \, d\tau + \int_{0}^{\infty} t^3 f(\mu + t) \, dt;$$

this difference is 0 because the last integrals are equal. The proof in the discrete case is similar.

5. Let X assume x_1 and x_2 with probabilities p_1 and $p_2 = 1 - p_1$. Then $\mu = x_1 p_1 + x_2 p_2$, and $E([X - \mu]^3) = (x_1 - \mu)^3 p_1 + (x_2 - \mu)^3 p_2 = 0$ gives $p_1 = 1/2, p_2 = 1/2$ (symmetry).

7. $2\sqrt{2}/5$

SECTION 6.6

1. $\sum_{x=0}^{\infty} e^{tx}q^x p = p \sum_{x=0}^{\infty} (e^t q)^x = \dfrac{p}{1 - e^t q}$

5. $|E(e^{itX})| = |\sum_j e^{itx_j} f(x_j)| \leq \sum_j |e^{itx_j}| \, f(x_j) = \sum_j f(x_j) = 1,$ because

$$|e^{itx_j}| = \sqrt{\cos^2(tx_j) + \sin^2(tx_j)} = 1.$$

In the continuous case,

$$|E(e^{itX})| = |\int e^{itx}f(x)\,dx| \leq \int |e^{itx}| f(x)\,dx = \int f(x)\,dx = 1.$$

7. $\mu = 1/\theta,\ \sigma^2 = 1/\theta^2$

SECTION 6.7

1. $G^*(t) = E(e^{tX^*}) = E(e^{t(c_1X+c_2)}) = E(e^{c_1 tX}e^{tc_2}) = e^{c_2 t}E(e^{c_1 tX}) = e^{c_2 t}G(c_1 t)$

5. This follows from (3).

7. $X^* - \mu^* = c_1X + c_2 - (c_1\mu + c_2) = c_1(X - \mu).$ From this the result follows.

9. $y = g(x) = x^2,\ x = h(y) = \sqrt{y},\ F^*(y) = F(\sqrt{y}) = \sqrt{y}\ (0 < y < 1),$
$f^*(y) = 1/2\sqrt{y}\ (0 < y < 1).$

SECTION 7.1

3. We see that $(n - x)p/(x + 1)q > 1\ (<1)$ when $x < np - q\ (> np - q).$ Hence, except for trivial cases, $f(x)$ at first increases and later decreases. The maximum is at the smallest integer $x \geq np - q.$ If $np - q$ is integral, then $f(np - q + 1) = f(np - q).$

SECTION 7.3

1. (a) 3/8, (b) 1/4, (c) 1/16

3. $\dfrac{1}{2^{15}}\left[\binom{15}{0} + \binom{15}{1}\right] = \dfrac{1}{2048}$, hence very small.

5. $f(x) = \binom{5}{x}0.5^5,\ f(0) = 0.03125,\ f(1) = 0.15625,\ 1 - f(0) = 0.96875,$
$1 - f(5) = 0.96875$

9. $P = 0.99^{10} \approx 90.4\%$

11. The probability of not hitting the target is $0.8^5 \approx 33\%.$ Ans. 67% (which is greater than the probability in Example 3).

13. The probability that a single bulb will not germinate is $p = 0.05.$ Hence the probability that 10 bulbs will have the guaranteed property is

$$\sum_{x=0}^{1}\binom{10}{x}0.05^x 0.95^{10-x} = 91\%.$$

Ans. $9\%.$

15. $\binom{10}{x}0.05^x 0.95^{10-x}$

17. (a) 0, (b) 1/2, (c) 3/4, (d) 3/8, (e) 5/8

SECTION 7.5

1. $f(x) = 1.5^x e^{-1.5}/x!$

3. $\displaystyle\sum_{x=11}^{1000} \binom{1000}{x} 0.01^x 0.99^{1000-x} \approx e^{-10} \sum_{x=11}^{\infty} \frac{10^x}{x!} = 1 - e^{-10} \sum_{x=0}^{10} \frac{10^x}{x!} = 42\%$

7. X = number of calls per minute, $\mu = 300/60 = 5$ = average number of calls per minute, $P(X \leq 10) = F(10) = 0.9863$ (cf. Table 2 in Appendix 4). Ans. 1.4%.

9. $p = 0.001$, $np = 1$, $P(X \leq 1) = 2e^{-1} = 0.736$. Ans. 26.4%.

SECTION 7.6

3. $\tilde{G}(t) = e^{\mu(e^t - t - 1)}$, $\tilde{G}(0) = 1$
$\tilde{G}'(t) = \mu(e^t - 1)\tilde{G}(t)$, $\tilde{G}'(0) = 0$
$\tilde{G}''(t) = \mu e^t \tilde{G}(t) + \mu(e^t - 1)\tilde{G}'(t)$, $\sigma^2 = \tilde{G}''(0) = \mu$

SECTION 7.7

1. By direct calculation,

$$x\binom{M}{x} = M\binom{M-1}{x-1}.$$

Hence, from the definition of μ and (11), Sec. 4.10, with $p = M - 1$, $k = x - 1$, $q = N - M$, $r - k = n - x$, we obtain

$$\mu = \frac{1}{\binom{N}{n}} \sum_x x\binom{M}{x}\binom{N-M}{n-x} = \frac{M}{\binom{N}{n}} \sum_x \binom{M-1}{x-1}\binom{N-M}{n-x}$$

$$= \frac{M}{\binom{N}{n}} \binom{N-1}{n-1} = n\frac{M}{N}.$$

3. If a package of $N = 100$ items contains precisely $M = 10$ defectives, then the probability that 10 items drawn without replacement contain no defectives is

$$f(0) = \binom{10}{0}\binom{90}{10} \bigg/ \binom{100}{10} = \frac{90 \cdot 89 \cdots 81}{100 \cdot 99 \cdots 91} = 33\%.$$

Ans. 67%, so the method is very poor.

5. $P(X = x) = f(x) = \binom{9}{x}\binom{3}{8-x} \bigg/ \binom{12}{8}$, $f(x) = 0$ when $x = 0, 1, 2, 3, 4$,

$f(5) = 126/495$, $f(6) = 252/495$, $f(7) = 108/495$, $f(8) = 9/495$

SECTION 7.8

1. $npq = \dfrac{nM(N - M)}{N^2} > \dfrac{nM(N - M)}{N^2}\left(\dfrac{N-n}{N-1}\right) = \sigma^2$

3. Writing out the binomial coefficients, we see that $f(x) = \binom{n}{x} \dfrac{AB}{C}$ where

$$A = M(M - 1) \cdots (M - x + 1) \leqq M^x$$
$$B = (N - M)(N - M - 1) \cdots (N - M - n + x + 1) \leqq (N - M)^{n-x}$$
$$C = N(N - 1) \cdots (N - n + 1) > (N - n)^n$$

(and $A = 1$ when $x = 0$, $B = 1$ when $x = n$). This implies

$$f(x) < \binom{n}{x} \frac{M^x(N - M)^{n-x}}{(N - n)^n} = \binom{n}{x}\left(\frac{M}{N}\right)^x\left(\frac{N - M}{N}\right)^{n-x} \bigg/ \left(\frac{N - n}{N}\right)^n.$$

5. 22%, 43%, 29%, 6% and 17%, 50%, 30%, 3%; $\mu = 1.2$; $\sigma^2 = 0.72$ and 0.56, respectively

SECTION 8.2

1. $\Phi^2(\infty) = \dfrac{1}{2\pi} \displaystyle\int_{-\infty}^{\infty} e^{-u^2/2}\, du \int_{-\infty}^{\infty} e^{-v^2/2}\, dv$

$$= \frac{1}{2\pi} \int_{-\infty}^{\infty}\int_{-\infty}^{\infty} e^{-(u^2+v^2)/2}\, du\, dv = \frac{1}{2\pi}\int_{0}^{2\pi}\int_{0}^{\infty} e^{-r^2/2} r\, dr\, d\theta$$

$$= \frac{1}{2\pi}\int_{0}^{2\pi} d\theta \int_{0}^{\infty} e^{-r^2/2} r\, dr = \frac{1}{2\pi}\cdot 2\pi \cdot 1 = 1$$

$(u = r\cos\theta,\ v = r\sin\theta,\ du\, dv = r\, dr\, d\theta)$

3. Writing β at first instead of σ, we obtain from (1), Sec. 8.1,

$$\sigma^2 = \frac{1}{\sqrt{2\pi}\,\beta}\int_{-\infty}^{\infty} (x - \mu)^2 e^{-[(x-\mu)/\beta]^2/2}\, dx \qquad\qquad \left(u = \frac{x - \mu}{\beta}\right)$$

$$= \frac{1}{\sqrt{2\pi}\,\beta}\int_{-\infty}^{\infty} \beta^2 u^2 e^{-u^2/2}\,\beta\, du = \frac{\beta^2}{\sqrt{2\pi}}\int_{-\infty}^{\infty} u^2 e^{-u^2/2}\, du$$

$$= \frac{\beta^2}{\sqrt{2\pi}}\int_{-\infty}^{\infty} (-u)(-u e^{-u^2/2})\, du$$

$$= \beta^2\left(\frac{1}{\sqrt{2\pi}}(-u)e^{-u^2/2}\bigg|_{-\infty}^{\infty} + \frac{1}{\sqrt{2\pi}}\int_{-\infty}^{\infty} e^{-u^2/2}\, du\right) = \beta^2.$$

5. $P = \Phi(c) - \Phi(-c) = 2\Phi(c) - 1 = \gamma$

7. $\tilde{G}(t) = E(e^{t(X-\mu)}) = \dfrac{1}{\sqrt{2\pi}\,\sigma}\displaystyle\int_{-\infty}^{\infty} e^{t(x-\mu) - [(x-\mu)/\sigma]^2/2}\, dx$

$$= \frac{1}{\sqrt{2\pi}}\int_{-\infty}^{\infty} e^{t\sigma u - u^2/2}\, du$$

$$= \frac{1}{\sqrt{2\pi}} e^{t^2\sigma^2/2}\int_{-\infty}^{\infty} e^{-(u-t\sigma)^2/2}\, du = e^{t^2\sigma^2/2},$$

$\tilde{G}(0)^{\mathrm{IV}} = 3\sigma^4$, $\gamma^* = 3\sigma^4/\sigma^4 = 3$

SECTION 8.3

1. 4.8%, 79.7%, 90.5%

3. 68%, 98.8%

5. (*a*) 32, (*b*) 32

11. $P(9.97 \leq X \leq 10.03) = \Phi\left(\dfrac{0.03}{\sigma}\right) - \Phi\left(\dfrac{-0.03}{\sigma}\right) = 99\%, \quad 0.03/\sigma = 2.576$ (from Table 3*b*), $\sigma = 0.012$

13. $\sigma = 0.608$

15. 2

17. $P(X_0 > c) = 1 - \Phi\left(\dfrac{c - 10}{3}\right) = \alpha = 0.05, \dfrac{c - 10}{3} = 1.645, c = 14.94,$

$$P(X_1 \leq 14.94) = \Phi\left(\dfrac{14.94 - 20.00}{3}\right) = \Phi(-1.69) = 4.5\%,$$

which is much less than in the preceding problem (49%).

SECTION 8.4

1. $P = \displaystyle\sum_{x=0}^{10} \binom{1000}{x} 0.01^x\, 0.99^{1000-x}$

$\approx \Phi\left(\dfrac{10 - 10 + 0.5}{\sqrt{9.9}}\right) - \Phi\left(\dfrac{0 - 10 - 0.5}{\sqrt{9.9}}\right) = 0.564$

(exact 0.583)

3. $\Phi\left(\dfrac{6 - 1.6 + 0.5}{\sqrt{1.28}}\right) - \Phi\left(\dfrac{4 - 1.6 - 0.5}{\sqrt{1.28}}\right) = 1.0000 - 0.9535 = 0.0465'$

(from the table, 0.0562)

5. $\Phi\left(\dfrac{4040 - 2020 + 0.5}{\sqrt{1010}}\right) - \Phi\left(\dfrac{2048 - 2020 - 0.5}{\sqrt{1010}}\right) = 19.3\%$

7. $\Phi\left(\dfrac{3000 - 1500 + 0.5}{\sqrt{750}}\right) - \Phi\left(\dfrac{1578 - 1500 - 0.5}{\sqrt{750}}\right) = 0.23\%.$

This small value indicates that our assumption may be false.

SECTION 9.1

1. $F(b_1, b_2) =$ probability that (X, Y) assumes any value in $A, B, C,$ or D;
$F(a_1, b_2) =$ probability that (X, Y) assumes any value in A or C, etc. (Here B is the rectangle under consideration.)

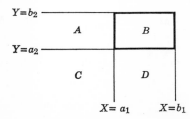

SECTION 9.2

5. $f(x_1, x_2) = \dfrac{20!}{x_1! x_2! (20 - x_1 - x_2)!} \, 0.03^{x_1} 0.05^{x_2} 0.92^{20 - x_1 - x_2}$

7. 5/36, 4/36, 13/36, 6/36, 17/36

SECTION 9.3

1. $F(x, y) = 0$ when $x \leqq \alpha_1$ or $y \leqq \alpha_2$,

$$F(x, y) = (a - \alpha_1)(b - \alpha_2)/k \qquad \text{when } x > \alpha_1 \text{ and } y > \alpha_2$$

where

$$a = \begin{cases} x & \text{when } \alpha_1 < x \leqq \beta_1 \\ \beta_1 & \text{when } x > \beta_1 \end{cases} \quad \text{and} \quad b = \begin{cases} y & \text{when } \alpha_2 < y \leqq \beta_2 \\ \beta_2 & \text{when } y > \beta_2 \end{cases}$$

5. $P = (e^{-a_1} - e^{-b_1})(e^{-a_2} - e^{-b_2})$

7. (a) 12%, (b) 40%, (c) 50%, (d) 0

9. 0.5

SECTION 9.4

3. $f_1(x) = \dfrac{1}{\beta_1 - \alpha_1} \, (\alpha_1 < x < \beta_1), f_2(y) = \dfrac{1}{\beta_2 - \alpha_2} \, (\alpha_2 < y < \beta_2)$

5. $f_1(x) = 0.5x \; (0 < x < 2), f_2(y) = 1 - 0.5y \; (0 < y < 2)$

9. $k = 1/\pi, f_1(x) = \dfrac{2}{\pi} \sqrt{1 - x^2}, f_2(y) = \dfrac{2}{\pi} \sqrt{1 - y^2}, 25\%$

SECTION 9.5

1. From (3), Sec. 5.4, we obtain

$$P(a_1 < X \leqq b_1) P(a_2 < Y \leqq b_2) = [F_1(b_1) - F_1(a_1)][F_2(b_2) - F_2(a_2)].$$

In the case of independence we may apply (1) and see that the right-hand side is equal to

$$F(b_1, b_2) - F(a_1, b_2) - F(b_1, a_2) + F(a_1, a_2).$$

From this and (2), Sec. 9.1, we obtain (3). Conversely, suppose that (3) holds for any pair of those events. Then we may let $a_1 \to -\infty, a_2 \to -\infty$; writing x instead of b_1 and y instead of b_2, we see that (3) becomes identical with (1).

3. $f(0, 0) = \dfrac{N - M}{N} \cdot \dfrac{N - M - 1}{N - 1}, \qquad f(0, 1) = \dfrac{N - M}{N} \cdot \dfrac{M}{N - 1} = f(1, 0),$

$f_1(0) = f(0, 0) + f(0, 1) = \dfrac{N - M}{N} = f_2(0), \; f_1(0) f_2(0) \neq f(0, 0)$

5. Dependent

9. $c = 2/\pi$, dependent

SECTION 9.6

1. $f(x, y) = 1$ in S, $F(z) = \iint_{x+y\leq z} dx\, dy$ = area of the portion of S "below" the straight line $x + y = z$; thus $F = 0$ if $z \leq 0$, $F = z^2/2$ if $0 < z \leq 1$, $F = 1 - 2^{-1}(2 - z)^2$ if $1 < z \leq 2$, $F = 1$ if $z > 2$. Differentiation gives the density $f = 0$ if $z < 0$ or $z > 2$, $f = z$ if $0 < z < 1$, $f = 2 - z$ if $1 < z < 2$.

3. $F(z) = 0$ if $z \leq 0$, $F(z) = \sqrt{z}$ if $0 \leq z \leq 1$, $F(z) = 1$ if $z > 1$

5. $F(z) = \iint_{x+y\leq z} f(x, y)\, dx\, dy = \iint_{x\leq z-y} f_1(x) f_2(y)\, dx\, dy$

$$= \int_{-\infty}^{\infty} f_2(y) \left[\int_{-\infty}^{z-y} f_1(x)\, dx \right] dy.$$

From this we obtain (5a) by differentiation under the integral sign.

7. $F(z) = 1 - (1 + z)e^{-z}$ if $z \geq 0$, $f(z) = ze^{-z}$ if $z \geq 0$

9. (a) $f(0, 0) = 1/128$, $f(0, 1) = 6/128$, $f(0, 2) = 9/128$, $f(1, 0) = 3/128$, etc. (b) To $z_1 = x + 2y = 0, \cdots, 7$ there corresponds $f(z_1) = 1/128, 3/128, 9/128, 19/128, 27/128, 33/128, 27/128, 9/128$. (c) $f(0) = 1/128$, $f(1) = 9/128$, $f(2) = 18/128$, $f(3) = 0$, $f(4) = 12/128$, $f(5) = 45/128$, etc.

SECTION 9.7

1. $G_j(t) = E(e^{tX_j})$. To $X_1 + \cdots + X_n$ there corresponds

$$G(t) = E(e^{t(X_1+\cdots+X_n)}) = E(e^{tX_1} \cdots e^{tX_n}) = E(e^{tX_1}) \cdots E(e^{tX_n})$$
$$= G_1(t) \cdots G_n(t).$$

3. $Z = X_1 + \cdots + X_n$, X_j = number of red balls drawn in the jth performance. $E(X_j) = r/(r + b)$. Ans. $nr/(r + b)$.

5. Use (2), Sec. 6.7, and then Theorem 1.

SECTION 9.8

1. X_j = number the jth die turns up, $\mu_j = 3.5$, $\sigma_j^2 = 35/12$ (cf. Example 1, Sec. 6.4) Ans. $\mu = 3.5n$, $\sigma^2 = 35n/12$.

3. By Theorem 1 and formula (4), Sec. 6.7, the variance of Z is

$$\sigma^2 = (a_1^2\sigma_1^2 + \cdots + a_k^2\sigma_k^2)/(\sum a_j)^2,$$

and $\partial\sigma^2/\partial a_j = 0$ ($j = 1, \cdots, k$) yields

$$a_j\sigma_j^2 = \sum a_m^2\sigma_m^2/(a_1 + \cdots + a_k).$$

Since in all k equations the right-hand sides are identical,

$$a_1\sigma_1^2 = a_2\sigma_2^2 = \cdots = a_k\sigma_k^2.$$

SECTION 10.1

1. $\Gamma(\lambda + 1) = \int_0^\infty e^{-t}t^\lambda\, dt = -e^{-t}t^\lambda \Big|_0^\infty + \lambda\int_0^\infty e^{-t}t^{\lambda-1}\, dt = 0 + \lambda\Gamma(\lambda)$

3. $\Gamma(\tfrac{1}{2}) = \int_0^\infty e^{-\tau}\tau^{-1/2}\, d\tau = \sqrt{2}\int_0^\infty e^{-t^2/2}\, dt = \dfrac{\sqrt{2}}{2}\int_{-\infty}^\infty e^{-t^2/2}\, dt = \dfrac{\sqrt{2\pi}}{\sqrt{2}}$

7. Use (3) and integrate.

9. $F(x) = 1 - (0.5x + 1)e^{-0.5x}$.

SECTION 10.2

1. $\mu = \dfrac{1}{2^{n/2}\Gamma\left(\dfrac{n}{2}\right)} \displaystyle\int_0^\infty x^{n/2}e^{-x/2}\,dx = \dfrac{2^{(n+2)/2}}{2^{n/2}\Gamma\left(\dfrac{n}{2}\right)} \displaystyle\int_0^\infty e^{-t}\,t^{n/2}\,dt = \dfrac{2\Gamma\left(\dfrac{n}{2}+1\right)}{\Gamma\left(\dfrac{n}{2}\right)} = n$

5. Equate the derivative to zero.

SECTION 10.3

1. $\sigma^2 = I\,\Gamma\left(\dfrac{n+1}{2}\right)\Big/ \sqrt{n\pi}\,\Gamma\left(\dfrac{n}{2}\right)$

where

$$I = 2\int_0^\infty z^2\left(1 + \frac{z^2}{n}\right)^{-(n+1)/2} dz = n^{3/2}\int_0^1 t^{(n-4)/2}(1-t)^{1/2}\,dt$$

$$= n^{3/2}\,\dfrac{\Gamma\left(\dfrac{n}{2}-1\right)\Gamma\left(\dfrac{3}{2}\right)}{\Gamma\left(\dfrac{n+1}{2}\right)};$$

here

$$1 + \frac{z^2}{n} = \frac{1}{t}.$$

Hence

$$\sigma^2 = n\Gamma\left(\frac{n}{2}-1\right)\Gamma\left(\frac{3}{2}\right)\Big/ \sqrt{\pi}\,\Gamma\left(\frac{n}{2}\right), \qquad \Gamma\left(\frac{3}{2}\right) = \frac{1}{2}\Gamma\left(\frac{1}{2}\right) = \frac{\sqrt{\pi}}{2},$$

$$\Gamma\left(\frac{n}{2}\right) = \left(\frac{n}{2}-1\right)\Gamma\left(\frac{n}{2}-1\right).$$

3. (*a*) 9.93, (*b*) 4.03, (*c*) 2.85, (*d*) 2.63

SECTION 11.2

1.

x	1	1.5	2	2.5	3	3.5	4	4.5	5	5.5	6
$f(x)$	$\dfrac{1}{36}$	$\dfrac{2}{36}$	$\dfrac{3}{36}$	$\dfrac{4}{36}$	$\dfrac{5}{36}$	$\dfrac{6}{36}$	$\dfrac{5}{36}$	$\dfrac{4}{36}$	$\dfrac{3}{36}$	$\dfrac{2}{36}$	$\dfrac{1}{36}$

Here it is assumed that the die is fair.

3. $S^2 = \dfrac{1}{n-1}\sum [(X_j - \mu) - (\bar{X} - \mu)]^2$

$\qquad = \dfrac{1}{n-1}\sum (X_j - \mu)^2 - \dfrac{2}{n-1}(\bar{X} - \mu)\sum (X_j - \mu) + \dfrac{n}{n-1}(\bar{X} - \mu)^2$

$\qquad = \dfrac{1}{n-1}\sum (X_j - \mu)^2 - \dfrac{n}{n-1}(\bar{X} - \mu)^2,$

because from (3) it follows that

$$\sum (X_j - \mu) = n(\bar{X} - \mu).$$

Hence, by (8),

$$E(S^2) = \frac{1}{n-1} \sum E([X_j - \mu]^2) - \frac{n}{n-1} E([\bar{X} - \mu]^2)$$

$$= \frac{n}{n-1} \sigma^2 - \frac{n}{n-1} \left(\frac{\sigma^2}{n}\right) = \sigma^2.$$

7. $E(c_1\hat{\Theta}_1 + c_2\hat{\Theta}_2) = c_1 E(\hat{\Theta}_1) + c_2 E(\hat{\Theta}_2) = c_1\theta + c_2\theta = \theta$
9. $\sigma^2 = c_1{}^2\sigma_1{}^2 + c_2{}^2\sigma_2{}^2$ (cf. Sec. 9.8)
   $= c_1{}^2\sigma_1{}^2 + (1 - c_1)^2\sigma_2{}^2$.
   $d\sigma^2/dc_1 = 0$ gives $c_1\sigma_1{}^2 = (1 - c_1)\sigma_2{}^2 = c_2\sigma_2{}^2$.
11. Using the distribution function of the chi-square distribution (Sec. 10.1), we find by differentiation that S has the density

$$f(s) = 2\left(\frac{n-1}{2\sigma^2}\right)^{(n-1)/2} \left[\Gamma\left(\frac{n-1}{2}\right)\right]^{-1} e^{-(n-1)s^2/2\sigma^2} s^{n-2} \qquad (s > 0).$$

From this we obtain the result by expressing

$$E(S) = \int_0^\infty s f(s)\, ds$$

in terms of the gamma function.

SECTION 11.3

1. $P(|\bar{X} - \mu| \geq a\sigma) \leq \dfrac{\sigma^2/n}{a^2\sigma^2} = \dfrac{1}{a^2 n} = 0.05$, $n = \dfrac{1}{0.05a^2}$. Ans. $n = 20, 80, 320$.
3. From (2), $P(|X - \mu| \geq 2\sigma) \leq 0.25$, $P(|X - \mu| \geq 3\sigma) \leq 1/9$.
5. If X assumes $-2, 0, 2$ with probability $1/8, 3/4, 1/8$, respectively, then $\mu = 0$, $\sigma^2 = 1, 2\sigma = 2$,

$$P(|X - \mu| \geq 2) = 1/8 + 1/8 = 1/4,$$

thus

$$P(|X - \mu| < 2) = 3/4.$$

SECTION 11.4

1. Computed values $\bar{x} = 100.25$, $s = 1.37$
3. Computed values $\bar{x} = 165.05$, $s = 5.86$

SECTION 11.6

1. $l = 1/(b - a)^n$ is maximum if $b - a$ is as small as possible, that is, a equal to the smallest sample value and b equal to the largest.
3. Inserting the inverse $\theta = \psi(\varphi)$ of $\varphi(\theta)$ into the likelihood function $l(\theta)$, we obtain $l(\psi(\varphi))$. Since l has its maximum when $\theta = \hat{\theta}$, it follows that the $\varphi = \hat{\varphi}$ for which l is maximum must satisfy $\hat{\theta} = \psi(\hat{\varphi})$. This implies $\hat{\varphi} = \varphi(\hat{\theta})$.
5. $\dfrac{\partial \ln l}{\partial p} = \dfrac{\partial \ln f}{\partial p} = \dfrac{1}{p} - \dfrac{x-1}{1-p} = 0$ gives $\hat{p} = \dfrac{1}{x}$.

9. $f(x) = \binom{2}{x} p^x q^{2-x}, p = 0, 0.5, 1$ maximizes $f(x)$ when $x = 0, 1, 2$, respectively.

11. $k = \theta, \hat{\theta} = n/\sum x_j = 1/\bar{x}$

SECTION 12.1

1. CONF $\{3.14 \leqq \mu \leqq 6.86\}$, CONF $\{4.814 \leqq \mu \leqq 5.186\}$

3. $k = 2.576 \cdot 2.4/15 = 0.41$

5. $n \approx 6000$

7. About 4, 16, 385, 38500

9. $k = c\sigma/\sqrt{n}$ in (a), k from $\sigma^2/k^2 n = 1 - \gamma$ in (b), thus $k = c^*\sigma/\sqrt{n}$ where $c^* = 1/\sqrt{1 - \gamma}$. $c^*/c = 1.9, 2.3, 3.9, 9.6$.

11. CONF $\{x_1 - 2.576\sigma \leqq \mu \leqq x_1 + 2.576\sigma\}$

SECTION 12.2

1. Normal distributions with $\mu = 8$, $\sigma^2 = 100$, $\mu = -4$, $\sigma^2 = 25$, and $\mu = 0$, $\sigma^2 = 225$, respectively

3. $Z = X + Y$ is normal with mean $\mu = 105$ and variance $\sigma^2 = 1.25$ Ans. $P(104 \leqq Z \leqq 106) = 63\%$.

5. $X_2 - X_1$ is normal with mean $\mu = \mu_2 - 1$ and variance $\sigma^2 = 0.2$. Hence

$$P(X_2 - X_1 \leqq 0) = \Phi\left(\frac{0 - (\mu_2 - 1)}{\sqrt{0.2}}\right) = \frac{1}{1000}, \quad \frac{\mu_2 - 1}{\sqrt{0.2}} = 3.090,$$

$\mu_2 = 2.38$.

9. CONF $\{4.48 \leqq \mu \leqq 5.75\}$

11. For fixed γ, σ, and n the quantity $(c_1 + c_2)\sigma/\sqrt{n}$ is minimum when $c_1 + c_2$ is minimum. From (8) we see that this holds for $c_1 = c_2$.

13. $Z = Y - X$ is normal with mean 0.01 and variance 0.0002,

$$P(0.002 \leqq Z \leqq 0.018) = \Phi\left(\frac{0.018 - 0.010}{0.0141}\right) - \Phi\left(\frac{0.002 - 0.010}{0.0141}\right) = 43\%.$$

15. $f(y) = \displaystyle\sum_{x_1 + x_2 = y} e^{-\mu_1} \frac{\mu_1^{x_1}}{x_1!} e^{-\mu_2} \frac{\mu_2^{x_2}}{x_2!}$

$\qquad = e^{-\mu} \displaystyle\sum_{x_1=0}^{y} \frac{\mu_1^{x_1} \mu_2^{y-x_1}}{x_1!(y-x_1)!} = \frac{e^{-\mu}}{y!} \sum_{x_1=0}^{y} \binom{y}{x_1} \mu_1^{x_1} \mu_2^{y-x_1}$

$\qquad = e^{-\mu} \dfrac{(\mu_1 + \mu_2)^y}{y!} = e^{-\mu} \dfrac{\mu^y}{y!}$

SECTION 12.3

1. CONF $\{0.726 \leqq \mu \leqq 0.751\}$

3. $c/\sqrt{n} = 0.715$, $\bar{x} = 4.37$, $s = 0.157$, CONF $\{4.25 \leqq \mu \leqq 4.49\}$

5. $c/\sqrt{n} = 0.198$, $\bar{x} = 165.05$, $s = 5.858$, CONF $\{163.8 \leqq \mu \leqq 166.3\}$

7. $c = 1.98$, $\bar{x} = 0.445$, $s = 0.035$, CONF $\{0.438 \leqq \mu \leqq 0.453\}$

9. $n = 8$

11. CONF $\{6.82 \leqq \mu \leqq 13.18\}$, CONF $\{8.04 \leqq \mu \leqq 11.96\}$

13. $n = 3$ (2 degrees of freedom), $n = 4$ (3 degrees of freedom)

15. CONF $\{2.21 \leqq \mu \leqq 2.63\}$

SECTION 12.4

1. 95%

3. 19

5. $F(s) = P(S \leqq s) = P(S^2 \leqq s^2) = P\left(\dfrac{(n-1)S^2}{\sigma^2} \leqq \dfrac{(n-1)s^2}{\sigma^2}\right).$

Using (3) in Sec. 10.1 with $n-1$ instead of n, we obtain the formula for $F(s)$, and differentiation yields $f(s)$.

SECTION 12.5

1. $c_1 = 0.41$, $c_2 = 16.7$, CONF $\{0.000\ 04 \leqq \sigma^2 \leqq 0.001\ 67\}$

3. $c_1 = (\sqrt{253} - 2.58)^2/2 = 88.79$, $c_2 = 170.87$, CONF $\{1.42 \leqq \sigma^2 \leqq 2.75\}$

5. $(n-1)s^2 = 0.01301$, CONF $\{0.0005 \leqq \sigma^2 \leqq 0.0076\}$

7. $(n-1)s^2 = 3396.75$, CONF $\{24.4 \leqq \sigma^2 \leqq 51.1\}$

9. CONF$\{69.8 \leqq \sigma^2 \leqq 155.1\}$

SECTION 12.6

1. CONF $\{0.507 \leqq p \leqq 0.516\}$. This seems to indicate that the die was biased.

3. CONF $\{0.491 \leqq p \leqq 0.523\}$,   CONF $\{0.492 \leqq p \leqq 0.511\}$,
CONF $\{0.494 \leqq p \leqq 0.507\}$

7. From (3), $0.04 = 2k = 2\dfrac{1.96}{n}\sqrt{\dfrac{m(n-m)}{n}}$, $\left(\dfrac{0.02}{1.96}\right)^2 n^3 = m(n-m)$, where m is
unknown but the right-hand side is maximum when $m = n/2$. Then $(0.02/1.96)^2 n = 1/4$, $n = 2400$. More economically, we may estimate m from a small preliminary sample and arrive at a smaller n if m differs substantially from $n/2$.

9. 95%

SECTION 12.7

1. $\bar{x} = 1502.7$, $s^2 = 41{,}665$, CONF $\{1479 \leqq \mu \leqq 1526\}$,
CONF $\{35{,}766 \leqq \sigma^2 \leqq 49{,}333\}$

3. $\bar{x} = 154.1$, $s^2 = 353.2$, CONF $\{151.7 \leqq \mu \leqq 156.5\}$,
CONF $\{298 \leqq \sigma^2 \leqq 426\}$

5. The approximating normal distribution has mean 4.5 and variance $8.25/5 = 1.65$.

7. CONF $\{0.441 \leqq \mu \leqq 0.559\}$

SECTION 13.2

1. If the hypothesis is true, $X = $ *number of heads in* 4040 *trials* is approximately normal with mean $\mu = np = 2020$ and $\sigma^2 = npq = 1010$, $q = 1 - p$. We choose $\alpha = 5\%$ and determine c_1 and c_2 from $P(X \leqq c_1) = 2\frac{1}{2}\%$, $P(X \geqq c_2) = 2\frac{1}{2}\%$, thus

$$P(X \leqq c_1) = \Phi\left(\frac{c_1 - 2020}{\sqrt{1010}}\right) = 0.025, \qquad \frac{c_1 - 2020}{\sqrt{1010}} = -1.96,$$

$$c_1 = 2020 - 62.29 \approx 1958, \qquad c_2 = 2020 + 62.29 \approx 2082.$$

Since 2048 lies in the acceptance region $1958 \leqq x \leqq 2082$, we do not reject the hypothesis.

3. $P(X \leq c_1) = \Phi\left(\dfrac{c_1 - 6000}{\sqrt{3000}}\right) = 0.025, \qquad \dfrac{c_1 - 6000}{\sqrt{3000}} = -1.96,$

$\qquad c_1 = 6000 - 107.35 \approx 5893, \qquad c_2 = 6000 + 107.35 \approx 6107.$

Do not reject the hypothesis. For the second sample,

$\qquad c_1 = 12{,}000 - 151.82 \approx 11{,}848, \qquad c_2 = 12{,}000 + 151.82 \approx 12{,}152.$

Do not reject the hypothesis.

5. $P(X > c)_{\theta_0} = \displaystyle\int_c^\infty e^{-x}\,dx = e^{-c} = \alpha = 5\%,\ c = 2.996,$

$\qquad \beta = P(X \leq c)_{\theta_1} = \dfrac{1}{\theta_1}\displaystyle\int_0^c e^{-x/\theta_1}\,dx = 1 - e^{-c/\theta_1},$

$\qquad \eta = 1 - \beta = e^{-2.996/\theta_1}$ increases as θ_1 increases.

7. $c = 0.95,\ \eta = (\theta_1 - 0.95)/\theta_1$

9. $c = 3.9,\ \beta = 40\%$

11. $\alpha = 36\%,\ \beta = 33\%,\ \beta = 21\%$

13. $\alpha = 20\%$ as before, $\beta = 40\%$

15. $\alpha = 2/90;$ let $\theta =$ number of red balls in the box, then

θ	2	3	4	5	6	7	8	9	10
β	$\dfrac{88}{90}$	$\dfrac{84}{90}$	$\dfrac{78}{90}$	$\dfrac{70}{90}$	$\dfrac{60}{90}$	$\dfrac{48}{90}$	$\dfrac{34}{90}$	$\dfrac{18}{90}$	0

SECTION 13.3

1. $\alpha = 5\%$. $t = \sqrt{10}\,(0.811 - 0.800)/\sqrt{0.000054} = 4.73$, $P(-c \leq T \leq c) = 0.95$ gives $c = 2.26$ $(n - 1 = 9$ degrees of freedom). Reject the hypothesis.

3. $t = \sqrt{10}\,(1.193 - 1.200)/0.038 = -0.58 > c = -1.83$ $(\alpha = 5\%)$. Do not reject the hypothesis.

5. $t = \sqrt{7}\,(0.286 - 0)/4.31 = 0.18 < c = 1.94$ $(\alpha = 5\%)$. Do not reject the hypothesis.

7. $n = 16$, $\bar{x} = 0.75$, $s^2 = 2.87$, $t = 1.77 < c = 2.13$ $[\alpha = 5\%$, alternative $\mu \neq 0$, c from $P(-c \leq T \leq c) = 1 - \alpha]$, do not reject the hypothesis.

9. The logical alternative from the manufacturer's point of view is $H_1 : p > 0.03$. Let $X =$ *number of defectives among* 500 *parts.* Applying the normal approximation to the binomial distribution and choosing $\alpha = 5\%$, we obtain the critical value c from

$$P(X > c)_{p=0.03} = 1 - P(X \leq c)_{p=0.03} = 1 - \Phi\left(\dfrac{c - 15}{\sqrt{14.55}}\right) = 0.05;$$

thus $(c - 15)/3.814 = 1.645$, $c = 21.27 < 26$, and we reject the hypothesis.

11. Hypothesis H_0: not better. Alternative H_1: better. Under H_0 the variable $X =$ *number of cases cured in* 200 *cases* is approximately normal with mean $\mu = np = 140$ and variance $\sigma^2 = npq = 42$; $\alpha = 5\%$ gives $(c - 140)/\sqrt{42} = 1.645$, $c = 150.65 > 148$. We do not reject the hypothesis. This indicates that the results obtained thus far do not establish the superiority.

13. $Y = 27S^2/25 = 1.08S^2$, $P(Y < c) = \alpha = 5\%$, $c = 16.2$ (27 degrees of freedom), $c^* = 16.2/1.08 = 15.00 > 3.5^2$, reject the hypothesis and assert that $\sigma^2 < 25$, that is, it will be less expensive to replace all batteries simultaneously.

17. $\bar{X}$ has variance $\sigma^2/9 = 1$.

$$\Phi\left(\frac{c - 10}{1}\right) = 0.05$$

gives $c = 10 - 1.645 = 8.355$, and

$$\beta = 1 - \Phi\left(\frac{c - 7.36}{1}\right) = 1 - \Phi(1) = 16\%.$$

19. $5^2 = 25$ times the original sample size

21. $P(\bar{X} \le 23)_{\mu_0} = \Phi\left(\dfrac{23 - 20}{\sigma_{\bar{X}}}\right) = 90\%$, $\quad \dfrac{23 - 20}{\sigma_{\bar{X}}} = 1.282$,

$$\sigma_{\bar{X}} = \frac{3}{1.282} = \frac{\sigma}{\sqrt{n}} = \frac{10}{\sqrt{n}}, \quad \sqrt{n} = \frac{10}{2.34} = 4.27, \quad n = 19$$

SECTION 13.4

1. $\bar{x} = 376.3$, $\bar{y} = 335.3$, $s_x^2 = 1009.3$, $s_y^2 = 869.3$, $t_0 = 1.64 < c = 2.13$ ($\alpha = 5\%$, 4 degrees of freedom), do not reject the hypothesis.

3. Hypothesis $\mu_X = \mu_Y$, alternative $\mu_X \ne \mu_Y$, $\bar{x} = 106.22$, $\bar{y} = 106.34$, $s_x^2 = 0.717$, $s_y^2 = 0.243$, $t_0 = -0.27$ lies between $c_1 = -2.31$ and $c_2 = 2.31$ ($\alpha = 5\%$, 8 degrees of freedom), do not reject the hypothesis.

5. Second method: $\bar{x} = 260$, $s_x^2 = 796.4$. First method: $\bar{y} = 236$, $s_y^2 = 607.1$, $t_0 = 1.9 > c = 1.75$ ($\alpha = 5\%$), reject the hypothesis and assert that the second method is better.

7. $t_0 = \sqrt{16}(110 - 105)/\sqrt{100 + 64} = 1.56 < c = 2.04$ ($\alpha = 5\%$, 30 degrees of freedom), do not reject the hypothesis.

9. No ($\alpha = 5\%$, two-sided alternative, 12 degrees of freedom).

11. $t_0 = \sqrt{n}\,\dfrac{1120 - 1064}{\sqrt{75^2 + 82^2}} = 0.5\sqrt{n}$. From Table 8 and (5), $c_1 = -2$, $c_2 = 2$,

approximately, when $\alpha = 5\%$ and n is between 20 and 200. Now $0.5\sqrt{n} = 2$ when $n = 16$. Ans. $n = 16$.

13. $t_0 = 4.7 > c = 1.68$ ($\alpha = 5\%$, 54 degrees of freedom), reject the hypothesis.

SECTION 13.6

1. $v_0 = 2.5 < 6.00$ [$\alpha = 5\%$, $(9, 4)$ degrees of freedom], do not reject the hypothesis.

3. $v_0 = 679/254 = 2.67$. We choose $\alpha = 5\%$. Table 9a does not contain a value corresponding to $(11, 5)$ degrees of freedom, but we see from the neighboring values that this missing value must be greater than v_0, and we do not reject the hypothesis.

5. $v_0 = 2.4 < c = 3.18$ [$\alpha = 5\%$, $(9, 9)$ degrees of freedom].

7. $\bar{x} = 219$, $\bar{y} = 183$, $s_x^2 = 111$, $s_y^2 = 133$, $t_0 = 6.8 > c = 2.12$ ($\alpha = 5\%$, two-sided). Ans. Yes.

9. $v_0 = 13.61/2.36 = 5.77 > c = 3.79$. Ans. Yes.

11. $F(x) = P(T^2 \leq x) = P(-\sqrt{x} \leq T \leq \sqrt{x}) = 2P(0 \leq T \leq \sqrt{x})$

$$= 2 \frac{\Gamma\left(\dfrac{n+1}{2}\right)}{\sqrt{n\pi}\,\Gamma\left(\dfrac{n}{2}\right)} \int_0^{\sqrt{x}} \frac{du}{\left(1 + \dfrac{u^2}{n}\right)^{(n+1)/2}} = \frac{\Gamma\left(\dfrac{n+1}{2}\right)}{\sqrt{n\pi}\,\Gamma\left(\dfrac{n}{2}\right)} \int_0^x \frac{t^{-\frac{1}{2}}}{\left(1 + \dfrac{t}{n}\right)^{(n+1)/2}}\, dt$$

$$= \frac{\Gamma\left(\dfrac{n+1}{2}\right)}{\Gamma\left(\dfrac{1}{2}\right)\Gamma\left(\dfrac{n}{2}\right)}\, n^{n/2} \int_0^x \frac{t^{-\frac{1}{2}}}{(t+n)^{(n+1)/2}}\, dt,$$

which is (2) with $m = 1$; here we put $u^2 = t$ and used $\sqrt{\pi} = \Gamma(1/2)$.

13. $F(x) = 2 \cdot 2 \displaystyle\int_0^x \frac{dt}{(2t+2)^2} = 1 - \frac{1}{x+1} = 0.95$, $x = 19$, etc.

SECTION 14.1

1. LCL $= 1 - 2.58 \cdot 0.02/2 = 0.974$, UCL $= 1.026$

3. LCL and UCL will correspond to a significance level α which, in general, is not equal to 1%.

5. $\mu_0 = 20.50$, LCL $= 4.05 \cdot 5 = 20.25$, UCL $= 20.75$

7. Trend of sample means to increase. Abrupt change of sample means.

9. LCL $= 3$, UCL $= 7$

17. The sample range tends to increase with increasing n whereas σ remains unchanged.

19. $0.27 \cdot 5 = 1.35$ ($s = 1.37$)

SECTION 14.2

1. $(1 - \theta)^2$

3. $P(A; \theta) \approx e^{-500\theta}$

5. (a) $(1 - \theta)^5$, (b) $(1 - \theta)^5 + 5\theta(1 - \theta)^4$

7. 50%

11. Because n is finite.

13. The values corresponding to $\theta = 0.1, 0.2, \cdots, 1.0$ are $0.9619, 0.7969, \cdots, 0$.

15. About 100

17. About $k = 0.22$

SECTION 14.3

1. $\alpha = 5\%$, $\beta = 44\%$, which is unsatisfactorily large.

3. α decreases, β increases (for fixed θ_1).

5. $\theta_1 = 25\%$. θ_1 is too large to use that formula.

SECTION 14.4

3. $P(A; \theta) = \left[\dbinom{N - N\theta}{4} + N\theta \dbinom{N - N\theta}{3} \right] \Big/ \dbinom{N}{4}$

$$\approx (1 - \theta)^4 + 4\theta(1 - \theta)^3,$$

$$\text{AOQ}(\theta) \approx \theta(1 - \theta)^4 + 4\theta^2(1 - \theta)^3$$

5. $[\theta(1 - \theta)^5]' = 0$ yields $\theta = 1/6$. Ans. 0.07.

SECTION 14.6

1. (*a*) 3, (*b*) 21

3. Critical lines $x = 0.415w - 2.59$ and $x = 0.415w + 3.09$

5. $x = 0.078w - 4.29$ and $x = 0.078w + 5.57$

SECTION 15.2

1. It supports the theory because $\chi_0^2 = 0.47 < c = 7.81$ ($\alpha = 5\%$).

3. $n = 100$, $K = 6$, $e_j = 100/6$, $b_1 = 16$, $|b_1 - e_1| = 2/3$, etc. $\chi_0^2 = 1.28 < c = 11.07$ ($\alpha = 5\%$), do not reject the hypothesis.

5. $a \geq 32$ because

$$\chi_0^2 = \tfrac{1}{25}[(a - 25)^2 + (50 - a - 25)^2] > c = 3.84$$

when $a \geq 32$ (or $a \leq 18$, of course).

7. $n = 944{,}000$, $e_1 = (31/365)n = 80{,}175$, $e_2 = (28/365)n = 72{,}416$, etc., $\chi_0^2 = 2300 > c = 19.68$ ($\alpha = 5\%$, 11 degrees of freedom). Reject the hypothesis.

9. $n = 200$, $\bar{x} = 122/200 = 0.61$, $f(x) = e^{-0.61} \, 0.61^x/x!$

x_j	0	1	2	≥ 3
b_j	109	65	22	4
e_j	108.67	66.29	20.22	4.82

$\chi_0^2 = 0.3 < c = 5.99$ ($\alpha = 5\%$, 2 degrees of freedom). Do not reject the hypothesis.

11. $p = \bar{x}/8 = 0.5147$, $e_1 = 165$, $e_2 = 1402$, $e_3 = 5203$, $e_4 = 11035$, $e_5 = 14628$, $e_6 = 12410$, $e_7 = 6580$, $e_8 = 1994$, $e_9 = 264$, $\chi_0^2 = 92 > c = 14.07$ ($\alpha = 5\%$, 7 degrees of freedom), reject the hypothesis. This indicates that for a refined investigation the model is too simple. Large deviations appear at the ends (only in part caused by twin births) and in the middle.

13. $K = 8$, $\hat{\mu} = \bar{x} = 43.62$, $\tilde{\sigma} = \sqrt{1.8705} = 1.368$, $\chi_0^2 = 2.292 < c = 11.07$ ($\alpha = 5\%$, $K - 2 - 1 = 5$ degrees of freedom). Do not reject the hypothesis.

15. (*a*) $\chi_0^2 = 42.5$, (*b*) 157, (*c*) 214

17. $(10 + 2 + 15)/300 = 0.09$ is an estimate for the probability that a can does not meet the specifications.

$$\chi_0^2 = \tfrac{1}{9}[(10 - 9)^2 + (2 - 9)^2 + (15 - 9)^2] = \tfrac{86}{9} = 9.56 > 3.84$$

($\alpha = 5\%$, 1 degree of freedom). Reject the hypothesis.

19. H_0: Number of defective screws the same for all 3 machines. We estimate $p = 15/600 = 2.5\%$. Then

$$\chi_0^2 = \tfrac{1}{5}(2^2 + 3^2 + 1^2) = 2.8 < 3.84$$

($\alpha = 5\%$, 1 degree of freedom). Ans. No.

SECTION 15.4

1. $n = 100$, $\bar{x} = 1.944$, $s = 0.053$, $a = 0.072 < c = 0.134$ ($\alpha = 5\%$), do not reject the hypothesis.

3. $n = 247$, $\bar{x} = 154.1$, $s = 18.79$, $a = 0.14 > 1.36/\sqrt{247} = 0.09$, reject the hypothesis. The result is typical; also other (larger) samples exhibit skewness.

5. $n = 291$, $\bar{x} = 112.96$, $s = 4.61$, $a = 0.14 > 1.36/\sqrt{291} = 0.08$ ($\alpha = 5\%$), reject the hypothesis.

SECTION 15.5

1. $\chi_0^2 = 86^2 \cdot 0.018035 = 133 > c = 3.84$ ($\alpha = 5\%$, 1 degree of freedom), reject the hypothesis and assert that the eye color of father and son are dependent.

3. $\chi_0^2 = 4 < c = 5.99$ ($\alpha = 5\%$, 2 degrees of freedom), do not reject the hypothesis that preference is independent of sex.

5. $\chi_0^2 = 0.43 < c = 3.84$ ($\alpha = 5\%$, 1 degree of freedom), do not reject the hypothesis.

7. $\chi_0^2 = 45 > c = 9.49$ ($\alpha = 5\%$, 4 degrees of freedom), reject the hypothesis.

SECTION 16.2

1. $r - 1 = 4$, $n - r = 15$, $v_0 = \dfrac{66/4}{30/15} = 8.25 > c = 3.06$ ($\alpha = 5\%$), reject the hypothesis.

3. $n = 6$, $r = 3$, $n_i = 2$, $q_1 = 0.028$, $q_2 = 0.471$, $v_0 = 0.09 < c = 9.55$ ($\alpha = 5\%$), not significant.

5. $n = 27$, $n_i = 9$, $r = 3$, $\bar{x}_1 = 259.9$, $\bar{x}_2 = 255.8$, $\bar{x}_3 = 246.3$, $q_1 = 869.6$, $q_2 = 15260$, $v_0 = 0.68 < c = 3.40$ ($\alpha = 5\%$), do not reject the hypothesis that there is no difference between positions.

7. $n = 12$, $r = 3$, $n_i = 4$, $q_1 = 0.505$, $q_2 = 4.70$, $v_0 = 0.48 < c = 4.26$ ($\alpha = 5\%$), do not reject the hypothesis that the planting date does not affect the yield.

9. $n = 30$, $r = 3$, $q_1 = 9.89$, $q_2 = 36.3$, $v_0 = 3.68 > c = 3.35$ ($\alpha = 5\%$). Ans. Yes.

11. $n = 12$, $r = 3$, $q_1 = 5$, $q_2 = 29$, $v_0 = 0.78 < c = 4.26$ ($\alpha = 5\%$). Ans. No.

13. $v_0 = \dfrac{1636/3}{2018/20} = 5.4 > 3.10$ [$\alpha = 5\%$, (3, 20) degrees of freedom], reject the hypothesis that the fat absorption is independent of the type of fat.

SECTION 16.6

1. In addition to Problem 5, Sec. 16.2, we merely have to compute the column sums and then a new $q_2 = 12051$ and $q_3 = q - q_1 - q_2 = 3209$. Then $v_1 = 2.17 < c_1 = 3.63$ [$\alpha = 5\%$, (2, 16) degrees of freedom], $v_2 = 7.51 > c_2 = 2.59$ [(8, 16) degrees of freedom], and we assert that there is no significant difference between the rows (positions), but the difference between the columns (the workers) is significant.

3. $q_1 = 0.0188$, $q_2 = 0.0991$, $q_3 = 0.0238$, $v_1 = 1.58 < c_1 = 6.94$ [$\alpha = 5\%$, (2, 4) degrees of freedom], $v_2 = 8.31 > c_2 = 6.94$ [(2, 4) degrees of freedom], and we assert that the weight does not have a significant effect, but the difference between the types of motion is significant.

5. $q_1 = 565$, $q_2 = 259$, $q_3 = 93.1$, $v_1 = 24.28 > c_1 = 4.46$ [$\alpha = 5\%$, (2, 8) degrees of freedom], $v_2 = 5.56 > c_2 = 3.84$ [(4, 8) degrees of freedom], and we assert that the difference between the kinds of barley as well as between the places is significant.

7. $q_1 = 2.72$, $q_2 = 109.23$, $q_3 = 0.20$, $v_1 = 13.4 < c_1 = 19.0$ [$\alpha = 5\%$, (2, 2) degrees of freedom], $v_2 = 1074.4 > c_2 = 18.5$ [(1, 2) degrees of freedom], and we assert that the difference between the groups is not significant, but the difference between the two methods is significant.

9. $q_1 = 76$, $q_2 = 32/3$, $q_3 = 4/3$, $v_1 = 57 > c_1 = 19$ ($\alpha = 5\%$), $v_2 = 16 < c_2 = 18.5$, assert that the difference between rows is significant, whereas the difference between columns is not significant.

11. $\mu_{i\cdot} = \dfrac{1}{p} \displaystyle\sum_{k=1}^{p} \mu_{ik} = \dfrac{1}{p}\left(p\mu + p\alpha_i + \displaystyle\sum_{k=1}^{p} \beta_k\right) = \mu + \alpha_i$, etc.

SECTION 17.1

3. About 160 lb

SECTION 17.2

1. $(n-1)s_{xy} = \sum (x_j - \bar{x})(y_j - \bar{y}) = \sum c_1(x_j{}^* - \bar{x}^*)c_2(y_j{}^* - \bar{y}^*) = c_1 c_2 (n-1)s_{xy}{}^*$

3. $y = x - 0.1$

5. $y - 281.16 = 1.93(x - 50)$

7. $y - 40.9 = -0.17(x - 47.5)$

9. $y - 14.0 = 0.84(x - 29.5)$

SECTION 17.5

1. $\gamma = 95\%$, $c = 3.18$, $4s_x{}^2 = 82000$, $4s_{xy} = 354100$, $4s_y{}^2 = 1530080$, $b = 4.31829$, $q = 974$, $k = 0.2$, CONF $\{4.1 \leq \beta \leq 4.5\}$

3. $k = 2.2$, $b = 1$, CONF $\{-1.2 \leq \beta \leq 3.2\}$

5. $c = 2.10$, $19s_x{}^2 = 337$, $19s_{xy} = 1817.5$, $19s_y{}^2 = 11550$, $b = 5.39$, $q = 1748$, $k = 1.13$, CONF $\{4.26 \leq \beta \leq 6.52\}$

SECTION 17.6

1. $\gamma = 95\%$, $c = 2.37$, $8s_x{}^2 = 0.2956$, $8s_{xy} = 3.5667$, $8s_y{}^2 = 90$, $b = 12.06765$, $q = 47$, $y = 12.07x - 7.99$, $k = 6.1h$,

$$h^2 = \frac{1}{9} + \frac{(x - 3.1)^2}{0.3}$$

3. $\gamma = 95\%$, $c = 2.31$, $9s_x{}^2 = 44.4$, $9s_{xy} = 24.2$, $9s_y{}^2 = 21.6$, $b = 0.55$, $q = 8.4$, $y = 0.55x + 7.7$, $k = 2.4h$,

$$h^2 = \frac{1}{10} + \frac{(x - 50.4)^2}{44.4}$$

SECTION 17.7

1. $\alpha^* = 5\%$, $c = 1.86$, $9s_x{}^2 = 86.1$, $9s_y{}^2 = 1258.9$, $b = 3.5$, $t_0 = 6.34 > c$. Reject the hypothesis.

3. $\alpha^* = 5\%$, $c = 6.31$, $s_x{}^2 = 1$, $s_y{}^2 = (3 + p^2)/3$, $b = 1$, $q = 2p^2/3$. $t_0 = \sqrt{3}/|p|$, hence $t_0 = c$ when $|p| = \sqrt{3}/c = 0.27$, $t_0 < c$ when $|p| > 0.27$. Hence if the points are sufficiently scattered, the hypothesis $\beta = 0$ will not be rejected although b is relatively large.

5. $t_0 = 0.3\sqrt{42} \cdot 0.31/\sqrt{0.4} = 0.95 < c = 1.94$ ($\alpha^* = 5\%$), do not reject the hypothesis.

SECTION 17.9

1. $\tilde{q} = 4$, $q_1 = 2$, $q_2 = 2$, $v_0 = 2 < c = 18.5$ ($\alpha = 5\%$), do not reject the hypothesis.

3. $n = 10$, $\tilde{q} = 40.1$, $q_1 = 14.9$, $q_2 = 25.2$, $v_0 = 4.73 < c = 5.32$ ($\alpha = 5\%$), do not reject the hypothesis.

5. $n = 10$, $\tilde{q} = 1259$, $q_1 = 1050$, $q_2 = 209$, $v_0 = 40.25 > c = 5.32$ ($\alpha = 5\%$), reject the hypothesis.

SECTION 17.10

1.
$$\sum_{j=1}^{n_i} (y_{ij} - \eta_i)^2 = \sum_{j=1}^{n_i} [(\bar{y}_i - \eta_i) + (y_{ij} - \bar{y}_i)]^2$$
$$= n_i(\bar{y}_i - \eta_i)^2 + \sum_{j=1}^{n_i} (y_{ij} - \bar{y}_i)^2 + 2(\bar{y}_i - \eta_i) \sum_{j=1}^{n_i} (y_{ij} - \bar{y}_i).$$

The last sum is zero, cf. (1). Summation over i from 1 to r gives (4).

3. $n = 10$, $r = 5$, $q = 31.8$, $q_1 = 9.8$, $q_2 = 22.0$, $v_0 = 0.75 < c = 5.41$ ($\alpha^* = 5\%$), do not reject the hypothesis.

5. $n = 12$, $r = 6$, $q = 9697$, $q_1 = 9623$, $q_2 = 74$, $v_0 = 196 > c = 4.53$ ($\alpha^* = 5\%$), reject the hypothesis.

SECTION 17.11

1. $y = 0.5 + 1.5x^2$

3. $y = 6642 + 762.3x - 156.1x^2$

5. $y = 795 - 37.1x + 1.75x^2$

7. $y = 5.355 - 0.761x + 0.093x^2$

SECTION 17.12

1. $y = 29.12 - 0.17x + 0.00028x^2$, $q_1 = 2.56$, $q_2 = 0.12$, $v_0 = 32 > c = 3.37$ [$\alpha^* = 5\%$, (6, 9) degrees of freedom], reject the hypothesis.

3. Compute $y_{ij}^* = \ln y_{ij}$, then the regression line
$$y^* - 2.59 = -0.007(x - 116.7)$$
of the (x_i, y_{ij}^*)-values and finally
$$y = e^{y^*} = 30e^{-0.007x}.$$

SECTION 18.1

1. -0.028

3. 0.98

5. 0

7. 1 when $k > 0$, -1 when $k < 0$

9. 0.6

SECTION 18.2

3. $m_{10} = m_{01} = 7/12 = 0.58$, $m_{20}^* = m_{02}^* = 11/144 = 0.076$, $m_{11}^* = -1/144 = -0.0069$, $\rho = -1/11 = -0.091$

5. $m_{10} = m_{01} = 1/3$, $m_{20}^* = m_{02}^* = 1/18$, $m_{11}^* = 0$, $\rho = 0$

9. $-1/9$

SECTION 18.3

1. $\sigma_{XY} = E([X - \mu_X][Y - \mu_Y]) = E(\sigma_X X^*[\rho\sigma_Y X^* + \sqrt{1 - \rho^2}\,\sigma_Y Y^*])$,
$$E(X^{*2}) = 1, \qquad E(X^* Y^*) = E(X^*)E(Y^*) = 0,$$
hence $\sigma_{XY} = \sigma_X \rho \sigma_Y$, $\sigma_{XY}/\sigma_X \sigma_Y = \rho$, cf. (4), Sec. 18.2.

3. $45°$

5. Ellipses with principal axes parallel to the coordinate axes

7. Use (1), Sec. 4.7.

11. $P(X^2 + Y^2 < 1) = \dfrac{1}{2\pi} \displaystyle\int_0^1 \int_0^{2\pi} e^{-r^2/2}\, r\, dr\, d\theta$

$$= -e^{-r^2/2}\Big|_0^1 = 1 - e^{-\frac{1}{2}} = 0.39$$

13. $P(\chi^2 < z) = P(X^2 + Y^2 < z) = \dfrac{1}{2\pi} \displaystyle\iint\limits_{x^2 + y^2 < z} e^{-(x^{*2}+v^{*2})/2}\, dx^*\, dy^*$

$$= \dfrac{1}{2\pi} \int_0^{2\pi} \int_0^{\sqrt{z}} e^{-r^2/2}\, r\, dr\, d\theta = 1 - e^{-z/2},$$

which is (3), Sec. 10.1, (with $n = 2$) in integrated form, with z instead of x.

SECTION 18.4

1. $c = 2.576$, $r = 0.47$, $z_0 = 0.51$, $k = 1.82$, CONF $\{-0.87 \leq \rho \leq 0.99\}$

3. $c = 2.576$, $r = 0.128$, $z_0 = 0.129$, $k = 0.974$, CONF $\{-0.69 \leq \rho \leq 0.81\}$

5. $c = 2.576$, $r = 0.66$, $z_0 = 0.79$, $k = 0.13$, CONF $\{0.58 \leq \rho \leq 0.73\}$

7. $t_0 > 1.81$; $t_0 < -1.81$; t_0 greater than 2.23 or less than -2.23

9. (a) $r = 0.24$ (5%), 0.33 (1%), (b) $|r| = 0.28$ (5%), 0.36 (1%)

SECTION 19.1

1. 2434.46 ± 4.39

3. 80.02 ± 0.13

5. CONF $\{0.8 \leq \sigma^2 \leq 6.0\}$

7. CONF $\{1.77 \leq \mu \leq 2.43\}$

9. $\bar{X}$ is approximately normal with mean 0 and variance 1/1200 (1/12 is the variance of the present uniform distribution), and
$$P(-0.05 \leq \bar{X} \leq 0.05) = \Phi(0.05\sqrt{1200}) - \Phi(-0.05\sqrt{1200}) = 91.6\%.$$

SECTION 19.2

1. X_j has the density
$$f_j(x_j) = \dfrac{\sqrt{c_j}}{\sqrt{2\pi}\,\sigma} \exp\left[-\dfrac{c_j}{2}\left(\dfrac{x_j - \mu}{\sigma}\right)^2\right].$$

Obtain l from (1), Sec. 11.5, then $\ln l$. Equate
$$\dfrac{\partial \ln l}{\partial \mu} = \dfrac{1}{\sigma^2}\,[c_1(x_1 - \mu) + \cdots + c_n(x_n - \mu)]$$

to zero. Solve for μ to get the estimate
$$\hat{\mu} = \dfrac{c_1 x_1 + \cdots + c_n x_n}{c_1 + \cdots + c_n}.$$

Because of (3) the c_j are proportional to the reciprocals of the variances. Hence we may set $c_j = g_j$. Then $\hat{\mu} = \bar{x}^*$.

3. (a) $\bar{x}^* = \dfrac{1}{n+m}\,(x_1 + \cdots + x_n + x_1' + \cdots + x_m')$

$\qquad = \dfrac{n\bar{x}}{n+m} + \dfrac{m\bar{x}'}{n+m}$

because $x_1 + \cdots + x_n = n\bar{x}$ and $x_1' + \cdots + x_m' = m\bar{x}'$.
(b) $\bar{X}$ and $\bar{X}' = (X_1' + \cdots + X_m')/m$ have variance σ^2/n and σ^2/m, respectively, cf. Theorem 2 in Sec. 9.8. Hence, by (4) in Sec. 6.7 and Theorem 1 in Sec. 9.8, the random variable $\bar{X}^* = g_1\bar{X} + g_2\bar{X}'$ has variance

$$\sigma^{*2} = \left(\frac{g_1^2}{n} + \frac{g_2^2}{m}\right)\sigma^2.$$

Substitute $g_2 = 1 - g_1$ and set $d\sigma^{*2}/dg_1 = 0$.
5. $73°2'8''$

SECTION 19.3

1. $A = ab = 12000 \pm 17$ sq. in.
3. $\gamma = 8.014 \pm 0.039$ g/cm^3
5. $m \approx \sqrt{a^2 m_x^2 + b^2 m_y^2}$.

SECTION 19.4

1. $y - 1.76 = 0.04(x - 55)$
3. $y - 0.038 = 0.0086(x - 6)$
5.

$$\begin{aligned} 4b_0 + 2b_1 + 6b_2 &= 4 \\ 2b_0 + 6b_1 + 8b_2 &= 4 \\ 6b_0 + 8b_1 + 18b_2 &= 10 \end{aligned}$$

$y = 0.3 - 0.1x + 0.5x^2$

SECTION 20.1

1. Hypothesis $\mu = 0$, alternative $\mu > 0$, $\bar{x} = 0.83$, $t = \sqrt{10}\cdot 0.83/0.82 = 3.21 > c = 1.83$ ($\alpha = 5\%$, 9 degrees of freedom, cf. Table 8), reject the hypothesis (also when $\alpha = 1\%$).
3. Hypothesis $\mu = 0$, alternative $\mu > 0$, $\bar{x} = 1.58$, $t = \sqrt{10}\cdot 1.58/1.23 = 4.06 > c = 2.26$ ($\alpha = 5\%$, two-sided), reject the hypothesis.
5. $n = 8, P(X \geq 7) = 1 - P(X \leq 6) = 1 - 0.9648 = 3.5\%$ (cf. Table 1d in Appendix 4), reject the hypothesis that the difference is not significant, at the 5%-level.
7. $\bar{x} = 9.67$, $s = 11.87$, $t_0 = \sqrt{15}\cdot 9.67/11.87 = 3.15 > c = 1.76$ ($\alpha = 5\%$, 14 degrees of freedom). Even $3.15 > c = 2.98$ ($\alpha = 0.5\%$), which shows that the present test is better.

SECTION 20.2

3. $n = 7$. Hypothesis *no trend*, alternative *negative trend*. Two transpositions (5.6 and 5.4 before 6.0). $P(T \leq 2) = 0.5\%$ (cf. Table 10a in Appendix 4). Reject the hypothesis.
5. Hypothesis *no trend*, alternative *positive trend*. $P(T \leq 10) = 1.4\%$ (cf. Table 10a in Appendix 4). Reject the hypothesis.

SECTION 20.3

1. $n = 20$, $M^* = 84$, $m = 9$, $u = 4 < c_1 = 5$ ($\alpha = 5\%$, $\alpha^* = 2.5\%$), reject the hypothesis that the sample values are arranged at random.

3. $n = 20$, $M = 35$, $m = 10$, $u = 10 > c_1 = 6$ ($\alpha = 5\%$), do not reject the hypothesis that the sample values are arranged at random.

5. Do not reject the hypothesis that the digits are randomly arranged.

SECTION 20.4

1. $n_1 = 8$, $n_2 = 9$, critical values $c_1 = 5$, $c_2 = 13$ ($\alpha^* = 2.5\%$), reject the hypothesis.

3. $n_1 = n_2 = 10$, 5 runs, $c_1 = 6$, $c_2 = 15$ ($\alpha^* = 2.5\%$), reject the hypothesis.

5. $n_1 = n_2 = 20$, 11 runs, $c_1 = 14$, $c_2 = 28$ ($\alpha = 5\%$, two-sided), reject the hypothesis.

SECTION 20.5

1. $n = 7$, $m = 6$, $u_0 = 8$, do not reject the hypothesis that the population has mean 0.

5. Yes, the corresponding probability is smaller.

SECTION 20.6

1. $1 + 2 + \cdots + n_1 = \dfrac{n_1(n_1 + 1)}{2}$

$(n_2 + 1) + (n_2 + 2) + \cdots + (n_2 + n_1)$
$$= \frac{(n_1 + n_2)(n_1 + n_2 + 1) - n_2(n_2 + 1)}{2} = \frac{n_1(n_1 + 2n_2 + 1)}{2}$$

3. $n_1 = 5$, $n_2 = 6$, $w = 43 > c_2 = 42$, reject the hypothesis.

5. $n_1 = 15$, $n_2 = 20$, $\mu_W = 270$, $\sigma_W = 30$, $c_1 = 211$, $c_2 = 329$, $w = 216 > c_1$, do not reject the hypothesis.

SECTION 21.2

1. $\Omega = \{1, 2\}$, $A = \{1, 2\}$, where 1 means odd and 2 means even.

	$\theta_1 = 1$	$\theta_2 = 2$
$a_1 = 1$	-1	2
$a_2 = 2$	2	-3

I should choose $\theta = 1$. If II is permitted to choose first, he should choose $a = 2$.

3. 9 decision functions. 5 of them are nonsensical, because $x = 0$ makes $\theta = 2$ impossible, etc. The other 4 decision functions are listed in Problem 4.

5.
$R(0, d_1) = 0$, $\quad R(1, d_1) = 0.5$, $\quad R(2, d_1) = 1$,
$R(0, d_2) = 0$, $\quad R(1, d_2) = 1$, $\quad R(2, d_2) = 0$,
$R(0, d_3) = 1$, $\quad R(1, d_3) = 0$, $\quad R(2, d_3) = 1$,
$R(0, d_4) = 1$, $\quad R(1, d_4) = 0.5$, $\quad R(2, d_4) = 0$.

7. $R(\theta, d_1) = 0$, 0.25, 1; $\quad R(\theta, d_2) = 0$, 0.5, 0; $\quad R(\theta, d_3) = 1$, 0, 1; $\quad R(\theta, d_4) = 1$, 0.25, 0

SECTION 21.3

1. $R(\mu, d) = E([\bar{X} - \mu]^2) = 0.5$; cf. Theorem 2, Sec. 9.8

3. $R(\mu, d_2) = k^2 + (1 - k)^2$, $k = 0.5$

5. $R(\mu, d) = (k_1^2 + \cdots + k_n^2)\sigma^2$, $k_1 = \cdots = k_n = 1/n$

SECTION 21.6

1. d_2

3. d_2 is better than d_3.

5. Suppose that there is a complete class C not containing d. Then C contains a d^* which is better than d. This contradicts the assumption that d is admissible.

7. Let D_1 be a minimal complete class and D_2 the class of admissible decision functions. By Problem 5, $D_2 \subset D_1$. Show that $d_1 \in D_1$ implies $d_1 \in D_2$, thus $D_1 = D_2$. Suppose not. Then $d_1 \notin D_2$, d_1 is not admissible; there exists a d_2 better than d_1. Show $d_2 \notin D_1$. Suppose not. Then $d_2 \in D_1$. Since $d_1 \in D_1$ and d_2 is better than d_1, $D_1 - \{d_1\}$ is complete, and D_1 is not minimal, a contradiction. Thus $d_2 \in D_1$ is false, and $d_2 \notin D_1$. Since D_1 is complete, it contains a d_3 better than d_2; hence d_3 is better than d_1, $D_1 - \{d_1\}$ is complete, and D_1 is not minimal. Hence $d_1 \notin D_2$ is false, and $d_1 \in D_2$.

9. $k = 5/8$, $R_{\min} = 1/8$. Maximum risk $R(\theta_1, d_k) = 2 - 3k$ when $k \leqq 5/8$ and $R(\theta_2, d_k) = -3 + 5k$ when $k \geqq 5/8$.

11. d_2

SECTION 21.7

1. (a) d_4, (b) d_2, (c) d_1

5. k remains arbitrary; $\bar{R}(q, d_k) = 1/8$, which is the value of $R(\theta_1, d_k)$ and $R(\theta_2, d_k)$ in the case of the minimax decision function.

11. d_2 when $0 \leqq q_1 \leqq 1/3$, d_1 when $1/3 \leqq q_1 \leqq 1/2$

13. d_2 when $0 \leqq q_1 \leqq 0.6$, d_1 when $0.6 \leqq q_1 \leqq 0.75$

15. The Bayes decision function corresponds to

$$a_0 = \frac{1.2}{2 + q_1}, \qquad a_1 = \frac{1.8 - q_1}{3 - q_1}.$$

APPENDIX 3

References

Acton, F. S. (1959), *Analysis of Straight Line Data*. Wiley, New York

Anderson, R. L. and T. A. Bancroft (1952), *Statistical Theory in Research*. McGraw-Hill, New York

Anderson, T. W. (1958), *An Introduction to Multivariate Statistical Analysis*. Wiley, New York

Army Ordnance Corps (1952), *Tables of the Cumulative Binomial Probabilities*. ORDP, 20-11

Bartlett, M. S. (1955), *An Introduction to Stochastic Processes*. Cambridge University Press, Cambridge

Barucha-Reid, A. T. (1960), *Elements of the Theory of Stochastic Processes and Their Applications*. McGraw-Hill, New York

Bennet, C. A. and N. L. Franklin (1954), *Statistical Analysis in Chemistry and the Chemical Industry*. Wiley, New York

Blackwell, D. and M. A. Girshick (1966), *Theory of Games and Statistical Decisions*. 5th printing. Wiley, New York

Bowker, A. H. and H. P. Goode (1952), *Sampling Inspection by Variables*. McGraw-Hill, New York

British Association Mathematical Tables (1951), *Circular and Hyperbolic Functions, Exponential, Sine and Cosine Integrals, Factorial (Gamma) and Derived Functions, Integrals of Probability Integral*. 3rd ed. Cambridge University Press, Cambridge

Brownlee, K. A. (1949), *Industrial Experimentation*. Chemical Publishing Co., New York

Cauchy, A. L. (1853), Sur les résultats moyens d'observations de même nature et sur les résultats les plus probables. *Comp. Rend. Acad. Sci. Paris*, **37**, 198–206

Chapin, F. S. (1947), *Experimental Designs in Sociological Research*. Harper, New York

Chernoff, H. and L. E. Moses (1967), *Elementary Decision Theory*. 5th printing. Wiley, New York

Chung, J. H. and D. B. DeLury (1950), *Confidence Limits for the Hypergeometric Distribution*. University of Toronto Press, Toronto

Clopper, C. J. and E. S. Pearson (1934), The use of confidence or fiducial limits illustrated in the case of the binomial. *Biometrika*, **26**, 404–413

Cochran, W. G. (1963), *Sampling Techniques*. 2nd ed. Wiley, New York

Cochran, W. G. and G. M. Cox (1957), *Experimental Designs*. 2nd ed. Wiley, New York

Comrie, L. J. (1949), *Chamber's Six-Figure Mathematical Tables*. *Vol. II. Natural Values*. Chambers, Edinburgh

Comrie, L. J. (1962), *Barlow's Tables*. 4th ed. New Impression. Chemical Publishing Co., New York

Cox, D. R. (1958), *Planning of Experiments*. Wiley, New York

Cramér, H. (1961). *Mathematical Methods of Statistics*. 9th printing. Princeton University Press, Princeton, N.J.

Croxton, F. E. and D. J. Cowden (1955), *Applied General Statistics*. 2nd ed. Prentice-Hall, Englewood Cliffs, N.J.

Davies, O. L., editor (1956), *The Design and Analysis of Industrial Experiments*. 2nd ed. Oliver and Boyd, Edinburgh

Davis, H. T. (1941), *The Analysis of Economic Time Series*. Principia Press, Bloomington, Ind.

Deming, W. (1950), *Some Theory of Sampling*. Wiley, New York

Deming, W. (1960), *Sample Design in Business Research*. Wiley, New York

Dixon, W. J. (1940), A criterion for testing the hypothesis that two samples are from the same population. *Annals Math. Stat.*, **11**, 199–204

Dodge, H. F. and H. G. Romig (1929), A method of sampling inspection. *Bell System Tech. J.*, **8**, 613–631

Dodge, H. F. and H. G. Romig (1959), *Sampling Inspection Tables*. 2nd ed. Wiley, New York

Doob, J. L. (1953), *Stochastic Processes*. Wiley, New York

Draper, N. and H. Smith (1966), *Applied Regression Analysis*. Wiley, New York

Dwyer, P. S. (1951), *Linear Computations*. Wiley, New York

Dynkin, E. B. (1965), *Markov Processes*. 2 vols. (Translated from the Russian.) Springer, Berlin

Edwards, A. L. (1950), *Experimental Design in Psychological Research*. Rinehart, New York

Federer, W. T. (1955), *Experimental Design*. MacMillan, New York

Feller, W. (1935), Über den zentralen Grenzwertsatz der Wahrscheinlichkeitsrechnung. *Math. Zeitschr.*, **40**, 521–559

Feller, W. (1961), *An Introduction to Probability Theory and Its Applications*. Vol. I. 2nd ed. 6th printing, 1961. Vol. II. 2nd printing, 1966. Wiley, New York

Finney, D. J. (1952), *Statistical Method in Biological Assay*. Griffin, London

Finney, D. J., R. Latscha, B. M. Bennet, and P. Hsu (1963), *Tables for Testing Significance in a 2 × 2 Contingency Table*. Cambridge University Press, Cambridge

Fisher, R. A. (1915), Frequency distribution of the values of the correlation coefficient in samples from an indefinitely large population. *Biometrika*, **10**, 507–521

Fisher, R. A. (1922), On the mathematical foundations of theoretical statistics. *Phil. Trans. Roy. Soc. London* (A), **222**, 309–368

Fisher, R. A. (1925), Theory of statistical estimation. *Proc. Camb. Phil. Soc.*, **22**, 700–725

Fisher, R. A. (1950), *Contributions to Mathematical Statistics*. Editor W. A. Shewhart. Wiley, New York

Fisher, R. A. (1958), *Statistical Methods for Research Workers*. 13th ed. Oliver and Boyd, Edinburgh

Fisher, R. A. (1960), *The Design of Experiments*. 7th printing. Oliver and Boyd, Edinburgh

Fisher, R. A. and F. Yates (1957), *Statistical Tables for Biological, Agricultural and Medical Research*. 5th ed. Oliver and Boyd, Edinburgh

Fraser, D. A. S. (1966), *Nonparametric Methods in Statistics*. 5th printing. Wiley, New York

Garwood, F. (1936), Fiducial limits for the Poisson distribution. *Biometrika*, **28**, 437–442

Gnedenko, B. V. and A. N. Kolmogorov (1954), *Limit Distributions for Sums of Independent Random Variables*. (Translated from the Russian.) Addison-Wesley, Reading, Mass.

Goodman, L. A. (1954), Simple methods for analyzing three-factor interaction in contingency tables. *J. Amer. Stat. Assn.*, **59**, 319–352

Goodman, L. A. and W. H. Kruskal (1954), Measures of association for cross classification. I, II, III. *J. Amer. Stat. Assn.*, **49**, 1954, 732–764; **54**, 1959, 123–163; **58**, 1963, 310–364

Grant, E. L. (1952), *Statistical Quality Control.* 2nd ed. McGraw-Hill, New York

Graybill, F. A. (1961), *An Introduction to Linear Statistical Models.* McGraw-Hill, New York

Greenwood, J. A. and H. O. Hartley (1961), *Guide to Tables in Mathematical Statistics.* Princeton University Press, Princeton, N.J.

Grenander, U. and M. Rosenblatt (1957), *Statistical Analysis of Stationary Time Series.* Wiley, New York

Hald, A. (1962), *Statistical Tables and Formulas.* 4th printing. Wiley, New York

Hansen, M. H., W. N. Hurwitz, and W. G. Madow (1966), *Sample Survey Methods and Theory.* Wiley, New York

Harvard Computation Laboratory (1955), *Tables of the Cumulative Binomial Probability Distribution.* Harvard University Press, Cambridge, Mass.

Helmert, F. R. (1876), Ueber die Wahrscheinlichkeit der Potenzsummen der Beobachtungsfehler und über einige damit im Zusammenhange stehende Fragen. *Zeitschr. für Math. und Phys.*, **21**, 192–218

Hill, A. B. (1955), *Principles of Medical Statistics.* 6th ed. Oxford University Press, London

Huff, D. (1954), *How to Lie With Statistics.* Norton, New York

Kelley, T. L. (1948), *The Kelley Statistical Tables.* 2nd ed. Harvard University Press, Cambridge, Mass.

Kempthorne, O. (1952), *The Design and Analysis of Experiments.* Wiley, New York

Kendall, M. G. (1953), *Rank Correlation Methods.* 2nd ed. Griffin, London

Kendall, M. G. (1957), *A Course in Multivariate Analysis.* Griffin, London

Kendall, M. G. and A. Stuart (1946), *The Advanced Theory of Statistics.* 2 vols. Griffin, London

Kendall, M. G. and R. M. Sundrum (1953), Distribution-free methods and order properties. *Rev. Int. Stat. Inst.*, **23**, 124–134

Kitagawa, T. (1951), *Tables of Poisson Distributions.* Baifukan, Tokyo

Kitagawa, T. and M. Mitome (1953), *Tables for the Design of Factorial Experiments.* Baifukan, Tokyo

Kolmogorov, A. N. (1956), *Foundations of the Theory of Probability.* 2nd English ed. (Translated from the German.) Chelsea, New York

Kullback, S. (1959), *Information Theory and Statistics.* Wiley, New York

Laplace, P. S. de (1812), *Théorie analytique des probabilités.* Paris

Lehmann, E. L. (1959), *Testing Statistical Hypotheses.* Wiley, New York

Lévy, P. (1935), Propriétes asymptotiques des sommes des variables aléatoires indépendantes ou enchainees. *J. Math. Pures et Appl.*, **14**, 347–402

Lieberman, G. J. and D. B. Owen (1961), *Tables of the Hypergeometric Probability Distribution.* Stanford University Press, Stanford, Cal.

Lindeberg, J. W. (1922), Eine neue Herleitung des Exponentialgesetzes in der Wahrscheinlichkeitsrechnung. *Math. Zeitschr.*, **15**, 211–225

Lindquist, E. F. (1953), *Design and Analysis of Experiments in Psychology and Education.* Houghton Mifflin Co., Boston, Mass.

Loève, M. (1963), *Probability Theory.* Van Nostrand, Princeton, N.J.

Luce, R. D. and H. Raiffa (1966), *Games and Decisions.* 6th printing. Wiley, New York

Lukacs, E. (1960), *Characteristic Functions.* Griffin, London

Lukacs, E. and R. G. Laha (1964), *Applications of Characteristic Functions.* Griffin, London

Mann, H. B. (1949), *Analysis and Design of Experiments.* Dover, New York

Mann, H. B. and D. R. Whitney (1947), On a test of whether one of two random variables is stochastically larger than the other. *Annals Math. Stat.*, **18**, 50–60

Mathisen, H. C. (1943), A method of testing the hypothesis that two samples are from the same population. *Annals Math. Stat.*, **14**, 188–194

Moivre, A. de (1718), *The Doctrine of Chances.* Millar, London

Molina, E. C. (1942), *Poisson's Exponential Binomial Limit.* Van Nostrand, New York

Mood, A. M. (1940), The distribution theory of runs. *Annals Math. Stat.*, **11**, 367–392

Moore, G. H. and W. A. Wallis (1943), Time series significance tests based on signs of differences. *J. Amer. Stat. Assn.*, **38**, 153–164

Moran, P. A. P., J. W. Whitfield, and H. E. Daniels (1950), Symposium on ranking methods. *J. Roy. Stat. Soc.* (B), **12**, 153–191

Morse, P. M. (1958), *Queues, Inventories and Maintenance.* Wiley, New York

Mosteller, F. (1941), Note on an application of runs to quality control charts. *Annals Math. Stat.*, **12**, 228–232

National Bureau of Standards (1947), *Table of Circular and Hyperbolic Tangents and Cotangents for Radian Arguments.* 2nd printing. U.S. Government Printing Office, Washington, D.C.

National Bureau of Standards (1949), *Tables of the Binomial Probability Distribution.* U.S. Government Printing Office, Washington, D.C.

National Bureau of Standards (1951), *Tables of the Exponential Function e^x.* U.S. Government Printing Office, Washington, D.C.

National Bureau of Standards (1953), *Tables of Normal Probability Functions.* U.S. Government Printing Office, Washington, D.C.

Neumann, J. von (1928), Zur Theorie der Gesellschaftsspiele. *Math. Ann.*, **100**, 295–320

Neumann, J. von and O. Morgenstern (1953), *Theory of Games and Economic Behavior.* 3rd ed. Princeton University Press, Princeton, N.J.

Neyman, J. (1935), On the problem of confidence intervals. *Annals Math. Stat.*, **6**, 111–116

Neyman, J. (1937), Outline of a theory of statistical estimation based on the classical theory of probability. *Phil. Trans. Roy. Soc. London* (A), **236**, 333–380

Neyman, J. (1952), *Lectures and Conferences on Mathematical Statistics and Probability.* 2nd ed. Graduate School of the U.S. Department of Agriculture, Washington, D.C.

Neyman, J. and E. S. Pearson (1928), On the use and interpretation of certain test criteria for purposes of statistical inference. *Biometrika*, **20A**, 175–240 and 263–294

Neyman, J. and E. S. Pearson (1933), On the p.oblem of the most efficient tests of statistical hypotheses. *Phil. Trans. Roy. Soc. London* (A), **231**, 289–337

Noether, G. E. (1967). *Elements of Nonparametric Statistics.* Wiley, New York

Olmstead, P. S. (1946), Distribution of sample arrangements for runs up and down. *Annals Math. Stat.*, **17**, 24–33

Parzen, E. (1960), *Modern Probability Theory and its Applications.* Wiley, New York

Pearson, E. S. (1938), *Karl Pearson.* Cambridge University Press, Cambridge

Pearson, E. S. and J. Wishart, editors (1942), *"Student's" Collected Papers.* Biometrika Office, London

Pearson, E. S. and H. O. Hartley (1954), *Biometrika Tables for Statisticians.* Cambridge University Press, Cambridge

Pearson, K. (1900), On the criterion that a system of deviations from the probable in the case of a correlated system of variables is such that it can be reasonably supposed to have arisen in random sampling. *Phil. Mag.* V, **50**, 157–175

Pearson, K., editor (1922), *Tables of the Incomplete Gamma Function.* Cambridge University Press, Cambridge

Pearson, K., editor (1968), *Tables of the Incomplete Beta Function.* 2nd ed. (prepared by E. S. Pearson and N. L. Johnson). Cambridge University Press, Cambridge

Peters, J. (1957), *Zehnstellige Logarithmentafel*. (Original German edition 1922.) Ungar, New York

Putter, J. (1955), The treatment of ties in some nonparametric tests. *Annals Math. Stat.*, **26**, 368–386

Raiffa, H. and R. Schlaifer (1961), *Applied Statistical Decision Theory*. Graduate School of Business Administration, Harvard University, Cambridge, Mass.

Rand Corporation (1955), *A Million Random Digits With 100,000 Normal Deviates*. Free Press, Glencoe, Ill.

Rao, C. R. (1952), *Advanced Statistical Methods in Biometric Research*. Wiley, New York

Rice, W. B. (1947), *Control Charts in Factory Management*. Wiley, New York

Ricker, W. E. (1937), The concept of confidence or fiducial limits applied to the Poisson frequency distribution, *J. Amer. Stat. Assn.*, **32**, 349–356

Romig, H. G. (1953), 50–100 *Binomial Tables*. Wiley, New York

Roy, S. N. (1957), *Some Aspects of Multivariate Analysis*. Wiley, New York

Royal Society Mathematical Tables (1954), *Table of Binomial Coefficients*. Editor J. C. P. Miller. Cambridge University Press, Cambridge

Saaty, T. L. (1961), *Elements of Queuing Theory*. McGraw-Hill, New York

Sarhan, A. E. and B. G. Greenberg, editors (1962), *Contributions to Order Statistics*. Wiley, New York

Savage, I. R. (1962), *Bibliography of Nonparametric Statistics*. Harvard University Press, Cambridge, Mass.

Savage, L. J. (1954), *The Foundations of Statistics*. Wiley, New York

Scheffé, H. (1943), Statistical inference in the non-parametric case. *Annals Math. Stat.*, **14**, 305–332

Scheffé, H. (1953), A method for judging all contrasts in the analysis of variance. *Biometrika*, **40**, 87–104

Scheffé, H. (1963), *The Analysis of Variance*. 2nd ed. Wiley, New York

Sheppard, W. F. (1898), On the calculation of the most probable values of frequency-constants for data arranged according to equidistant divisions of a scale. *Proc. London Math. Soc.*, **29**, 353–380

Shewhart, W. A. (1939), *Statistical Method from the Viewpoint of Quality Control*. Graduate School of the U.S. Department of Agriculture, Washington, D.C.

Smirnov, N. (1939), On the estimation of the discrepancy between empirical curves of distribution for two independent samples. *Bull. Math. Univ. Moscow*, **2** (2), 3–14

Smirnov, N. (1961), *Tables for the Distribution and Density Functions of the t-distribution*. Pergamon Press, New York

Stephan, F. F. and P. J. McCarthy (1958), *Sampling Opinions*. Wiley, New York

Stevens, W. L. (1939), Distribution of groups in a sequence of alternatives. *Annals of Eugenics*, **9**, 10–17

"Student" (1908), The probable error of a mean. *Biometrika*, **6**, 1–25

Sukatme, P. V. (1954), *Sampling Theory of Surveys with Applications*. Iowa State College Press, Ames, Iowa

Swed, F. S. and C. Eisenhart (1943), Tables for testing randomness of grouping in a sequence of alternatives. *Annals Math. Stat.*, **14**, 66–87

Takacs, L. (1962), *Introduction to the Theory of Queues*. Oxford University Press, London

Todhunter, I. (1949), *A History of the Mathematical Theory of Probability*. (Macmillan, London, 1865) Chelsea, New York

Uspensky, J. V. (1937), *Introduction to Mathematical Probability*. McGraw-Hill, New York

Wald, A. (1947), *Sequential Analysis*. Wiley, New York

Wald, A. (1949), Statistical decision functions. *Annals Math. Stat.*, **20**, 165–205

Wald, A. (1950), *Statistical Decision Functions*. Wiley, New York

Wald, A. and J. Wolfowitz (1940), On a test whether two samples are from the same population. *Annals Math. Stat.*, **11**, 147–162

Walsh, J. E. (1949), Some significance tests for the median which are valid under very general conditions. *Annals Math. Stat.*, **20**, 64–81

Weiss, L. (1961), *Statistical Decision Theory*. McGraw-Hill, New York

Wilcoxon, F. (1945), Individual comparisons by ranking methods. *Biometrics*, **1**, 80–83

Wilcoxon, F. (1947), Probability tables for individual comparisons by ranking methods. *Biometrics*, **3**, 119–122

Wilcoxon, F. (1949), *Some Rapid Approximate Statistical Procedures*. American Cyanimid Co., Stamford, Conn.

Wilks, S. S. (1959), *Nonparametric statistical inference. Probability and Statistics*, The Harald Cramér Volume. Almqvist and Wiksell, Uppsala

Wilks, S. S. (1961), A combinatorial test for the problem of two samples from continuous distributions. *Proc. Fourth Berkeley Symp. on Math. Stat. and Prob.* University of California Press, Berkeley, Cal.

Wilks, S. S. (1962), *Mathematical Statistics*. Wiley, New York

Williams, E. J. (1959), *Regression Analysis*. Wiley, New York

Wilson, E. B. (1927), Probable inference, the law of succession, and statistical inference. *J. Amer. Stat. Assn.*, **22**, 209–212

Wold, H. (1934), Sulla correzione di Sheppard. *Giorn. Ist. Italiano d. Attuari*, **5**, 304

Wolfowitz, J. (1944), Asymptotic distribution of runs up and down. *Annals Math. Stat.*, **15**, 163–172

Wolfowitz, J. (1949), Non-parametric statistical inference. *Proc. Berkeley Symp. on Math. Stat. and Prob.* University of California Press, Berkeley, Cal.

Yaglom, A. M. (1962), *Stationary Random Functions*. (Translated from the Russian.) Prentice-Hall, Englewood Cliffs, N.J.

Yates, F. (1949), *Sampling Methods for Censuses and Surveys*. Hafner, New York

Yule, G. U. and M. G. Kendall (1965), *An Introduction to the Theory of Statistics*. 14th ed., 4th printing. Griffin, London

APPENDIX **4**

Tables

1 Factorial Function. Binomial Coefficients. Binomial Distribution. Gamma Function

Table 1a. Factorial Function

More extended tables: Fisher and Yates (1957), Peters (1957) (cf. Appendix 3).

n	$n!$	n	$n!$	n	$n!$	n	$n!$
1	1	6	720	11	39 916 800	16	20 922 789 888 000
2	2	7	5 040	12	479 001 600	17	355 687 428 096 000
3	6	8	40 320	13	6 227 020 800	18	6 402 373 705 728 000
4	24	9	362 880	14	87 178 291 200	19	121 645 100 408 832 000
5	120	10	3 628 800	15	1 307 674 368 000	20	2 432 902 008 176 640 000

Table 1b. Logarithm of the Factorial Function

More extended tables: Fisher and Yates (1957), Peters (1957) (cf. Appendix 3).

n	$\log(n!)$	n	$\log(n!)$	n	$\log(n!)$	n	$\log(n!)$
1	0.000 000	6	2.857 332	11	7.601 156	16	13.320 620
2	0.301 030	7	3.702 431	12	8.680 337	17	14.551 069
3	0.778 151	8	4.605 521	13	9.794 280	18	15.806 341
4	1.380 211	9	5.559 763	14	10.940 408	19	17.085 095
5	2.079 181	10	6.559 763	15	12.116 500	20	18.386 125

Table 1c. Binomial Coefficients

More extended tables: Royal Society Mathematical Tables (1954), Peters (1957) (cf. Appendix 3)

k	$\binom{1}{k}$	$\binom{2}{k}$	$\binom{3}{k}$	$\binom{4}{k}$	$\binom{5}{k}$	$\binom{6}{k}$	$\binom{7}{k}$	$\binom{8}{k}$	$\binom{9}{k}$	$\binom{10}{k}$	$\binom{11}{k}$	$\binom{12}{k}$	$\binom{13}{k}$
0	1	1	1	1	1	1	1	1	1	1	1	1	1
1	1	2	3	4	5	6	7	8	9	10	11	12	13
2		1	3	6	10	15	21	28	36	45	55	66	78
3			1	4	10	20	35	56	84	120	165	220	286
4				1	5	15	35	70	126	210	330	495	715
5					1	6	21	56	126	252	462	792	1287
6						1	7	28	84	210	462	924	1716
7							1	8	36	120	330	792	1716
8								1	9	45	165	495	1287
9									1	10	55	220	715
10										1	11	66	286
11											1	12	78
12												1	13
13													1

k	$\binom{14}{k}$	$\binom{15}{k}$	$\binom{16}{k}$	$\binom{17}{k}$	$\binom{18}{k}$	$\binom{19}{k}$	$\binom{20}{k}$
0	1	1	1	1	1	1	1
1	14	15	16	17	18	19	20
2	91	105	120	136	153	171	190
3	364	455	560	680	816	969	1140
4	1001	1365	1820	2380	3060	3876	4845
5	2002	3003	4368	6188	8568	11628	15504
6	3003	5005	8008	12376	18564	27132	38760
7	3432	6435	11440	19448	31824	50388	77520
8	3003	6435	12870	24310	43758	75582	125970
9	2002	5005	11440	24310	48620	92378	167960
10	1001	3003	8008	19448	43758	92378	184756
11	364	1365	4368	12376	31824	75582	167960
12	91	455	1820	6188	18564	50388	125970
13	14	105	560	2380	8568	27132	77520
14	1	15	120	680	3060	11628	38760
15		1	16	136	816	3876	15504
16			1	17	153	969	4845
17				1	18	171	1140
18					1	19	190
19						1	20
20							1

Table 1*d*. Binomial Distribution

Cf. (4) and (7) in Sec. 7.1.

More extended tables: Army Ordnance Corps (1952), Harvard Computation Laboratory (1955), National Bureau of Standards (1949), Romig (1953); cf. Appendix 3.

n	x	p = 0.1 f(x)	F(x)	p = 0.2 f(x)	F(x)	p = 0.3 f(x)	F(x)	p = 0.4 f(x)	F(x)	p = 0.5 f(x)	F(x)
		0.		0.		0.		0.		0.	
1	0	9000	0.9000	8000	0.8000	7000	0.7000	6000	0.6000	5000	0.5000
	1	1000	1.0000	2000	1.0000	3000	1.0000	4000	1.0000	5000	1.0000
	0	8100	0.8100	6400	0.6400	4900	0.4900	3600	0.3600	2500	0.2500
2	1	1800	0.9900	3200	0.9600	4200	0.9100	4800	0.8400	5000	0.7500
	2	0100	1.0000	0400	1.0000	0900	1.0000	1600	1.0000	2500	1.0000
	0	7290	0.7290	5120	0.5120	3430	0.3430	2160	0.2160	1250	0.1250
3	1	2430	0.9720	3840	0.8960	4410	0.7840	4320	0.6480	3750	0.5000
	2	0270	0.9990	0960	0.9920	1890	0.9730	2880	0.9360	3750	0.8750
	3	0010	1.0000	0080	1.0000	0270	1.0000	0640	1.0000	1250	1.0000
	0	6561	0.6561	4096	0.4096	2401	0.2401	1296	0.1296	0625	0.0625
	1	2916	0.9477	4096	0.8192	4116	0.6517	3456	0.4752	2500	0.3125
4	2	0486	0.9963	1536	0.9728	2646	0.9163	3456	0.8208	3750	0.6875
	3	0036	0.9999	0256	0.9984	0756	0.9919	1536	0.9744	2500	0.9375
	4	0001	1.0000	0016	1.0000	0081	1.0000	0256	1.0000	0625	1.0000
	0	5905	0.5905	3277	0.3277	1681	0.1681	0778	0.0778	0313	0.0313
	1	3281	0.9185	4096	0.7373	3602	0.5282	2592	0.3370	1563	0.1875
5	2	0729	0.9914	2048	0.9421	3087	0.8369	3456	0.6826	3125	0.5000
	3	0081	0.9995	0512	0.9933	1323	0.9692	2304	0.9130	3125	0.8125
	4	0005	1.0000	0064	0.9997	0284	0.9976	0768	0.9898	1563	0.9688
	5	0000	1.0000	0003	1.0000	0024	1.0000	0102	1.0000	0313	1.0000
	0	5314	0.5314	2621	0.2621	1176	0.1176	0467	0.0467	0156	0.0156
	1	3543	0.8857	3932	0.6554	3025	0.4202	1866	0.2333	0938	0.1094
	2	0984	0.9841	2458	0.9011	3241	0.7443	3110	0.5443	2344	0.3438
6	3	0146	0.9987	0819	0.9830	1852	0.9295	2765	0.8208	3125	0.6563
	4	0012	0.9999	0154	0.9984	0595	0.9891	1382	0.9590	2344	0.8906
	5	0001	1.0000	0015	0.9999	0102	0.9993	0369	0.9959	0938	0.9844
	6	0000	1.0000	0001	1.0000	0007	1.0000	0041	1.0000	0156	1.0000
	0	4783	0.4783	2097	0.2097	0824	0.0824	0280	0.0280	0078	0.0078
	1	3720	0.8503	3670	0.5767	2471	0.3294	1306	0.1586	0547	0.0625
	2	1240	0.9743	2753	0.8520	3177	0.6471	2613	0.4199	1641	0.2266
7	3	0230	0.9973	1147	0.9667	2269	0.8740	2903	0.7102	2734	0.5000
	4	0026	0.9998	0287	0.9953	0972	0.9712	1935	0.9037	2734	0.7734
	5	0002	1.0000	0043	0.9996	0250	0.9962	0774	0.9812	1641	0.9375
	6	0000	1.0000	0004	1.0000	0036	0.9998	0172	0.9984	0547	0.9922
	7	0000	1.0000	0000	1.0000	0002	1.0000	0016	1.0000	0078	1.0000
	0	4305	0.4305	1678	0.1678	0576	0.0576	0168	0.0168	0039	0.0039
	1	3826	0.8131	3355	0.5033	1977	0.2553	0896	0.1064	0313	0.0352
	2	1488	0.9619	2936	0.7969	2965	0.5518	2090	0.3154	1094	0.1445
	3	0331	0.9950	1468	0.9437	2541	0.8059	2787	0.5941	2188	0.3633
8	4	0046	0.9996	0459	0.9896	1361	0.9420	2322	0.8263	2734	0.6367
	5	0004	1.0000	0092	0.9988	0467	0.9887	1239	0.9502	2188	0.8555
	6	0000	1.0000	0011	0.9999	0100	0.9987	0413	0.9915	1094	0.9648
	7	0000	1.0000	0001	1.0000	0012	0.9999	0079	0.9993	0313	0.9961
	8	0000	1.0000	0000	1.0000	0001	1.0000	0007	1.0000	0039	1.0000

Table 1d. Binomial Distribution (*Continued*)

$F(x)$ for $p = 0.5$.   Cf. (7) in Sec. 7.1.

x	$n = 9$	$n = 10$	$n = 11$	$n = 12$	$n = 13$	$n = 14$	$n = 15$	$n = 16$	$n = 17$
0	0.0020	0.0010	0.0005	0.0002	0.0001	0.0001	0.0000	0.0000	0.0000
1	0.0195	0.0107	0.0059	0.0032	0.0017	0.0009	0.0005	0.0003	0.0001
2	0.0898	0.0547	0.0327	0.0193	0.0112	0.0065	0.0037	0.0021	0.0012
3	0.2539	0.1719	0.1133	0.0730	0.0461	0.0287	0.0176	0.0106	0.0064
4	0.5000	0.3770	0.2744	0.1938	0.1334	0.0898	0.0592	0.0384	0.0245
5	0.7461	0.6230	0.5000	0.3872	0.2905	0.2120	0.1509	0.1051	0.0717
6	0.9102	0.8281	0.7256	0.6128	0.5000	0.3953	0.3036	0.2272	0.1662
7	0.9805	0.9453	0.8867	0.8062	0.7095	0.6047	0.5000	0.4018	0.3145
8	0.9980	0.9893	0.9673	0.9270	0.8666	0.7880	0.6964	0.5982	0.5000
9	1.0000	0.9990	0.9941	0.9807	0.9539	0.9102	0.8491	0.7728	0.6855
10		1.0000	0.9995	0.9968	0.9888	0.9713	0.9408	0.8949	0.8338
11			1.0000	0.9998	0.9983	0.9935	0.9824	0.9616	0.9283
12				1.0000	0.9999	0.9991	0.9963	0.9894	0.9755
13					1.0000	0.9999	0.9995	0.9979	0.9936
14									
15						1.0000	1.0000	0.9997	0.9988
							1.0000	1.0000	0.9999
16								1.0000	1.0000

x	$n = 18$	$n = 19$	$n = 20$	$n = 21$	$n = 22$	$n = 23$	$n = 24$	$n = 25$	$n = 26$
0	0.0000	0.0000	0.0000	0.0000	0.0000	0.0000	0.0000	0.0000	0.0000
1	0.0001	0.0000	0.0000	0.0000	0.0000	0.0000	0.0000	0.0000	0.0000
2	0.0007	0.0004	0.0002	0.0001	0.0001	0.0000	0.0000	0.0000	0.0000
3	0.0038	0.0022	0.0013	0.0007	0.0004	0.0002	0.0001	0.0001	0.0000
4	0.0154	0.0096	0.0059	0.0036	0.0022	0.0013	0.0008	0.0005	0.0003
5	0.0481	0.0318	0.0207	0.0133	0.0085	0.0053	0.0033	0.0020	0.0012
6	0.1189	0.0835	0.0577	0.0392	0.0262	0.0173	0.0113	0.0073	0.0047
7	0.2403	0.1796	0.1316	0.0946	0.0669	0.0466	0.0320	0.0216	0.0145
8	0.4073	0.3238	0.2517	0.1917	0.1431	0.1050	0.0758	0.0539	0.0378
9	0.5927	0.5000	0.4119	0.3318	0.2617	0.2024	0.1537	0.1148	0.0843
10	0.7597	0.6762	0.5881	0.5000	0.4159	0.3388	0.2706	0.2122	0.1635
11	0.8811	0.8204	0.7483	0.6682	0.5841	0.5000	0.4194	0.3450	0.2786
12	0.9519	0.9165	0.8684	0.8083	0.7383	0.6612	0.5806	0.5000	0.4225
13	0.9846	0.9682	0.9423	0.9054	0.8569	0.7976	0.7294	0.6550	0.5775
14	0.9962	0.9904	0.9793	0.9608	0.9331	0.8950	0.8463	0.7878	0.7214
15	0.9993	0.9978	0.9941	0.9867	0.9738	0.9534	0.9242	0.8852	0.8365
16	0.9999	0.9996	0.9987	0.9964	0.9915	0.9827	0.9680	0.9461	0.9157
17	1.0000	1.0000	0.9998	0.9993	0.9978	0.9947	0.9887	0.9784	0.9622
18	1.0000	1.0000	1.0000	0.9999	0.9996	0.9987	0.9967	0.9927	0.9855
19		1.0000	1.0000	1.0000	0.9999	0.9998	0.9992	0.9980	0.9953
20			1.0000	1.0000	1.0000	1.0000	0.9999	0.9995	0.9988
21				1.0000	1.0000	1.0000	1.0000	0.9999	0.9997
22					1.0000	1.0000	1.0000	1.0000	1.0000

Table 1e. Confidence Interval for the Parameter *p* of the Binomial Distribution

γ = Confidence level, n = size of sample, m = observed number of successes
Cf. Sec. 12.6

Example. When $n = 20$ and $m = 8$, then $m/n = 40\%$, and a 95%-confidence interval
is CONF $\{0.19 \leqq p \leqq 0.64\}$.

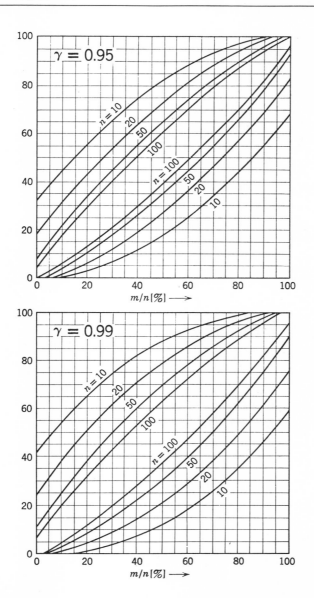

Table 1*f*. Gamma Function

Definition in Sec. 10.1. For computing values outside the interval from 1 to 2, use formula (6) in Sec. 10.1.

Example. $\Gamma(3.4) = 2.4 \cdot \Gamma(2.4) = 2.4 \cdot 1.4 \cdot \Gamma(1.4) = 2.4 \cdot 1.4 \cdot 0.8873$

More extended tables: British Association Mathematical Tables (1951), Comrie (1949) (cf. Appendix 3).

λ	$\Gamma(\lambda)$	λ	$\Gamma(\lambda)$	λ	$\Gamma(\lambda)$	λ	$\Gamma(\lambda)$
	0.		0.		0.		0.
1.01	9943	1.26	9044	1.51	8866	1.76	9214
1.02	9888	1.27	9025	1.52	8870	1.77	9238
1.03	9835	1.28	9007	1.53	8876	1.78	9262
1.04	9784	1.29	8990	1.54	8882	1.79	9288
1.05	9735	1.30	8975	1.55	8889	1.80	9314
1.06	9687	1.31	8960	1.56	8896	1.81	9341
1.07	9642	1.32	8946	1.57	8905	1.82	9368
1.08	9597	1.33	8934	1.58	8914	1.83	9397
1.09	9555	1.34	8922	1.59	8924	1.84	9426
1.10	9514	1.35	8912	1.60	8935	1.85	9456
1.11	9474	1.36	8902	1.61	8947	1.86	9487
1.12	9436	1.37	8893	1.62	8959	1.87	9518
1.13	9399	1.38	8885	1.63	8972	1.88	9551
1.14	9364	1.39	8879	1.64	8986	1.89	9584
1.15	9330	1.40	8873	1.65	9001	1.90	9618
1.16	9298	1.41	8868	1.66	9017	1.91	9652
1.17	9267	1.42	8864	1.67	9033	1.92	9688
1.18	9237	1.43	8860	1.68	9050	1.93	9724
1.19	9209	1.44	8858	1.69	9068	1.94	9761
1.20	9182	1.45	8857	1.70	9086	1.95	9799
1.21	9156	1.46	8856	1.71	9106	1.96	9837
1.22	9131	1.47	8856	1.72	9126	1.97	9877
1.23	9108	1.48	8857	1.73	9147	1.98	9917
1.24	9085	1.49	8859	1.74	9168	1.99	9958
1.25	9064	1.50	8862	1.75	9191	2.00	*0000

2 Poisson Distribution

Table 2. Density $f(x)$ and Distribution Function $F(x)$ of the Poisson Distribution

Cf. (1) and (2) in Sec. 7.4.

More extended tables: Molina (1942), Kitagawa (1951), also see Pearson and Hartley (1954) (cf. Appendix 3).

x	$\mu = 0.1$		$\mu = 0.2$		$\mu = 0.3$		$\mu = 0.4$		$\mu = 0.5$	
	$f(x)$	$F(x)$	$f(x)$	$F(x)$	$f(x)$	$F(x)$	$f(x)$	$F(x)$	$f(x)$	$F(x)$
0	0. 9048	0.9048	0. 8187	0.8187	0. 7408	0.7408	0. 6703	0.6703	0. 6065	0.6065
1	0905	0.9953	1637	0.9825	2222	0.9631	2681	0.9384	3033	0.9098
2	0045	0.9998	0164	0.9989	0333	0.9964	0536	0.9921	0758	0.9856
3	0002	1.0000	0011	0.9999	0033	0.9997	0072	0.9992	0126	0.9982
4	0000	1.0000	0001	1.0000	0003	1.0000	0007	0.9999	0016	0.9998
5							0001	1.0000	0002	1.0000

x	$\mu = 0.6$		$\mu = 0.7$		$\mu = 0.8$		$\mu = 0.9$		$\mu = 1$	
	$f(x)$	$F(x)$	$f(x)$	$F(x)$	$f(x)$	$F(x)$	$f(x)$	$F(x)$	$f(x)$	$F(x)$
0	0. 5488	0.5488	0. 4966	0.4966	0. 4493	0.4493	0. 4066	0.4066	0. 3679	0.3679
1	3293	0.8781	3476	0.8442	3595	0.8088	3659	0.7725	3679	0.7358
2	0988	0.9769	1217	0.9659	1438	0.9526	1647	0.9371	1839	0.9197
3	0198	0.9966	0284	0.9942	0383	0.9909	0494	0.9865	0613	0.9810
4	0030	0.9996	0050	0.9992	0077	0.9986	0111	0.9977	0153	0.9963
5	0004	1.0000	0007	0.9999	0012	0.9998	0020	0.9997	0031	0.9994
6			0001	1.0000	0002	1.0000	0003	1.0000	0005	0.9999
7									0001	1.0000

x	$\mu = 1.5$		$\mu = 2$		$\mu = 3$		$\mu = 4$		$\mu = 5$	
	$f(x)$	$F(x)$	$f(x)$	$F(x)$	$f(x)$	$F(x)$	$f(x)$	$F(x)$	$f(x)$	$F(x)$
0	0. 2231	0.2231	0. 1353	0.1353	0. 0498	0.0498	0. 0183	0.0183	0. 0067	0.0067
1	3347	0.5578	2707	0.4060	1494	0.1991	0733	0.0916	0337	0.0404
2	2510	0.8088	2707	0.6767	2240	0.4232	1465	0.2381	0842	0.1247
3	1255	0.9344	1804	0.8571	2240	0.6472	1954	0.4335	1404	0.2650
4	0471	0.9814	0902	0.9473	1680	0.8153	1954	0.6288	1755	0.4405
5	0141	0.9955	0361	0.9834	1008	0.9161	1563	0.7851	1755	0.6160
6	0035	0.9991	0120	0.9955	0504	0.9665	1042	0.8893	1462	0.7622
7	0008	0.9998	0034	0.9989	0216	0.9881	0595	0.9489	1044	0.8666
8	0001	1.0000	0009	0.9998	0081	0.9962	0298	0.9786	0653	0.9319
9			0002	1.0000	0027	0.9989	0132	0.9919	0363	0.9682
10					0008	0.9997	0053	0.9972	0181	0.9863
11					0002	0.9999	0019	0.9991	0082	0.9945
12					0001	1.0000	0006	0.9997	0034	0.9980
13							0002	0.9999	0013	0.9993
14							0001	1.0000	0005	0.9998
15									0002	0.9999
16									0000	1.0000

3 Normal Distribution

Table 3a. Distribution Function (3), Sec. 8.2

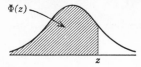 

$D(z) = \Phi(z) - \Phi(-z)$
$\Phi(-z) = 1 - \Phi(z),\qquad \Phi(0) = 0.5$

More extended tables: National Bureau of Standards (1953), Hald (1962). Index for further tables: Greenwood and Hartley (1961) (cf. Appendix 3).

z	$\Phi(-z)$	$\Phi(z)$	$D(z)$	z	$\Phi(-z)$	$\Phi(z)$	$D(z)$	z	$\Phi(-z)$	$\Phi(z)$	$D(z)$
	0.	0.	0.		0.	0.	0.		0.	0.	0.
0.01	4960	5040	0080	0.51	3050	6950	3899	1.01	1562	8438	6875
0.02	4920	5080	0160	0.52	3015	6985	3969	1.02	1539	8461	6923
0.03	4880	5120	0239	0.53	2981	7019	4039	1.03	1515	8485	6970
0.04	4840	5160	0319	0.54	2946	7054	4108	1.04	1492	8508	7017
0.05	4801	5199	0399	0.55	2912	7088	4177	1.05	1469	8531	7063
0.06	4761	5239	0478	0.56	2877	7123	4245	1.06	1446	8554	7109
0.07	4721	5279	0558	0.57	2843	7157	4313	1.07	1423	8577	7154
0.08	4681	5319	0638	0.58	2810	7190	4381	1.08	1401	8599	7199
0.09	4641	5359	0717	0.59	2776	7224	4448	1.09	1379	8621	7243
0.10	4602	5398	0797	0.60	2743	7257	4515	1.10	1357	8643	7287
0.11	4562	5438	0876	0.61	2709	7291	4581	1.11	1335	8665	7330
0.12	4522	5478	0955	0.62	2676	7324	4647	1.12	1314	8686	7373
0.13	4483	5517	1034	0.63	2643	7357	4713	1.13	1292	8708	7415
0.14	4443	5557	1113	0.64	2611	7389	4778	1.14	1271	8729	7457
0.15	4404	5596	1192	0.65	2578	7422	4843	1.15	1251	8749	7499
0.16	4364	5636	1271	0.66	2546	7454	4907	1.16	1230	8770	7540
0.17	4325	5675	1350	0.67	2514	7486	4971	1.17	1210	8790	7580
0.18	4286	5714	1428	0.68	2483	7517	5035	1.18	1190	8810	7620
0.19	4247	5753	1507	0.69	2451	7549	5098	1.19	1170	8830	7660
0.20	4207	5793	1585	0.70	2420	7580	5161	1.20	1151	8849	7699
0.21	4168	5832	1663	0.71	2389	7611	5223	1.21	1131	8869	7737
0.22	4129	5871	1741	0.72	2358	7642	5285	1.22	1112	8888	7775
0.23	4090	5910	1819	0.73	2327	7673	5346	1.23	1093	8907	7813
0.24	4052	5948	1897	0.74	2296	7704	5407	1.24	1075	8925	7850
0.25	4013	5987	1974	0.75	2266	7734	5467	1.25	1056	8944	7887
0.26	3974	6026	2051	0.76	2236	7764	5527	1.26	1038	8962	7923
0.27	3936	6064	2128	0.77	2206	7794	5587	1.27	1020	8980	7959
0.28	3897	6103	2205	0.78	2177	7823	5646	1.28	1003	8997	7995
0.29	3859	6141	2282	0.79	2148	7852	5705	1.29	0985	9015	8029
0.30	3821	6179	2358	0.80	2119	7881	5763	1.30	0968	9032	8064
0.31	3783	6217	2434	0.81	2090	7910	5821	1.31	0951	9049	8098
0.32	3745	6255	2510	0.82	2061	7939	5878	1.32	0934	9066	8132
0.33	3707	6293	2586	0.83	2033	7967	5935	1.33	0918	9082	8165
0.34	3669	6331	2661	0.84	2005	7995	5991	1.34	0901	9099	8198
0.35	3632	6368	2737	0.85	1977	8023	6047	1.35	0885	9115	8230
0.36	3594	6406	2812	0.86	1949	8051	6102	1.36	0869	9131	8262
0.37	3557	6443	2886	0.87	1922	8078	6157	1.37	0853	9147	8293
0.38	3520	6480	2961	0.88	1894	8106	6211	1.38	0838	9162	8324
0.39	3483	6517	3035	0.89	1867	8133	6265	1.39	0823	9177	8355
0.40	3446	6554	3108	0.90	1841	8159	6319	1.40	0808	9192	8385
0.41	3409	6591	3182	0.91	1814	8186	6372	1.41	0793	9207	8415
0.42	3372	6628	3255	0.92	1788	8212	6424	1.42	0778	9222	8444
0.43	3336	6664	3328	0.93	1762	8238	6476	1.43	0764	9236	8473
0.44	3300	6700	3401	0.94	1736	8264	6528	1.44	0749	9251	8501
0.45	3264	6736	3473	0.95	1711	8289	6579	1.45	0735	9265	8529
0.46	3228	6772	3545	0.96	1685	8315	6629	1.46	0721	9279	8557
0.47	3192	6808	3616	0.97	1660	8340	6680	1.47	0708	9292	8584
0.48	3156	6844	3688	0.98	1635	8365	6729	1.48	0694	9306	8611
0.49	3121	6879	3759	0.99	1611	8389	6778	1.49	0681	9319	8638
0.50	3085	6915	3829	1.00	1587	8413	6827	1.50	0668	9332	8664

Table 3a. Distribution Function (3), Sec. 8.2 (*Continued*)

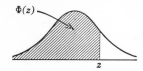

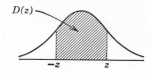

z	$\Phi(-z)$	$\Phi(z)$	$D(z)$	z	$\Phi(-z)$	$\Phi(z)$	$D(z)$	z	$\Phi(-z)$	$\Phi(z)$	$D(z)$
	0.	0.	0.		0.	0.	0.		0.	0.	0.
1.51	0655	9345	8690	2.01	0222	9778	9556	2.51	0060	9940	9879
1.52	0643	9357	8715	2.02	0217	9783	9566	2.52	0059	9941	9883
1.53	0630	9370	8740	2.03	0212	9788	9576	2.53	0057	9943	9886
1.54	0618	9382	8764	2.04	0207	9793	9586	2.54	0055	9945	9889
1.55	0606	9394	8789	2.05	0202	9798	9596	2.55	0054	9946	9892
1.56	0594	9406	8812	2.06	0197	9803	9606	2.56	0052	9948	9895
1.57	0582	9418	8836	2.07	0192	9808	9615	2.57	0051	9949	9898
1.58	0571	9429	8859	2.08	0188	9812	9625	2.58	0049	9951	9901
1.59	0559	9441	8882	2.09	0183	9817	9634	2.59	0048	9952	9904
1.60	0548	9452	8904	2.10	0179	9821	9643	2.60	0047	9953	9907
1.61	0537	9463	8926	2.11	0174	9826	9651	2.61	0045	9955	9909
1.62	0526	9474	8948	2.12	0170	9830	9660	2.62	0044	9956	9912
1.63	0516	9484	8969	2.13	0166	9834	9668	2.63	0043	9957	9915
1.64	0505	9495	8990	2.14	0162	9838	9676	2.64	0041	9959	9917
1.65	0495	9505	9011	2.15	0158	9842	9684	2.65	0040	9960	9920
1.66	0485	9515	9031	2.16	0154	9846	9692	2.66	0039	9961	9922
1.67	0475	9525	9051	2.17	0150	9850	9700	2.67	0038	9962	9924
1.68	0465	9535	9070	2.18	0146	9854	9707	2.68	0037	9963	9926
1.69	0455	9545	9090	2.19	0143	9857	9715	2.69	0036	9964	9929
1.70	0446	9554	9109	2.20	0139	9861	9722	2.70	0035	9965	9931
1.71	0436	9564	9127	2.21	0136	9864	9729	2.71	0034	9966	9933
1.72	0427	9573	9146	2.22	0132	9868	9736	2.72	0033	9967	9935
1.73	0418	9582	9164	2.23	0129	9871	9743	2.73	0032	9968	9937
1.74	0409	9591	9181	2.24	0125	9875	9749	2.74	0031	9969	9939
1.75	0401	9599	9199	2.25	0122	9878	9756	2.75	0030	9970	9940
1.76	0392	9608	9216	2.26	0119	9881	9762	2.76	0029	9971	9942
1.77	0384	9616	9233	2.27	0116	9884	9768	2.77	0028	9972	9944
1.78	0375	9625	9249	2.28	0113	9887	9774	2.78	0027	9973	9946
1.79	0367	9633	9265	2.29	0110	9890	9780	2.79	0026	9974	9947
1.80	0359	9641	9281	2.30	0107	9893	9786	2.80	0026	9974	9949
1.81	0351	9649	9297	2.31	0104	9896	9791	2.81	0025	9975	9950
1.82	0344	9656	9312	2.32	0102	9898	9797	2.82	0024	9976	9952
1.83	0336	9664	9328	2.33	0099	9901	9802	2.83	0023	9977	9953
1.84	0329	9671	9342	2.34	0096	9904	9807	2.84	0023	9977	9955
1.85	0322	9678	9357	2.35	0094	9906	9812	2.85	0022	9978	9956
1.86	0314	9686	9371	2.36	0091	9909	9817	2.86	0021	9979	9958
1.87	0307	9693	9385	2.37	0089	9911	9822	2.87	0021	9979	9959
1.88	0301	9699	9399	2.38	0087	9913	9827	2.88	0020	9980	9960
1.89	0294	9706	9412	2.39	0084	9916	9832	2.89	0019	9981	9961
1.90	0287	9713	9426	2.40	0082	9918	9836	2.90	0019	9981	9963
1.91	0281	9719	9439	2.41	0080	9920	9840	2.91	0018	9982	9964
1.92	0274	9726	9451	2.42	0078	9922	9845	2.92	0018	9982	9965
1.93	0268	9732	9464	2.43	0075	9925	9849	2.93	0017	9983	9966
1.94	0262	9738	9476	2.44	0073	9927	9853	2.94	0016	9984	9967
1.95	0256	9744	9488	2.45	0071	9929	9857	2.95	0016	9984	9968
1.96	0250	9750	9500	2.46	0069	9931	9861	2.96	0015	9985	9969
1.97	0244	9756	9512	2.47	0068	9932	9865	2.97	0015	9985	9970
1.98	0239	9761	9523	2.48	0066	9934	9869	2.98	0014	9986	9971
1.99	0233	9767	9534	2.49	0064	9936	9872	2.99	0014	9986	9972
2.00	0228	9772	9545	2.50	0062	9938	9876	3.00	0013	9987	9973

Table 3b. Normal Distribution. Values of z for Given Values of (3), Sec. 8.2, and $D(z)$

$D(z) = \Phi(z) - \Phi(-z)$
Example. $\Phi(z) = 61\%$
for $z = 0.279$,
$D(z) = 61\%$ for $z = 0.860$
More extended tables: Comrie (1949), Fisher and Yates (1957), Hald (1962), Kelley (1948) (cf. Appendix 3).

%	$z(\Phi)$	$z(D)$	%	$z(\Phi)$	$z(D)$	%	$z(\Phi)$	$z(D)$
1	−2.326	0.013	41	−0.228	0.539	81	0.878	1.311
2	−2.054	0.025	42	−0.202	0.553	82	0.915	1.341
3	−1.881	0.038	43	−0.176	0.568	83	0.954	1.372
4	−1.751	0.050	44	−0.151	0.583	84	0.994	1.405
5	−1.645	0.063	45	−0.126	0.598	85	1.036	1.440
6	−1.555	0.075	46	−0.100	0.613	86	1.080	1.476
7	−1.476	0.088	47	−0.075	0.628	87	1.126	1.514·
8	−1.405	0.100	48	−0.050	0.643	88	1.175	1.555
9	−1.341	0.113	49	−0.025	0.659	89	1.227	1.598
10	−1.282	0.126	50	0.000	0.674	90	1.282	1.645
11	−1.227	0.138	51	0.025	0.690	91	1.341	1.695
12	−1.175	0.151	52	0.050	0.706	92	1.405	1.751
13	−1.126	0.164	53	0.075	0.722	93	1.476	1.812
14	−1.080	0.176	54	0.100	0.739	94	1.555	1.881
15	−1.036	0.189	55	0.126	0.755	95	1.645	1.960
16	−0.994	0.202	56	0.151	0.772	96	1.751	2.054
17	−0.954	0.215	57	0.176	0.789	97	1.881	2.170
18	−0.915	0.228	58	0.202	0.806	97.5	1.960	2.241
19	−0.878	0.240	59	0.228	0.824	98	2.054	2.326
20	−0.842	0.253	60	0.253	0.842	99	2.326	2.576
21	−0.806	0.266	61	0.279	0.860	99.1	2.366	2.612
22	−0.772	0.279	62	0.305	0.878	99.2	2.409	2.652
23	−0.739	0.292	63	0.332	0.896	99.3	2.457	2.697
24	−0.706	0.305	64	0.358	0.915	99.4	2.512	2.748
25	−0.674	0.319	65	0.385	0.935	99.5	2.576	2.807
26	−0.643	0.332	66	0.412	0.954	99.6	2.652	2.878
27	−0.613	0.345	67	0.440	0.974	99.7	2.748	2.968
28	−0.583	0.358	68	0.468	0.994	99.8	2.878	3.090
29	−0.553	0.372	69	0.496	1.015	99.9	3.090	3.291
30	−0.524	0.385	70	0.524	1.036			
31	−0.496	0.399	71	0.553	1.058	99.91	3.121	3.320
32	−0.468	0.412	72	0.583	1.080	99.92	3.156	3.353
33	−0.440	0.426	73	0.613	1.103	99.93	3.195	3.390
34	−0.412	0.440	74	0.643	1.126	99.94	3.239	3.432
35	−0.385	0.454	75	0.674	1.150	99.95	3.291	3.481
36	−0.358	0.468	76	0.706	1.175	99.96	3.353	3.540
37	−0.332	0.482	77	0.739	1.200	99.97	3.432	3.615
38	−0.305	0.496	78	0.772	1.227	99.98	3.540	3.719
39	−0.279	0.510	79	0.806	1.254	99.99	3.719	3.891
40	−0.253	0.524	80	0.842	1.282			

Table 3c. Density $f(z) = e^{-z^2/2}/\sqrt{2\pi}$

Cf. (3) in Sec. 8.2.

$f(-z) = f(z), f(0) = 1/\sqrt{2\pi} = 0.3989$

More extended tables: Comrie (1949), National Bureau of Standards (1953), Pearson and Hartley (1954) (cf. Appendix 3).

z	$f(z)$	z	$f(z)$	z	$f(z)$	z	$f(z)$	z	$f(z)$
	0.		0.		0.		0.		0.
0.01	3989	0.41	3668	0.81	2874	1.21	1919	1.61	1092
0.02	3989	0.42	3653	0.82	2850	1.22	1895	1.62	1074
0.03	3988	0.43	3637	0.83	2827	1.23	1872	1.63	1057
0.04	3986	0.44	3621	0.84	2803	1.24	1849	1.64	1040
0.05	3984	0.45	3605	0.85	2780	1.25	1826	1.65	1023
0.06	3982	0.46	3589	0.86	2756	1.26	1804	1.66	1006
0.07	3980	0.47	3572	0.87	2732	1.27	1781	1.67	0989
0.08	3977	0.48	3555	0.88	2709	1.28	1758	1.68	0973
0.09	3973	0.49	3538	0.89	2685	1.29	1736	1.69	0957
0.10	3970	0.50	3521	0.90	2661	1.30	1714	1.70	0940
0.11	3965	0.51	3503	0.91	2637	1.31	1691	1.71	0925
0.12	3961	0.52	3485	0.92	2613	1.32	1669	1.72	0909
0.13	3956	0.53	3467	0.93	2589	1.33	1647	1.73	0893
0.14	3951	0.54	3448	0.94	2565	1.34	1626	1.74	0878
0.15	3945	0.55	3429	0.95	2541	1.35	1604	1.75	0863
0.16	3939	0.56	3410	0.96	2516	1.36	1582	1.76	0848
0.17	3932	0.57	3391	0.97	2492	1.37	1561	1.77	0833
0.18	3925	0.58	3372	0.98	2468	1.38	1539	1.78	0818
0.19	3918	0.59	3352	0.99	2444	1.39	1518	1.79	0804
0.20	3910	0.60	3332	1.00	2420	1.40	1497	1.80	0790
0.21	3902	0.61	3312	1.01	2396	1.41	1476	1.81	0775
0.22	3894	0.62	3292	1.02	2371	1.42	1456	1.82	0761
0.23	3885	0.63	3271	1.03	2347	1.43	1435	1.83	0748
0.24	3876	0.64	3251	1.04	2323	1.44	1415	1.84	0734
0.25	3867	0.65	3230	1.05	2299	1.45	1394	1.85	0721
0.26	3857	0.66	3209	1.06	2275	1.46	1374	1.86	0707
0.27	3847	0.67	3187	1.07	2251	1.47	1354	1.87	0694
0.28	3836	0.68	3166	1.08	2227	1.48	1334	1.88	0681
0.29	3825	0.69	3144	1.09	2203	1.49	1315	1.89	0669
0.30	3814	0.70	3123	1.10	2179	1.50	1295	1.90	0656
0.31	3802	0.71	3101	1.11	2155	1.51	1276	1.91	0644
0.32	3790	0.72	3079	1.12	2131	1.52	1257	1.92	0632
0.33	3778	0.73	3056	1.13	2107	1.53	1238	1.93	0620
0.34	3765	0.74	3034	1.14	2083	1.54	1219	1.94	0608
0.35	3752	0.75	3011	1.15	2059	1.55	1200	1.95	0596
0.36	3739	0.76	2989	1.16	2036	1.56	1182	1.96	0584
0.37	3725	0.77	2966	1.17	2012	1.57	1163	1.97	0573
0.38	3712	0.78	2943	1.18	1989	1.58	1145	1.98	0562
0.39	3697	0.79	2920	1.19	1965	1.59	1127	1.99	0551
0.40	3683	0.80	2897	1.20	1942	1.60	1109	2.00	0540

4 Square Roots. Squares. Exponential Function. Constants

Table 4a. Square Roots and Squares

More extended table: Comrie (1962) (cf. Appendix 3).

n	$\sqrt{n}$	$\sqrt{10n}$	n^2	n	$\sqrt{n}$	$\sqrt{10n}$	n^2
1	1.000 000	3.162 278	1	51	7.141 428	22.583 180	2601
2	1.414 214	4.472 136	4	52	7.211 103	22.803 509	2704
3	1.732 051	5.477 226	9	53	7.280 110	23.021 729	2809
4	2.000 000	6.324 555	16	54	7.348 469	23.237 900	2916
5	2.236 068	7.071 068	25	55	7.416 198	23.452 079	3025
6	2.449 490	7.745 967	36	56	7.483 315	23.664 319	3136
7	2.645 751	8.366 600	49	57	7.549 834	23.874 673	3249
8	2.828 427	8.944 272	64	58	7.615 773	24.083 189	3364
9	3.000 000	9.486 833	81	59	7.681 146	24.289 916	3481
10	3.162 278	10.000 000	100	60	7.745 967	24.494 897	3600
11	3.316 625	10.488 088	121	61	7.810 250	24.698 178	3721
12	3.464 102	10.954 451	144	62	7.874 008	24.899 799	3844
13	3.605 551	11.401 754	169	63	7.937 254	25.099 801	3969
14	3.741 657	11.832 160	196	64	8.000 000	25.298 221	4096
15	3.872 983	12.247 449	225	65	8.062 258	25.495 098	4225
16	4.000 000	12.649 111	256	66	8.124 038	25.690 465	4356
17	4.123 106	13.038 405	289	67	8.185 353	25.884 358	4489
18	4.242 641	13.416 408	324	68	8.246 211	26.076 810	4624
19	4.358 899	13.784 049	361	69	8.306 624	26.267 851	4761
20	4.472 136	14.142 136	400	70	8.366 600	26.457 513	4900
21	4.582 576	14.491 377	441	71	8.426 150	26.645 825	5041
22	4.690 416	14.832 397	484	72	8.485 281	26.832 816	5184
23	4.795 832	15.165 751	529	73	8.544 004	27.018 512	5329
24	4.898 979	15.491 933	576	74	8.602 325	27.202 941	5476
25	5.000 000	15.811 388	625	75	8.660 254	27.386 128	5625
26	5.099 020	16.124 515	676	76	8.717 798	27.568 098	5776
27	5.196 152	16.431 677	729	77	8.774 964	27.748 874	5929
28	5.291 503	16.733 201	784	78	8.831 761	27.928 480	6084
29	5.385 165	17.029 386	841	79	8.888 194	28.106 939	6241
30	5.477 226	17.320 508	900	80	8.944 272	28.284 271	6400
31	5.567 764	17.606 817	961	81	9.000 000	28.460 499	6561
32	5.656 854	17.888 544	1024	82	9.055 385	28.635 642	6724
33	5.744 563	18.165 902	1089	83	9.110 434	28.809 721	6889
34	5.830 952	18.439 089	1156	84	9.165 151	28.982 753	7056
35	5.916 080	18.708 287	1225	85	9.219 544	29.154 759	7225
36	6.000 000	18.973 666	1296	86	9.273 618	29.325 757	7396
37	6.082 763	19.235 384	1369	87	9.327 379	29.495 762	7569
38	6.164 414	19.493 589	1444	88	9.380 832	29.664 794	7744
39	6.244 998	19.748 418	1521	89	9.433 981	29.832 868	7921
40	6.324 555	20.000 000	1600	90	9.486 833	30.000 000	8100
41	6.403 124	20.248 457	1681	91	9.539 392	30.166 206	8281
42	6.480 741	20.493 902	1764	92	9.591 663	30.331 502	8464
43	6.557 439	20.736 441	1849	93	9.643 651	30.495 901	8649
44	6.633 250	20.976 177	1936	94	9.695 360	30.659 419	8836
45	6.708 204	21.213 203	2025	95	9.746 794	30.822 070	9025
46	6.782 330	21.447 611	2116	96	9.797 959	30.983 867	9216
47	6.855 655	21.679 483	2209	97	9.848 858	31.144 823	9409
48	6.928 203	21.908 902	2304	98	9.899 495	31.304 952	9604
49	7.000 000	22.135 944	2401	99	9.949 874	31.464 265	9801
50	7.071 068	22.360 680	2500	100	10.000 000	31.622 777	10000

Table 4*b*. Exponential Function and Hyperbolic Tangent

More extended tables: National Bureau of Standards (1947, 1951), Comrie (1949) (cf. Appendix 3).

x	e^x	tanh x	x	e^x	tanh x	x	e^x	tanh x
0.00	1.0000	0.00000	0.40	1.4918	0.37995	0.80	2.2255	0.66404
0.01	1.0101	0.01000	0.41	1.5068	0.38847	0.81	2.2479	0.66959
0.02	1.0202	0.02000	0.42	1.5220	0.39693	0.82	2.2705	0.67507
0.03	1.0305	0.02999	0.43	1.5373	0.40532	0.83	2.2933	0.68048
0.04	1.0408	0.03998	0.44	1.5527	0.41364	0.84	2.3164	0.68581
0.05	1.0513	0.04996	0.45	1.5683	0.42190	0.85	2.3396	0.69107
0.06	1.0618	0.05993	0.46	1.5841	0.43008	0.86	2.3632	0.69626
0.07	1.0725	0.06989	0.47	1.6000	0.43820	0.87	2.3869	0.70137
0.08	1.0833	0.07983	0.48	1.6161	0.44624	0.88	2.4109	0.70642
0.09	1.0942	0.08976	0.49	1.6323	0.45422	0.89	2.4351	0.71139
0.10	1.1052	0.09967	0.50	1.6487	0.46212	0.90	2.4596	0.71630
0.11	1.1163	0.10956	0.51	1.6653	0.46995	0.91	2.4843	0.72113
0.12	1.1275	0.11943	0.52	1.6820	0.47770	0.92	2.5093	0.72590
0.13	1.1388	0.12927	0.53	1.6989	0.48538	0.93	2.5345	0.73059
0.14	1.1503	0.13909	0.54	1.7160	0.49299	0.94	2.5600	0.73522
0.15	1.1618	0.14889	0.55	1.7333	0.50052	0.95	2.5857	0.73978
0.16	1.1735	0.15865	0.56	1.7507	0.50798	0.96	2.6117	0.74428
0.17	1.1853	0.16838	0.57	1.7683	0.51536	0.97	2.6379	0.74870
0.18	1.1972	0.17808	0.58	1.7860	0.52267	0.98	2.6645	0.75307
0.19	1.2092	0.18775	0.59	1.8040	0.52990	0.99	2.6912	0.75736
0.20	1.2214	0.19738	0.60	1.8221	0.53705	1.00	2.7183	0.76159
0.21	1.2337	0.20697	0.61	1.8404	0.54413	1.1	3.0042	0.80050
0.22	1.2461	0.21652	0.62	1.8589	0.55113	1.2	3.3201	0.83365
0.23	1.2586	0.22603	0.63	1.8776	0.55805	1.3	3.6693	0.86172
0.24	1.2712	0.23550	0.64	1.8965	0.56490	1.4	4.0552	0.88535
0.25	1.2840	0.24492	0.65	1.9155	0.57167	1.5	4.4817	0.90515
0.26	1.2969	0.25430	0.66	1.9348	0.57836	1.6	4.9530	0.92167
0.27	1.3100	0.26362	0.67	1.9542	0.58498	1.7	5.4739	0.93541
0.28	1.3231	0.27291	0.68	1.9739	0.59152	1.8	6.0496	0.94681
0.29	1.3364	0.28213	0.69	1.9937	0.59798	1.9	6.6859	0.95624
0.30	1.3499	0.29131	0.70	2.0138	0.60437	2.0	7.3891	0.96403
0.31	1.3634	0.30044	0.71	2.0340	0.61068	2.1	8.1662	0.97045
0.32	1.3771	0.30951	0.72	2.0544	0.61691	2.2	9.0250	0.97574
0.33	1.3910	0.31852	0.73	2.0751	0.62307	2.3	9.9742	0.98010
0.34	1.4049	0.32748	0.74	2.0959	0.62915	2.4	11.023	0.98367
0.35	1.4191	0.33638	0.75	2.1170	0.63515	2.5	12.182	0.98661
0.36	1.4333	0.34521	0.76	2.1383	0.64108	2.6	13.464	0.98903
0.37	1.4477	0.35399	0.77	2.1598	0.64693	2.7	14.880	0.99101
0.38	1.4623	0.36271	0.78	2.1815	0.65271	2.8	16.445	0.99263
0.39	1.4770	0.37136	0.79	2.2034	0.65841	2.9	18.174	0.99396
0.40	1.4918	0.37995	0.80	2.2255	0.66404	3.0	20.086	0.99505

Table 4b (*Continued*)

x	e^x	tanh x	x	e^x	tanh x	x	e^x	tanh x
3.0	20.086	0.99505	4.0	54.598	0.99933	5.0	148.41	0.99991
3.1	22.198	0.99595	4.1	60.340	0.99945	5.1	164.02	0.99993
3.2	24.533	0.99668	4.2	66.686	0.99955	5.2	181.27	0.99994
3.3	27.113	0.99728	4.3	73.700	0.99963	5.3	200.34	0.99995
3.4	29.964	0.99777	4.4	81.451	0.99970	5.4	221.41	0.99996
3.5	33.115	0.99818	4.5	90.017	0.99975	5.5	244.69	0.99997
3.6	36.598	0.99851	4.6	99.484	0.99980	5.6	270.43	0.99997
3.7	40.447	0.99878	4.7	109.95	0.99983	5.7	298.87	0.99998
3.8	44.701	0.99900	4.8	121.51	0.99986	5.8	330.30	0.99998
3.9	49.402	0.99918	4.9	134.29	0.99989	5.9	365.04	0.99998
4.0	54.598	0.99933	5.0	148.41	0.99991	6.0	403.43	0.99999

Table 4c. Some Important Constants

$$
\begin{aligned}
e &= 2.718\,281\,828 = 1/0.367\,879\,441 \\
e^2 &= 7.389\,056\,099 = 1/0.135\,335\,283 \\
\sqrt{e} &= 1.648\,721\,271 = 1/0.606\,530\,660 \\[6pt]
\pi &= 3.141\,592\,654 = 1/0.318\,309\,886 \\
\pi^2 &= 9.869\,604\,401 = 1/0.101\,321\,184 \\
\sqrt{\pi} &= 1.772\,453\,851 = 1/0.564\,189\,584 \\[6pt]
\sqrt{2\pi} &= 2.506\,628\,275 = 1/0.398\,942\,280 \\
\sqrt{\pi/2} &= 1.253\,314\,137 = 1/0.797\,884\,561 \\
\sqrt[3]{\pi} &= 1.464\,591\,888 = 1/0.682\,784\,063 \\[6pt]
e^{\pi} &= 23.140\,692\,633 = 1/0.043\,213\,918 \\
e^{\pi/2} &= 4.810\,477\,381 = 1/0.207\,879\,576 \\
e^{\pi/4} &= 2.193\,280\,051 = 1/0.455\,938\,128 \\
\log_{10}\pi &= 0.497\,149\,873 \\
\log_e\pi &= 1.144\,729\,886 \\[6pt]
\sqrt{2} &= 1.414\,213\,562 = 1/0.707\,106\,781 \\
\sqrt{3} &= 1.732\,050\,808 = 1/0.577\,350\,269 \\
\sqrt{10} &= 3.162\,277\,660 = 1/0.316\,227\,766 \\[6pt]
\sqrt[3]{2} &= 1.259\,921\,050 = 1/0.793\,700\,526 \\
\sqrt[3]{10} &= 2.154\,434\,690 = 1/0.464\,158\,883 \\[6pt]
\log_e 2 &= 0.693\,147\,181 \\
\log_e 3 &= 1.098\,612\,289 \\
\log_e 10 &= 2.302\,585\,093 = 1/0.434\,294\,482
\end{aligned}
$$

5 Auxiliary Table for Random Selection

Table 5. Random Digits

More extended table: Rand Corporation (1955) (cf. Appendix 3).

Row Number	Column Number									
	0	1	2	3	4	5	6	7	8	9
0	87331	82442	28104	26432	83640	17323	68764	84728	37995	96106
1	33628	17364	01409	87803	65641	33433	48944	64299	79066	31777
2	54680	13427	72496	16967	16195	96593	55040	53729	62035	66717
3	51199	49794	49407	10774	98140	83891	37195	24066	61140	65144
4	78702	98067	61313	91661	59861	54437	77739	19892	54817	88645
5	55672	16014	24892	13089	00410	81458	76156	28189	40595	21500
6	18880	58497	03862	32368	59320	24807	63392	79793	63043	09425
7	10242	62548	62330	05703	33535	49128	66298	16193	55301	01306
8	54993	17182	94618	23228	83895	73251	68199	64639	83178	70521
9	22686	50885	16006	04041	08077	33065	35237	02502	94755	72062
10	42349	03145	15770	70665	53291	32288	41568	66079	98705	31029
11	18093	09553	39428	75464	71329	86344	80729	40916	18860	51780
12	11535	03924	84252	74795	40193	84597	42497	21918	91384	84721
13	35066	73848	65351	53270	67341	70177	92373	17604	42204	60476
14	57477	22809	73558	96182	96779	01604	25748	59553	64876	94611
15	48647	33850	52956	45410	88212	05120	99391	32276	55961	41775
16	86857	81154	22223	74950	53296	67767	55866	49061	66937	81818
17	20182	36907	94644	99122	09774	29189	27212	79000	50217	71077
18	83687	31231	01133	41432	54542	60204	81618	09586	34481	87683
19	81315	12390	46074	47810	90171	36313	95440	77583	28506	38808
20	87026	52826	58341	76549	04105	66191	12914	55348	07907	06978
21	34301	76733	07251	90524	21931	83695	41340	53581	64582	60210
22	70734	24337	32674	49508	49751	90489	63202	24380	77943	09942
23	94710	31527	73445	32839	68176	53580	85250	53243	03350	00128
24	76462	16987	07775	43162	11777	16810	75158	13894	88945	15539
25	14348	28403	79245	69023	34196	46398	05964	64715	11330	17515
26	74618	89317	30146	25606	94507	98104	04239	44973	37636	88866
27	99442	19200	85406	45358	86253	60638	38858	44964	54103	57287
28	26869	44399	89452	06652	31271	00647	46551	83050	92058	83814
29	80988	08149	50499	98584	28385	63680	44638	91864	96002	87802
30	07511	79047	89289	17774	67194	37362	85684	55505	97809	67056
31	49779	12138	05048	03535	27502	63308	10218	53296	48687	61340
32	47938	55945	24003	19635	17471	65997	85906	98694	56420	78357
33	15604	06626	14360	79542	13512	87595	08542	03800	35443	52823
34	12307	27726	21864	00045	16075	03770	86978	52718	02693	09096
35	02450	28053	66134	99445	91316	25727	89399	85272	67148	78358
36	57623	54382	35236	89244	27245	90500	75430	96762	71968	65838
37	91762	78849	93105	40481	99431	03304	21079	86459	21287	76566
38	87373	31137	31128	67050	34309	44914	80711	61738	61498	24288
39	67094	41485	54149	86088	10192	21174	39948	67268	29938	32476
40	94456	66747	76922	87627	71834	57688	04878	78348	68970	60048
41	68359	75292	27710	86889	81678	79798	58360	39175	75667	65782
42	52393	31404	32584	06837	79762	13168	76055	54833	22841	98889
43	59565	91254	11847	20672	37625	41454	86861	55824	79793	74575
44	48185	11066	20162	38230	16043	48409	47421	21195	98008	57305
45	19230	12187	86659	12971	52204	76546	63272	19312	81662	96557
46	84327	21942	81727	68735	89190	58491	55329	96875	19465	89687
47	77430	71210	00591	50124	12030	50280	12358	76174	48353	09682
48	12462	19108	70512	53926	25595	97085	03833	59806	12351	64253
49	11684	06644	57816	10078	45021	47751	38285	73520	08434	65627

Table 5. Random Digits (*Continued*)

Row Number	0	1	2	3	4	5	6	7	8	9
50	12896	36576	68686	08462	65652	76571	70891	09007	04581	01684
51	59090	05111	27587	90349	30789	50304	70650	06646	70126	15284
52	42486	67483	65282	19037	80588	73076	41820	46651	40442	40718
53	88662	03928	03249	85910	97533	88643	29829	21557	47328	36724
54	69403	03626	92678	53460	15465	83516	54012	80509	55976	46115
55	56434	70543	38696	98502	32092	95505	62091	39549	30117	98209
56	58227	62694	42837	29183	11393	68463	25150	86338	95620	39836
57	41272	94927	15413	40505	33123	63218	72940	98349	57249	40170
58	36819	01162	30425	15546	16065	68459	35776	64276	92868	07372
59	31700	66711	26115	55755	33584	18091	38709	57276	74660	90392
60	69855	63699	36839	90531	97125	87875	62824	03889	12538	24740
61	44322	17569	45439	41455	34324	90902	07978	26268	04279	76816
62	62226	36661	87011	66267	78777	78044	40819	49496	39814	73867
63	27284	19737	98741	72531	52741	26699	98755	19657	08665	16818
64	88341	21652	94743	77268	79525	44769	66583	30621	90534	62050
65	53266	18783	51903	56711	38060	69513	61963	80470	88018	86510
66	50527	49330	24839	42529	03944	95219	88724	37247	84166	23023
67	15655	07852	77206	35944	71446	30573	19405	57824	23576	23301
68	62057	22206	03314	83465	57466	10465	19891	32308	01900	67484
69	41769	56091	19892	96253	92808	45785	52774	49674	68103	65032
70	25993	72416	44473	41299	93095	17338	69802	98548	02429	85238
71	22842	57871	04470	37373	34516	04042	04078	35336	34393	97573
72	55704	31982	05234	22664	22181	40358	28089	15790	33340	18852
73	94258	18706	09437	96041	90052	80862	20420	24323	11635	91677
74	74145	20453	29657	98868	56695	53483	87449	35060	98942	62697
75	88881	12673	73961	89884	73247	97670	69570	88888	58560	72580
76	01508	56780	52223	35632	73347	71317	46541	88023	36656	76332
77	92069	43000	23233	06058	82527	25250	27555	20426	60361	63525
78	53366	35249	02117	68620	39388	69795	73215	01846	16983	78560
79	88057	54097	49511	74867	32192	90071	04147	46094	63519	07199
80	85492	82238	02668	91854	86149	28590	77853	81035	45561	16032
81	39453	62123	69611	53017	34964	09786	24614	49514	01056	18700
82	82627	98111	93870	56969	69566	62662	07353	84838	14570	14508
83	61142	51743	38209	31474	96095	15163	54380	77849	20465	03142
84	12031	32528	61311	53730	89032	16124	58844	35386	45521	59368
85	31313	59838	29147	76882	74328	09955	63673	96651	53264	29871
86	50767	41056	97409	44376	62219	35439	70102	99248	71179	26052
87	30522	95699	84966	26554	24768	72247	84993	85375	92518	16334
88	74176	19870	89874	64799	03792	57006	57225	36677	46825	14087
89	17114	93248	37065	91346	04657	93763	92210	43676	44944	75798
90	53005	11825	64608	87587	05742	31914	55044	41818	29667	77424
91	31985	81539	79942	49471	46200	27639	94099	42085	79231	03932
92	63499	60508	77522	15624	15088	78519	52279	79214	43623	69166
93	30506	42444	99047	66010	91657	37160	37408	85714	21420	80996
94	78248	16841	92357	10130	68990	38307	61022	56806	81016	38511
95	64996	84789	50185	32200	64382	29752	11876	00664	54547	62597
96	11963	13157	09136	01769	30117	71486	80111	09161	08371	71749
97	44335	91450	43456	90449	18338	19787	31339	60473	06606	89788
98	42277	11868	44520	01113	11341	11743	97949	49718	99176	42006
99	77562	18863	58515	90166	78508	14864	19111	57183	85808	59385

6   Chi-Square Distribution

Table 6. Values of x for Given Values of the Distribution Function (3) in Sec. 10.1

More extended tables: Fisher (1958), Hald (1962), Pearson and Hartley (1954) (cf. Appendix 3).

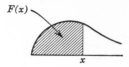

Example. For 3 degrees of freedom, $F = 0.99$ when $x = 11.34$.

$F(x)$	Number of Degrees of Freedom									
	1	2	3	4	5	6	7	8	9	10
0.001	0.00	0.00	0.02	0.09	0.21	0.38	0.60	0.86	1.15	1.48
0.005	0.00	0.01	0.07	0.21	0.41	0.68	0.99	1.34	1.73	2.16
0.01	0.00	0.02	0.11	0.30	0.55	0.87	1.24	1.65	2.09	2.56
0.025	0.00	0.05	0.22	0.48	0.83	1.24	1.69	2.18	2.70	3.25
0.05	0.00	0.10	0.35	0.71	1.15	1.64	2.17	2.73	3.33	3.94
0.1	0.02	0.21	0.58	1.06	1.61	2.20	2.83	3.49	4.17	4.87
0.25	0.10	0.58	1.21	1.92	2.67	3.45	4.25	5.07	5.90	6.74
0.5	0.45	1.39	2.37	3.36	4.35	5.35	6.35	7.34	8.34	9.34
0.75	1.32	2.77	4.11	5.39	6.63	7.84	9.04	10.22	11.39	12.55
0.9	2.71	4.61	6.25	7.78	9.24	10.64	12.02	13.36	14.68	15.99
0.95	3.84	5.99	7.81	9.49	11.07	12.59	14.07	15.51	16.92	18.31
0.975	5.02	7.38	9.35	11.14	12.83	14.45	16.01	17.53	19.02	20.48
0.99	6.63	9.21	11.34	13.28	15.09	16.81	18.48	20.09	21.67	23.21
0.995	7.88	10.60	12.84	14.86	16.75	18.55	20.28	21.96	23.59	25.19
0.999	10.83	13.82	16.27	18.47	20.52	22.46	24.32	26.13	27.88	29.59

$F(x)$	Number of Degrees of Freedom									
	11	12	13	14	15	16	17	18	19	20
0.001	1.83	2.21	2.62	3.04	3.48	3.94	4.42	4.90	5.41	5.92
0.005	2.60	3.07	3.57	4.07	4.60	5.14	5.70	6.26	6.84	7.43
0.01	3.05	3.57	4.11	4.66	5.23	5.81	6.41	7.01	7.63	8.26
0.025	3.82	4.40	5.01	5.63	6.26	6.91	7.56	8.23	8.91	9.59
0.05	4.57	5.23	5.89	6.57	7.26	7.96	8.67	9.39	10.12	10.85
0.1	5.58	6.30	7.04	7.79	8.55	9.31	10.09	10.86	11.65	12.44
0.25	7.58	8.44	9.30	10.17	11.04	11.91	12.79	13.68	14.56	15.45
0.5	10.34	11.34	12.34	13.34	14.34	15.34	16.34	17.34	18.34	19.34
0.75	13.70	14.85	15.98	17.12	18.25	19.37	20.49	21.60	22.72	23.83
0.9	17.28	18.55	19.81	21.06	22.31	23.54	24.77	25.99	27.20	28.41
0.95	19.68	21.03	22.36	23.68	25.00	26.30	27.59	28.87	30.14	31.41
0.975	21.92	23.34	24.74	26.12	27.49	28.85	30.19	31.53	32.85	34.17
0.99	24.73	26.22	27.69	29.14	30.58	32.00	33.41	34.81	36.19	37.57
0.995	26.76	28.30	29.82	31.32	32.80	34.27	35.72	37.16	38.58	40.00
0.999	31.26	32.91	34.53	36.12	37.70	39.25	40.79	42.31	43.82	45.32

Table 6. Values of x for Given Values of the Distribution Function (3) in Sec. 10.1 (*Continued*)

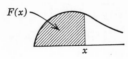

$F(x)$

$F(x)$	\multicolumn{10}{c}{Number of Degrees of Freedom}
	21	22	23	24	25	26	27	28	29	30
0.001	6.4	7.0	7.5	8.1	8.7	9.2	9.8	10.4	11.0	11.6
0.005	8.0	8.6	9.3	9.9	10.5	11.2	11.8	12.5	13.1	13.8
0.01	8.9	9.5	10.2	10.9	11.5	12.2	12.9	13.6	14.3	15.0
0.025	10.3	11.0	11.7	12.4	13.1	13.8	14.6	15.3	16.0	16.8
0.05	11.6	12.3	13.1	13.8	14.6	15.4	16.2	16.9	17.7	18.5
0.1	13.2	14.0	14.8	15.7	16.5	17.3	18.1	18.9	19.8	20.6
0.25	16.3	17.2	18.1	19.0	19.9	20.8	21.7	22.7	23.6	24.5
0.5	20.3	21.3	22.3	23.3	24.3	25.3	26.3	27.3	28.3	29.3
0.75	24.9	26.0	27.1	28.2	29.3	30.4	31.5	32.6	33.7	34.8
0.9	29.6	30.8	32.0	33.2	34.4	35.6	36.7	37.9	39.1	40.3
0.95	32.7	33.9	35.2	36.4	37.7	38.9	40.1	41.3	42.6	43.8
0.975	35.5	36.8	38.1	39.4	40.6	41.9	43.2	44.5	45.7	47.0
0.99	38.9	40.3	41.6	43.0	44.3	45.6	47.0	48.3	49.6	50.9
0.995	41.4	42.8	44.2	45.6	46.9	48.3	49.6	51.0	52.3	53.7
0.999	46.8	48.3	49.7	51.2	52.6	54.1	55.5	56.9	58.3	59.7

$F(x)$	\multicolumn{8}{c}{Number of Degrees of Freedom}
	40	50	60	70	80	90	100	>100 (Approximation)
0.001	17.9	24.7	31.7	39.0	46.5	54.2	61.9	$\frac{1}{2}(h - 3.09)^2$
0.005	20.7	28.0	35.5	43.3	51.2	59.2	67.3	$\frac{1}{2}(h - 2.58)^2$
0.01	22.2	29.7	37.5	45.4	53.5	61.8	70.1	$\frac{1}{2}(h - 2.33)^2$
0.025	24.4	32.4	40.5	48.8	57.2	65.6	74.2	$\frac{1}{2}(h - 1.96)^2$
0.05	26.5	34.8	43.2	51.7	60.4	69.1	77.9	$\frac{1}{2}(h - 1.64)^2$
0.1	29.1	37.7	46.5	55.3	64.3	73.3	82.4	$\frac{1}{2}(h - 1.28)^2$
0.25	33.7	42.9	52.3	61.7	71.1	80.6	90.1	$\frac{1}{2}(h - 0.67)^2$
0.5	39.3	49.3	59.3	69.3	79.3	89.3	99.3	$\frac{1}{2}h^2$
0.75	45.6	56.3	67.0	77.6	88.1	98.6	109.1	$\frac{1}{2}(h + 0.67)^2$
0.9	51.8	63.2	74.4	85.5	96.6	107.6	118.5	$\frac{1}{2}(h + 1.28)^2$
0.95	55.8	67.5	79.1	90.5	101.9	113.1	124.3	$\frac{1}{2}(h + 1.64)^2$
0.975	59.3	71.4	83.3	95.0	106.6	118.1	129.6	$\frac{1}{2}(h + 1.96)^2$
0.99	63.7	76.2	88.4	100.4	112.3	124.1	135.8	$\frac{1}{2}(h + 2.33)^2$
0.995	66.8	79.5	92.0	104.2	116.3	128.3	140.2	$\frac{1}{2}(h + 2.58)^2$
0.999	73.4	86.7	99.6	112.3	124.8	137.2	149.4	$\frac{1}{2}(h + 3.09)^2$

In the last column, $h = \sqrt{2m - 1}$, where m is the number of degrees of freedom.

7 Kolmogorov-Smirnov Test

Table 7. Solutions c of Equation (1) in Sec. 15.3

n = Size of sample

n	$\alpha = 20\%$	$\alpha = 10\%$	$\alpha = 5\%$	$\alpha = 2\%$	$\alpha = 1\%$
	0.	0.	0.	0.	0.
1	900	950	975	990	995
2	684	776	842	900	929
3	565	636	708	785	829
4	493	565	624	689	734
5	447	509	563	627	669
6	410	468	519	577	617
7	381	436	483	538	576
8	359	410	454	507	542
9	339	387	430	480	513
10	323	369	409	457	486
11	308	352	391	437	468
12	296	338	375	419	449
13	285	325	361	404	432
14	275	314	349	390	418
15	266	304	338	377	404
16	258	295	327	366	392
17	250	286	318	355	381
18	244	279	309	346	371
19	237	271	301	337	361
20	232	265	294	329	352
21	226	259	287	321	344
22	221	253	281	314	337
23	216	247	275	307	330
24	212	242	269	301	323
25	208	238	264	295	317
26	204	233	259	290	311
27	200	229	254	284	305
28	197	225	250	279	300
29	193	221	246	275	295
30	190	218	242	270	290
35	177	202	224	251	269
40	165	189	210	235	252
45	156	179	198	222	238
50	148	170	188	211	226
55	142	162	180	201	216
60	136	155	172	193	207
65	131	149	166	185	199
70	126	144	160	179	192
75	122	139	154	173	185
80	118	135	150	167	179
85	114	131	145	162	174
90	111	127	141	158	169
95	108	124	137	154	165
100	106	121	134	150	161
Approximation for large n	$1.07/\sqrt{n}$	$1.22/\sqrt{n}$	$1.36/\sqrt{n}$	$1.52/\sqrt{n}$	$1.63/\sqrt{n}$

8 Student's *t*-Distribution

Table 8. Values of *z* for Given Values of the Distribution Function (3) in Sec. 10.3

More extended tables: Fisher (1958), Hald (1962), Pearson and Hartley (1954) (cf. Appendix 3).

$F(z)$

z

Example. For 9 degrees of freedom, $F(z) = 0.95$ when $z = 1.83$.

$$F(-z) = 1 - F(z).$$

Example. For 9 degrees of freedom, $F(-1.83) = 1 - F(1.83) = 1 - 0.95 = 0.05$.

(handwritten margin note: if there's no # equal to your F(z), sub. & itp. 1 + use F(-z))

$F(z)$	Number of Degrees of Freedom									
	1	2	3	4	5	6	7	8	9	10
0.5	0.00	0.00	0.00	0.00	0.00	0.00	0.00	0.00	0.00	0.00
0.6	0.33	0.29	0.28	0.27	0.27	0.27	0.26	0.26	0.26	0.26
0.7	0.73	0.62	0.58	0.57	0.56	0.55	0.55	0.55	0.54	0.54
0.8	1.38	1.06	0.98	0.94	0.92	0.91	0.90	0.89	0.88	0.88
0.9	3.08	1.89	1.64	1.53	1.48	1.44	1.42	1.40	1.38	1.37
0.95	6.31	2.92	2.35	2.13	2.02	1.94	1.90	1.86	1.83	1.81
0.975	12.7	4.30	3.18	2.78	2.57	2.45	2.37	2.31	2.26	2.23
0.99	31.8	6.97	4.54	3.75	3.37	3.14	3.00	2.90	2.82	2.76
0.995	63.7	9.93	5.84	4.60	4.03	3.71	3.50	3.36	3.25	3.17
0.999	318.3	22.3	10.2	7.17	5.89	5.21	4.79	4.50	4.30	4.14

$F(z)$	Number of Degrees of Freedom									
	11	12	13	14	15	16	17	18	19	20
0.5	0.00	0.00	0.00	0.00	0.00	0.00	0.00	0.00	0.00	0.00
0.6	0.26	0.26	0.26	0.26	0.26	0.26	0.26	0.26	0.26	0.26
0.7	0.54	0.54	0.54	0.54	0.54	0.54	0.53	0.53	0.53	0.53
0.8	0.88	0.87	0.87	0.87	0.87	0.87	0.86	0.86	0.86	0.86
0.9	1.36	1.36	1.35	1.35	1.34	1.34	1.33	1.33	1.33	1.33
0.95	1.80	1.78	1.77	1.76	1.75	1.75	1.74	1.73	1.73	1.73
0.975	2.20	2.18	2.16	2.15	2.13	2.12	2.11	2.10	2.09	2.09
0.99	2.72	2.68	2.65	2.62	2.60	2.58	2.57	2.55	2.54	2.53
0.995	3.11	3.06	3.01	2.98	2.95	2.92	2.90	2.88	2.86	2.85
0.999	4.03	3.93	3.85	3.79	3.73	3.69	3.65	3.61	3.58	3.55

$F(z)$	Number of Degrees of Freedom									
	22	24	26	28	30	40	50	100	200	∞
0.5	0.00	0.00	0.00	0.00	0.00	0.00	0.00	0.00	0.00	0.00
0.6	0.26	0.26	0.26	0.26	0.26	0.26	0.26	0.25	0.25	0.25
0.7	0.53	0.53	0.53	0.53	0.53	0.53	0.53	0.53	0.53	0.52
0.8	0.86	0.86	0.86	0.86	0.85	0.85	0.85	0.85	0.84	0.84
0.9	1.32	1.32	1.32	1.31	1.31	1.30	1.30	1.29	1.29	1.28
0.95	1.72	1.71	1.71	1.70	1.70	1.68	1.68	1.66	1.65	1.65
0.975	2.07	2.06	2.06	2.05	2.04	2.02	2.01	1.98	1.97	1.96
0.99	2.51	2.49	2.48	2.47	2.46	2.42	2.40	2.37	2.35	2.33
0.995	2.82	2.80	2.78	2.76	2.75	2.70	2.68	2.63	2.60	2.58
0.999	3.51	3.47	3.44	3.41	3.39	3.31	3.26	3.17	3.13	3.09

9 F-Distribution

Table 9a. Values of x for which the Distribution Function (2) in Sec. 13.6 of the F-Distribution with (m, n) Degrees of Freedom has the Value 0.95

More extended tables: Pearson and Hartley (1954), Hald (1962) (cf. Appendix 3).

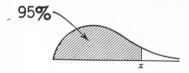

Example. For (7, 4) degrees of freedom, $F = 0.95$ when $x = 6.09$.

The value of x for which $F = 0.05$ in the case (n, m) degrees of freedom equals the reciprocal of that x for which $F = 0.95$ in the case of (m, n) degrees of freedom.

Example. For (7, 4) degrees of freedom, $F = 0.05$ when $x = 1/4.12 = 0.24$.

n	$m = 1$	$m = 2$	$m = 3$	$m = 4$	$m = 5$	$m = 6$	$m = 7$	$m = 8$	$m = 9$
1	161	200	216	225	230	234	237	239	241
2	18.5	19.0	19.2	19.2	19.3	19.3	19.4	19.4	19.4
3	10.1	9.55	9.28	9.12	9.01	8.94	8.89	8.85	8.81
4	7.71	6.94	6.59	6.39	6.26	6.16	6.09	6.04	6.00
5	6.61	5.79	5.41	5.19	5.05	4.95	4.88	4.82	4.77
6	5.99	5.14	4.76	4.53	4.39	4.28	4.21	4.15	4.10
7	5.59	4.74	4.35	4.12	3.97	3.87	3.79	3.73	3.68
8	5.32	4.46	4.07	3.84	3.69	3.58	3.50	3.44	3.39
9	5.12	4.26	3.86	3.63	3.48	3.37	3.29	3.23	3.18
10	4.96	4.10	3.71	3.48	3.33	3.22	3.14	3.07	3.02
11	4.84	3.98	3.59	3.36	3.20	3.09	3.01	2.95	2.90
12	4.75	3.89	3.49	3.26	3.11	3.00	2.91	2.85	2.80
13	4.67	3.81	3.41	3.18	3.03	2.92	2.83	2.77	2.71
14	4.60	3.74	3.34	3.11	2.96	2.85	2.76	2.70	2.65
15	4.54	3.68	3.29	3.06	2.90	2.79	2.71	2.64	2.59
16	4.49	3.63	3.24	3.01	2.85	2.74	2.66	2.59	2.54
17	4.45	3.59	3.20	2.96	2.81	2.70	2.61	2.55	2.49
18	4.41	3.55	3.16	2.93	2.77	2.66	2.58	2.51	2.46
19	4.38	3.52	3.13	2.90	2.74	2.63	2.54	2.48	2.42
20	4.35	3.49	3.10	2.87	2.71	2.60	2.51	2.45	2.39
22	4.30	3.44	3.05	2.82	2.66	2.55	2.46	2.40	2.34
24	4.26	3.40	3.01	2.78	2.62	2.51	2.42	2.36	2.30
26	4.23	3.37	2.98	2.74	2.59	2.47	2.39	2.32	2.27
28	4.20	3.34	2.95	2.71	2.56	2.45	2.36	2.29	2.24
30	4.17	3.32	2.92	2.69	2.53	2.42	2.33	2.27	2.21
32	4.15	3.30	2.90	2.67	2.51	2.40	2.31	2.24	2.19
34	4.13	3.28	2.88	2.65	2.49	2.38	2.29	2.23	2.17
36	4.11	3.26	2.87	2.63	2.48	2.36	2.28	2.21	2.15
38	4.10	3.24	2.85	2.62	2.46	2.35	2.26	2.19	2.14
40	4.08	3.23	2.84	2.61	2.45	2.34	2.25	2.18	2.12
50	4.03	3.18	2.79	2.56	2.40	2.29	2.20	2.13	2.07
60	4.00	3.15	2.76	2.53	2.37	2.25	2.17	2.10	2.04
70	3.98	3.13	2.74	2.50	2.35	2.23	2.14	2.07	2.02
80	3.96	3.11	2.72	2.49	2.33	2.21	2.13	2.06	2.00
90	3.95	3.10	2.71	2.47	2.32	2.20	2.11	2.04	1.99
100	3.94	3.09	2.70	2.46	2.31	2.19	2.10	2.03	1.97
150	3.90	3.06	2.66	2.43	2.27	2.16	2.07	2.00	1.94
200	3.89	3.04	2.65	2.42	2.26	2.14	2.06	1.98	1.93
1000	3.85	3.00	2.61	2.38	2.22	2.11	2.02	1.95	1.89
∞	3.84	3.00	2.60	2.37	2.21	2.10	2.01	1.94	1.88

Table 9a. Values of *x* for which the Distribution Function (2) in Sec. 13.6 of the *F*-Distribution with (*m, n*) Degrees of Freedom has the Value 0.95 (*Continued*)

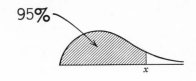

n	*m* = 10	*m* = 15	*m* = 20	*m* = 30	*m* = 40	*m* = 50	*m* = 100	∞
1	242	246	248	250	251	252	253	254
2	19.4	19.4	19.4	19.5	19.5	19.5	19.5	19.5
3	8.79	8.70	8.66	8.62	8.59	8.58	8.55	8.53
4	5.96	5.86	5.80	5.75	5.72	5.70	5.66	5.63
5	4.74	4.62	4.56	4.50	4.46	4.44	4.41	4.37
6	4.06	3.94	3.87	3.81	3.77	3.75	3.71	3.67
7	3.64	3.51	3.44	3.38	3.34	3.32	3.27	3.23
8	3.35	3.22	3.15	3.08	3.04	3.02	2.97	2.93
9	3.14	3.01	2.94	2.86	2.83	2.80	2.76	2.71
10	2.98	2.85	2.77	2.70	2.66	2.64	2.59	2.54
11	2.85	2.72	2.65	2.57	2.53	2.51	2.46	2.40
12	2.75	2.62	2.54	2.47	2.43	2.40	2.35	2.30
13	2.67	2.53	2.46	2.38	2.34	2.31	2.26	2.21
14	2.60	2.46	2.39	2.31	2.27	2.24	2.19	2.13
15	2.54	2.40	2.33	2.25	2.20	2.18	2.12	2.07
16	2.49	2.35	2.28	2.19	2.15	2.12	2.07	2.01
17	2.45	2.31	2.23	2.15	2.10	2.08	2.02	1.96
18	2.41	2.27	2.19	2.11	2.06	2.04	1.98	1.92
19	2.38	2.23	2.16	2.07	2.03	2.00	1.94	1.88
20	2.35	2.20	2.12	2.04	1.99	1.97	1.91	1.84
22	2.30	2.15	2.07	1.98	1.94	1.91	1.85	1.78
24	2.25	2.11	2.03	1.94	1.89	1.86	1.80	1.73
26	2.22	2.07	1.99	1.90	1.85	1.82	1.76	1.69
28	2.19	2.04	1.96	1.87	1.82	1.79	1.73	1.65
30	2.16	2.01	1.93	1.84	1.79	1.76	1.70	1.62
32	2.14	1.99	1.91	1.82	1.77	1.74	1.67	1.59
34	2.12	1.97	1.89	1.80	1.75	1.71	1.65	1.57
36	2.11	1.95	1.87	1.78	1.73	1.69	1.62	1.55
38	2.09	1.94	1.85	1.76	1.71	1.68	1.61	1.53
40	2.08	1.92	1.84	1.74	1.69	1.66	1.59	1.51
50	2.03	1.87	1.78	1.69	1.63	1.60	1.52	1.44
60	1.99	1.84	1.75	1.65	1.59	1.56	1.48	1.39
70	1.97	1.81	1.72	1.62	1.57	1.53	1.45	1.35
80	1.95	1.79	1.70	1.60	1.54	1.51	1.43	1.32
90	1.94	1.78	1.69	1.59	1.53	1.49	1.41	1.30
100	1.93	1.77	1.68	1.57	1.52	1.48	1.39	1.28
150	1.89	1.73	1.64	1.53	1.48	1.44	1.34	1.22
200	1.88	1.72	1.62	1.52	1.46	1.41	1.32	1.19
1000	1.84	1.68	1.58	1.47	1.41	1.36	1.26	1.08
∞	1.83	1.67	1.57	1.46	1.39	1.35	1.24	1.00

Table 9b. Values of x for which the Distribution Function (2) in Sec. 13.6 of the F-Distribution with (m, n) Degrees of Freedom has the Value 0.99

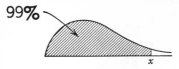

99%

x

Example. For (7, 4) degrees of freedom, $F = 0.99$ when $x = 15.0$.

The value of x for which $F = 0.01$ in the case of (n, m) degrees of freedom equals the reciprocal of that x for which $F = 0.99$ in the case of F (m, n) degrees of freedom.

Example. For (7, 4) degrees of freedom, $F = 0.01$ when $x = 1/7.85 = 0.13$.

n	$m = 1$	$m = 2$	$m = 3$	$m = 4$	$m = 5$	$m = 6$	$m = 7$	$m = 8$	$m = 9$
1	4052	4999	5403	5625	5764	5859	5928	5982	6022
2	98.5	99.0	99.2	99.3	99.3	99.3	99.4	99.4	99.4
3	34.1	30.8	29.5	28.7	28.2	27.9	27.7	27.5	27.3
4	21.2	18.0	16.7	16.0	15.5	15.2	15.0	14.8	14.7
5	16.3	13.3	12.1	11.4	11.0	10.7	10.5	10.3	10.2
6	13.7	10.9	9.78	9.15	8.75	8.47	8.26	8.10	7.98
7	12.2	9.55	8.45	7.85	7.46	7.19	6.99	6.84	6.72
8	11.3	8.65	7.59	7.01	6.63	6.37	6.18	6.03	5.91
9	10.6	8.02	6.99	6.42	6.06	5.80	5.61	5.47	5.35
10	10.0	7.56	6.55	5.99	5.64	5.39	5.20	5.06	4.94
11	9.65	7.21	6.22	5.67	5.32	5.07	4.89	4.74	4.63
12	9.33	6.93	5.95	5.41	5.06	4.82	4.64	4.50	4.39
13	9.07	6.70	5.74	5.21	4.86	4.62	4.44	4.30	4.19
14	8.86	6.51	5.56	5.04	4.70	4.46	4.28	4.14	4.03
15	8.68	6.36	5.42	4.89	4.56	4.32	4.14	4.00	3.89
16	8.53	6.23	5.29	4.77	4.44	4.20	4.03	3.89	3.78
17	8.40	6.11	5.18	4.67	4.34	4.10	3.93	3.79	3.68
18	8.29	6.01	5.09	4.58	4.25	4.01	3.84	3.71	3.60
19	8.18	5.93	5.01	4.50	4.17	3.94	3.77	3.63	3.52
20	8.10	5.85	4.94	4.43	4.10	3.87	3.70	3.56	3.46
22	7.95	5.72	4.82	4.31	3.99	3.76	3.59	3.45	3.35
24	7.82	5.61	4.72	4.22	3.90	3.67	3.50	3.36	3.26
26	7.72	5.53	4.64	4.14	3.82	3.59	3.42	3.29	3.18
28	7.64	5.45	4.57	4.07	3.75	3.53	3.36	3.23	3.12
30	7.56	5.39	4.51	4.02	3.70	3.47	3.30	3.17	3.07
32	7.50	5.34	4.46	3.97	3.65	3.43	3.26	3.13	3.02
34	7.44	5.29	4.42	3.93	3.61	3.39	3.22	3.09	2.98
36	7.40	5.25	4.38	3.89	3.57	3.35	3.18	3.05	2.95
38	7.35	5.21	4.34	3.86	3.54	3.32	3.15	3.02	2.92
40	7.31	5.18	4.31	3.83	3.51	3.29	3.12	2.99	2.89
50	7.17	5.06	4.20	3.72	3.41	3.19	3.02	2.89	2.79
60	7.08	4.98	4.13	3.65	3.34	3.12	2.95	2.82	2.72
70	7.01	4.92	4.08	3.60	3.29	3.07	2.91	2.78	2.67
80	6.96	4.88	4.04	3.56	3.26	3.04	2.87	2.74	2.64
90	6.93	4.85	4.01	3.54	3.23	3.01	2.84	2.72	2.61
100	6.90	4.82	3.98	3.51	3.21	2.99	2.82	2.69	2.59
150	6.81	4.75	3.92	3.45	3.14	2.92	2.76	2.63	2.53
200	6.76	4.71	3.88	3.41	3.11	2.89	2.73	2.60	2.50
1000	6.66	4.63	3.80	3.34	3.04	2.82	2.66	2.53	2.43
∞	6.63	4.61	3.78	3.32	3.02	2.80	2.64	2.51	2.41

Table 9*b*. Values of *x* for which the Distribution Function (2) in Sec. 13.6 of the *F*-Distribution with (*m*, *n*) Degrees of Freedom has the Value 0.99 (*Continued*)

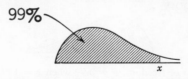

n	*m* = 10	*m* = 15	*m* = 20	*m* = 30	*m* = 40	*m* = 50	*m* = 100	∞
1	6056	6157	6209	6261	6287	6300	6330	6366
2	99.4	99.4	99.4	99.5	99.5	99.5	99.5	99.5
3	27.2	26.9	26.7	26.5	26.4	26.4	26.2	26.1
4	14.5	14.2	14.0	13.8	13.7	13.7	13.6	13.5
5	10.1	9.72	9.55	9.38	9.29	9.24	9.13	9.02
6	7.87	7.56	7.40	7.23	7.14	7.09	6.99	6.88
7	6.62	6.31	6.16	5.99	5.91	5.86	5.75	5.65
8	5.81	5.52	5.36	5.20	5.12	5.07	4.96	4.86
9	5.26	4.96	4.81	4.65	4.57	4.52	4.42	4.31
10	4.85	4.56	4.41	4.25	4.17	4.12	4.01	3.91
11	4.54	4.25	4.10	3.94	3.86	3.81	3.71	3.60
12	4.30	4.01	3.86	3.70	3.62	3.57	3.47	3.36
13	4.10	3.82	3.66	3.51	3.43	3.38	3.27	3.17
14	3.94	3.66	3.51	3.35	3.27	3.22	3.11	3.00
15	3.80	3.52	3.37	3.21	3.13	3.08	2.98	2.87
16	3.69	3.41	3.26	3.10	3.02	2.97	2.86	2.75
17	3.59	3.31	3.16	3.00	2.92	2.87	2.76	2.65
18	3.51	3.23	3.08	2.92	2.84	2.78	2.68	2.57
19	3.43	3.15	3.00	2.84	2.76	2.71	2.60	2.49
20	3.37	3.09	2.94	2.78	2.69	2.64	2.54	2.42
22	3.26	2.98	2.83	2.67	2.58	2.53	2.42	2.31
24	3.17	2.89	2.74	2.58	2.49	2.44	2.33	2.21
26	3.09	2.82	2.66	2.50	2.42	2.36	2.25	2.13
28	3.03	2.75	2.60	2.44	2.35	2.30	2.19	2.06
30	2.98	2.70	2.55	2.39	2.30	2.25	2.13	2.01
32	2.93	2.66	2.50	2.34	2.25	2.20	2.08	1.96
34	2.89	2.62	2.46	2.30	2.21	2.16	2.04	1.91
36	2.86	2.58	2.43	2.26	2.17	2.12	2.00	1.87
38	2.83	2.55	2.40	2.23	2.14	2.09	1.97	1.84
40	2.80	2.52	2.37	2.20	2.11	2.06	1.94	1.80
50	2.70	2.42	2.27	2.10	2.01	1.95	1.82	1.68
60	2.63	2.35	2.20	2.03	1.94	1.88	1.75	1.60
70	2.59	2.31	2.15	1.98	1.89	1.83	1.70	1.54
80	2.55	2.27	2.12	1.94	1.85	1.79	1.66	1.49
90	2.52	2.24	2.09	1.92	1.82	1.76	1.62	1.46
100	2.50	2.22	2.07	1.89	1.80	1.73	1.60	1.43
150	2.44	2.16	2.00	1.83	1.73	1.66	1.52	1.33
200	2.41	2.13	1.97	1.79	1.69	1.63	1.48	1.28
1000	2.34	2.06	1.90	1.72	1.61	1.54	1.38	1.11
∞	2.32	2.04	1.88	1.70	1.59	1.52	1.36	1.00

10 Tables for Nonparametric Methods

Table 10a. Distribution Function $F(x) = P(T \leq x)$ of the Random Variable T in Sec. 20.2

For $n = 3$, $F(2) = 1 - 0.167 = 0.833$.
For $n = 4$, $F(3) = 1 - 0.375 = 0.625$, $F(4) = 1 - 0.167 = 0.833$, etc.

x	$n=3$ 0.
0	167
1	500

x	$n=4$ 0.
0	042
1	167
2	375

x	$n=5$ 0.
0	008
1	042
2	117
3	242
4	408

x	$n=6$ 0.
0	001
1	008
2	028
3	068
4	136
5	235
6	360
7	500

x	$n=7$ 0.
1	001
2	005
3	015
4	035
5	068
6	119
7	191
8	281
9	386
10	500

x	$n=8$ 0.
2	001
3	003
4	007
5	016
6	031
7	054
8	089
9	138
10	199
11	274
12	360
13	452

x	$n=9$ 0.
4	001
5	003
6	006
7	012
8	022
9	038
10	060
11	090
12	130
13	179
14	238
15	306
16	381
17	460

x	$n=10$ 0.
6	001
7	002
8	005
9	008
10	014
11	023
12	036
13	054
14	078
15	108
16	146
17	190
18	242
19	300
20	364
21	431
22	500

x	$n=11$ 0.
8	001
9	002
10	003
11	005
12	008
13	013
14	020
15	030
16	043
17	060
18	082
19	109
20	141
21	179
22	223
23	271
24	324
25	381
26	440
27	500

x	$n=12$ 0.
11	001
12	002
13	003
14	004
15	007
16	010
17	016
18	022
19	031
20	043
21	058
22	076
23	098
24	125
25	155
26	190
27	230
28	273
29	319
30	369
31	420
32	473

x	$n=13$ 0.
14	001
15	001
16	002
17	003
18	005
19	007
20	011
21	015
22	021
23	029
24	038
25	050
26	064
27	082
28	102
29	126
30	153
31	184
32	218
33	255
34	295
35	338
36	383
37	429
38	476

x	$n=14$ 0.
18	001
19	002
20	002
21	003
22	005
23	007
24	010
25	013
26	018
27	024
28	031
29	040
30	051
31	063
32	079
33	096
34	117
35	140
36	165
37	194
38	225
39	259
40	295
41	334
42	374
43	415
44	457
45	500

x	$n=15$ 0.
23	001
24	002
25	003
26	004
27	006
28	008
29	010
30	014
31	018
32	023
33	029
34	037
35	046
36	057
37	070
38	084
39	101
40	120
41	141
42	164
43	190
44	218
45	248
46	279
47	313
48	349
49	385
50	423
51	461
52	500

x	$n=16$ 0.
27	001
28	002
29	002
30	003
31	004
32	006
33	008
34	010
35	013
36	016
37	021
38	026
39	032
40	039
41	048
42	058
43	070
44	083
45	097
46	114
47	133
48	153
49	175
50	199
51	225
52	253
53	282
54	313
55	345
56	378
57	412
58	447
59	482

x	$n=17$ 0.
32	001
33	002
34	002
35	003
36	004
37	005
38	007
39	009
40	011
41	014
42	017
43	021
44	026
45	032
46	038
47	046
48	054
49	064
50	076
51	088
52	102
53	118
54	135
55	154
56	174
57	196
58	220
59	245
60	271
61	299
62	328
63	358
64	388
65	420
66	452
67	484

x	$n=18$ 0.
38	001
39	002
40	003
41	003
42	004
43	005
44	007
45	009
46	011
47	013
48	016
49	020
50	024
51	029
52	034
53	041
54	048
55	056
56	066
57	076
58	088
59	100
60	115
61	130
62	147
63	165
64	184
65	205
66	227
67	250
68	275
69	300
70	327
71	354
72	383
73	411
74	441
75	470
76	500

x	$n=19$ 0.
43	001
44	002
45	002
46	003
47	003
48	004
49	005
50	006
51	008
52	010
53	012
54	014
55	017
56	021
57	025
58	029
59	034
60	040
61	047
62	054
63	062
64	072
65	082
66	093
67	105
68	119
69	133
70	149
71	166
72	184
73	203
74	223
75	245
76	267
77	290
78	314
79	339
80	365
81	391
82	418
83	445
84	473
85	500

x	$n=20$ 0.
50	001
51	002
52	002
53	003
54	004
55	005
56	006
57	007
58	008
59	010
60	012
61	014
62	017
63	020
64	023
65	027
66	032
67	037
68	043
69	049
70	056
71	064
72	073
73	082
74	093
75	104
76	117
77	130
78	144
79	159
80	176
81	193
82	211
83	230
84	250
85	271
86	293
87	315
88	339
89	362
90	387
91	411
92	436
93	462
94	487

Table 10b. Critical Values for the Test in Sec. 20.3

c_1 is the largest integer such that $P(U \leq c_1) \leq \alpha^*$.
c_2 is the smallest integer such that $P(U \geq c_2) \leq \alpha^*$.

m	$\alpha^* = 5\%$		$\alpha^* = 2.5\%$		$\alpha^* = 1\%$		$\alpha^* = 0.5\%$	
	c_1	c_2	c_1	c_2	c_1	c_2	c_1	c_2
5	3	8	2	9	2	9		
6	3	10	3	10	2	11	2	11
7	4	11	3	12	3	12	3	12
8	5	12	4	13	4	13	3	14
9	6	13	5	14	4	15	4	15
10	6	15	6	15	5	16	5	16
11	7	16	7	16	6	17	5	18
12	8	17	7	18	7	18	6	19
13	9	18	8	19	7	20	7	20
14	10	19	9	20	8	21	7	22
15	11	20	10	21	9	22	8	23
16	11	22	11	22	10	23	9	24
17	12	23	11	24	10	25	10	25
18	13	24	12	25	11	26	11	26
19	14	25	13	26	12	27	11	28
20	15	26	14	27	13	28	12	29

Table 10c. Critical Values for the Test in Sec. 20.4

c_1 is the largest integer such that $P(U \leqq c_1) \leqq \alpha^*$.
c_2 is the smallest integer such that $P(U \geqq c_2) \leqq \alpha^*$.

n_1	n_2	$\alpha^* = 5\%$		$\alpha^* = 2.5\%$		$\alpha^* = 1\%$		$\alpha^* = 0.5\%$	
		c_1	c_2	c_1	c_2	c_1	c_2	c_1	c_2
4	4	2	7						
	5	2	8	2	8				
	6	3	8	2	8	2	9		
	7	3	8	2	9	2	9		
	8	3	9	3	9	2	9	2	9
	9	3	9	3	9	2	9	2	9
	10	3	9	3	9	2	9	2	9
5	5	3	8	2	9	2	9		
	6	3	9	3	9	2	10	2	10
	7	3	9	3	10	2	10	2	11
	8	3	10	3	10	2	11	2	11
	9	4	10	3	11	3	11	2	11
	10	4	10	3	11	3	11	3	11
6	6	3	10	3	10	2	11	2	11
	7	4	10	3	11	3	11	2	12
	8	4	11	3	11	3	12	3	12
	9	4	11	4	12	3	12	3	13
	10	5	11	4	12	3	13	3	13
7	7	4	11	3	12	3	12	3	12
	8	4	12	4	12	3	13	3	13
	9	5	12	4	13	4	13	3	14
	10	5	12	5	13	4	14	3	14
8	8	5	12	4	13	4	13	3	14
	9	5	13	5	13	4	14	3	14
	10	6	13	5	14	4	14	4	15
9	9	6	13	5	14	4	15	4	15
	10	6	14	5	15	5	15	4	16
10	10	6	15	6	15	5	16	5	16

Table 10d. Rank Test in Sec. 20.5

Two-sided test. Reject the hypothesis if the quantity u_0 used in the test is equal to or smaller than the number given in the table.

m	5%	1%	m	5%	1%	m	5%	1%
6	0		11	11	5	16	30	19
7	2		12	14	7	17	35	23
8	4	0	13	17	10	18	40	28
9	6	1	14	21	13	19	46	32
10	8	3	15	25	16	20	52	38

For large m the critical value is approximately equal to

$$M - 1.96\sqrt{N} \quad (5\%) \quad \text{and} \quad M - 2.58\sqrt{N} \quad (1\%),$$

respectively, where

$$M = \frac{m(m+1)}{4} \quad \text{and} \quad N = \frac{(2m+1)(m+1)m}{24}.$$

Table 10e. Critical Values for the Test in Sec. 20.6

c_1 is the largest integer such that $P(W \leqq c_1) \leqq \alpha^*$.
c_2 is the smallest integer such that $P(W \geqq c_2) \leqq \alpha^*$.

n_1	n_2	$\alpha^* = 5\%$ c_1	c_2	$\alpha^* = 2.5\%$ c_1	c_2	$\alpha^* = 1\%$ c_1	c_2	$\alpha^* = 0.5\%$ c_1	c_2
2	5	3	13						
	6	3	15						
	7	3	17						
	8	4	18	3	19				
	9	4	20	3	21				
	10	4	22	3	23				
3	3	6	15						
	4	6	18						
	5	7	20	6	21				
	6	8	22	7	23				
	7	8	25	7	26	6	27		
	8	9	27	8	28	6	30		
	9	10	29	8	31	7	32	6	33
	10	10	32	9	33	7	35	6	36
4	4	11	25	10	26				
	5	12	28	11	29	10	30		
	6	13	31	12	32	11	33	10	34
	7	14	34	13	35	11	37	10	38
	8	15	37	14	38	12	40	11	41
	9	16	40	15	41	13	43	11	45
	10	17	43	15	45	13	47	12	48
5	5	19	36	17	38	16	39	15	40
	6	20	40	18	42	17	43	16	44
	7	21	44	20	45	18	47	17	48
	8	23	47	21	49	19	51	17	53
	9	24	51	22	53	20	55	18	57
	10	26	54	23	57	21	59	19	61
6	6	28	50	26	52	24	54	23	55
	7	29	55	27	57	25	59	24	60
	8	31	59	29	61	27	63	25	65
	9	33	63	31	65	28	68	26	70
	10	35	67	32	70	29	73	27	75
7	7	39	66	36	69	34	71	32	73
	8	41	71	38	74	36	76	34	78
	9	43	76	40	79	37	82	35	84
	10	45	81	42	84	39	87	37	89
8	8	51	85	49	87	46	90	43	93
	9	54	90	51	93	48	96	45	99
	10	56	96	53	99	50	102	47	105
9	9	66	105	63	108	59	112	56	115
	10	69	111	65	115	61	119	58	122
10	10	82	128	78	132	74	136	71	139

Index